We make lives worth living.

Meet George and Bill, two of our younger residents at Erskine Hospital, the foremost care facility for ex-Service men and women in Scotland.

George (left) was a 19 year old Argyll and Sutherland Highlander when he was caught in a bomb blast which killed three of his mates. He came to Erskine almost completely paralysed, unable to walk or talk. Today, he lives in a cottage in the grounds of the Hospital with his wife and children and has a job he enjoys in our print workshop. "Erskine gave me back my life," he says. "It's that simple."

It was the mental scars left by service in the Falklands conflict which brought Bill, a proud Scots Guardsman to Erskine. "Until I came here, no-one took the trauma I was going through seriously," said Bill who has lived at Erskine for four years now and runs our computer system. "Coming here has turned my life around."

The Hospital, which opened in 1916, has cared for more than 64,000 men and women from the Royal Navy, Royal Air Force and Army from both World Wars and the many modern day conflicts.

As a registered charity, it is the generosity of our supporters which allows us to care for people like George and Bill. More than 500 ex-Service men and women need that care, on a permanent or respite basis, each and every year. Your donation, no matter how large or small, will help us continue to make lives worth living.

Scottish Charity no SC006609

Please send your donations to:
Iain W. Grimmond, Director of Finance, Room CSYB00, Erskine Hospital, Bishopton PA7 5PU.

I enclose £ .... as a donation.

Please debit my Access/Visa account £ ....

Card No:-

Expiry Date ....

Signature ....

Web: www.erskine.org

Please send, without obligation, forms for
Deed of covenant ☐   Bankers Order ☐
Gift Aid ☐   Payroll Giving ☐

BLOCK LETTERS PLEASE

NAME...

ADDRESS...

....

....

POSTCODE..

ERSKINE HOSPITAL   ERSKINE CARE

Local people

supported by a unique, caring organisation.
That's what makes us different.

Your local Funeral Home is part of the nationwide Co-operative Movement.
A Movement owned by local people like you.
The Co-op is founded on strong principles of caring for others and concern for the community.
Those traditions are as strong today as they have ever been.
As part of the local community, we can offer you a genuinely local funeral service backed
by the strength and reassurance of a unique, caring national organisation.

PLAN AHEAD. For all of us, it is sensible and practical to plan
ahead. The Co-operative Funeral Bond allows you to tailor-make
your own plan and pay for your funeral at today's prices. There are
no hidden extras, no medical is required and there is no age limit.

For an Information Pack simply call us free on
0800 289 120 *or contact your local branch.*

FUNERALS

We understand

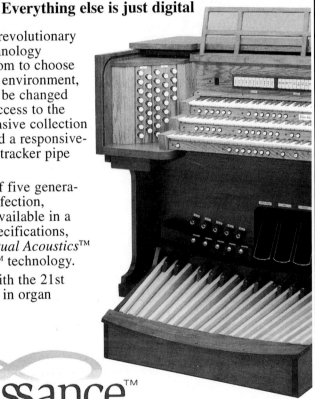

The Right Reverend Andrew R.C. McLellan MA BD STM

MODERATOR

The Church of Scotland
YEAR BOOK
—— 2000/2001 ——

Editor
Rev. Ronald S. Blakey
MA BD MTh

Published on behalf of
THE CHURCH OF SCOTLAND
BOARD OF COMMUNICATION
by SAINT ANDREW PRESS
121 George Street, Edinburgh EH2 4YN

THE OFFICES OF THE CHURCH

121 George Street   Tel: 0131 225 5722
Edinburgh EH2 4YN   Fax: 0131 220 3113
                            Internet: http://www.churchofscotland.org.uk/

Office Hours: Monday–Friday 9.00 am–5.00 pm
Office Manager: Mr Robert Simpson

PARISH EDUCATION
Annie Small House   18 Inverleith Terrace, Edinburgh EH3 5NS   Tel: 0131 332 0343

SOCIAL RESPONSIBILITY
Charis House   47 Milton Road East, Edinburgh EH15 2SR   Tel: 0131 657 2000
                    [e-mail: info@charis.org.uk]   Fax: 0131 657 5000

NATIONAL MISSION
Glasgow Office   59 Elmbank Street, Glasgow G2 4PQ   Tel: 0141 333 1948
Kirkcaldy Office   St Brycedale Church Centre,
                    St Brycedale Avenue, Kirkcaldy KY1 1ET   Tel/Fax: 01592 646406

(Youth Adviser: Presbytery of Glasgow)
                    110 St. James Road, Glasgow G4 0PS   Tel: 0141 400 7788

QUICK DIRECTORY

A.C.T.S. 01786   823588
Badenoch Centre 01540   651373
Board of Communication 0131 240 2236
Bridgeton, St Francis-in-the-East Church House 0141 554 8045
Carberry 0131 665 3135/7604
Christian Aid Scotland 0131 220 1254
Christian Aid London 0171 620 4444
Lodging House Mission 0141 552 0285
Netherbow 0131 556 9579/2647
Pathway Productions 0131 447 3531
Media Relations Unit (Press Office) 0131 240 2243
Society, Religion and Technology Project 0131 556 2953
St Ninian's Crieff 01764   653766

First published in 2000 by SAINT ANDREW PRESS, 121 George Street, Edinburgh EH2 4YN on behalf of the BOARD of COMMUNICATION of the CHURCH of SCOTLAND

ISBN 0 86153 306 2

British Library Cataloguing in Publication Data
A catalogue record for this book
is available from the British Library.

ISBN 0861533062

Printed and bound by Bell and Bain Ltd, Glasgow.

CONTENTS

All correspondence regarding the Year Book should be sent to
The Editor, *Church of Scotland Year Book*,
Saint Andrew Press, 121 George Street, Edinburgh EH2 4YN
Fax: 0131 220 3113
[e-mail: cofs.standrew@dial.pipex.com]

GENERAL ASSEMBLY OF 2001
The General Assembly of 2001 will convene on
Saturday, 19th May 2001.

FROM THE MODERATOR

I collect old Year Books. The earliest I have is that for 1880; and I have one or two for each generation since then. How much of the story of the Church of Scotland is contained in their pages! The glories and the disappointments, the achievements and the blind spots, the courage and the vision and the prayers - only a very limited vision would see the Year Book as merely a collection of statistics.

Perhaps very prosaic people think that church facts and figures are boring and unnecessary: but anyone with any feel for the life of the Church of Scotland today will be able to read behind the facts of this year's book so much that is important in our Church: the Presbyteries and congregations, the Boards and Committees, names, addresses, telephone numbers; other churches; chaplains; the Church of Scotland overseas; proper procedures; decisions of the General Assembly. The Year Book is most certainly useful; more than that, however - it is positively fascinating! I would like to think that it might also serve as a tool to help us all to pray in various ways for the Church of Scotland.

For years we have all been in debt to the Editor, Rev. Gordon McGillivray. He lays down the work in the sure knowledge that it has been appreciated throughout the Church. The new Editor, Rev. Ronald Blakey, is marvellously well equipped for the task, and takes up his duties with the thanks and encouragement of all.

Andrew R. C. McLellan
June 2000

FROM THE EDITOR

It was with an uneasy mix of apprehension and excitement that I accepted the invitation of the Board of Communication to become Editor of the Year Book. A long-time admirer and frequent user of it, I knew how useful a tool it is to many, how important it is to keep errors and omissions to a minimum and how easy it would be, with even the most modern computerised aids, to achieve a frustrating blend of the incomplete and the inconsistent. Coming to the post midway through June, with only some nine weeks in which to have the material ready for the printer, I recognised with some relief that significant changes to the format and content, even if such were flooding my mind, would need to wait a further year. The mixture, then, is much as before, offered with the hope that those who turn to it will find easily and accurately all that they want to find.

It is the intention of the Board of Communication to issue a questionnaire with the aim of establishing what the users of this book want to see included in or excluded from future editions. Already I have received a goodly number of firm, if mutually contradictory, suggestions - "more of this", "less of that", "introduce a section on", "bring back the section on". I cannot promise that every suggestion received will be incorporated: I can promise that each one will be carefully considered.

I am indebted to all who have assisted me in bringing the book to the point where it could be published. Presbytery Clerks and the Secretaries of Boards and Committees (particularly those whose writing I could read), those - almost anyone really - who knew more than I did about the computer software used in its publication and who unscrambled some early confusions, and above all my patient and kindly predecessor, Gordon McGillivray, have all contributed nobly.

Ronald S. Blakey
August 2000

SECTION 1

Assembly Boards
and Committees

MEETINGS OF BOARDS AND COMMITTEES

The following Boards and Committees have indicated that they plan to meet on the dates listed.

ARTISTIC MATTERS
2000	SEPTEMBER 7, OCTOBER 5, NOVEMBER 2, DECEMBER 14
2001	FEBRUARY 1, MARCH 1, APRIL 5, MAY 3, JUNE 7, JULY 5, (AUGUST 2), SEPTEMBER 6

ASSEMBLY COUNCIL
2000	SEPTEMBER 7, NOVEMBER 2
2001	JANUARY 11, MARCH 8, MAY 3, JUNE 13-14, SEPTEMBER 6

CHURCH OF SCOTLAND TRUST
2000	SEPTEMBER 22
2001	(TO BE CONFIRMED)

DOCTRINE
2000	DECEMBER 6
2001	FEBRUARY 7, JUNE 6

ECUMENICAL RELATIONS
2000	SEPTEMBER 28-29
2001	JANUARY 25, MARCH 22, JUNE 28, SEPTEMBER 27-28

GENERAL TRUSTEES
(A) GENERAL TRUSTEES
2000	SEPTEMBER 26, OCTOBER 24, NOVEMBER 21, DECEMBER 19
2001	JANUARY 23, FEBRUARY 20, MARCH 20, APRIL 24, MAY 29, JULY 3, SEPTEMBER 25

(B) FABRIC AND CHAIRMAN'S
2000	SEPTEMBER 5, OCTOBER 10, NOVEMBER 7, DECEMBER 5
2001	JANUARY 9, FEBRUARY 6, MARCH 6, APRIL 3, MAY 15, JUNE 12, JULY 24, SEPTEMBER 4

(C) GLEBES
2000	SEPTEMBER 6, OCTOBER 11, NOVEMBER 8, DECEMBER 6
2001	JANUARY 10, FEBRUARY 7, MARCH 7, APRIL 4, MAY 16, JUNE 13, JULY 25, SEPTEMBER 5

GUILD
(A) NATIONAL EXECUTIVE
2000	OCTOBER 31
2001	FEBRUARY 6, MARCH 28

(B) FINANCE AND GENERAL PURPOSES
2000	OCTOBER 3
2001	JANUARY 30

(C) MARKETING AND PUBLICITY
2000	OCTOBER 16
2001	JANUARY 25, MARCH 22

(D) PROGRAMMES AND RESOURCES
2000	OCTOBER 12, NOVEMBER 9
2001	MARCH 8

(E) PROJECTS AND TOPICS
2000   OCTOBER 24
2001   JANUARY 23, MARCH 13

(F) MATTERS CONCERNING YOUNGER WOMEN
2000   OCTOBER 4
2001   JANUARY 17, MARCH 14

(G) JOINT CONFERENCE
2000   SEPTEMBER 19-20

INVESTORS TRUST
2000   OCTOBER 24
2001   FEBRUARY 27, APRIL 24, JULY 24

MINISTRY
(A) BOARD
2000   SEPTEMBER 20-21, DECEMBER 13
2001   FEBRUARY 7, FEBRUARY 21, JUNE 13, SEPTEMBER 26-27

(B) MINISTRY SUPPORT
2000   OCTOBER 12, NOVEMBER 9
2001   JANUARY 11, MARCH 8, APRIL 26, JUNE 6

(C) VOCATIONAL GUIDANCE
2000   OCTOBER 11, NOVEMBER 8
2001   JANUARY 10, MARCH 14

(D) EDUCATION AND TRAINING
2000   SEPTEMBER 27, (OTHER DATES TO BE CONFIRMED)
2001   JANUARY 17, MARCH 21, (OTHER DATES TO BE CONFIRMED)

(E) MINISTRY DEVELOPMENT
2000   OCTOBER 12, NOVEMBER 9
2001   JANUARY 11, MARCH 8, APRIL 26

(F) HOUSING AND LOAN TRUSTEES
2000   SEPTEMBER 19, DECEMBER 12
2001   FEBRUARY 13, APRIL 10, JUNE 12, SEPTEMBER 11, DECEMBER 11

NATIONAL MISSION
(A) BOARD: Wednesdays 10 am
2000   SEPTEMBER 6, DECEMBER 6
2001   FEBRUARY 7, JUNE 6, SEPTEMBER 5, DECEMBER 5

(B) COMMITTEE ON PARISH REAPPRAISAL: Tuesdays 2 pm
2000   SEPTEMBER 19, OCTOBER 17, NOVEMBER 21, DECEMBER 19
2001   FEBRUARY 20, MARCH 20, APRIL 17, JUNE 19, SEPTEMBER 18, OCTOBER 16,
        NOVEMBER 20, DECEMBER 18

(C) COMMITTEE ON NEW CHARGE DEVELOPMENT: Wednesdays 10.30 am
2000   SEPTEMBER 20, NOVEMBER 22
2001   JANUARY 17, MARCH 21, JUNE 20, SEPTEMBER 19, NOVEMBER 21

(D) COMMITTEE ON PARISH ASSISTANCE: Wednesdays 10.45 am
2000   SEPTEMBER 27 (ALL DAY), NOVEMBER 29
2001   JANUARY 17, JUNE 13, SEPTEMBER 26 (ALL DAY), NOVEMBER 28

(E) COMMITTEE ON MISSION AND EVANGELISM RESOURCES: Thursdays 10.30 am
2000   AUGUST 22/23, OCTOBER 26
2001   JANUARY 18, MARCH 15, JUNE 7, AUGUST 21/22, NOVEMBER 29

(F)   COMMITTEE ON CHAPLAINCIES: Wednesdays 2pm
2000   JUNE 14, NOVEMBER 1
2001   JANUARY 24, JUNE 13, NOVEMBER 7

(G)   HOSPITALS, HEALTHCARE AND UNIVERSITIES SUB-COMMITTEE: Tuesdays 10.30 am
2000   SEPTEMBER 26, NOVEMBER 21
2001   JANUARY 16, MARCH 13, MAY 29, SEPTEMBER 25, NOVEMBER 20

(H)   CHURCH AND INDUSTRY SUB-COMMITTEE: Wednesdays 6.30 pm
2000   SEPTEMBER 20, NOVEMBER 15
2001   JANUARY 17, APRIL 18, JUNE 20, SEPTEMBER 19, NOVEMBER 14

(I)   PRISON CHAPLAINCIES SUB-COMMITTEE: Wednesdays 10.30 am
2000   OCTOBER 4
2001   JANUARY 10, MAY 30, OCTOBER 3

(J)   JOINT FAITHS ADVISORY BOARD ON CRIMINAL JUSTICE
DATES TO BE ARRANGED

(K)   IONA COMMUNITY BOARD: Thursdays 11.30 am
DATES TO BE ARRANGED

NOMINATION OF MODERATOR OF ASSEMBLY
2000   AUGUST 29, OCTOBER 17

PENSION TRUSTEES
2000   NOVEMBER 7
2001   TO BE CONFIRMED

PERSONNEL
2000   SEPTEMBER 4, DECEMBER 7
2001   FEBRUARY 15, APRIL 26

PRACTICE AND PROCEDURE
2000   SEPTEMBER 14, NOVEMBER 21
2001   JANUARY 16, FEBRUARY 20, APRIL 17

STEWARDSHIP AND FINANCE
2000   NOVEMBER 8-9
2001   FEBRUARY 28, MARCH 28, JUNE 20

WORLD MISSION
(A)   BOARD
2000   OCTOBER 11, DECEMBER 6
2001   FEBRUARY 21, (APRIL DATE TO BE DECIDED)
(B)   EUROPE
2000   SEPTEMBER 26
(C)   FINANCE
2000   SEPTEMBER 26
(D)   FURLOUGH HOUSES
2000   SEPTEMBER 8
(E)   LOCAL INVOLVEMENT
2000   SEPTEMBER 6, SEPTEMBER 21
2001   MARCH 29

(F) OVERSEAS PARTNERSHIP AND OVERSEAS CHARGES
2000 SEPTEMBER 7, NOVEMBER 9
2001 JANUARY 25, MARCH 15
(G) WORLD CHURCH IN SCOTLAND
2000 NOVEMBER 14
2001 JANUARY 23, MARCH 13

WORSHIP
2000 SEPTEMBER 14, NOVEMBER 9
2001 FEBRUARY 22, JUNE 7, SEPTEMBER 13

[NOTE: Years, where given, indicate the year of appointment.]

(1) GENERAL ADMINISTRATION
(PRACTICE AND PROCEDURE)

MEMBERSHIP
BOARD OF PRACTICE AND PROCEDURE
(38 members: 32 appointed by the Assembly, plus Moderator, Moderator Designate, Clerks, Procurator and Law Agent *ex officiis*)
Convener: Rev. David W. Lacy (2000)
Vice Convener: Rev. William C. Hewitt BD
Secretary: The Principal Clerk

COMMITTEE TO NOMINATE THE MODERATOR
(54 members: 3 surviving immediate past Moderators, 3 elders appointed through the Nomination Committee and 1 member from each UK Presbytery and the Presbytery of Europe)
Convener: The latest serving former Moderator present and willing to act
Secretary: The Principal Clerk

JUDICIAL COMMISSION OF THE GENERAL ASSEMBLY
Chairman: Sheriff J. Douglas Allan
Vice Chairman: Rev. Alistair G.C. McGregor QC BD
Secretaries: The Clerks of Assembly

STAFF
Principal Clerk: Rev. Finlay A.J. Macdonald MA BD PhD
Depute Clerk: Rev. Marjory A. MacLean LLB BD
Administrative Officer: Miss Chris Brown MBE BA

REMIT: BOARD OF PRACTICE AND PROCEDURE
(a)   To advise the General Assembly on questions of Church Law and of Constitutional Law affecting the relationship between Church and State.
(b)   To advise and assist Committees of the General Assembly in the preparation of proposed legislation and on questions of interpretation, including interpretation of and proposed changes to their remits.
(c)   To make all necessary arrangements for the General Assembly each year.
(d)   To advise the Moderator anent his or her official duties, if so required.
(e)   To be responsible to the General Assembly for the care and maintenance of all Assembly buildings and its other property.
(f)   To compile the statistics of the Church, except Youth and Finance; and to supervise on behalf of the General Assembly all arrangements for care of Church Records and for Quinquennial Visitations.
(g)   To attend to the general interests of the Church in matters which are not covered by the remit of any other Committee; and to perform such other duties as may be assigned to it by Act or Deliverance of the General Assembly.
(h)   To deal with urgent issues arising between meetings of the General Assembly or the Commission of Assembly which do not fall within the remit of any Board, provided that
       (a)   it shall not be competent for the Board to take or authorise an action which is

(i)   of such a nature that it would have been *ultra vires* of the Commission of Assembly, or
(ii) of a legislative or judicial nature, or
(iii) an order or instruction to any Court or Courts of the Church.

(b) any action taken in terms of this Clause shall be reported by the Board to the next meeting of the General Assembly or the Commission of Assembly, whichever is the sooner.

(2) GENERAL TRUSTEES

MEMBERSHIP

(New Trustees are appointed, as required, by the General Assembly, on the recommendation of the General Trustees)

Chairman:	Mr William S. Carswell MA LLB (1999)
Vice Chairman:	Rev. James H. Simpson BD LLB (1999)
Secretary and Clerk:	Mr Alan W. Cowe MA LLB (Tel: 0131 225 5722)
Depute Secretary and Clerk:	Mr T.R.W. Parker LLB

COMMITTEES:

Fabric Committee
Convener: Rev. James H. Simpson BD LLB (1994)

Chairman's Committee
Convener: Mr William S. Carswell MA LLB (1999)

Glebes Committee
Convener: Mr A.S. Chalmers FRICS (1988)

Finance Committee
Convener: Mr R.G. Burnett BComm CA FCMA (1999)

Law Committee
Convener: Professor J. Alistair M. Inglis CBE MA LLB (1999)

STAFF

Secretary and Clerk:	Mr Alan W. Cowe MA LLB
Depute Secretary and Clerk:	Mr T.R.W. Parker LLB
Assistants:	Miss P.M. Burnside LLB NP (Glebes)
	Mr David D. Robertson LLB NP (Ecclesiastical Buildings)
Treasurer:	Mr D.F. Ross MA CA
Deputy Treasurer:	Mr W.J. McKean BAcc CA

REMIT

The General Trustees are a Property Corporation created and incorporated under the Church of Scotland (General Trustees) Order Confirmation Act 1921. Their duties, powers and responsibilities were greatly extended by the Church of Scotland (Property & Endowments) Acts and Orders 1925 to 1995, and they are also charged with the administration of the Central Fabric Fund (see below) and the Consolidated Fabric Fund and the Consolidated Stipend Fund in which monies held centrally for the benefit of individual congregations are lodged.

The scope of the work of the Trustees is broad, covering all facets of property administration, but particular reference is made to the following matters:

1. **ECCLESIASTICAL BUILDINGS.** The Trustees' Fabric Committee considers proposals for work at buildings, regardless of how they are vested, and plans of new buildings. Details of all such projects should be submitted to the Committee before work is commenced. The Committee also deals with applications for the release of fabric monies held by the General Trustees for individual congregations, and considers applications for assistance from the Central Fabric Fund from which grants and/or loans may be given to assist congregations faced with expenditure on fabric. Application forms relating to consents for work and possible financial assistance from the Central Fabric Fund are available from the Secretary of the Trustees and require to be submitted through Presbytery with its approval. The Committee normally meets on the first or second Tuesday of each month, apart from July when it meets on the last Tuesday and August when there is no meeting.

2. **SALE, PURCHASE AND LETTING OF PROPERTIES.** All sales or lets of properties vested in the General Trustees fall to be carried out by them in consultation with the Financial Board of the congregation concerned, and no steps should be taken towards any sale or let without prior consultation with the Secretary of the Trustees. Where property to be purchased is to be vested in the General Trustees it is essential that contact be made at the earliest possible stage with the Solicitor to the Trustees who is responsible for the lodging of offers for such properties and all subsequent legal procedure.

3. **GLEBES.** The Trustees are responsible for the administration of Glebes vested in their ownership. All lets fall to be granted by them in consultation with the Minister concerned. It should be noted that neither Ministers nor Kirk Sessions may grant lets of Glebe land vested in the General Trustees. As part of their Glebe administration the Trustees review regularly all Glebe rents.

4. **INSURANCE.** Properties vested in the General Trustees must be insured with the Church of Scotland Insurance Co. Ltd, a company wholly owned by the Church of Scotland whose profits are applied for Church purposes. Insurance enquiries should be sent directly to the Company at 67 George Street, Edinburgh EH2 2JG. (Tel: 0131 220 4119 Fax: 0131 220 4120)

---

(3) NOMINATION

MEMBERSHIP – NOMINATION COMMITTEE
(44 members)
Convener: Rev. Fraser R. Aitken MA BD (1999)
Vice-Convener: Rev. Keith F. Hall BD
Secretary: The Principal Clerk

REMIT
To bring before the General Assembly names of persons to serve on the Boards and Standing Committees of the General Assembly.

(4) CHURCH OF SCOTLAND INVESTORS TRUST

MEMBERSHIP

(Trustees are appointed by the General Assembly, on the nomination of the Investors Trust)

Chairman:	Mr. J.B.M. Dick ACIB
Vice Chairman:	Mr D.M. Simpson BA FFA
Treasurer:	Mr D.F. Ross MA CA
Secretary:	Mr J.L. Henderson MCIBS

REMIT

The Church of Scotland Investors Trust, established in 1994 by Act of Parliament, offers to Boards, Committees and congregations of the Church a simple and economical medium for the investment of their funds. Investors are at liberty to invest in the Church of Scotland Investors Trust to an unlimited extent and it is felt that the facilities afforded thereby are preferable to the powers of investment offered by the Trustee Investments Act 1961, with all the attendant restrictions and conditions. The Church of Scotland Investors Trust provides three Funds for Church investors:

(a) **THE DEPOSIT FUND** is intended for short term money, and deposits are repayable on demand. Interest is calculated quarterly, but paid gross, half yearly on 15th May and 15th November. The Fund is invested in short term loans to Banks, Building Societies and Licensed Deposit-Taking Institutions. There is no capital appreciation in the Deposit Fund and hence there is no protection for capital against inflation. The Deposit Fund is professionally managed by Noble Grossart Limited, Edinburgh.

(b) **THE GROWTH FUND** previously known as the "General Investment Fund" is an equity-based Fund, intended for long-term investment. The Fund, which is operated on a unitised basis, is designed to provide capital growth whilst endeavouring to maintain an income distribution which increases in line with inflation. Units can be purchased or sold monthly. Income is distributed gross, half-yearly on 15th May and 15th November. The Growth Fund is professionally managed by Murray Johnstone Ltd, Glasgow.

(c) **THE INCOME FUND** is intended for medium term investment of capital on which it is essential to obtain an immediate and consistent high yield. The Fund is invested predominantly in fixed interest securities. It offers little protection against inflation for income or capital. The Income Fund is operated on a unitised basis and units can be purchased or sold monthly. Income is distributed gross, half-yearly, on 15th March and 15th September. The Income Fund is professionally managed by Baillie Gifford & Co., Edinburgh.

Application Forms for investment and further information may be had from the Secretary of the Church of Scotland Investors Trust, 121 George Street, Edinburgh EH2 4YN.

(5) STEWARDSHIP AND FINANCE

MEMBERSHIP
BOARD OF STEWARDSHIP AND FINANCE
(77 Members: 24 appointed by the Assembly, plus Convener and Vice-Convener, the Convener, Vice-Convener and Secretary of the Co-ordinating Forum, and 47 from Presbyteries who attend three meetings of the Board at which they have full rights of Board members)
Convener: Mr Leon M. Marshall CA (1997)
Vice Convener: Rev. J. Colin Caskie BA BD (1998)

STAFF
General Treasurer's Department
General Treasurer: Mr Donald F. Ross MA CA
Deputy General Treasurers: Mr Alexander F. Gemmill BAcc CA
                                   Mr John S. Steven CA
                                   Mr William J. McKean BAcc CA
Assistant Treasurer: Mrs Anne Macintosh BA CA
Accountant: Mr Ross Donaldson
Stewardship Department
Director of Stewardship: Rev. Gordon D. Jamieson MA BD
Deputy Director: Mr Crawford Conochie
Stewardship Consultants: Mrs Gillian Paterson
                                   Mr W. John Gray
                                   Mrs Edith Scott
Board Administration
Administrative Secretary: Mr Fred E. Marsh MCIBS

BOARD REMIT
1.   To promote teaching and understanding of Christian Stewardship throughout the Church. To provide programmes to assist congregations in visiting members, making known the work of the Church and promoting Christian giving. To help congregations through the service of its Stewardship Consultants in running conferences, advising office-bearers and training visitors.
2.   To prepare a Co-ordinated Budget for the costs of Local Mission, Ministry, and the Mission and Aid Fund and submit it to the General Assembly each year for approval.
3.   To be responsible with the Board of Ministry and Presbyteries for allocating among congregations the Co-ordinated Budget approved by the General Assembly and to seek to ensure that congregations meet their obligations by transmitting contributions towards their allocations regularly throughout the year to the General Treasurer of the Church.
4.   To provide financial, administrative and accounting services for the General Assembly, the Boards and Committees of the Church.

The Board has a duty to report annually to the General Assembly on the general financial position of the Church and powers to examine the financial and statistical information of such Boards and Committees of the General Assembly as the Board shall consider appropriate.

The Board exercises control of the General Treasurer's Department and the Stewardship Department and maintains a close liaison with the Church of Scotland Investors Trust, which is serviced by officials of the Board.

GENERAL TREASURER'S DEPARTMENT

The General Treasurer's Department provides a central finance service for the General Assembly Boards and Committees and for the Statutory Corporations. Its responsibilities include:

- Payroll processing for the Board of Ministry and the Personnel Committee
- Issuing to congregations their requirement figures for Ministry Funds and the Mission and Aid Fund
- Receiving payments from congregations towards their central requirements
- Providing accountancy systems and services for Boards and Committees
- Providing banking arrangements and operating a central banking system for Boards and Committees
- Making Gift Aid and Deed of Covenant tax recoveries on behalf of Boards and Committees
- Making Deed of Covenant tax recoveries on behalf of congregations
- Providing financial and secretarial services for the Church of Scotland Investors Trust
- Providing financial services for the Church of Scotland General Trustees
- Providing financial services for the Trustees of the Church's Pension Schemes

STEWARDSHIP DEPARTMENT

The Stewardship Department is responsible for the promotion of Christian Stewardship throughout the Church (part 1 of the Board Remit). This involves the production of material to assist congregations in developing an understanding of Christian Stewardship and encouraging a higher level of giving of time, talents and money from the members of the Church. The staff of the Stewardship Department are regularly involved in meetings with congregations and Presbyteries.

The Stewardship Department is also responsible for processing the allocating of the Mission and Aid Fund among the self-supporting congregations of the Church.

NEW GIFT AID

As a result of changes to the Gift Aid Scheme which were introduced in April 2000, the £250 minimum for Gift Aid donations has been abolished, so that the scheme now applies to all donations from taxpayers, whether large or small, regular or one-off.

The separate tax relief for payments made under Deed of Covenant has been withdrawn, and relief for such payments will in future be under the Gift Aid Scheme.

Gift Aid Certificates have been replaced by new, simpler and more flexible Gift Aid Declarations, which can be made in advance of the donation, at the time of the donation, or at any time after the donation (subject to the normal six year limit), and can cover one or more donations.

Donors no longer must pay basic rate income tax - they simply have to pay an amount of income tax or capital gains tax, whether at the basic rate or some other rate, equal to the tax deducted from their donations.

Donors who pay tax at the higher rate will be able to claim further relief in their Self-Assessment tax return against either income tax or capital gains tax.

Companies will no longer be required to deduct tax from their donations to charities.

The New Gift Aid Scheme offers an opportunity for congregations to increase the tax recovered on both regular offerings and one-off donations from taxpayers. In order to meet Inland Revenue requirements, offerings must be received from the donor by cheque, Banker's Order, or cash through Offering Envelopes. Cash put into the Open Plate, which cannot be recorded against the name of a particular person, cannot be treated as Gift Aid donations.

Each congregation is responsible for maintaining proper records, for obtaining Gift Aid Declarations from the donors, and for making repayment claims to the Inland Revenue.

Claims should be submitted on Charity Repayment Claim Form R68 (2000), supported by

Schedule R68 (New Gift Aid), to the Inland Revenue, FICO (Scotland), Trinity Park House, South Trinity Road, Edinburgh EH5 3SD.

GIVING WITH A WILL
Making a will is a sensitive but wise decision. It is also an aspect of good stewardship. The provisions of a will can show our love and concern for our families and friends. They can also provide us with an opportunity to continue supporting the work of the Church of Scotland. The Church acknowledges with gratitude the many legacies it has received over the years and the kind and generous thoughts which have been their inspiration. Such giving is encouraged by the government: gifts of money to the Church are exempt from Inheritance Tax without limit.

The General Treasurer or the Solicitor of the Church of Scotland will always be ready to give information about the work of the Church to members (and their solicitors) interested in providing a legacy.

(6) CHURCH OF SCOTLAND PENSION TRUSTEES

Chairman: Mr W.D.B. Cameron CA
Vice Chairman: Mr W.J. McCafferty ACII ASFA CIP
Secretary: Mrs S. Dennison BA

STAFF
Pensions Manager: Mrs S. Dennison BA
Assistant Pensions Administrators: Mrs M. Marshall
                                     Mr M. Hannam

REMIT

The body acts as Trustees for the Church of Scotland's three Pension Schemes:
(a)   The Church of Scotland Pension Scheme for Ministers and Overseas Missionaries;
(b)   The Church of Scotland Pension Scheme for Staff;
(c)   The Church of Scotland Pension Scheme for the Board of National Mission.

The Trustees have wide-ranging duties and powers detailed in the Trust Law, Pension Acts and other regulations, but in short the Trustees are responsible for the administration of the Pension Schemes and for the investment of the Scheme Funds. Six Trustees are appointed by the General Assembly, and members nominate up to three Trustees for each Scheme.
    The investment of the Funds is delegated to external Investment Managers under the guidelines and investment principles set by the Trustees: Baillie Gifford & Co for the Ministers' Scheme and National Mission Scheme; and Tilney Fund Management and Scottish Value Management for the Staff Scheme.
    The benefits provided by the three Pension Schemes differ in detail, but all provide a pension to the Scheme member and dependants on death of the member, and a lump sum death benefit on death in service. Scheme members also have the option to improve their benefits by paying additional voluntary contributions (AVCs) to plans set up by the Trustees with leading Insurance Companies. Ministers' benefits can also be increased by additional contributions by their congregations.

Further information on any of the Church of Scotland Pension Schemes or on individual benefits can be obtained from the Pensions Manager, Mrs S. Dennison, at the Church Offices, 121 George Street, Edinburgh EH2 4YN.

(7) PERSONNEL

MEMBERSHIP
PERSONNEL COMMITTEE
(14 Members: 6 appointed by the Assembly)
Convener: Mr Graham Charters MBE FCIS
Vice-Convener: Mr Gordon A. Murison MBE
Secretary: Mr George B.B. Eadie BA

STAFF
Personnel Manager: Mr George B.B. Eadie BA
Assistant Personnel Manager: Miss Angela Brady MIPD
Personnel Officer: Miss Maria Carena
Personnel Assistant: Mrs Dorothy Menzies

REMIT
This body was set up in 1978 on the Report of the Advisory Board to determine salaries, length of service and conditions generally for Secretaries and Members of Office Staff. In 1991, and again in 1996, the General Assembly made certain minor adjustments to the remit, including a requirement that the Personnel Committee should conduct an annual salary review of those members of staff for which it is the employing agency.

In recognition of the aim that the Personnel Committee may in time operate as the co-ordinating body for the Church in respect of the salaries and conditions of employment of all persons employed by the five employing agencies, the other four employing agencies are required to provide all information on such matters as requested by the Personnel Committee.

(8) THE CHURCH OF SCOTLAND GUILD

NATIONAL OFFICE-BEARERS AND EXECUTIVE STAFF
Convener: Mrs Elva A.M. Carlisle MA
Vice-Convener: Mrs Elspeth Kerr DCE NFU
General Secretary: Mrs Alison Twaddle MA JP
                            [e-mail: atwaddle@cofscotland.org.uk]
Information Officer: Mrs Fiona J. Lange
                            [e-mail: fjlange@cofscotland.org.uk]
                            (Tel: 0131 225 5722 ext 317; 0131 240 2217)

The Church of Scotland Guild is a movement within the Church of Scotland, whose aim is **"to invite and encourage all women to commit their lives to Jesus Christ and to enable them to express their faith in worship, prayer, and action"**.

Membership of the Guild is open to all who subscribe to that aim. At 31st December 1999 there were 44,364 members in 1429 affiliated groups throughout Scotland and beyond. The revised 1997 Constitution opens the way for other groups at congregational level – fellowship groups, prayer and study groups, single issue groups – to affiliate to the movement.

Groups at congregational level are free to organise themselves under the authority of the Kirk Session, as best suits their own local needs and circumstances. Large groups with frequent meetings and activities continue to operate with a committee or leadership team, while other, smaller groups simply share whatever tasks need to be done amongst the membership as a whole. Similarly, at Presbyterial Council level, frequency and style of meetings vary according to local needs, as do leadership patterns. Each Council may nominate one person to serve at national level, where six committees made up of these representatives take forward the work of the Guild in accordance with the stated aim. These Committees are:

- Executive
- Finance and General Purposes
- Projects and Topics
- Programmes and Resources
- Marketing and Publicity
- Matters Concerning Younger Women

There has always been a close relationship between the Boards and Committees of the Church and the Guild, latterly through a system of delegates. Many Departments of the Church have since set up a link system, and the Guild is delighted that many former delegates have become congregational links to the major Boards of the Church. In addition the Guild continues to relate to the wider work of the Church through the Project Partnership Scheme .

This scheme affords groups at congregational level the opportunity to select a project, or projects, from a range of up to six, selected by the Projects and Topics Committee from submissions by a wide range of Church Departments and other Church-related bodies. A project partner in each group seeks ways of promoting the project locally, increasing awareness of the issues raised by it, and encouraging support of a financial and practical nature. She is helped in these tasks by the Project Co-ordinator at Council level and by the Information Officer based at the Guild Office.

The Guild is very aware of the importance of good communication in any large organisation, and regularly sends mailings to its branches to pass on information and resources to the members. In addition the Newsletter, sent to members three times per session, is a useful communication tool. It is a means of sharing both local news and experiences, and of communicating some-thing of the wider interest and influence of the Guild, which is represented on other national bodies such as ACTS Network of Ecumenical Women in Scotland and the Women's National Commission.

Each year the Guild has a Theme and produces a resources pack covering worship and study material. In recent years there has also been a Discussion Topic with supporting material and background information. The theme, topic and projects all relate to a common three year strategy which, for 2000-2003, is **"Strength for Living"**. Each of the six current projects – from National Mission, World Mission, Communication, The Lodging House Mission, the National Bible Society, and Mission Aviation Fellowship – reflects some aspect of strength for living. The 2000-2001 Theme is **"Strength Through God's Promises"** and Guilds are invited to explore this in a variety of ways, looking at the Biblical account of the nature of God's promises and the current contextual outworking of them. The related Discussion Topic is **"Commitment, What Price?"** which addresses the seemingly unfashionable nature of commit-ment of any kind in today's society, whilst reflecting on the constancy of God's commitment to His creation.

(9) ASSEMBLY COUNCIL

MEMBERSHIP
(12 members appointed by the Assembly)
Convener: Mrs Helen M. McLeod MA, Forfar (1999)
Vice Convener: Rev. Duncan E. McClements MA BD MTh, Falkirk (1999)

[The Principal Clerk attends in an advisory capacity, but without the right to vote.]

STAFF
Research & Development Officer: Sophia Marriage MA PhD
                                                           [e-mail: SMarriage@cofscotland.org.uk]
                                                           (Tel: 0131 225 5722)

REMIT
The revised remit of the Assembly Council, as determined by the General Assembly of 1999, is as follows:

> In ongoing consultation with *inter alia* Presbyteries, Boards, Committees, congregations, other denominations, and appropriate ecumenical bodies, and in collaboration with the Co-ordinating Forum, to assess the changing needs, challenges, and responsibilities of the Church, to identify priority areas and tasks, and to make recommendations to the General Assembly.

---

(10) CHURCH AND NATION

MEMBERSHIP
CHURCH AND NATION COMMITTEE
(48 members: 32 appointed by the Assembly; 16 appointed by Presbyteries)
Convener: Rev. Alan McDonald LLB BD MTh (2000)
Vice Convener: Rev. Erik M. Cramb LTh (1999)
Secretary: Rev. David I. Sinclair BSc BD PhD DipSW

REMIT
The remit of the Church and Nation Committee as defined by the Assembly is:

> "to watch over developments of the Nation's life in which moral and spiritual considerations specially arise, and to consider what action the Church from time to time may be advised to take to further the highest interests of the people."

There are five Sub-Committees:
- International Interests
- Economic and Industrial Interests
- Social Interests
- Media Interests
- Constitutional Issues

(11) PANEL ON DOCTRINE

MEMBERSHIP
16 members: 12 appointed by the Assembly, and four from the four University Faculties/Departments of Divinity, with the Principal Clerk, the Procurator and the Convener of the Board of Practice and Procedure *ex officiis*.
Convener: Rev. John McPake BA BD PhD (1999)
Vice Convener: Mrs Katharina Nimmo (1999)

STAFF
Administrative Secretary: Rev. Douglas Galbraith MA BD BMus MPhil ARSCM

REMIT
The responsibilities of the Panel on Doctrine include: the fulfilling of remits from the General Assembly on matters concerning doctrine; drawing the attention of the General Assembly to matters inside the Church of Scotland or elsewhere which might have significant doctrinal implications, with recommendations for action; being available for consultation by other Committees of the General Assembly on any matter which might be of doctrinal significance; communicating and consulting in an ecumenical context on matters involving doctrine.

(12) PANEL ON WORSHIP

MEMBERSHIP
28 members: all appointed by the Assembly
Convener: Very Rev. Gilleasbuig I. Macmillan CVO MA BD Drhc (1999)
Vice Convener: Rev. Colin Renwick BMus BD (1998)

STAFF
Administrative Secretary: Rev. Douglas Galbraith MA BD BMus MPhil ARSCM

REMIT
The Panel on Worship exists to witness to the importance of worship as a primary function of the Church. It has three major committees:

• The Liturgical Committee is concerned with the provision of worship materials for public use and is responsible, among other things, for the production of *Common Order*.
• The Prayer and Devotion Committee is responsible for *Pray Now* and for courses and retreats to promote spiritual growth.
• The Music Committee encourages new developments in church music, the training of musicians, and the publication of relevant materials.

The Panel is engaged also in providing materials for worship in Gaelic and is involved in the compilation of new hymn books and supplements. From time to time, it publishes occasional papers on aspects of the practice of Public Worship.

(13) COMMITTEE ON ARTISTIC MATTERS

MEMBERSHIP
22 members (of whom not less than five shall have professional or practical skills and knowledge) appointed by the General Assembly, one appointed from the General Trustees and two appointed from the Committee on New Charge Development, plus up to five co-opted persons with special knowledge.

Convener: Mr Douglas Laird RIBA FRIAS (1999)
Vice Convener: Rev. Roy Wilson DA ARIBA ARIAS (1998)

STAFF
Administrative Secretary: Rev. Douglas Galbraith MA BD BMus MPhil ARSCM

REMIT
The Committee advises congregations and Presbyteries regarding the most appropriate way of carrying out renovations, alterations and re-ordering of interiors, having regard to the architectural quality of Church buildings. It also advises on the installation of stained glass, tapestries, memorials, furniture and furnishings, and keeps a list of accredited artists and craftsworkers.

Any alteration to the exterior or interior of a Church building which affects its appearance must be referred to the Committee for approval, which is given on behalf of the General Trustees. Congregations contemplating alterations are urged to consult the Committee at an early stage.

Members of the Committee and of its local area panels are prepared, when necessary, to visit churches and meet office-bearers. The Committee's services are given free.

In recent years the General Assembly has conferred these additional duties on the Committee:
(a) preparation of reports on the architectural, historical and aesthetic merit of the buildings of congregations involved in questions of readjustment;
(b) verification of the propriety of repair and renovation work forming the basis of grant applications to Historic Scotland;
(c) the offering of advice on the maintenance and installation of organs;
(d) facilitating the transfer of unwanted furnishings etc. from one church to another through the quarterly *Exchange and Transfer*;
(e) the compilation of a Register of Churches;
(f) the processing of applications from congregations for permission to dispose of surplus communion plate.

(14) DEPARTMENT OF MINISTRY

BOARD OF MINISTRY
Convener: Rev. Professor William F. Storrar MA BD PhD
General Secretary: The Very Rev. Alexander McDonald
                                   BA CMIWSc DUniv
Depute General Secretary: Rev. John P. Chalmers BD
Director of Educational Services: Rev. Nigel J. Robb MA BD ThM MTh
Accountant: Mrs Pauline Willder MA PgDipIS

COMMITTEES:
Ministry Support   (25 members)
Convener: Rev. Shaw J. Paterson BSc BD
Secretary: Very Rev. Alexander McDonald BA CMIWSc DUniv

Vocational Guidance   (25 members)
Convener: Rev. Christine M. Goldie LLB BD DMin
Secretary: Mrs Elizabeth Chalmers

Education and Training   (25 members)
Convener: Rev. Ian Taylor BD ThM
Secretary: Rev. Robert S. T. Allan LLB DipLD BD

Ministry Development   (25 members)
Convener: Mr William Greenock MA
Secretary: Rev. Angus R. Mathieson MA BD

Trustees of Housing and Loan Fund   (10 members)
Chairman: Mr William McVicar CA
Secretary: Mr Ronald C. Mather

Chaplains to HM Forces   (20 members)
Convener: Rev. Professor Iain R. Torrance TD MA BD DPhil (1998)
Vice Convener: Professor Herbert A. Kerrigan QC
Secretary: Mr Douglas M. Hunter WS
                          19 Ainslie Place, Edinburgh EH3 6AU (Tel: 0131 226 6881)

STAFF
General Secretary: Very Rev. Alexander McDonald
                                        BA CMIWSc DUniv
Depute General Secretary: Rev. John P. Chalmers BD
Director of Educational Services: Rev. Nigel J. Robb MA BD MTh ThM
Assistant Secretary: Mr Ronald C. Mather
Education and
   Development Officers: Rev. Robert S.T. Allan LLB DipLP BD
                                        Rev. Angus R. Mathieson MA BD
                                        Rev. Martin Scott DipMusEd RSAM BD PhD
                                        Mrs Yvonne Teague DCS
Vocational Guidance Officer: Mrs Elizabeth Chalmers
Accountant: Mrs Pauline Willder MA PgDipIS
Finance Officer: Miss Elizabeth Dailly

REMIT
The Board of Ministry is responsible for all aspects of the recruitment, education, training, in-service training and support of ministers, auxiliary ministers and deacons as well as making the financial provision for that work. To enable the Board to discharge these responsibilities and fulfil its remit, the Board shall determine from time to time what constituent Committees are required. The exceptions to this will be in respect of the Housing and Loan Fund for Retired Ministers and Widows and Widowers of Ministers and the Committee on Chaplains to Her Majesty's Forces, the Trustees and members respectively of which continue to be appointed as at present and report separately to the General Assembly.

The work of the Board is under the care of the following Committees:

A. MINISTRY SUPPORT

The responsibilities of the Committee are:
(a) To determine and declare the Minimum Stipend.
(b) To advise the Church in matters relating to stipend levels and arrangements.
(c) To deal with appropriate matters relating to endowments.
(d) To deal with appropriate matters relating to allowances, expenses, loans and the like for which those engaged in ministry in the Church and their families are, or may be, eligible.
(e) The pastoral care of all in the Ministry, insofar as centralised co-ordination and support are desired or required.

The Ministry
The Church of Scotland is a National Church and has the responsibility of providing the ministry of Word and Sacrament to all the people of Scotland on a territorial basis. This is achieved through the parish ministry, which is supported by the Board of Ministry.

Consolidated Stipend Endowment Fund
The General Assembly of 1981 approved the creation of the Consolidated Stipend Endowment Fund. The creation of this Fund, which meets all the requirements of the Church of Scotland (Property and Endowments) Act 1925, has greatly facilitated the administration of stipend endowments. The Fund is administered by the Church of Scotland General Trustees and is invested through the medium of the Church of Scotland Trust.

Each congregation which had endowment income for stipend purposes in 1981 was given a proportionate share in the Fund. While income from Glebe Rents does not form part of the Consolidated Stipend Endowment Fund, the net sale proceeds of Glebe land constitutes new capital for the Fund and this is used to purchase shares in the Fund.

Endowment Grants
The Committee makes grants to allow congregations to improve their endowment income for stipend purposes through the Grants for Further Endowment Scheme. Information about the availability of endowment grants and the terms and conditions on which they are made can be obtained from Mr Ronald C. Mather, Assistant Secretary, at the Church Offices.

Stipend and Aid
The Ministry Support Committee has the responsibility of exercising the delegated authority of the General Assembly in the matter of the declaration of the Minimum Stipend. The actual level of the Minimum Stipend from year to year depends on various factors, but the most important factor is the continuing response of members and adherents through their offerings. Stipends above the level of the Minimum Stipend are determined by Presbyteries and the Committee acting together.

Congregations without sufficient resources to meet the full stipend have an agreed level of Aid granted to them from the Fund, to assist in meeting the stipend. The level of aid to be received is determined in advance by the Committee and the Presbytery acting together. The amount of stipend provision to Aid Receiving congregations forms the major requirement on the Fund.

MISCELLANEOUS PROVISIONS FROM THE FUND

Centralised Payment of Travelling Expenses
The General Assembly in 1990 approved the introduction of the Centralised payment of Travelling Expenses. At the Board of Ministry meeting in June 1999 it was agreed that from January 2000 the payment of a minister's travelling expenses would be based on actual miles travelled, thus meeting the regulations contained in current fiscal policy.

A minister providing a car for pastoral travel will receive an agreed lump sum paid in twelve equal parts along with the stipend. This is intended to assist with capital costs in car provision and does not require a separate claim. In addition, travelling expenses at the current level will be reimbursed through the payroll on receipt of the travelling expense claim. The Board reclaims these expenses from congregations.

Rates for Year 2001:   Lump Sum: £960
                            Pastoral Travel: First 4000 miles: 40p per mile
                                               Remaining Miles: 22.5p per mile.

Pulpit Supply
A minister is entitled annually to six Sundays' Pulpit Supply in respect of holidays and to one Sunday's Pulpit Supply when he or she is a Commissioner to the General Assembly. Presbyteries have had responsibility for this provision since 1st January 1998. Those wishing to give or to receive supply should contact their local Presbytery.

Supply Fee and Expenses
The General Assembly of 2000 approved new regulations governing the amount of Supply Fee and Expenses. They are as follows:

In charges where there is only one diet of worship, the Pulpit Supply Fee shall be a standard Fee of £45 (or as from time to time agreed by the Board of Ministry).

In Charges where there are additional diets of worship on a Sunday, the person fulfilling the Supply will be paid £10 for each additional Service (or as from time to time agreed by the Board of Ministry).

Where the person is unwilling to conduct more than one diet of worship on a given Sunday, he or she will receive a pro-rata payment based on the total available Fee shared on the basis of the number of Services conducted.

The Fee thus calculated shall be payable in the case of all persons permitted to conduct Services under Act II 1986.

In all cases necessary Travelling Expenses shall be paid. Where there is no convenient public conveyance, the use of a private car shall be paid at 22p per mile and updated from time to time by the Board of Ministry. In exceptional circumstances, to be approved in advance, the cost of hiring a car may be met.

Where weekend board and lodging are agreed as necessary, these may be claimed for the weekend at a maximum rate of that allowed when attending the General Assembly. The Fee and Expenses should be paid to the person providing the Supply before he or she leaves on the Sunday.

Provision of Cars
The current Terms and Conditions of the Car Provision Scheme are available from the Board of Ministry.

Pre-Retirement Course
The Board of Ministry arranges Pre-Retirement Courses for ministers and spouses. The courses, which are residential, include sessions on such topics as Finance in Retirement, Health in Retirement, and Leisure in Retirement.

Study Leave Scheme
The General Assembly of 1997 approved the introduction of a Study Leave Scheme for ministers, provided they have five years' qualifying service, have completed any compulsory Ministry Development Courses, and are not within five years of anticipated retirement. Those qualifying may take two weeks' study leave annually, or they may save up their entitlement to a maximum of seven years and take it in blocks to a maximum of fourteen weeks at any one time. For every two weeks of leave taken, a minister may claim funding from central funds up to £250. An Education and Development Officer has been appointed to promote and oversee the Scheme. The use to be made of the period of leave will require the approval of the Ministry Development Committee.

B.   VOCATIONAL GUIDANCE

The Vocational Guidance Committee has responsibility for all aspects of Recruitment, Assessment and Selection, and Admission and Readmission.

C.   EDUCATION AND TRAINING

The Education and Training Committee has responsibility for all aspects of the Education and Training of the Ministry.

D.   MINISTRY DEVELOPMENT

The Ministry Development Committee is responsible for maintaining present courses and promoting all aspects of Ministry Development.

E.   THE HOUSING AND LOAN FUND

The Church of Scotland Housing and Loan Fund for Retired Ministers and Widows and Widowers of Ministers endeavours, wherever possible, to assist with their retirement housing, ministers who are about to retire and surviving widows or widowers of ministers, by way of a house to rent or a house purchase loan. The main source from which the Trustees obtain funds for the purchase of houses or the granting of loans is the levy, at present 2% of stipend, made on all congregations for this specific Fund.

The Trustees may grant the tenancy on advantageous terms of one of their existing houses or, if necessary, they will purchase a house for renting. Alternatively, the Trustees may grant a house purchase loan up to a normal maximum of £59,500 or 70% of the house purchase price whichever is lower, at favourable rates of interest.

It would be helpful to the Trustees if ministers, who wish to be considered for possible help in the future, could submit their applications about ten years before their proposed date of retirement, so that the Trustees have an indication of their possible future commitment, and give the applicant a place on their waiting list.

The Trustees are prepared to consider assisting those who are already housed, but are seeking to move to more suitable accommodation.

Further information may be obtained from The Secretary: Mr Ronald C. Mather, 121 George Street, Edinburgh EH2 4YN. (Home Tel: 0131 334 1085)

F. CHAPLAINS TO HM FORCES

Recruitment
The Chaplains' Committee is entrusted with the task of recruitment of Chaplains for the Regular, Reserve and Auxiliary Forces. Vacancies occur periodically and the Committee is happy to receive enquiries from all interested Ministers.

Forces Registers
The Committee maintains a Register of all those who have been baptised and/or admitted to Communicant Membership by Service Chaplains.
    At the present time registers are being meticulously prepared and maintained. Parish Ministers are asked to take advantage of the facilities by applying for Certificates from the Secretary of the Committee.
    Full information may be obtained from the Honorary Secretary, Mr Douglas M. Hunter WS, 19 Ainslie Place, Edinburgh EH3 6AU. (Tel: 0131 226 6881)

A list of Chaplains may be found in List B in Section 6.

(15) NATIONAL MISSION

MEMBERSHIP –
BOARD OF NATIONAL MISSION (34 members)
Convener: Rev. James Gibson TD LTh (2000)
Vice Conveners: Rev. David Randall MA BD ThM (1998)
                         Mrs Fiona Campbell (2000)

PARISH REAPPRAISAL (52 members)
Convener: Rev. Arthur Barrie LTh (1999)
Vice Convener: Mr Noel Glen (1999)

NEW CHARGE DEVELOPMENT (23 members)
Convener: Rev. Andrew Ritchie BD DipMin (1999)
Vice Convener: Rev. A. Drummond BD (1999)

PARISH ASSISTANCE (16 Members)
Convener: Rev. Stanley A. Brook BD (2000)
Vice-Convener: Mrs Alison Henderson (2000)

MISSION AND EVANGELISM RESOURCES (30 members)
Convener: Rev. Colin A.M. Sinclair BA BD (1999)
Vice Conveners: Mrs Nena Dinnes (1998)
                         Rev. Howard G. Taylor BSc BD MTh (2000)

CHAPLAINCIES (25 members)
Convener: Rev. Max Homewood MSc BD (1998)
Vice-Conveners:
  Church and Industry: Mr James Greig (1999)
  Hospitals, Healthcare and
    Universities: Rev. T. Stewart McGregor MBE MA BD (1999)
  Prisons: Rev. William R. Taylor MA BD (1999)

IONA COMMUNITY BOARD
Convener: Rev. Tom Gordon MA BD (2000)

JOINT FAITHS ADVISORY BOARD ON CRIMINAL JUSTICE
Appointment pending

SCOTTISH CHURCHES COMMUNITY TRUST
Church of Scotland representative: Rev. Ian A. Moir MA BD (2000)

STAFF
General Secretary: Rev. Douglas A.O. Nicol MA BD
Secretary Depute (Parish Staffing):   Mrs Norma Henderson
Secretary Depute (Parish Resourcing):   Rev. Frank D. Bardgett MA BD PhD
Accountant: Miss Elizabeth Orr BSc CA
Property Administrator: Mr Colin Wallace
Chaplaincies Administrator: Mr John K. Thomson
Congregational Links Administrator: Mrs Georgina Payne

REMIT

1.   THE BOARD OF NATIONAL MISSION

Established on 1st January 1990 the Board, with its Constituent Committees, has the responsibility for planning and co-ordinating the Church's strategy and provision for the fulfilment of its mission as the National Church.
    The Board's policy is that the most effective missionary strategy for our time is "the development of strong congregations, adequately resourced, with a missionary concern for the parishes they are called to serve - and all this work at congregational level backed by chaplaincy in strategic areas of Scottish life".

Subject to the General Assembly, the Board's remit is as follows:
(a) Development of Policy:
      Aided by reflecting on the deliberations of a regular National Mission Conference, the Board will develop its policy which will be communicated to, and pursued by, the five Constituent Committees: Parish Reappraisal, New Charge Development, Parish Assistance, Mission and Evangelism Resources, and Chaplaincies.
(b) Finance:
      The agreement of the annual budget and the monitoring of income and expenditure will be the responsibility of the Board.
(c) New Work:
      Constituent Committees will refer to the Board new work and work which is likely to exceed the budget of the Committee. The Board will consider such referrals and grant permission if agreed.
(d) Property:
      The Board will have responsibility for the acquisition and disposal of properties and for the proper maintenance of all its properties.
(e) Presbytery Representatives:
      The Board will have the responsibility of resolving on which Constituent Committees Presbytery representatives would serve.

(f)   **General Assembly Report:**
The Board will have the responsibility for the approval of the Report to the General Assembly on the work of the Board and the five Constituent Committees.

Reporting to the General Assembly in association with the Board of National Mission are:
The Iona Community Board
The Joint Faiths Advisory Board on Criminal Justice
The Scottish Churches Community Trust

In addition the Board receives reports from the following groups:
(i)   **Congregational Link Group:** This group has the responsibility of communicating the whole range of the Board's work directly with congregations through congregational links appointed by Kirk Sessions.
(ii)   **Glasgow Lodging House Mission:** This work is based in the Institute in East Campbell Street, Glasgow and its object is to care for the thousands of homeless in Scotland's industrial capital. Oversight of the work is by a Management Committee appointed by the Presbytery of Glasgow: telephone 0141 552 0285.
(iii) **Project Rejoice Group:** This group, which seeks ecumenical support, produces visual materials for use by congregations in mission related to the key Christian Festivals. Email: NMrejoice@dial.pipex.com
(iv)   **Residential Centres' Executive:** On behalf of the Board, this group manages National Mission's two residential centres:
Badenoch Christian Centre: Situated at Kincraig in Strathspey, the Badenoch Christian Centre offers individuals, families and groups opportunities for enjoying retreats, short breaks and the many outdoor pursuits of the area from a base of Christian fellowship. Opened in 1976, the Centre is mainly self-catering. Full information from the Manager: telephone 01450 651373. Email: Badenoch@dial.pipex.com
St. Ninian's Centre, Crieff: The special concern of St. Ninian's, Crieff, is the advancement of the Church's mission and the renewal of its life as it seeks to serve the Church as a training and resource centre through courses offered and programmes specifically prepared for incoming groups. Its comfortable accommodation and extensive facilities are also available for self-programming groups and for individual or congregational retreat purposes. A programme of youth events and weekends is offered through the year. Both the Director and the Youth Worker are happy to respond to requests for advice and help in the planning and preparation of programmes. Full information from the Centre: telephone: 01764 653766: fax: 01764 655824: Email: StNinians@dial.pipex.com

2.   THE COMMITTEE ON PARISH REAPPRAISAL

In accordance with the overall policy of the Board, the Committee on Parish Reappraisal:
–   Will undertake full responsibilities and rights in connection with the implementation of Act IV (1984) and Act V (1984) and equivalent subsequent legislation directly to the General Assembly:
–   Will be responsible for dealing with all matters coming from Presbyteries regarding planning and vacancies:
–   Will deal with proposals for the staffing needs of parishes:
–   Will, in consultation with the Presbyteries concerned, and following detailed discussion with the Committee on New Charge Development, determine where new charges shall be established or where, as a result of population growth in an existing charge, an alternative location for the place of worship is deemed desirable:

– Will be available, when requested, to assist and advise Presbyteries in regard to their own forward and readjustment planning.

The Committee also supports ministry to deaf people, has responsibility for seven Community and eight Associate Ministers and for students employed through the Summer Appointment Scheme.

3.   THE COMMITTEE ON NEW CHARGE DEVELOPMENT

In accordance with the overall policy of the Board of National Mission, the Committee on New Charge Development, without prejudice to any other body (such as the Committee on Parish Reappraisal) which may have prior rights or jurisdiction, will be responsible for the following areas of work:
1.   Following the instructions of the Committee on Parish Reappraisal, to facilitate the creation of new charges. The Committee, in co-operation with other bodies, including Boards, Committees and Presbyteries, will enable the new charge to begin its mission in the new parish area, and will be responsible for:
    (a)   The development of the Charge:
    (b)   The appointment of the Minister:
    (c)   The provision of a suitable building as the place of worship which may be a new church funded and erected by the Committee, or an existing location within a community which would be suitable for the purpose of worship.
2.   In the case of established charges, where significant population growth is being established by the construction of new housing, the Committee on New Charge Development will, on the instruction of the Committee on Parish Reappraisal, enter into discussion with Presbyteries and appropriate Committees to determine the needs of the area with respect to the provision of a place of witness.
3.   Will be responsible for facilitating and supporting the mission of new charges and those not yet in full status, in co-operation with other Committees or Boards as deemed necessary.
4.   (a) Will be responsible for advising on and, within the limitations of its budget, assisting with major problems and expenditure associated with ongoing necessary maintenance of buildings, where there are building debts outstanding on the part of the congregations concerned, or where the congregation concerned is not yet in full status.
    (b) The responsibility of the Committee on New Charge Development for the purchase of land and the purchase or erection, maintenance, and disposal of buildings pertaining to the work of that Committee are the express responsibility of the Committee.
5.   To provide arbiters to make the choice of buildings to be retained in a readjustment situation.

The Committee has a responsibility for four new church developments and 13 church extension charges, with a number of other projects at various stages of development.

4.   THE COMMITTEE ON PARISH ASSISTANCE

In accordance with the overall policy of the Board and to meet the staffing needs of parishes in regard to National Mission Appointments as determined by Presbytery with the approval of the Committee on Parish Reappraisal, the Committee will:
    (a) Be responsible for investigating all applications for National Mission Appointments:
    (b) Be responsible for the Departmental matters relating to the selection, recruitment, training, personal development, employment, deployment and support of National Mission Appointments.

The Committee has responsibility for 77 Deacons, Parish Assistants and Project Workers. Following the General Assembly of 2000, the Committee will in the course of time also have responsibility for ministers employed through National Mission Appointments. Posts are advertised and people recruited who have the relevant educational standards, expertise, skills and who are called to the work of mission and outreach. Many staff serve in the large housing areas of our towns and cities where the number of ordained ministers is low in relation to the population.

For more than thirty years the Board has been providing financial support to **Bridgeton, St. Francis-in-the-East Church House,** which centre provides club facilities for young and old who have little or no church connection. A Club Leader and Assistant are in charge of the work under a Committee of Management whose Chair is the Minister of the Parish: telephone 0141 554 8045.

5. THE COMMITTEE ON MISSION AND EVANGELISM RESOURCES

In accordance with the overall policy of the Board, the Committee on Mission and Evangelism Resources will be responsible for:
–   Developing vision for the work of mission and evangelism in Scotland;
–   Encouraging mission and evangelism in Presbyteries and parishes through congregations of the Church of Scotland by means of research, development and training;
–   Ensuring that the personnel and Centres under the Committee's direction are serving the missionary and evangelistic purposes of the Church to the best advantage;
–   Identifying, originating and supporting projects which are advancing mission and evangelism in key areas of life in Scotland.
The Committee is responsible for the work of the team of Advisers in Mission and Evangelism who encourage and resource both Presbyteries and congregations. Training is provided for the network of Presbytery Mission Resource appointments: and Mission Contracts are offered to congregations by the Congregational Development Adviser and a team of Contract Enablers. In addition, the team supports the networks of Prayer Correspondents and Secretaries, circulates the "Praying Across Scotland" materials, and runs Schools of Mission and Evangelism. Regional offices are maintained in Glasgow, Inverness, Kirkcaldy and Kirriemuir from which the mission seminar materials, "Towards Tomorrow", are available. Contact the Senior Adviser: telephone 01698 428345: e-mail: NMadvisersouth@dial.pipex.com

A full list of Advisers will be found in List J in Section 6.

The Committee is also responsible for the work of a number of component Committees, projects and centres:

(a)   **The Apologetics Committee** engages in the work of apologetics with key areas of Scottish thought and culture; and produces resources to equip churches in the task of giving a reason for the Christian faith.

(b)   **The Netherbow: Scottish Storytelling Centre:** The integrated facilities of the **Netherbow Theatre** and the **John Knox House Museum,** together with the **Scottish Storytelling Centre,** are an important cultural and visitor centre on the Royal Mile in Edinburgh and provide advice and assistance nationally in the use of the arts in mission, education and worship. "Story Source", "Script Aid" and other resources are available. Contact the Director: The Netherbow, 43-45 High Street, Edinburgh EH1 1SR: telephone 0131 556 9579/2647): Website: http://www.storytellingcentre.org.uk

(c)   The Projects in Evangelism Committee oversees the work of Mission Projects and Summer Missions, whereby teams of volunteers are recruited and trained to assist parish-based and High School missions: youth mission is a priority. Details can be obtained from the Missions Co-ordinator's office at 59 Elmbank Street, Glasgow G2 4PQ: telephone: 0141 352 6946. In addition, the Committee's remit is to identify, originate and support projects in mission and evangelism of a short-term, trial or temporary nature and to liaise with and advise on local or national evangelistic campaigns.
Website: http://www.summermission.org.uk

(d)   The Rural Committee maintains an awareness of developments in rural Scottish life on both regional and topical bases and seeks to share good practice in mission and evangelism in rural Scotland through its publication "The Rural Spirit", local consultations and the Church of Scotland Stand at the Royal Highland Show. Contact the National Mission Kirkcaldy office: telephone 01592 646406.
Email: MatMissKdy@dial.pipex.com

(e)   The Society, Religion and Technology Project: This unique project, initiated in 1970, studies the impact of new technologies on society and helps the Church to form its response in ways which are practical and prophetic. The Project is a forum for all wishing to shape the Church's response to some of the most pressing issues of our time. A Newssheet, the "SRT Bulletin", is available. Contact the SRT Director, John Knox House, 45 High Street, Edinburgh EH1 1SR: telephone 0131 556 2953): e-mail: srtp@srtp.org.uk
Website: http://www.srtp.org.uk

(f)   The Urban Priority Areas Committee oversees the implementation of relevant strategies within Urban Priority Areas and monitors the work of the church within these areas at both local and national levels. Consultations are held on an annual basis and a regular publication, "UPA News" is circulated. Contact the UPA Adviser's office, 59 Elmbank Street, Glasgow G2 4PQ: telephone 0141 333 1948: e-mail: natmisnglasoffice@dial.pipex.com

(g)   The Well Asian Information and Advice Centre: the Committee provides support and funding for the Presbytery of Glasgow's innovative project that serves the south side of Glasgow by assisting with welfare, housing, immigration, asylum and personal problems. The Well has a strong mission basis on the clear principles that sharing the love of Christ has to include accepting people for who they are and respecting the beliefs of others. A regular prayer letter is available. Contact the Well, 48/50 Albert Road, Glasgow G42 8DN: telephone 0141 424 4523: Fax: 0141 422 1722: e-mail: info@the-well.clara.co.uk

6. THE COMMITTEE ON CHAPLAINCIES

In accordance with the overall policy of the Board, the Committee on Chaplaincies will be responsible, through its sub-committees on Hospitals, Healthcare and Universities, Church and Industry, and Prisons, for the encouragement, development, support and, where appropriate, review of chaplaincies in Hospitals, Healthcare, Universities, Industry, and Prisons.

Healthcare Chaplaincies The Committee administers the scheme by which, under the 1947 National Health Act, ministers and others are appointed as Chaplains in all hospitals in Scotland. There are currently 32 full-time and around 230 part-time Chaplains. Appointments of Chaplains are made by the General Secretary of the Board as the "appointing authority" after consultation with, where appropriate, the Presbytery of the bounds and the relevant Hospital Authority. Presbyteries are responsible for the oversight of part-time Chaplains' work. The Committee also employs four whole-time and two half-time chaplains' assistants.

A list of Hospital Chaplains will be found in List C in Section 6.

Church and Industry: The aim of Industrial Mission is threefold:
(a)   to provide pastoral care and witness to the Gospel for men and women in all branches of industry in their place of work;
(b)   to assess in the interest of the Gospel the nature of the influence which industry exerts both on individuals and on society;
(c)   to promote the desire for just relationships and understanding at all levels of our industrial society. The work, which is fully ecumenical in character, is now involved in most key industrial sectors. There are about 80 part-time Industrial Chaplains and seven full-time Industrial Chaplains. The co-ordinator of Scottish Churches Industrial Mission is the Rev. Erik M. Cramb: telephone: 01382 458764.

A list of Industrial Chaplains will be found in List D in Section 6.

Prison Chaplaincies: The Committee takes an interest in all matters relating to Church of Scotland Prison Chaplains appointed by the Scottish Prison Service.

A list of Church of Scotland Prison Chaplains will be found in List E in Section 6.

Universities: The Committee takes an interest in all matters relating to the appointment and support of Chaplains to Universities.

A list of University Chaplains will be found in List F in Section 6.

7.   BOARDS AND COMMITTEES ASSOCIATED WITH THE BOARD OF NATIONAL MISSION

(a) The Iona Community Board: The Iona Community Board is the body through which the Iona Community reports to the General Assembly. It is made up of Members of the Community and members of the Church appointed by the Assembly. It meets twice yearly, to hear reports of the Community's work both on Iona and Mull and on the mainland, and to assist and guide the Community in its task of seeking "new ways to touch the hearts of all".

(b) Joint Faiths Advisory Board on Criminal Justice: The General Assembly of 2000 set up this Board with representatives from the Church of Scotland, the Roman Catholic Church, the Scottish Episcopal Church, Action of Churches Together in Scotland (ACTS) and the Scottish Interfaith Council. Its principal remit is to contribute to the development of Criminal Justice philosophy, penal reform, and to the rights of offenders, untried persons and their families: and to stimulate the interest and participation of all faiths in ministry within the Criminal Justice System.

(c) Scottish Churches Community Trust: By the end of 2000, the Priority Areas Fund will have moved on to become part of the new Scottish Churches Community Trust (SCCT). The Board of National Mission is responsible for monitoring the Church of Scotland's involvement in this new inter-church funding body. SCCT gives grants, resources and support for local work with disadvantaged people which addresses spiritual, social and economic needs. The Trust is in the process of formation: in the meantime, for further information and details please contact National Mission: telephone 0131 225 5722.

(16) SOCIAL RESPONSIBILITY
Charis House, 47 Milton Road East, Edinburgh EH15 2SR
Tel: 0131 657 2000   Fax: 0131 657 5000
[e-mail: info@charis.org.uk]

BOARD OF SOCIAL RESPONSIBILITY
The Board of Social Responsibility engages in social care as part of the Christian witness of the Church to the people of Scotland. In addition, the Board offers guidance to the Church and the media about social, moral and ethical issues.

MEMBERSHIP
(96 Members: 44 appointed by the Assembly plus Convener and two Vice Conveners; 47 from Presbyteries; a representative of the Church of Scotland Guild; and a representative from the Committee on Church and Nation. They attend three meetings of the Board per year, in February, June and October, and may be asked to serve on one of the five committees.)

Convener:	Mrs Ann Allen (1997)
Vice-Conveners:	Rev. James M. Cowie (1997)
	Rev. Gilbert C. Nisbet (2000)

COMMITTEES –
EXECUTIVE
Convener: Mrs Ann Allen

CENTRAL SERVICES
Convener: Rev. Gilbert C. Nisbet

OPERATIONS
Convener: Rev. David L. Court

PLANNING AND DEVELOPMENT
Convener: Mr Ronald C. Lavalette

SOCIAL INTERESTS
Convener: Mrs Ann Allen

STAFF
Director of Social Work:	Mr Ian D. Baillie CBE
Deputy Director (Central Services):	Mr James Maguire
Deputy Director (Operations):	Mr David J. Kellock
Deputy Director (Planning and Development):	Mrs Joyce M. Buchanan

REMIT

The Board of Social Responsibility is Scotland's largest social work agency in the voluntary sector employing 2300 full and part-time staff. The range and breadth of its work is ever-increasing, but the purpose of the Board of Social Responsibility could be broadly defined as follows:

1. To offer care and help through the varied establishments and projects it operates, and to encourage and enable caring work at parish level;
2. To offer to the Church informed opinion on contemporary social, moral and ethical issues;
3. To encourage balanced judgements on these issues in the light of the Christian faith, and to put forward these judgements at all levels of influence.

DIVISIONAL STRUCTURE

Operationally, the Board's work is split into five geographical areas which cover Scotland. Each of these areas is administered by a Divisional Manager and Assistant Divisional Managers. They are physically located in their own Division, and manage and develop services at a local level. The general administration of the Board, which includes finance, publicity, training, and fundraising is carried out by staff based at the Board's offices in Charis House, Edinburgh. (Tel: 0131 657 2000).

DIVISION 1   **CITY OF GLASGOW, EAST DUMBARTONSHIRE, NORTH LANARKSHIRE**

Divisional Office: Tom Allan Centre, 23 Elmbank Street, Glasgow G2 4PD
(Tel: 0141 243 2897   Fax: 0141 229 0423)
[e-mail: division1.cos@uk.uumail.com]

Divisional Manager: Paul Robinson
A.D.M. (Planning and Development):   Flora Mackenzie
A.D.M. (Operations):   Marlene Smith

Services for Older People
Baxter House, 8-10 Lowther Terrace, Glasgow G12 0RN
(Tel: 0141 334 1231   Fax: 0141 334 3965)
Queen Mary House, 52 Queen Mary Avenue, Crosshill, Glasgow G42 8DT
(Tel: 0141 423 2736   Fax: 0141 424 1820)
Tollcross Mansionhouse, 601-641 Tollcross Road, Glasgow G32 8TF
(Tel: 0141 778 5406   Fax: 0141 778 5406)

Drug Dependency
Rainbow, 1 Belhaven Terrace, Glasgow G12 0TF
(Tel: 0141 339 2691   Fax: 0141 337 1656)

Alcohol/Drug Dependency
Victoria View, 21 Westland Drive, Glasgow G14 9NY
(Tel: 0141 959 1679   Fax: 0141 954 2572)

Counselling and Support
Tom Allan Centre, Counselling Service, 23 Elmbank Street, Glasgow G2 4PD
(Tel: 0141 221 1535   Fax: 0141 248 8452)

Learning Disabilities
Florentine, 33 Queen Mary Avenue, Glasgow G42 8DS
(Tel: 0141 423 0279   Fax: 0141 423 0635)
Saltmarket Project, Flat 1/2, 85 Saltmarket, Glasgow G1 5LE
(Tel: 0141 552 3207   Fax: 0141 552 5096)

Learning Disabilities (Children)
9 Cairnhill Place, Rosshall, Glasgow G52 3NR
(Tel: 0141 401 8037   Fax: 0141 401 8037)
The Mallard, 100 Morrin Street, Springburn, Glasgow G21 1AW
(Tel: 0141 558 7575   Fax: 0141 558 3883)

Mental Illness
Allarton, 32 Laurel Street, Glasgow G11 7QR
(Tel: 0141 339 1383   Fax: 0141 339 1314)

Offenders
Dick Stewart Hostels:
40 Circus Drive, Glasgow G31 2JE
(Tel: 0141 554 0277   Fax: 0141 554 6646)
2 Westercraigs, Dennistoun, Glasgow G31 2HZ
(Tel: 0141 554 0212)

Single Homeless
Kirkhaven Project, 107 Summerfield Street, Dalmarnock, Glasgow G40 4QT
(Tel: 0141 550 4889   Fax: 0141 556 2932)

Supported Accommodation
Whiteinch Project, 13 Victoria Park Drive South, Whiteinch, Glasgow G14 9RN
(Tel: 0141 959 5069   Fax: 0141 950 1991)

DIVISION 2   CENTRAL AND SOUTH WEST SCOTLAND

Divisional Office: Adams House, 136 Auchenlodment Road, Elderslie, Johnstone,
Renfrewshire PA5 9NX
(Tel: 01505 337303   Fax: 01505 382022)
[e-mail: division2.cos@uk.uumail.com]

Divisional Manager: Archie Henderson
A.D.M. (Planning and Development):   David Clark
A.D.M. (Operations):   John McShane

Epilepsy
Westhaven, 2 Upper Bourtree Drive, High Burnside, Rutherglen G73 4EH
(Tel: 0141 634 4563   Fax: 0141 634 0599)

Services for Older People
Auchinlee, Campbeltown, Argyll PA28 6EN
(Tel: 01586 552568   Fax: 01586 553241)
Clyde View, 12 East Montrose Street, Helensburgh G84 7HP
(Tel: 01436 674529   Fax: 01436 674529)
Cumnor Hall, 18 Racecourse View, Ayr KA7 2TY
(Tel: 01292 266450   Fax: 01292 886740)
Devorgilla House, 33 George Street, Dumfries DG1 1ED
(Tel: 01387 254007   Fax: 01387 254642)
Dunselma, 55 Main Road, Fenwick, Kilmarnock KA3 6DR
(Tel: 01560 600218   Fax: 01560 600644)

Eastwoodhill, 238 Fenwick Road, Giffnock, Glasgow G46 6UU
    (Tel: 0141 638 5127   Fax: 0141 621 4371)
Invereck, Sandbank, Dunoon, Argyll PA23 8QS
    (Tel: 01369 706231   Fax: 01369 702423)
South Beach House, 7 South Crescent Road, Ardrossan KA22 8DU
    (Tel: 01294 468234   Fax: 01294 604223)
Well Hall, 60 Wellhall Road, Hamilton ML3 9DL
    (Tel: 01698 286151   Fax: 01698 286476)

Dementia
Adams House, 136 Auchenlodment Road, Elderslie, Johnstone, Renfrewshire PA5 9NX
    (Tel: 01505 337322   Fax: 01505 337872)
Williamwood House, Strathtay Avenue, Netherlee, Glasgow G44 3YA
    (Tel: 0141 637 1168   Fax: 0141 637 6398)

Holiday Home/Conference Centre
Crosbie Tower, South Beach Road, Troon KA25 6EH
    (Tel: 01292 313696   Fax: 01292 311454)

Alcohol/Drug Dependency
Ronachan, Clachan, By Tarbet, Argyll PA29 6XW
    (Tel: 01880 740252   Fax: 01880 740616)

Learning Disabilities
Cornerstone Project, 15 Mill Road, Hamilton ML3 8AA
    (Tel: 01698 282377   Fax: 01698 283122)
Kilpatrick House, 3 Bridge Street, Alexandria, Dumbartonshire G83 0TA
    (Tel: 01389 752085   Fax: 01389 751679)
Threshold, Well Hall, 60 Wellhall Road, Hamilton ML3 9DL
    (Tel: 01698 423335   Fax: 01698 423398)

Mental Illness
Morven Day Services, Ardbeg Avenue, Kilmarnock KA3 2AR
    (Tel: 01563 572459   Fax: 01563 571086)

Residential Schools
Ballikinrain School, Balfron, Stirlingshire G63 0LL
    (Tel: 01360 440244   Fax: 01360 440946)
Geilsland School, Beith, Ayrshire KA15 1HD
    (Tel: 01505 504044   Fax: 01505 502635)

DIVISION 3   EDINBURGH AND SOUTH EAST SCOTLAND

Divisional Office: Gate Lodge, 27 Milton Road East, Edinburgh EH15 2NL
                          (Tel: 0131 669 9576   Fax: 0131 669 5185)
                          [e-mail: division3.cos@uk.uumail.com]

Divisional Manager: Jeannette S. Deacon
A.D.M. (Planning and Development):   Graham Lumb
A.D.M. (Operations):   Jennifer Spiers

Services for Older People
Mayburn House, 2 Hawthorn Gardens, Loanhead EH20 9EE
    (Tel: 0131 440 0299   Fax: 0131 440 3448)
Morlich House, 11 Church Hill, Edinburgh EH10 4BG
    (Tel: 0131 447 3239   Fax: 0131 447 2512)
Queen's Bay, 49 Milton Road East, Edinburgh EH15 2NN
    (Tel: 0131 669 2828   Fax: 0131 669 6407)
St Andrew's Centre, 9 Bayswell Road, Dunbar EH42 1AB
    (Tel: 01368 862961   Fax: 01368 863066)
The Elms, 148 Whitehouse Loan, Edinburgh EH9 2EZ
    (Tel: 0131 447 4924   Fax: 0131 447 9051)

Alcohol/Drug Dependency
Malta House, 1 Malta Terrace, Edinburgh EH4 1HR
    (Tel: 0131 332 3217   Fax: 0131 315 2313)
Rankeillor Initiative, 140 The Pleasance, Edinburgh EH8 9RR
    (Tel: 0131 662 0322   Fax: 0131 662 8293)

Counselling and Support
Connections Counselling Service, St Andrew's Centre, 9 Bayswell Road, Dunbar EH42 1AB
    (Tel: 01368 865218   Fax: 01368 863066)
Elderly Persons Project, Wallace House, 3 Boswell Road, Edinburgh EH5 3RJ
    (Tel: 0131 552 8901   Fax: 0131 552 2319)
National Counselling Service, Wallace House, 3 Boswell Road, Edinburgh EH5 3RJ
    (Tel: 0131 552 8901   Fax: 0131 552 2319)
Number 21 Counselling Service, 21 Rutland Square, Edinburgh EH1 2BB
    (Tel: 0131 221 9377   Fax: 0131 221 9399)
Post Natal Depression Project, Wallace House, 3 Boswell Road, Edinburgh EH5 3RJ
    (Tel: 0131 538 7288   Fax: 0131 552 2319)
Simpson House, Drugs Counselling and Related Services, 52 Queen Street, Edinburgh EH2 3NS
    (Tel: 0131 225 6028   Fax: 0131 220 0064)

Learning Disabilities
Dunforth, 46 Park Road, Newhaven, Edinburgh EH6 4LD
    (Tel: 0131 552 3767   Fax: 0131 552 9101)
Eskmills Project, The Old Engine House, Eskmills Business Park, Station Road,
    Musselburgh EH21 7PQ
    (Tel: 0131 665 1966   Fax: 0131 665 1966)
Gorgie Park, 21 Gorgie Park Close, Edinburgh EH14 1NQ
    (Tel: 0131 443 6844   Fax: 0131 443 7569)
Wolfson House, 95 Milton Road East, Edinburgh EH15 2NL
    (Tel: 0131 669 1216   Fax: 0131 669 1323)

Mental Illness
Tynepark Resource and Day Centre, Poldrate, Haddington EH41 4DA
    (Tel: 01620 822444   Fax: 01620 822977)

Homelessness
Cunningham House, 205 Cowgate, Edinburgh EH1 1JH
    (Tel: 0131 225 4795   Fax: 0131 220 1354)
McGregor House, 35 Spring Gardens, Edinburgh EH8 8HR
    (Tel: 0131 661 6359)

DIVISION 4   FORTH VALLEY AND NORTH EAST SCOTLAND

Divisional Office: Leslie House, Leslie, Fife KY6 3EP
(Tel: 01592 741343   Fax: 01592 743624)
[e-mail: division4.cos@uk.uumail.com]

Divisional Manager: John Wyllie
A.D.M. (Planning and Development):   Clark Bremner

Services for Older People
Ashley Lodge, 253 Great Western Road, Aberdeen AB10 6PP
    (Tel: 01224 585558   Fax: 01224 591429)
Balmedie House, Balmedie, Aberdeen AB33 8XU
    (Tel: 01358 742244   Fax: 01358 742382)
Bellfield, 1 Dee Street, Banchory AB31 5XS
    (Tel: 01330 822692   Fax: 01330 822633)
Belmont Castle, Meigle, Perthshire PH12 8TH
    (Tel: 01828 640244   Fax: 01828 640249)
Chequers, 12 Atholl Road, Pitlochry PH16 5DH
    (Tel: 01796 472521   Fax: 01796 472381)
Clashfarquhar, 23 Robert Street, Stonehaven AB39 2DJ
    (Tel: 01569 762438   Fax: 01569 762438)
Duneaves, 7 Claypotts Road, Broughty Ferry, Dundee DD5 1BX
    (Tel: 01382 738559   Fax: 01382 775728)
Kinloch Day Care and Support Services, 10A Newburgh Road, Auchtermuchty,
    Fife KY14 7BS
    (Tel: 01337 827242   Fax: 01337 828515)
Leslie House, Leslie, Fife KY6 3EP
    (Tel: 01592 741228   Fax: 01592 743432)
Rubislaw Park, Rubislaw Park Road, Aberdeen AB1 8DA
    (Tel: 01224 310641   Fax: 01224 323882)
Tryst Day Care Centre, Church Road, Pitlochry PH16 5EB
    (Tel: 01796 472160)

Dementia
St. Margaret's, St Margaret's Crescent, Polmont, Falkirk FK2 0UP
    (Tel: 01324 716149   Fax: 01324 716070)

Alcohol/Drug Dependency
Deeford, 59 Riverside Drive, Aberdeen AB10 7LE
    (Tel: 01224 585453   Fax: 01224 582626)

Counselling and Support
Dundee Women and Children Project, 11 Dock Street, Dundee DD1 4BT
    (Tel: 01382 201854   Fax: 01382 201854)

Learning Disabilities (Children)
Keith Lodge, Cameron Street, Stonehaven AB39 2HS
    (Tel: 01569 762213   Fax: 01569 764161)

Mental Illness
Gaberston House, 82 Whins Road, Alloa FK10 3SB
(Tel: 01259 722402   Fax: 01259 725930)

DIVISION 5   HIGHLANDS AND ISLANDS

Divisional Office: Cameron House, Culduthel Road, Inverness IV2 4YG
(Tel: 01463 236136   Fax: 01463 236247)
[e-mail: division5.cos@uk.uumail.com]

Divisional Manager: Margaret Wilkinson
A.D.M. (Planning and Development):   Gerald Robson

Services for Older People
Achvarasdal, Reay, Thurso KW14 7RR
(Tel: 01847 811226   Fax: 01847 811570)
Budhmor House, Portree, Isle of Skye IV51 9DJ
(Tel: 01478 612012   Fax: 01478 613580)
The Walter & Joan Gray, Main Street, Scalloway, Shetland ZE1 0XJ
(Tel: 01595 880691   Fax: 01595 880908)
Oversteps, Earls Cross Road, Dornoch IV25 3PJ
(Tel: 01862 810393   Fax: 01862 811559)
Whinnieknowe, Mill Road, Nairn IV12 5EN
(Tel: 01667 452387   Fax: 01667 451190)

Dementia
Cameron House, Culduthel Road, Inverness IV2 4YG
(Tel: 01463 243241   Fax: 01463 235808)

Alcohol/Drug Dependency
Beechwood House, 69/71 Old Perth Road, Inverness IV1 3JH
(Tel: 01463 711355/711335   Fax: 01463 711544)
Lifestyle Centre, Town Hall, Francis Street, Stornoway, Isle of Lewis HS1 2XS
(Tel: 01851 701010   Fax: 01851 704209)

Homelessness
Beechwood House, 73/79 Old Perth Road, Inverness IV1 3JH
(Tel: 01463 716206   Fax: 01463 711544)
Cale House, Flat 1, Millburn Road, Inverness IV1 3PX
(Tel: 01463 718616   Fax: 01463 718616)

Supported Accommodation
Lewis Street Flat 3/5, 6 Lewis Street, Stornoway, Isle of Lewis HS1 2JF
(Tel: 01851 706888   Fax: 01851 706376)

HOME SUPPORT
The Board is continuing to develop its Home Support Service which is available in many parts
of the country. This innovative service is designed to provide whatever kind of help a person
might need, from ironing to doing shopping, or even just providing companionship.

Home Support can help anyone, from babies to older people, and is available for as little as an hour, or a whole day or night. For more details about the service, telephone the Home Support Hotline FREE on 0800 389 7557. A video *"Home Support – The Gift of Care"* is available for hire.

SOCIAL INTERESTS
Social Interests Officer: Kristine Gibbs [e-mail: kristine@charis.org.uk]
The remit of the Board of Social Responsibility instructs it "to study and present essential Christian judgements on social and moral issues arising within the area of its concern". It does this through Study Groups, which present their findings to the Board of Social Responsibility. The Board then reports to the General Assembly. Some of the recent issues reported upon have been: Family Matters; Euthanasia; Human Sexuality; Human Genetics; Human Fertilisation and Embryology; Decriminilisation of Drugs; and Prostitution.

PRESS AND PUBLIC RELATIONS
Public Relations Officer: Hugh Brown [e-mail: hbrown@charis.org.uk]
The Board takes every opportunity to publicise the caring work of the Church, through *Life & Work*, newspapers, and articles in the Press. The Public Relations Officer co-ordinates contact with the various media, and is responsible for Press statements (in consultation with the Church's Media Relations Unit).

The *Circle of Care* Calendar, which is produced each year, highlights some of the Board's services, and sells 30,000 copies through the channels of the Guild and Church members; 45,000 copies of the *Circle of Care* newspaper are distributed three times a year with the latest news about the Board. Leaflets, brochures and videos are available to explain the Board's work. Some of the Board's reports to the General Assembly (*The Future of the Family, Euthanasia, Human Genetics, Human Fertilisation and Embryology, Health and Healing*) have been published as books by The Saint Andrew Press. There are 'user-friendly' packs on various topics: HIV/AIDS Resource Pack, Marriage PLUS – A Study Pack for Couples, and a Day Care Pack.

CONGREGATIONAL LIAISON
Congregational Liaison Officer:
The post of Congregational Liaison Officer links the social care managed and developed by the Board of Social Responsibility at a national level with the social work of the church initiated at parish level. The tasks of the Congregational Liaison Officer fall into three main categories:
1.   To encourage and enable local congregations to identify and meet the needs of local people.
2.   To ensure and enable local congregations to have knowledge and understanding of the Board's work.
3.   To maintain a database of projects which can be shared with other congregations wishing support and ideas.

CONGREGATIONAL CONTACTS
The Board has a network of Congregational Contacts around Scotland. Every parish was invited to nominate someone to be their contact with the Board, and to receive and distribute information about the Board's work. Over 1100 congregations have responded positively to this exciting initiative, and it is hoped that this will continue to increase awareness of the Board's work at local level.

FINANCIAL DEVELOPMENT
Central Fund Raiser: Maurice Houston [e-mail: mhouston@charis.org.uk]
This post exists to inform people who want to participate in the mission of Social Responsibility and to enable them to help us in our work with some of the most needy people in Scotland. We invite anyone who is interested to pray with us about the day-to-day running of Social Responsibility projects, to volunteer their time to help carry out essential tasks of all kinds and to give money to support our charitable work. If you want to know more, please get in touch with Maurice Houston on 0131 657 2000.

DEPUTATION WORK
Members of staff and of the Board will gladly visit congregations and other church organisations to speak about the work of the Board. To request a speaker and details of expenses, please write to the Congregational Liaison Officer at Charis House, 47 Milton Road East, Edinburgh EH15 2SR.

(17) WORLD MISSION
Tel: 0131 225 5722   Fax: 0131 226 6121
Update: 0131 226 4121   Ansaphone: 0131 240 2231
[e-mail: world@cofscotland.org.uk]

MEMBERSHIP: BOARD OF WORLD MISSION
(27 members: 12 from Presbyteries, 12 nominated by the General Assembly, Convener and two Vice-Conveners)

Convener:	Very Rev. Professor Alan Main
	TD MA BD STM PhD (2000)
Vice-Conveners:	Rev. Alan Greig BSc BD (1999)
	Rev. Elisabeth Cranfield MA BD (2000)

DEPARTMENTAL STAFF

General Secretary:	Rev. Prof. Kenneth R. Ross BA BD PhD
Sub-Saharan Africa:	Mr Walter T. Dunlop ARICS
Faithshare:	Miss Celeste Geddes MA
Partnership in Scotland:	Mrs Catherine Laidlaw ALA
Finance:	Mrs. Anne Macintosh BA CA
	(General Treasurer's Department)
Personnel:	Miss Sheila Ballantyne MA PgDipPM
Overseas Partnership:	Rev. Ian W. Alexander BA BD STM
Asia:	Ms Jill Hughes BA MTh

REMIT
The purpose of the Board is to enable the membership of the Church of Scotland at local, Presbytery and national levels, to experience and enjoy being part of the worldwide Church of Jesus Christ, sharing in the mission of God, as partners with other churches in the work of seeking God's kingdom on earth.

The Board carries on its work through the following constituent committees:

Overseas Partnership: Convener: Rev. Alan Greig, BSc BD (1999)
World Church in Scotland: Convener: Rev. Elisabeth Cranfield MA BD (2000)
Europe: Convener: Rev. Norman Hutcheson MA BD (1998)
Israel Centres: Convener: Rev. Alistair Bennett BSc BD (2000)
Overseas Charges: Convener: Rev. Malcolm Cuthbertson BA BD (1997)

PARTNERSHIP PRIORITIES

Following a consultation with Partner churches held in St. Andrews in September 1999, the Board has identified the following priority areas for partnership in mission:
1. **Theological Education:** developing ministerial and lay training at appropriate levels in all our churches.
2. **Evangelism:** helping one another to create new models and launch new initiatives to take the gospel to all people.
3. **Holistic Mission:** enabling one another to respond with Christian compassion to human needs in our rapidly changing societies.
4. **Mission in Pluralistic Societies:** strengthening Christian identity in our multi-religious and multi-cultural societies by supporting one another and sharing our experiences.
5. **Prophetic Ministry:** inspiring one another to discern and speak God's Word in relation to critical issues which arise in our times.
6. **Human and Material Resources:** finding new and imaginative ways of sharing our resources at all levels of church life.

WORLD MISSION AND WORLD RESOURCES

Sharing in the mission of God worldwide requires a continuing commitment to sharing the Church of Scotland's resources of people and money for mission in six continents as contemporary evidence that it is "labouring for the advancement of the Kingdom of God throughout the world" (First Article Declaratory). Such resource sharing remains an urgent matter because most of our overseas work is in the so-called "Third World," or "South", in nations where the effects of the widening gap between rich and poor is *the* major issue for the Church. Our partner churches in Africa, most of Asia, in the Caribbean, South and Central America are desperately short of financial and technical resources which we can to some extent meet with personnel and grants. However, they are more than willing to share the resources of their Christian Faith with us, including things which the Church in the West often lacks: enthusiasm in worship, hospitality and evangelism, and a readiness to suffer and struggle for righteousness, and in many areas a readiness to sink denominational differences. Mutual sharing in the World Church witnesses to its international nature, and has much to offer a divided world, not least in Scotland.

VACANCIES OVERSEAS. The Board welcomes enquiries from men and women interested in serving in the Church overseas. This is usually with indigenous denominations and related organisations with which we are in partnership overseas, in Church of Scotland congregations mostly in Europe, or our work in Israel. Those interested in more information are invited to write to the Assistant Secretary (Personnel) in the first instance.

CHRISTIAN AID SCOTLAND. Christian Aid is an official relief development agency of churches in Britain and Ireland. Christian Aid's mandate is to challenge and enable us to fulfil our responsibilities to the poor of the world. Half a million volunteers and collectors and nearly 200 paid staff make this possible, with money given by millions of supporters. The Church of Scotland marks its commitment as a church to this vital part of its mission through an annual grant from the Mission and Aid Fund, transmitted through World Mission, which keeps in close touch with Christian Aid and its work.

Up-to-date information about projects and current emergency relief work can be obtained from the National Secretary, Rev. John Wylie, Christian Aid Scotland, 41 George IV Bridge, Edinburgh EH1 1EL (Tel: 0131 220 1254); the three area co-ordinators, Ms Eildon Dyer and Mrs Ailsa Henderson, Glasgow Office, 759a Argyle Street G3 8DS (Tel: 0141 221 7475), Miss Marjorie Clark, Perth Office, 28 Glasgow Road, Perth PH2 0NX (Tel: 01738 643982); or the Director, Dr Daleep Mukarji, Christian Aid Office, PO Box 100, London SE1 7RT (Tel: 0171 620 4444).

ACCOMMODATION IN ISRAEL. The Church of Scotland has two Christian Guest Houses in Israel which provide comfortable accommodation for pilgrims and visitors to the Holy Land. Further information is available from the St Andrew's Guest House, PO Box 8619, Jerusalem (Tel: 0097226732401; Fax: 0097226731711; e-mail: standjer@netvision.net il), and the Sea of Galilee Centre, PO Box 104, Tiberias (Tel: 0097266721165; Fax: 0097266790145; e-mail: scottie@rannet.com).

A list of Overseas Appointments will be found in List K in Section 6.

A World Mission Year Book is available with more details of our partner churches and of people currently serving abroad, including those with ecumenical bodies and para-church bodies.

A list of Retired Missionaries will be found in List M in Section 6.

(18) ECUMENICAL RELATIONS

MEMBERSHIP
COMMITTEE ON ECUMENICAL RELATIONS
(27 members: 12 nominated by the General Assembly, 13 appointed by the main Boards and Committees of the Church, plus five Corresponding Members – the General Secretary of ACTS, one from the Roman Catholic Church in Scotland and three on a rotating basis from the Congregational Union of Scotland, the Scottish Episcopal Church, the Synod of the Methodist Church in Scotland, the Salvation Army, the Religious Society of Friends, the United Free Church of Scotland, the United Reformed Church, and the Baptist Union of Scotland: Convener and Vice-Convener.)

Convener: Rev. Thomas Macintyre MA BD, Paisley (1998)
Secretary: Rev. Sheilagh M. Kesting BA BD

REMIT
The purpose of the Committee is to enable the Church of Scotland, at local, Presbytery and national levels, increasingly to maximise opportunities and resources for worship, witness and service together with other churches and related organisations in this country and overseas, working wherever possible through existing Boards and Committees of the Church.

In fulfilment of this Remit the Committee will:
(i)   be the body within the Church of Scotland through which WCC, ACTS, CTBI and, as appropriate, the other Ecumenical Instruments in Britain and Ireland relate;
(ii)   call together for planning, briefing and the exchanging of information, the Church of Scotland's representatives on WCC, ACTS (Central Council, Commissions and Committees), CTBI (the Assembly and the Church Representatives Meetings) and the like;
(iii) bring to the General Assembly for the approval of the General Assembly the names of those who might serve for the following year (or appropriate term) on ACTS, on CTBI and, as appropriate, on Committees, Commissions and the like of these bodies;
(iv)   following consultation with the Board of World Mission, bring to the General Assembly for the approval of the General Assembly the names of those who might serve for the following year (or appropriate term) on such Bodies as the World Alliance of Reformed Churches, the Conference of European Churches and the World Council of Churches;
(v)   bring to the General Assembly for the approval of the General Assembly the names of those who might be invited to represent the Church of Scotland at the Assemblies or Synods of other Churches in Britain and at Conferences and Gatherings organised on an ecumenical basis at which official Church of Scotland representation is appropriate;
(vi) (a)   call for and receive reports from representatives of the Church of Scotland attending the Assemblies or Synods of other Churches and those ecumenical Conferences and Gatherings which are from time to time held;
      (b)   ensure that appropriate parts of such reports are made available to relevant Boards and Committees.
(vii) (a)   be informed of, assist centrally where appropriate, and report to the General Assembly on the Local Ecumenical Projects/Parishes which already exist in Scotland and which may in the future come to exist;
      (b)   in consultation with the Board of Practice and Procedure (where matters of Church Law and Practice are involved), advise congregations and Presbyteries seeking to establish new Ecumenical Projects/Parishes or to amend existing Projects/Parishes.
(viii) be the Committee through which reports are submitted to the General Assembly from Groups appointed to take part on behalf of the Church of Scotland in formal conversations and doctrinal dialogues with other Church and ecumenical bodies.

INTERCHURCH ORGANISATIONS

WORLD COUNCIL OF CHURCHES
The Church of Scotland is a founder-member of the World Council of Churches formed in 1948. As its basis declares, it is "a fellowship of Churches which confess the Lord Jesus Christ as God and Saviour according to the Scriptures, and therefore seek to fulfil their common calling to the Glory of the one God, Father, Son and Holy Spirit". Its member Churches, which number over three hundred, are drawn from all continents and include all the major traditions (except the Roman Catholic) – Eastern and Oriental Orthodox, Reformed, Lutheran, Anglican, Baptist, Disciples, Methodist, Moravian, Friends, Pentecostalist, and others. Its Eighth Assembly was held in Harare, Zimbabwe from 3-14th December 1998. This Assembly marked the 50th Anniversary of the World Council with an act of recommitment by the member churches. The theme was:"Turn to God: Rejoice in Hope". The Council is once again restructuring to form a more flexible working pattern among the staff.
    The General Secretary is Rev. Dr Konrad Raiser, 150 route de Ferney, 1211 Geneva 2, Switzerland (Tel: 010 41 22 791 61 11   Fax: 010 41 22 791 03 61).

WORLD ALLIANCE OF REFORMED CHURCHES
The Church of Scotland is a founder member of the World Alliance of Reformed Churches, which began in 1875 as "The Alliance of the Reformed Churches Throughout the World Hold-

ing the Presbyterian System" and which now includes also Churches of the Congregational tradition. Today it is composed of nearly 200 Churches in nearly 100 countries, with an increasing number in Asia. It brings together, for mutual help and common action, large Churches which enjoy majority status and small minority Churches. It engages in theological dialogue with other Christian traditions – Orthodox, Roman Catholic, Lutheran, Methodist, Baptist, *etc*. It is organised in three main departments – Co-operation with Witness, Theology, and Partnership.

The General Secretary is Rev. Dr Sekri Nyomi, 150 route de Ferney, 1211 Geneva 2, Switzerland (Tel: 010 41 22 791 62 38   Fax: 010 41 22 791 65 05).

CONFERENCE OF EUROPEAN CHURCHES
The Church of Scotland is a founder member of the Conference of European Churches, formed in 1959 and until recently the only body which involved in common membership representatives of every European country (except Albania) from the Atlantic to the Urals. More than a hundred Churches, Orthodox and Protestant, are members. Although the Roman Catholic Church is not a member there is very close co-operation with the Council of European Catholic Bishops' Conferences. With the removal of the long-standing political barriers in Europe the Conference has now opportunities and responsibilities to assist the Church throughout the continent to offer united witness and service.

Its General Secretary is Rev Dr. Keith Clements, 150 route de Ferney, 1211 Geneva 2, Switzerland (Tel: 010 41 22 791 61 11   Fax: 010 41 22 791 03 61).

CEC: CHURCH AND SOCIETY COMMISSION
The Church of Scotland is a founder member of the European Ecumenical Commission for Church and Society (EECCS). The Commission owes its origins to the Christian concern and vision of a group of ministers and European civil servants about the future of Europe. It was established in 1973 by churches recognising the importance of this venture. Membership included churches and ecumenical bodies from the European Union. The process of integration with CEC is now complete, and the name, Church and Society Commission (CSC), established. In Brussels CSC monitors Community activity, maintains contact with MEPs and promotes dialogue between the churches and the institutions. It plays an educational role and encourages the churches' social and ethical responsibility in European affairs. It has a General Secretary, a study secretary and an executive secretary in Brussels and a small office in Strasbourg and Geneva.

The General Secretary is Keith Jenkins, Ecumenical Centre, 174 rue Joseph II, 1040 Brussels, Belgium (Tel: 010 32 2 230 17 32; Fax: 010 32 2 231 14 13).

CHURCHES TOGETHER IN BRITAIN AND IRELAND (CTBI)
and ACTION OF CHURCHES TOGETHER IN SCOTLAND (ACTS)
In September 1990 Churches throughout Britain and Ireland solemnly committed themselves to one another, promising to one another to do everything possible together. To provide frameworks for this commitment to joint action, the Churches established CTBI for the United Kingdom and Ireland, and for Scotland, ACTS, with sister organisations for Wales and for England.

CTBI has a large Assembly meeting every second year, a Church Representatives Meeting held two or three times a year, and a Steering Committee meeting five times a year. It has commissions on Mission, Racial Justice and Interfaith Relations. It is staffed by a General Secretary and Co-ordinating Secretaries for Church Life, Church and Society, and International Affairs.

The General Secretary of CTBI is Dr. David R. Goodbourn, Inter-Church House, 35-41 Lower Marsh, London SE1 7SA (Tel: 020 7523 2121   Fax: 020 7928 0010).

ACTS has a Central Council and three Commissions - on Unity, Faith and Order; on Mission, Evangelism and Education; and on Justice, Peace, and Social and Moral Issues. It has five Committees – on Local and Regional Unity, on Communications, on Youth Action, on Women's Participation (entitled Network of Ecumenical Women in Scotland) and on Scottish Churches House. All meet regularly. Every second year it calls a one thousand strong Scottish Christian Gathering. It is staffed by a General Secretary, a Director of Scottish Churches House, and two Associate Secretaries.

At local level there are corresponding arrangements and a continuation of the face-to-face inter-Church groups which came into being or were strengthened in the 1980s.

These structures facilitate more regular consultation and more intensive co-operation among those who frame the policies and deploy the resources of the Churches in Scotland and throughout Britain and Ireland; at the same time they afford greater opportunity for a wide range of members of different Churches to meet in common prayer and study.

The General Secretary of ACTS is Rev. Dr. Kevin Franz, Scottish Churches House, Dunblane FK15 OAJ (Tel: 01786 823588: Fax: 01786 825844)

(19) PARISH EDUCATION
Annie Small House, 18 Inverleith Terrace
Edinburgh EH3 5NS
Tel: 0131 332 0343

MEMBERSHIP: BOARD OF PARISH EDUCATION
(Convener, Vice-Convener, 50 members appointed by the General Assembly, one representative from The Church of Scotland Guild)

Convener:	Rev. G. Stewart Smith, Glasgow (1997)
Vice-Convener:	Mrs Lorna Paterson, West Lothian (2000)
Director and General Secretary:	Mr Iain W. Whyte BA DCE DMS
Depute Director:	Mr Steven Mallon

STAFF

Librarian:	Mr Michael Buck
National Adult Adviser:	Ms Lisa Clark
Youth Ministry Development Worker:	Mr Stewart Cutler
Publications Manager:	Ms Gillian Cloke
Director, Spirituality Programme:	Rev. Alison Newell
Counselling Course Leader:	Ms Martha Mount
Associate Counselling Course Leader:	Ms Morag Highet
TLS Regional Organiser:	Mrs Judy Page
National Adviser, Children's Ministry:	Miss Ionwen Roberts
National Adviser, Elder Training:	Mrs Sheilah Steven
TLS Regional Organiser:	Mrs Mary Stobo
Tutor Organiser, Full-time Training:	Rev. Ian Walker
Children's Ministry Development Worker	Mr Douglas Swanney
Glasgow Presbytery Youth Adviser:	Dr Kathleen Rankin
National Adviser, Child Protection:	Ms Gillian Scott/Ms Sue Wheatley
Principal, SCOC:	Rev. Jayne Scott
Vice-Principal, SCOC:	Rev. Dr Donald Macaskill

REMIT

Based at Annie Small House in Edinburgh, the Board of Parish Education's remit is to oversee the development of an education and leadership training service for the Church of Scotland and, through the Scottish Churches Open College, for members of other denominations. The Board's provision covers a wide spectrum of courses, publications (through PEP) and events catering for all ages and abilities. This involves training and resources for Children's workers, youth workers and elders, and reaches through to degree and higher degree level courses.

In addition, the Board's courses provide training for the Readership, Parish Assistants employed by the Board of National Mission, and the Diaconate.

COMMITTEES

The Board itself meets twice annually, in February and June, with its committees meeting four or five times per annum. The committees are organised to reflect the Board's commitment to learning for all, and to developing the concept of Faith Community.

(20) DEPARTMENT OF EDUCATION

MEMBERSHIP: The Education Committee (operating as the Department of Education) (20 members together with Convener and Vice-Convener)
Convener: Rev. John J. Laidlaw MA (1999)
Vice-Convener: Mr William T. Weatherspoon BSc DipEd (1999)

STAFF
General Secretary: Rev. John Stevenson MA BD FEIS

REMIT

The Education Committee is the oldest continuing Committee of the General Assembly (it was formed in 1825) and has a long and historic connection with Scottish Education. The key aspects of the Committee's remit are:

1. to represent the Church on matters of state education at every level:
2. to support the Church Representatives whom it appoints on behalf of the General Assembly to deal with education on each of Scotland's 32 Local Authorities:
3. to co-operate with Presbyteries and Local Authorities in undertaking the support and training of chaplains in schools and in Further Education Colleges:
4. to promote good learning and teaching in the curriculum and ensure the place of Religious and Moral Education:
5. to commission and produce resources to ensure that Scottish Christianity and the life and work of the Church of Scotland can be properly represented in the curriculum:
6. to co-operate with other churches and faith groups working to enhance Scottish Education.

The Committee responds to consultation documents from the Scottish Executive and seeks to develop and maintain links with Education Ministers, with Members of the Scottish Parliament and with the relevant Committees.

It participates in the work of the Scottish Joint Committee on Religious and Moral Education and is represented on the Religious Education Movement (Scotland) and the Association for the Teaching of Religious Education in Scotland (ATRES).

It has established useful and practical links with the Roman Catholic Church through its Education Commission and it has a good record of liaison with the Educational Institute of Scotland and other unions in the educational field. It nominates one person to represent the Church on the General Teaching Council.

(21) COMMUNICATION

MEMBERSHIP
BOARD OF COMMUNICATION
(18 Members: Assembly appointed)

Convener:	Rev. Jean B. Montgomerie (1999)
Vice Convener:	Rev. W. Peter Graham (1999)
Secretary:	Mr Brian McGlynn

STAFF

Secretary and Director:	Mr Brian McGlynn
Management Accountant:	Mr Steve Murray
Media Relations Unit:	Mrs Pat Holdgate, Head of Media Relations
Design Services:	Mr Peter J.F. Forrest, Head of Design Services
Life & Work:	Miss Rosemary Goring, Editor
Saint Andrew Press:	Mrs Ann Crawford, Head of Publishing
Pathway Productions:	Mr Laurence P. Wareing, Director
Ministers' Forum:	Rev. John A. Ferguson, Editor
Year Book:	Rev. Ronald S. Blakey, Editor

REMIT
Under a revised constitution approved by the General Assembly in 1995, the Board is responsible for providing the Church with professional communication services and, *inter alia*, promoting effective communication within the Church and to the outside world. The Board's services are as follows:

1.   MEDIA RELATIONS UNIT
(Tel: 0131 240 2243/0131 225 5722: Fax: 0131 225 6475: e-mail: cofsmedia@dial.pipex.com)
The Media Relations Unit is the link between the Media and the Church, and is the first point of contact for journalists seeking information on the work and views of the Church's Boards and Committees. The Unit issues regular press releases on matters of interest and provides an audio release service to independent local radio. Unit staff maintain close links with a large network of media contacts and are happy to facilitate interviews with key personnel within the Church. The Unit also supports Parish Ministers and Church members by promoting local news and events on their behalf and by offering advice on local media work.

2.   DESIGN SERVICES
(Tel: 0131 225 5722/0131 240 2224; Fax: 0131 220 5407; e-mail: cofs.design@dial.pipex.com)
This part of the Board's work is concerned with the design and production of a wide range of promotional literature, display materials and exhibitions. Members of staff are pleased to advise congregations and Presbyteries on their particular communications needs.

A mailing list is maintained to provide parish magazine editors with suitable material and resources for their publications. Anyone wishing to be added to this list should provide their name and address to the Department.

3.   PATHWAY PRODUCTIONS – the Church's audio-visual production unit
(Tel: 0131 447 3531; Fax: 0131 452 8745; e-mail: Pathway@dial.pipex.com)
From its premises at 22 Colinton Road, Edinburgh EH10 5EQ, the Unit produces and markets videos, tape-slide sets and audio cassettes. Short training courses in television, radio and video are also held here. The Unit has pioneered church production and use of video as a means of Christian communication. It also produces occasional programmes for broadcast television. In conjunction with the Media Relations Unit, Pathway supports religious output on Independent Local Radio.

Videos and audio cassettes may be hired or bought from Wesley Owen Bookshops in Scotland or bought through Pathway's distributor, Saint Andrew Press.

4.   LIFE & WORK
(Tel: 0131 225 5722; Fax: 0131 240 2207; e-mail: lifework@dial.pipex.com)
Life & Work is the Church of Scotland's monthly magazine. Its purpose is to keep the Church informed about events in church life at home and abroad and to provide a forum for Christian opinion and debate on a variety of topics. It has an independent editorial policy. Contributions which are relevant to any aspect of the Christian faith are welcome.

The price of *Life & Work* this year is 90 pence. With a circulation of around 50,000 it also offers advertisers a first-class opportunity to reach a discerning readership in all parts of Scotland.

5.   SAINT ANDREW PRESS
(Tel: 0131 225 5722; Fax: 0131 220 3113; e-mail: cofs.standrew@dial.pipex.com)
Since its creation in 1954, Saint Andrew Press has been responsible for a great number of publications, many of which have made a major contribution to Christian literature. The world-renowned series of New Testament commentaries by the late Professor William Barclay, *The Daily Study Bible,* continues to provide a large share of the sales of the Press. Saint Andrew Press has also published the bestselling *Glasgow Gospel* by Jamie Stuart, the critically acclaimed *Common Order* on behalf of the Church of Scotland Panel on Worship, and more recently the ecumenical songbook *Common Ground.*

Saint Andrew Press also acts as distributor for Wild Goose Publications, Pathway Productions and Church of Scotland Stationery.

All manuscripts should be sent to the Head of Publishing. The staff are always willing to offer professional help and advice.

LOCAL BROADCASTING.
The Board of Communication encourages the work of a number of ecumenical groups assisting local radio stations with their religious broadcasting. Enquiries about local religious broadcasting should be made to the Media Relations Unit (see above).

CHURCHES ADVISORY COUNCIL FOR LOCAL BROADCASTING (CACLB)
CACLB was formed in 1967 to provide an advisory body to the Churches and to the broadcasters. Membership of the Council is drawn from members of ACTS, the Roman Catholic Church and the Evangelical Alliance, with representatives of the BBC and ILR, together with three members co-opted from the Association of Christians in Broadcasting (see below).

Present Officers
President: Baroness Nicholson of Winterbourne MEP
Chairman: Rt. Rev. Dr Tom Butler
General Secretary: Jeff Bonser, PO Box 124, Westcliffe-on-Sea, Essex SS0 0QY
                                   (Tel: 01702 348369   Fax: 01702 305121)
                                   (e-mail: office@caclb.org.uk) (www.caclb.org.uk)

ASSOCIATION OF CHRISTIANS IN BROADCASTING (ACB)

ACB was formed at a CACLB Conference in 1980 to meet the evident need for an association to provide "mutual support, help and comfort" for Christians involved in local radio, in whatever role. Membership is also open to those who, though not directly involved in local radio, appreciate its importance and wish to keep in touch with its problems and development.

For further information about membership, consult Jeff Bonser: PO Box 124, Westcliff-on-Sea, Essex SS0 0QY (Tel: 01702 348369   Fax: 01702 305121)

(22) THE LAW DEPARTMENT

STAFF

Solicitor of the Church and of the General Trustees:	Mrs J.S. Wilson LLB NP
Depute Solicitor:	Miss M.E. Macleod LLB NP
Assistant Solicitors:	Mr I.K. Johnstone MA LLB
	Mrs E.M. Kemp MA LLB
	Mrs J.M. Hamilton BA NP
	Mrs Elspeth Annan LLB NP
	Miss Susan Killean LLB NP

The Law Department of the Church was created in 1937/38. The Department acts in legal matters for the Church and all of its Courts, Boards, Committees, the Church of Scotland General Trustees, the Church of Scotland Trust and the Church of Scotland Investors Trust. It also acts for individual Congregations and is available to give advice on any legal matter arising.

The Department is under the charge of the Solicitor of the Church, a post created at the same time as the formation of the Department and a post which is now customarily held along with the traditional posts of Law Agent of the General Assembly and the Custodier of former United Free Church titles.

(23) CHURCH OF SCOTLAND TRUST

MEMBERSHIP
(Members are appointed by the General Assembly, on the Nomination of the Trust)

Chairman:	Mr J.M. Hodge WS
Vice-Chairman:	Mr C.N. Mackay WS
Treasurer:	Mr D.F. Ross MA CA
Secretary and Clerk:	Mrs J.M. Hamilton BA

REMIT
The Church of Scotland Trust was established by Act of Parliament in 1932. The Trust's function since 1st January 1995 has been to hold properties outwith Scotland and to act as Trustee in a number of third party trusts.

Further information can be obtained from the Secretary and Clerk of the Church of Scotland Trust, 121 George Street, Edinburgh EH2 4YN.
(Tel: 0131 240 2222; e-mail: lawdept@cofscotland.org.uk)

SECTION 2

General Information

(1) OTHER CHURCHES IN THE UNITED KINGDOM

THE ASSOCIATED PRESBYTERIAN CHURCHES
Synod Clerk: Mr David Laing, 224 Queens Road, Aberdeen AB1 8DN (Tel: 01224 317250).

THE REFORMED PRESBYTERIAN CHURCH OF SCOTLAND
Stated Clerk: Rev. A. Sinclair Horne, Magdalene Chapel, 41 Cowgate, Edinburgh EH1 1JR (Tel: 0131 220 1450).

THE FREE CHURCH OF SCOTLAND
Principal Clerk: The Mound, Edinburgh EH1 2LS (Tel: 0131 226 4978/5286).

THE FREE PRESBYTERIAN CHURCH OF SCOTLAND
Synod Clerk: Napier House, 8 Colinton Road, Edinburgh EH10 5DS (Tel: 0131 447 1920).

THE UNITED FREE CHURCH OF SCOTLAND
General Secretary: Rev. John Fulton, United Free Church Offices, 11 Newton Place, Glasgow G3 7PR (Tel: 0141 332 3435).

THE PRESBYTERIAN CHURCH IN IRELAND
Clerk of the General Assembly and General Secretary: Very Rev. Dr. Samuel Hutchinson BA BD MTH DD, Church House, Fisherwick Place, Belfast BT1 6DW (Tel: 02890 322284).

THE PRESBYTERIAN CHURCHES OF WALES
General Secretary: Rev. Gareth Edwards, 53 Richmond Road, Cardiff CF24 3WJ (Tel: 02920 494913; Fax: 02920 464293; e-mail: ebcpcw@aol.com).

THE UNITED REFORMED CHURCH
General Secretary: Rev. Anthony Burnham, 86 Tavistock Place, London WC1H 9RT (Tel: 020 7916 2020; Fax: 020 7916 2021).

UNITED REFORMED CHURCH SCOTLAND SYNOD
General Secretary: Rev. Kenneth M. Forbes, Church House, PO Box 189, Glasgow G1 2BX (Tel: 0141 332 7667).

BAPTIST UNION OF SCOTLAND
Secretary: Rev. William Slack, 14 Aytoun Road, Glasgow G41 5RT (Tel: 0141 423 6169).

RELIGIOUS SOCIETY OF FRIENDS (QUAKERS)
Clerk to the General Meeting of Scotland: Margaret Peacock, 16 Drumlin Drive, Milngavie G62 6LN.

ROMAN CATHOLIC CHURCH
Rt. Rev. Mgr. Henry Docherty, General Secretariat, Bishops' Conference for Scotland, 64 Aitken Street, Airdrie ML6 6LT. (Tel: 01236 764061; Fax: 01236 762489)

SALVATION ARMY
Scotland Secretary: Colonel John Flett, Scotland Secretariat, 30 Rutland Square, Edinburgh EH1 2BW (Tel: 0131 221 9699).

SCOTTISH EPISCOPAL CHURCH
General Secretary: John F. Stuart, 21 Grosvenor Crescent, Edinburgh EH12 5EE (Tel: 0131 225 6357).

THE SYNOD OF METHODIST CHURCH IN SCOTLAND
Secretary: Rev. David Cooper, Methodist Central Hall, West Tollcross, Edinburgh EH3 9BP (Tel: 0131 221 9029).

GENERAL SYNOD OF THE CHURCH OF ENGLAND
Secretary General: Mr Philip Mawer, Church House, Great Smith Street, London SW1P 3NZ. (Tel: 020 7898 1000).

(2) OVERSEAS CHURCHES

PRESBYTERIAN CHURCH IN AMERICA
Stated Clerk: 1852 Century Place, Suite 190, Atlanta, GA, 30345-4305, USA

PRESBYTERIAN CHURCH IN CANADA
Clerk of Assembly: 50 Wynford Drive, North York, Ontario M3C 1J7, Canada.

UNITED CHURCH OF CANADA
General Secretary: 3250 Bloor Street West, Etobicoke, Ontario M8K 2Y4, Canada.

PRESBYTERIAN CHURCH (USA)
Stated Clerk: 100 Witherspoon Street, Louisville KY 40202-1396, USA.

REFORMED PRESBYTERIAN CHURCH IN NORTH AMERICA
General Synod: 1818 Missouri Avenue, Las Cruces, New Mexico, USA.

CUMBERLAND PRESBYTERIAN CHURCH
General Secretary: Box 5535, Memphis 4, Tennessee, USA.

REFORMED CHURCH IN AMERICA
General Secretary: 475 Riverside Drive NY 10115, USA.

UNITED CHURCH OF CHRIST
General Secretary: 297 Park Avenue South, New York 10, USA.

UNITING CHURCH IN AUSTRALIA
General Secretary: PO Box A2266, Sydney South, New South Wales 2000, Australia.

PRESBYTERIAN CHURCH OF AUSTRALIA
Clerk of Assembly: GPO Box 100, Sydney, New South Wales 2001, Australia.

PRESBYTERIAN CHURCH OF AOTEOROA NEW ZEALAND
Executive Secretary: PO Box 9049, Wellington, New Zealand.

EVANGELICAL PRESBYTERIAN CHURCH, GHANA
Synod Clerk: PO Box 18, Ho, Volta Region, Ghana.

PRESBYTERIAN CHURCH OF GHANA
Synod Clerk: PO Box 1800, Accra, Ghana.

PRESBYTERIAN CHURCH OF EAST AFRICA
Secretary General: PO Box 48268, Nairobi, Kenya.

CHURCH OF CENTRAL AFRICA PRESBYTERIAN
Senior Clerk of General Synod: PO Box 30398, Lilongwe, Malawi.
General Secretary of Blantyre Synod: PO Box 413, Blantyre, Malawi.
General Secretary of Livingstonia Synod: PO Box112, Mzuzu, Malawi.

IGREJA EVANGELICA DE CRISTO EM MOCAMIQUE
General Secretary: Cx. Postale 284, Nampula 70100, Mozambique.

PRESBYTERIAN CHURCH OF NIGERIA
Principal Clerk: PO Box 2635, Aba, Abia State, Nigeria.

UNITING PRESBYTERIAN CHURCH IN SOUTHERN AFRICA
General Secretary: PO Box 96188, Brixton 2019, South Africa.

PRESBYTERIAN CHURCH OF SUDAN (A)
General Secretary: PO Box 66168, Nairobi, Kenya.

PRESBYTERIAN CHURCH OF SUDAN (M)
General Secretary: PO Box 3421, Khartoum, Sudan.

UNITED CHURCH OF ZAMBIA
General Secretary: PO Box 50122, 15101 Ridgeway, Lusaka, Zambia.

CHURCH OF BANGLADESH
Moderator: Synod Office, 54 Johnson Road, Dhaka 1100, Bangladesh.

CHURCH OF NORTH INDIA
General Secretary: Synod Office, 16 Pandit Pant Marg, New Delhi, 110 001, India.

CHURCH OF SOUTH INDIA
General Secretary: Synod Office, 5 White's Road, Royapettah, Chennai 600 114, India.

PRESBYTERIAN CHURCH OF KOREA
General Secretary: CPO Box 1125, Seoul 110 611, Korea.

PRESBYTERIAN CHURCH IN THE REPUBLIC OF KOREA
General Secretary: 1501 The Korean Ecumenical Building, 136-56 Yunchi-Dong, Chongno-Ku, Seoul, Korea.

THE UNITED MISSION TO NEPAL
Executive Director: PO Box 126, Kathmandu, Nepal.

CHURCH OF PAKISTAN
General Secretary: Mission Compound, Daska, Distt Sialkot, Punjab, Pakistan.

PRESBYTERY OF LANKA
Moderator: 127/1 D S Senanayake Veedyan, Kandy, Sri Lanka.

PRESBYTERIAN CHURCH IN TAIWAN
General Secretary: 3 Lane 269 Roosevelt Road, Sec. 3, Taipei, Taiwan 10763, ROC.

CHURCH OF CHRIST IN THAILAND
General Secretary: 109 CCT (13th Floor), Surawong Road, Khet Bangrak, Bangkok 10500, Thailand.

PRESBYTERY OF GUYANA
Moderator: 81 Croall Street, PO Box 10151, Georgetown, Guyana.

NATIONAL PRESBYTERIAN CHURCH OF GUATEMALA
Executive Secretary: Av Simeon Canas 7-13, Zona 2, Aptdo 655, Guatemala City, Guatemala.

UNITED CHURCH IN JAMAICA AND THE CAYMAN ISLANDS
General Secretary: 12 Carlton Crescent, PO Box 359, Kingston 10, Jamaica.

PRESBYTERIAN CHURCH IN TRINIDAD AND TOBAGO
General Secretary: Box 92, Paradise Hill, San Fernando, Trinidad.

BELGIAN PROTESTANT CHURCH
Rue de Champ de Mars 5, B - 1050 Bruxelles, Belgium.

REFORMED CHRISTIAN CHURCH IN CROATIA
Bishop's Office: Vladimira Nazora 31, HR - 32101 Vinkovci, Croatia.

EVANGELICAL CHURCH OF THE CZECH BRETHREN
Moderator: Jungmannova 9, Post Pr 466, CZ 111 21 Praha 1, Czech Republic.

EGLISE REFORMEE DE FRANCE
General Secretary: 47, rue de Clichy, F - 75311, Paris, France.

HUNGARIAN REFORMED CHURCH
General Secretary: Abonyi utca 21, PO Box 5, H - 1146 Budapest, Hungary.

WALDENSIAN CHURCH
Moderator: Via Firenze 38, 00184, Rome, Italy.

NETHERLANDS REFORMED CHURCH
Overgoo 11, PO Box 405, NL - 2260, AK Leidschendam, Netherlands.

REFORMED CHURCH IN ROMANIA
Bishop's Office: Str IC Bratianu No. 51, R - 3400, Cluj-Napoca, Romania.

REFORMED CHURCH IN YUGOSLAVIA
Bishop's Office: Pap Pavla, YU - 21000 Novi Sad, Yugoslavia.

SYNOD OF THE NILE OF THE EVANGELICAL CHURCH
General Secretary: Synod of the Nile of the Evangelical Church, PO Box 1248, Cairo, Egypt.

DIOCESE OF THE EPISCOPAL CHURCH IN JERUSALEM AND THE MIDDLE EAST
Bishop's Office: PO Box 19122, Jerusalem 91191, via Israel.

NATIONAL EVANGELICAL SYNOD OF SYRIA AND LEBANON
General Secretary: PO Box 70890, Antelias, Lebanon

[Full information on churches overseas may be obtained from the Board of World Mission.]

(3) SCOTTISH DIVINITY FACULTIES
[*denotes a Minister of the Church of Scotland]
[(R) Reader   (SL) Senior Lecturer   (L) Lecturer]

ABERDEEN
(University Faculty of Arts and Divinity and Christ's College)
King's College, Old Aberdeen AB24 3UB
(Tel: 01224 272380   Fax: 01224 273750
e-mail: <divinity@abdn.ac.uk>)

Master of Christ's College: The Very Rev. Prof. Alan Main* TD MA BD STM PhD
**Head of Department
of Divinity with
Religious Studies:**   The Rev. Prof. I.R. Torrance* TD MA BD DPhil
(Patristics)

Professors: Rev. W. Johnstone* BD MA DLitt (Hebrew)
The Very Rev. A. Main* TD MA BD STM PhD
(Practical Theology)
Rev. I.R. Torrance* TD MA BD DPhil
(Patristics and Christian Ethics)
F.B. Watson BA DPhil (New Testament)

Lecturers:
K.T. Aitken BD PhD (Hebrew)
A.D. Clarke BA MA PhD (New Testament)
Rev. J.W. Drane MA PhD (SL) (Practical Theology)
S. Gathercole BA MA (New Testament)
S. Kunin BA PhD (SL) (Anthropology of Religion)
Ian A. McFarland BA MDiv ThM MPhil PhD (Systematic Theology)
M. A. Mills MA PhD (Anthropology of Religion)
F.A. Murphy BA MA PhD (Systematic Theology)
Rev. J. Swinton* BD PhD RNM (Practical Theology)
C.R. Trueman MA PhD (SL) (Church History).

ST ANDREWS
(University College of St Mary)
St Mary's College, St Andrews, Fife KY16 9JU
(Tel: 01334 462850/1   Fax: 01334 462852)

Principal and Head of School: R.A. Piper BA BD PhD
Dean of the Faculty: T.A. Hart BA PhD

Chairs: R.J. Bauckham BA MA PhD FBA (New Testament Studies)
                                      T.A. Hart BA PhD (Divinity)
                                      P.F. Esler BA LLB LLM DPhil (Biblical Criticism)
                                      B. Lang DipTheol Dr Theol Dr Theol Habil (Old Testament)
                                      R.A. Piper BA BD PhD (Christian Origins)
                                      C.R. Seitz AB MTS MA MPhil PhD
                                      (Old Testament and Theological Studies))
                                      A.J. Torrance* MA BD DrTheol (Systematic Theology)

Readerships, Senior Lectureships, Lectureships:

M.I. Aguilar BA MA STB PhD (SL) (Religion and Contextual Theology)
J.S. Alexander* MA BD BA PhD (Church History)
I.C. Bradley* BA MA BD DPhil (SL) (Practical Theology)
J.R. Davila BA MA PhD (Early Jewish Studies)
M.D. Hampson BA DPhil ThM ThD MA (R) (Divinity)
B.W. Longenecker BA MRel PhD (New Testament)
D.W. Lovegrove MA BD PhD (Church History)
E.D. Reed BA PhD (Theology and Ethics)
R.B. Salters* MA BD PhD (SL) (Old Testament and Hebrew)

EDINBURGH
(Faculty of Divinity and New College)
New College, Mound Place, Edinburgh EH1 2LX
(Tel: 0131 650 8900   Fax: 0131 650 6579   e-mail: Divinity.faculty@ed.ac.uk)

Dean of Faculty: Prof. Stewart J. Brown BA MA PhD FRHistS
Vice Dean and
   Head of Department: A.Peter Hayman BA PhD
Principal of New College: Rev. David Lyall* BSc BD STM PhD

Chairs: Rev. A. Graeme Auld* MA BD PhD DLitt FSAScot
                                   (Hebrew Bible)
                                   Stewart J. Brown BA MA PhD FRHistS
                                   (Ecclesiastical History)
                                   Rev. David A.S. Fergusson* MA BD DPhil (Divinity)

Rev. Duncan B. Forrester* MA BD DPhil DD
(Christian Ethics and Practical Theology)
Larry W Hurtado BA MA PhD
(New Testament Language, Literature and Theology)
A. Alistair Kee MA BD STM PhD DPhil (Religious Studies)
David Kerr MA BA DPhil
(Christianity in the Non-Western World)
Rev. William F. Storrar* MA BD PhD
(Christian Ethics and Practical Theology)
Sir Stewart Sutherland MA FBA (Philosophy of Religion)
David F. Wright MA FRHistS DD
(Patristics and Reformed Christianity)

Readers, Senior Lecturers and Lecturers:
Hebrew and Old Testament: A. Peter Hayman BA PhD (SL)
Timothy Lim BA MPhil DPhil (R)
David J. Reimer BTh BA MA MA (L)

New Testament Language, Literature and Theology:
Helen K. Bond MTheol PhD (L)
David L. Mealand MA MLitt PhD (SL)

Christian Ethics and Practical Theology:
Marcella Althaus Reid BTh PhD (L)
David Lyall* BSc BD STM PhD (SL)
Jolyon Mitchell BA MA (L)
Michael S. Northcott MA PhD (SL)
Murray Chalmers* MA (Part-time) (L)
Derek B. Murray MA BD PhD (Part-time) (L)
Ewan Kelly* MB ChB BD (Part-time) (L)

Ecclesiastical History: Jane E.A. Dawson BA PhD DipEd (SL)
Jack Thompson BA PhD (SL)

Systematic Theology: Nicholas S. Adams BA PhD (L)
John C. McDowell BD PhD (L)
Michael Purcell MA PhD PhL PhB (L)

Religious Studies: James L. Cox BA MDiv PhD (SL)
Jeanne Openshaw BA MA PhD (L)
Nicholas Wyatt BA BD MTh PhD (R)

Centre for Christianity in the Non-Western World:
Moonjang Lee BA MTh MDiv PhD (L)

Fulton Lecturer in Speech and Communication:
Richard Ellis BSc MEd LGSM

GLASGOW
(Faculty of Divinity and Trinity College)
4 The Square, University of Glasgow, Glasgow G12 8QQ
(Tel: 0141 330 6526 : Fax: 0141 330 4943)
(e-mail: M.Macmillan@arts.gla.ac.uk)

Dean of Faculty:	Rev. Professor David Jasper MA PhD BD
Principal of Trinity College	
and Vice-Dean of Faculty:	Rev. Douglas M. Murray* MA BD PhD

Chairs: John M. G. Barclay MA PhD (New Testament and Christian Origins)
Joseph Houston MA BD DPhil (Philosophical Theology)
Rev. David Jasper MA PhD BD (Literature and Theology)
Rev. Donald Macleod MA (Visiting Professor)
Rev. George M. Newlands* MA BD PhD (Divinity)
Rev. John K. Riches MA (Divinity and Biblical Criticism)
Perry Schmidt-Leukel Dipl theol MA Dr theol Dr theol habil (Munich)
(Systematic Theology and Religious Studies)
H.E. Cardinal Thomas J. Winning STL DCL DD DUniv LLD
(Honorary Professor)

Senior Lecturers and Lecturers: Theology and Religious Studies:
Julie P. Clague BSc PGCE PGDip MTh (L))
W. Ian P. Hazlett BA BD DrTheol (SL)
Rev. Alastair G. Hunter* MSc BD (SL)
Rev. Jeffrey F. Keuss BA MDiv (L)
Rev. Thomas F. Magill PhB LSS PhD (L) (part-time)
Rev. Douglas M. Murray* MA BD PhD (L)
Lloyd V.J. Ridgeon BA MA PhD (L)
Yvonne M. Sherwood BA PhD DipJS (SL)
Mona Siddiqui MA MLL PhD (L)
Kiyoshi Tsuchiya MA PhD (L)
Heather E. Walton BA MA(Econ) PhD (L)

Centre for Study of Literature, Theology and the Arts:
Director: Rev. Professor George M. Newlands* MA BD PhD
Assistant Director: Kyoshi Tsuchiya MA PhD

(4) SOCIETIES AND ASSOCIATIONS

The undernoted list shows the name of the Association, along with the name and address of the Secretary.

INTER-CHURCH ASSOCIATIONS

THE FELLOWSHIP OF ST ANDREW: Rev. Donald Reid, St John's Rectory, 21 Swinton Road, Glasgow G69 6DS.

THE FELLOWSHIP OF ST THOMAS: Promotes informed interest in Churches of Indian sub-continent. Contact: Rev. Margaret S. MacGregor, MA BD DipEd, 16 Learmonth Court, Edinburgh EH4 1PB (Tel. 0131 332 1089).

THE SCOTTISH ORDER OF CHRISTIAN UNITY: Secretary: Rev. William D. Brown MA, 121 Dalkeith Road, Edinburgh EH16 5AJ (Tel/Fax: 0131 667 1124 e-mail: wdbrown@conventus.co.uk).

CHURCH PASTORAL AID SOCIETY (CPAS): Consultant for Scotland: Rev. Richard W. Higginbottom, 2 Highfield Place, Bankfoot, Perth PH1 4AX (Tel: 01738 787429).

FRONTIER YOUTH TRUST: Encourages and resources those engaged in youth work, particularly with disadvantaged young people. Co-ordinator: Feri Salvesen, c/o Anderson/Kelvingrove Church, 759b Argyle Street, Glasgow G3 8DS (Tel: 0141 204 4800).

IONA COMMUNITY: Leader: Rev. Norman Shanks, Pearce Institute, 840 Govan Road, Glasgow G51 3UU (Tel: 0141 445 4561); Warden: Rev. Peter Millar, Iona Abbey, Isle of Iona, Argyll PA76 6SN (Tel: 01681 700404).

SCOTTISH CHRISTIAN YOUTH ASSEMBLY: Chairperson: Mr Eric Whitten, 41 Kingston Avenue, Glasgow G14 OEB.

SCOTTISH CHURCHES HOUSING AGENCY: Provides the Churches with information, education, advice and support concerning homelessness. Co-ordinator: Alastair Cameron, 28 Albany Street, Edinburgh EH1 3QH (Tel: 0131 477 4500; Fax: 0131 477 2710).

SCOTTISH CHURCHES WORLD EXCHANGE: Arranges Overseas placements for 30-40 volunteers annually. Placements are for 1-2 years. Director: Rev. Robert Anderson, 121 George Street, Edinburgh EH2 4YN (Tel: 0131 225 8115).

SCOTTISH JOINT COMMITTEE ON RELIGIOUS EDUCATION: Rev. John Stevenson MA BD and Mr Frederick L. Forrester MA DipEd MBIM FEIS, 46 Moray Place, Edinburgh EH3 6BH (Tel: 0131 225 6244).

SCOTTISH NATIONAL COUNCIL OF YMCAs: 11 Rutland Street, Edinburgh EH1 2AE (Tel: 0131 228 1464)

SCOTTISH SUNDAY SCHOOL UNION FOR CHRISTIAN EDUCATION: Offers financial assistance by way of grant or loan to help fund training and provide resources in the promotion of Christian Education for children in Scotland. General Secretary: Mrs Lynne Collingham, 2 Fraser Avenue, Newton Mearns, Glasgow G77 6HW (Tel: 0141 571 7359).

SCOTTISH TEMPERANCE ALLIANCE: Mr John Livingstone, The Gean House, Alloa FK10 2EL (Tel: 01592 2443).

SCRIPTURE UNION: Secretary: 9 Canal Street, Glasgow G4 OAB. (Tel: 0141 332 1162).

STUDENT CHRISTIAN MOVEMENT: Mr Nick Davies, 1 Bristo Square, Edinburgh EH8 9AL (Tel: 0131 667 4321).

UNIVERSITIES AND COLLEGES CHRISTIAN FELLOWSHIP: Freepost, Leicester LE1 7ZL.

WORLD DAY OF PRAYER: SCOTTISH COMMITTEE: Convener: Mrs Jenny Easson; Secretary: Mrs Margaret A. Broster, St Columba's Manse, Kilbirnie KA25 7JU (Tel: 01505 683342 Fax 01505 684024).

CHURCH OF SCOTLAND SOCIETIES

ASSOCIATION OF GENERAL ASSEMBLY AND PRESBYTERY CLERKS: Rev. R.A. Baigrie MA, 32 Inchcolm Terrace, South Queensferry EH30 9NA (Tel: 0131 331 4311).

ASSOCIATION OF RETURNED OVERSEAS STAFF: Mrs Lesley D. Wilson, 37 Kings Avenue, Longniddry EH32 0QN (Tel: 01875 852898).

CHURCH OF SCOTLAND TOTAL ABSTAINERS ASSOCIATION: Honorary Treasurer: R.J.M. Hart, 5 St Vincent Place, Glasgow G1 2HT (Tel: 0141 248 6820).

SCOTTISH CHURCH SOCIETY: Secretary: Rev. Matthew Z. Ross LLB BD FSAScot, The Manse, Ceres, Cupar, Fife KY15 5NQ (Tel. 01334 828233).

SCOTTISH CHURCH THEOLOGY SOCIETY: Rev. William D. Brown MA, 121 Dalkeith Road, Edinburgh EH16 5AJ (Tel: 0131 667 1124).

SOCIETY OF FRIENDS OF ST ANDREW'S JERUSALEM: Hon. Secretary: Major D.J. McMicking LVO, 10 Albert Terrace, Edinburgh EH10 5EA (Tel. 0131 447 6192); Hon. Treasurer: A.J. McGregor CA, Arden, 8c Merchiston Park, Edinburgh EH10 4PN.

THE CHURCH OF SCOTLAND CHAPLAINS' ASSOCIATION: Rev. W. Scott Reid MA DipPS BD PhD, 14/37 Ethel Terrace, Edinburgh EH10 5NA (Tel: 0131 447 7642).

THE CHURCH OF SCOTLAND RETIRED MINISTERS' ASSOCIATION: Hon. Secretary: Rev. James L. Hepburn MA BD, 16 Marchmont Road, Edinburgh EH9 1HZ (Tel: 0131 229 6170).

THE CHURCH SERVICE SOCIETY. Secretary: Rev. Rachel J.W. Dobie, The Manse, Broughton, Biggar ML12 6HQ (Tel: 01899 830331).

THE IRISH MINISTERS' FRATERNAL: Secretary: Rev. Colin R. Williamson LLB BD, Manse of Aberdalgie, Perth PH2 0QD (Tel: 01738 2585).

THE NATIONAL CHURCH ASSOCIATION: Secretary: Miss Margaret P. Milne, 10 Balfron Crescent, Hamilton ML3 9UH.

THE NATIONAL COUNCIL OF YOUTH FELLOWSHIPS: General Secretary: c/o Board of Parish Education, Annie Small House, 18 Inverleith Terrace, Edinburgh EH3 5NS (Tel: 0131 332 0343).

BIBLE SOCIETIES

NATIONAL BIBLE SOCIETY OF SCOTLAND: Rev. Graham R. Houston BSc BD MTh, 7 Hampton Terrace, Edinburgh EH12 5XU (Tel: 0131 337 9701).

WEST OF SCOTLAND BIBLE SOCIETY: Rev. Alexander Macdonald MA BD, Manse of Neilston, Glasgow G78 3NP (Tel: 0141 881 1958).

GENERAL

THE BOYS' BRIGADE: Scottish Headquarters, Carronvale House, Carronvale Road, Larbert FK5 3LH (Tel: 01324 562008).

THE GIRLS' BRIGADE: Scottish Headquarters, Boys' Brigade House, 168 Bath Street, Glasgow G2 4TQ (Tel: 0141 332 1765).

THE GIRL GUIDES: Scottish Headquarters, 16 Coates Crescent, Edinburgh EH3 7AH (Tel: 0131 226 4511); Glasgow Headquarters, 15 Elmbank Street, Glasgow G2 4PB.

THE SCOUT ASSOCIATION: Scottish Headquarters, Fordell Firs, Hillend, Dunfermline KY11 5HQ (Tel: 01383 419073).

BOYS' AND GIRLS CLUBS OF SCOTLAND: 88 Giles Street, Edinburgh EH6 6BZ (Tel: 0131 555 1729).

YOUTH CLUBS (SCOTLAND): 17 Bonnington Grove, Edinburgh EH6 (Tel: 0131 554 2561).

CHRISTIAN AID SCOTLAND: National Secretary: Rev. John Wyllie, 41 George IV Bridge, Edinburgh EH1 1EL (Tel: 0131 220 1254   Fax: 0131 225 8861).

FEED THE MINDS: Scottish Secretary, Miss Dorothy Armstrong, 41 George IV Bridge, Edinburgh EH1 1EL (Tel: 0131 226 5254).

LADIES' GAELIC SCHOOLS AND HIGHLAND BURSARY ASSOCIATION: Rev. John Campbell MA, 15 Foulden Place, Dunfermline KY12 7CQ (Tel: 01383 738055).

MARRIAGE COUNSELLING SCOTLAND: Mrs Frances Love, Director, 105 Hanover Street, Edinburgh EH2 1DJ (Tel: 0131 225 5006 Fax: 0131 220 0639).

RUTHERFORD HOUSE: Warden: Rev. David C. Searle MA, 17 Claremont Park, Edinburgh EH6 7PJ (Tel: 0131 554 1206   Fax: 0131 555 1002).

SCOTTISH CHURCH HISTORY SOCIETY: Rev. Peter H. Donald MA PhD BD, 39 Southside Road, Inverness IV2 4XA (Tel: 01463 231140).

SCOTTISH EVANGELICAL THEOLOGY SOCIETY: Secretary: Rev. Robert D. Higham BD, Abbeyfield House, 4 School Road, East Linton EH42 1JP.

SCOTTISH NATIONAL CHRISTIAN ENDEAVOUR UNION: Secretary: Headquarters, 134 Wellington Street, Glasgow G2 2XL (Tel: 0141 332 1105).

TEAR FUND: 100 Church Road, Teddington TW11 8QE (Tel: 0181 977 9144). Scottish Secretary: Peter Chirnside, Tear Fund Scotland, Challenge House, Canal Street, Glasgow G4 0AD (Tel: 0141 332 3621).

THE AFRICA EVANGELICAL FELLOWSHIP: Mrs R. Mackay, 280 St Vincent Street, Glasgow G2 5RT (Tel: 0141 248 5630).

THE LEPROSY MISSION: 89 Barnton Street, Stirling FK8 1HJ (Tel/Fax: 01786 449266). Area Organisers: Rev. J. G. M'Connell, 24 Craigmount Avenue North, Edinburgh EH12 8DF; and Rev. A. H. Swanson, 72 Mulben Crescent, Glasgow G53 7EH.

THE LORD'S DAY OBSERVANCE SOCIETY: Rev. A. Hanna, 2 The Gallolee, Edinburgh EH13 9QJ (Tel: 0131 441 3116).

THE MONTHLY VISITOR TRACT SOCIETY: 122 Thirlestane Road, Edinburgh EH9 1AN.

THE SCOTTISH REFORMATION SOCIETY: The Society, The Magdalene Chapel, 41 Cowgate, Edinburgh EH1 1JR (Tel: 0131 220 1450).

THE SOCIETY IN SCOTLAND FOR PROPAGATING CHRISTIAN KNOWLEDGE: David McLetchie, Esq., Tods, Murray WS, 66 Queen Street, Edinburgh: EH2 4NE (Tel: 0131 226 4771).

THE WALDENSIAN MISSIONS AID SOCIETY FOR WORK IN ITALY: David A. Lamb, Esq. LLB, 36 Liberton Drive, Edinburgh EH16 6NN (Tel: 0131 664 3059).

YOUNG WOMEN'S CHRISTIAN ASSOCIATION OF GREAT BRITAIN, SCOTTISH COUNCIL: Miss Isobel Carr, 7 Randolph Crescent, Edinburgh EH3 7TH (Tel: 0131 225 7592).

---

(5) TRUSTS AND FUNDS

THE SOCIETY FOR THE BENEFIT OF THE SONS AND DAUGHTERS
OF THE CLERGY OF THE CHURCH OF SCOTLAND
Chairman: The Hon. Lord Davidson
Secretary and Treasurer: R. Graeme Thom FCA
                                   17 Melville Street
                                   Edinburgh EH3 7PH (Tel: 0131 473 3500)

Annual grants are made to assist in the education of the children (normally between the ages of 12-25 years) of ministers of the Church of Scotland. The Society also gives grants to aged and infirm daughters of ministers and ministers' unmarried daughters and sisters who are in need. Applications to be lodged by 31st May in each year.

THE GLASGOW SOCIETY OF SONS OF MINISTERS
OF THE CHURCH OF SCOTLAND

President: Rev. I.M.P. Davidson MBE MA BD
Hon. Secretary and Treasurer: R. Graeme Thom FCA
                                   17 Melville Street
                                   Edinburgh EH3 7PH (Tel: 0131 473 3500)

The Society's primary purpose is to grant financial assistance to children (no matter what age) of deceased ministers of the Church of Scotland. Applications to be submitted by 1st February each year. To the extent that funds are available, grants are also given for the children of ministers or retired ministers, but such grants are normally restricted to students. These latter grants are considered in conjunction with the Edinburgh based Society. Limited funds are also available for individual application for special needs or projects. Applications to be submitted by 31st May each year. Emergency applications can be dealt with at any time when need arises. Application forms may be obtained from the Hon. Secretary.

HOLIDAYS FOR MINISTERS

The undernoted hotels provide special terms for ministers and their families Fuller information may be obtained from the establishments:

CRIEFF HYDRO: The William Meikle Fund and Paton Fund make provision whereby active ministers and their spouses, members of the Diaconate and other full time Church workers may enjoy the amenities of the Hydro in the off-peak periods at greatly reduced rates. Chalets are also available for families. Enquiries to the Resident Manager, The Hydro, Crieff PH7 3LQ (Tel: 01764 655555).

THE CINTRA BEQUEST: The Trust provides financial assistance towards the cost of accommodation in Scotland for Missionaries on leave, or for Ministers on temporary holiday, or on rest. Applications should be made to Mrs J.S. Wilson, Solicitor, 121 George Street, Edinburgh EH2 4YN.

THE LYALL BEQUEST: on behoof of the Ministers of the Church of Scotland makes available the following benefits:
1.   A payment towards the cost of holiday accommodation at any hotel or boarding house in St Andrews will be paid to any Minister and to his wife at the rate of £10 per day each for a minimum stay of three days and a maximum stay of one week. Due to the number of applications which the Trustees now receive, an applicant will not be considered to be eligible if he or she has received a grant from the Bequest during the three years prior to the holiday for which application is made. Applications, prior to the holiday, should be made to the Secretaries.
2.   Grants towards costs of sickness and convalescence so far as not covered by the National Health Service or otherwise may be available to applicants, who should apply to the Secretaries giving relevant details.
All communications should be addressed to Messrs Pagan Osborne, Solicitors, Secretaries to the Lyall Bequest, 106 South Street, St Andrews KY16 9QD. (Tel: 01334 475001).

MARGARET AND JOHN ROSS TRAVELLING FUND: Offers grants to Ministers and their spouses for travelling and other expenses for trips to the Holy Land where the purpose is recuperation or relaxation. Applications should be made to the Secretary and Clerk, Church of Scotland Trust, 121 George Street, Edinburgh EH2 4YN. (Tel: 0131 240 2222).

SUMMER SCHOOL AT ST ANDREWS: A School of Theology for Ministers, organised by the Staff of St Mary's College, St Andrews, is held each year, generally in the third week of June. Full information may be obtained from the Principal, St Mary's College, St Andrews.

The undernoted represents a list of the more important trusts available for ministers, students and congregations. A brief indication is given of the trust purposes, but application should be made in each case to the person named for full particulars and forms of application.

THE ABERNETHY TRUST: Offers residential outdoor courses for Youth Fellowships, Church family week-ends, Bible Classes, *etc* at four outdoor centres. Further details from: The Executive Director, Abernethy Trust, Nethybridge PH25 3ED (Tel/Fax: 01479 821279).

THE ARROL TRUST: The object of the Trust is "to promote the benefit and advance the education of young people between the ages of 16 and 25 years of age who are physically or mentally disadvantaged or are in necessitous circumstances by assisting such persons gain experience through education and training for their future careers through travel within or without the United Kingdom". Further details and forms of application can be obtained from: C.S. Kennedy WS, Lindsays WS, 11 Atholl Crescent, Edinburgh EH3 8HE (Tel: 0131 229 1212).

THE BAIRD TRUST: Assists in the building and repair of Churches and Halls, endows Parishes and generally assists the work of the Church of Scotland. Apply: Ronald D. Oakes CA ACMA, 182 Bath Street, Glasgow G2 4HG (Tel: 0141 332 0476 Fax: 0141 331 0874).

THE REV. ALEXANDER BARCLAY BEQUEST: Assists mother, daughter, sister or niece of deceased Minister of the Church of Scotland who at the time of his death was acting as his housekeeper and who is in needy circumstances. Apply: W.N. Pomphrey DL JP LLB, 2 Belhaven Terrace, Wishaw ML2 7AY.

BELLAHOUSTON BEQUEST FUND: Gives grants to Protestant evangelical denominations in the City of Glasgow and certain areas within five miles of the city boundary for building and repairing Churches and Halls and the promotion of religion. Apply: Mitchells Roberton, 36 North Hanover Street, Glasgow G1 2AD.

BEQUEST FUND FOR MINISTERS: Assists Ministers in outlying parts. Apply: A. Linda Parkhill CA, 60 Wellington Street, Glasgow G2 6HJ.

CARNEGIE TRUST: In cases of hardship the Carnegie Trust is prepared to consider applications by students of Scottish birth, extraction, or schooling for financial assistance with the payment of their fees at the Scottish Universities. If the applicant is in receipt of a Student's Allowance or a Local Education Authority award which includes payment of fees in full, he will not be eligible for assistance from the Trust for this purpose. For further details students should apply to the Secretary, Carnegie Trust, Cameron House, Abbey Park Place, Dunfermline KY12 7PT. (Tel: 01383 622148)

CHURCH OF SCOTLAND INSURANCE CO. LTD: Undertakes Insurance of Church property and pays surplus profits to Church schemes. At 67 George Street, Edinburgh EH2 2JG (Tel: 0131 220 4119 Fax: 0131 220 4120).

CHURCH OF SCOTLAND MINISTRY BENEVOLENT FUND: Makes grants to retired men and women who have been ordained or commissioned for the ministry of the Church of Scotland and to widows, widowers, orphans, spouses or children of such, who are in need. Applications to The Accountant, Board of Ministry, 121 George Street, Edinburgh EH2 4YN (Tel: 0131 225 5722).

CLARK BURSARY: Awarded to candidate(s) for the ministry of the Church of Scotland studying at the University of Aberdeen. Applications to the Clerk to the Presbytery of Aberdeen, Mastrick Church, Greenfern Road, Aberdeen AB16 6TR by 16th October annually.

THE REV. JOHN CLARK FUND: Provides annuities (1) for blind persons and (2) for orphan or fatherless children of ministers and missionaries of the Church of Scotland. Apply: Fyfe, Ireland & Co. WS, 27 Melville Street, Edinburgh EH3 7PE.

CRAIGCROOK MORTIFICATION:
Chairman: G.A. Henry WS
Clerk and Factor: R. Graeme Thom FCA
                      17 Melville Street
                      Edinburgh EH3 7PH (Tel: 0131 473 3500)
Pensions are paid to poor men and women over 60 years old, born in Scotland or who have resided in Scotland for not less than 10 years. At present pensions amount to £480 p.a.
    Ministers are invited to notify the Clerk and Factor of deserving persons and should be prepared to act as a referee on the application form.

THE ALASTAIR CRERAR TRUST FOR SINGLE POOR: Provides Churches, Christian Organisations and individual Christians with grants to help single adults, who live on low incomes and have little capital, to improve their quality of life. Apply to the Secretary: Michael I.D. Sturrock, 58 Frederick Street, Edinburgh EH2 1LS (Tel: 0131 200 1200).

CROMBIE SCHOLARSHIP: Provides grants of £100 after competitive examination at St Mary's College, St Andrews, to MA Students of Divinity. Apply: Anderson Strathern WS, 48 Castle Street, Edinburgh EH2 3LX.

THE DRUMMOND TRUST: Makes grants towards the cost of publication of books of "sound Christian doctrine and evangelical purpose". Applications for interest-free loans for similar purposes may also be considered. The Trustees are willing to receive grant requests towards the cost of audio-visual programme material, but not equipment. Requests for application forms should be made to the Secretary, c/o Hill and Robb, 3 Pitt Terrace, Stirling FK8 2EY. Manuscripts should *not* be sent.

THE DUNCAN TRUST: Makes grants annually to students for the Ministry in the Faculties of Arts and Divinity. Preference is given to those born or educated within the bounds of the former Presbytery of Arbroath. Applications not later than 31st October to: G.J.M. Dunlop, Brothockbank House, Arbroath DD11 1NJ; or Rev. J. Colin Caskie, 44 Terrace Road, Carnoustie, Angus DD7 7AR.

ESDAILE TRUST: Assists education and advancement of daughters of Ministers, Missionaries, and Widowed Deaconesses of Church of Scotland between 12 and 25 years of age Applications to: R. Graeme Thom FCA, Clerk and Treasurer to the Governors, 17 Melville Street, Edinburgh EH3 7PH.

FERGUSON BEQUEST FUND: For the maintenance and promotion of religious ordinances and education and missionary operations in the first instance in the Counties of Ayr, Kirkcudbright, Wigtown, Lanark, Renfrew and Dunbarton. Apply Ronald D. Oakes CA AC MA, 182 Bath Street, Glasgow G2 4HG (Tel: 0141 332 0476   Fax: 0141 331 0874).

GEIKIE BEQUEST: Makes small grants to students for the Ministry, including students studying for entry to the University, preference being given to those not eligible for SED awards Apply to the Secretary, Department of Ministry, 121 George Street, Edinburgh EH2 4YN.

JAMES GILLAN'S BURSARY FUND: Bursaries are available for students for the ministry who were born or whose parents or parent have resided and had their home for not less than three years continually in the old counties (not Districts) of Moray or Nairn. Apply: R. and R. Urquhart, 121 High Street, Forres IV36 OAB.

HALDANE TRUST FUND: Provides grants to Ministers of the Church of Scotland on their first induction, towards the purchase of theological books. Apply: A. C. Bennett and Robertsons WS, 21/25 George IV Bridge, Edinburgh EH1 1EP.

HAMILTON BURSARY TRUST: Makes awards annually to students at the University of Aberdeen intending missionary service overseas. Preference given to those born or residing in (a) Parish of Skene, (b) Parish of Echt, (c) Presbytery of Aberdeen or Kincardine and Deeside or Gordon, failing which to candidate(s) for the ministry of the Church of Scotland studying at the University of Aberdeen. Applications to the Clerk to the Presbytery of Aberdeen by 16th October annually.

MARTIN HARCUS BEQUEST: Makes grants to poor youths resident within the City of Edinburgh desirous of entering the Ministry of the Church. Apply: Rev. W. Peter Graham MA BD, 10 Palmerston Place, Edinburgh EH12 5AA.

THE HOGARTH FUND: Provides annuities to orphan or fatherless children of Ministers and Missionaries of the Church of Scotland. Apply Fyfe, Ireland & Co., WS, 27 Melville Street, Edinburgh EH3 7PE.

THE HOPE TRUST: Gives some support to organisations involved in combating drink and drugs, and has as its main purpose the promotion of the Reformed Faith throughout the world. There is also a Scholarship programme for Post-graduate Theology Study in Scotland. Apply Miss Carole Hope LLB, 31 Moray Place, Edinburgh EH3 6BY (Tel: 0131 226 5151).

IONA TRUST: Objects are the preservation of the Abbey buildings and others at Iona and the making of these available for public worship. Secretaries: Anderson Strathern WS, 48 Castle Street, Edinburgh EH2 3LX.

GILLIAN MACLAINE BURSARY FUND: Open to candidates for the Ministry of the Church of Scotland of Scottish or Canadian nationality. Preference is given to Gaelic speakers. Bursaries are awarded after an examination which is held annually in November. Information and application forms from Mr Michael A. J. Gossip, OBE JP BL, The Secretary, Synod of Argyll Trusts Committee, Tigh-na-Coille, Ardrishaig, Argyll PA30 8EP: Telephone and Fax: 01546 603454: [e-mail: Gossip@dial.pipex.com].

THE MISSES ANN AND MARGARET McMILLAN'S BEQUEST: Makes grants to Ministers of the Free and United Free Churches, and of the Church of Scotland, in charges within the Synod of Argyll, with income not exceeding the Minimum Stipend of the Church of Scotland. Apply by 30th June each year to Business Manager, Royal Bank of Scotland, 37 Victoria Street, Rothesay, Isle of Bute PA20 OAP.

THE MANSE AUXILIARY: Convener: Mrs Jean Baigrie, 32 Inchcolm Terrace, South Queensferry EH30 9NA (Tel: 0131 331 4311). Collects and distributes slightly used clothing, soft furnishings, household linen, *etc,* to Manses on small stipends, Missionaries, Ministers' Widows, and others, especially those in remote areas. Enquiries to the Convener or to the Secretary, Miss Joan McNeel-Caird, 2/26 Goldenacre Terrace, Edinburgh EH3 5RD (Tel: 0131 551 2720).

MORGAN BURSARY FUND: Makes grants to students for the Ministry in Arts and Divinity at the University of Glasgow. Apply: Rev. Alexander Cunningham MA BD, 260 Bath Street, Glasgow G2 4JP.

NOVUM TRUST: Provides small short-term grants to initiate projects in Christian research and action which cannot readily be financed from other sources. Special consideration is given to proposals aimed at the welfare of young people, the training of lay people, and new ways of communicating the faith. Applications to Rev. Dr. Frank D. Bardgett, 121 George Street Edinburgh EH2 4YN.

PATON TRUST: Assists Ministers in ill health to have recuperative holiday outwith, and free from the cares of their parishes. Apply: Iain A.T. Mowat, Esq., CA, Alexander Sloan & Co, 144 West George Street, Glasgow G2 2HG.

RENFIELD STREET TRUST: Assists in the building and repair of Churches and Halls. Apply Ronald D. Oakes CA ACMA, 182 Bath Street, Glasgow G2 4HG (Tel: 0141 332 0476 Fax 0141 331 0874).

SCOTTISH CHURCHES ARCHITECTURAL HERITAGE TRUST: Assists congregations of any denomination in the preservation of churches regularly used for public worship and of architectural value and historic interest. Apply to the Secretary, 15 North Bank Street, The Mound, Edinburgh EH1 2LP.

SMIETON FUND. Enables a few Ministers to have a holiday at Crieff. Applications to the Secretary, Department of Ministry, 121 George Street, Edinburgh EH2 4YN.

MARY DAVIDSON SMITH CLERICAL AND EDUCATIONAL FUND FOR ABERDEEN-SHIRE: Assists Ministers in Aberdeenshire and the North to purchase books, or to travel for educational purposes, and assists their families with scholarships for further education or vocational training. Apply: Alan J. Innes Esq., LLB, 100 Union Street, Aberdeen AB10 1QR.

LORD MOUNT STEPHEN TRUSTS: Assists with stipends of Ministers of certain parishes in former Presbyteries of Strathbogie and Fordyce, Abernethy and Elgin. Factor, Secretary of the Department of Ministry, 121 George Street, Edinburgh EH2 4YN.

THE NAN STEVENSON CHARITABLE TRUST FOR RETIRED MINISTERS: Provides houses, or loans to purchase houses for retired ministers or missionaries on similar terms to the Housing and Loan Fund, with preference given to those with a North Ayrshire connection. Secretary: Rev. David Broster, Manse of St Columba's, Kilbirnie KA25 7JU.

SYNOD OF ARGYLL BURSARY FUND: Provides book grants for Candidates for the Ministry of the Church of Scotland who are native to or have strong connections within the bounds of the former Synod of Argyll (*ie* the Presbyteries of Dunoon, Lorn and Mull and South Argyll). Applications should be made by 31st October to Mr Michael A. J. Gossip, OBE JP BL, The Secretary, Synod of Argyll Trusts Committee, Tigh-na-Coille, Ardrishaig, Argyll PA30 8EP: Telephone and Fax: 01546 603454: [e-mail: Gossip@dial.pipex.com].

SYNOD OF GRAMPIAN CHILDREN OF THE CLERGY FUND: Makes annual grants to children of deceased ministers. Apply to Rev. Iain U. Thomson, Clerk and Treasurer, The Manse, Skene, Westhill Aberdeenshire AB32 6XX.

SYNOD OF GRAMPIAN WIDOWS FUND: Makes annual grants (currently £200 p.a.) to widows of deceased ministers who have served in a charge in the former Synod. Apply to Rev. Iain U. Thomson, Clerk and Treasurer, The Manse, Skene, Westhill, Aberdeenshire AB32 6XX.

YOUNG MINISTERS' FURNISHING LOAN FUND: Makes loans (of £500) to young Ministers in first charge where stipend minimum to assist with furnishing manse. Apply: The Secretary, Department of Ministry, 121 George Street, Edinburgh EH2 4YN.

(6) RECENT LORD HIGH COMMISSIONERS
TO THE GENERAL ASSEMBLY

1965/66	The Hon Lord Birsay CBE QC TD
1967/68	The Right Hon Lord Reith of Stonehaven GCVO GBE CB TD
1969	Her Majesty the Queen attended in person
1970	The Right Hon Margaret Herbison PC
1971/72	The Right Hon Lord Clydesmuir of Braidwood CB MBE TD
1973/74	The Right Hon Lord Ballantrae of Auchairne and the Bay of Islands GCMG GCVO DSO OBE
1975/76	Sir Hector MacLennan KT FRCPGLAS FRCOG
1977	Francis David Charteris, Earl of Wemyss and March KT LLD
1978/79	The Right Hon William Ross MBE LLD
1980/81	Andrew Douglas Alexander Thomas Bruce, Earl of Elgin and Kincardine KT DL JP
1982/83	Colonel Sir John Edward Gilmour BT DSO TD
1984/85	Charles Hector Fitzroy Maclean, Baron Maclean of Duart and Morvern KT GCVO KBE
1986/87	John Campbell Arbuthnott, Viscount of Arbuthnott CBE DSC FRSE FRSA
1988/89	Sir Iain Mark Tennant KT FRSA
1990/91	The Right Hon Donald MacArthur Ross FRSE
1992/93	The Right Hon Lord Macfarlane of Bearsden
1994/95	Lady Marion Fraser
1996	Her Royal Highness The Princess Royal LG GCVO
1997	The Right Hon Lord Macfarlane of Bearsden
1998/99	The Right Hon Lord Hogg of Cumbernauld
2000	His Royal Highness The Prince Charles, Duke of Rothesay

(7) RECENT MODERATORS
OF THE GENERAL ASSEMBLY

1965	Archibald Watt STM DD, Edzell and Lethnot
1966	R. Leonard Small OBE DD, Edinburgh St Cuthbert's
1967	W. Roy Sanderson DD, Stenton with Whittingehame
1968	J.B. Longmuir TD DD, Principal Clerk of Assembly
1969	T.M. Murchison MA DD, Glasgow St Columba Summertown
1970	Hugh O. Douglas CBE DD LLD, Dundee St Mary's
1971	Andrew Herron MA BD LLB, Clerk to the Presbytery of Glasgow
1972	R.W.V. Selby Wright JP CVO TD DD FRSE, Edinburgh Canongate
1973	George T.H. Reid MC MA BD DD, Aberdeen Langstane
1974	David Steel MA BD DD, Linlithgow St Michael's
1975	James G. Matheson MA BD DD, Portree
1976	Thomas F. Torrance MBE DLitt DD FRSE, University of Edinburgh
1977	John R. Gray VRD MA BD ThM, Dunblane Cathedral
1978	Peter P. Brodie MA BD LLB DD, Alloa St Mungo's
1979	Robert A.S. Barbour MA BD STM DD, University of Aberdeen
1980	William B. Johnston MA BD DD, Edinburgh Colinton
1981	Andrew B. Doig BD STM DD, National Bible Society of Scotland
1982	John McIntyre CVO DD DLitt FRSE, University of Edinburgh
1983	J. Fraser McLuskey MC DD, London St Columba's
1984	John M.K. Paterson MA ACII BD, Milngavie St Paul's
1985	David M.B.A. Smith MA BD DUniv, Logie
1986	Robert Craig CBE DLitt LLD DD, Emeritus of Jerusalem
1987	Duncan Shaw *Bundesverdienstkreuz* JP PhD ThDr, Edinburgh Craigentinny St Christopher's
1988	James A. Whyte MA LLD, University of St Andrews
1989	William J.G. McDonald MA BD DD, Edinburgh Mayfield
1990	Robert Davidson MA BD DD FRSE, University of Glasgow
1991	William B.R. Macmillan MA BD LLD DD, Dundee St Mary's
1992	Hugh R. Wyllie MA MCIBS DD, Hamilton Old Parish Church
1993	James L. Weatherhead MA LLB DD, Principal Clerk of Assembly
1994	James A. Simpson BSc BD STM DD, Dornoch Cathedral
1995	James Harkness CB OBE MA DD, Chaplain General (Emeritus)
1996	John H. McIndoe MA BD STM DD, London: St Columba's linked with Newcastle: St Andrew's
1997	Alexander McDonald BA CMIWSc DUniv, General Secretary, Department of Ministry
1998	Alan Main TD MA BD STM PhD, Professor of Practical Theology at Christ's College, University of Aberdeen
1999	John B. Cairns LTh LLB, Dumbarton Riverside
2000	Andrew R.C. McLellan MA BD STM, Edinburgh St. Andrew's and St. George's

MATTER OF PRECEDENCE

The Lord High Commissioner to the General Assembly of the Church of Scotland (while the Assembly is sitting) ranks next to the Sovereign, the Duke of Edinburgh and the Duke of Rothesay, and before the rest of the Royal Family.

The Moderator of the General Assembly of the Church of Scotland ranks next to the Lord Chancellor of Great Britain and before the Prime Minister and the Dukes.

(8) HER MAJESTY'S HOUSEHOLD IN SCOTLAND
ECCLESIASTICAL

Dean of the Chapel Royal: Very Rev. James Harkness CB OBE MA DD
Dean of the Order of the Thistle: Very Rev. Gilleasbuig I. Macmillan
CVO MA BD Drhc
Domestic Chaplain: Rev. Robert P. Sloan MA BD

Chaplains in Ordinary:

Very Rev. Gilleasbuig I. Macmillan
CVO MA BD Drhc
Rev. Maxwell D. Craig MA BD ThM
Very Rev. James L. Weatherhead
CBE MA LLB DD
Rev. Charles Robertson MA JP
Very Rev. James A. Simpson BSc STM DD
Rev. Norman W. Drummond MA BD
Rev. John L. Paterson MA BD STM
Rev. Alastair H. Symington MA BD
Very Rev. John B. Cairns LTh LLB

Extra Chaplains:

Very Rev. W. Roy Sanderson DD
Very Rev. Prof. John McIntyre
CVO DD DLitt Drhc FRSE
Rev. H.W.M. Cant MA BD STM
Rev. Kenneth MacVicar MBE DFC TD MA
Very Rev. Prof. Robert A.S. Barbour
KCVO MC BD STM DD
Rev. Alwyn Macfarlane MA
Very Rev. William B. Johnston
MA BD DD DLitt
Rev. Colin Forrester-Paton MA BD
Rev. Mary I. Levison BA BD DD
Rev. J.A. Keith Angus LVO TD MA
Very Rev. William J. Morris
KCVO PhD LLD DD JP
Rev. John MacLeod MA
Rev. A. Stewart Todd MA BD DD
Very Rev. William B.R. Macmillan
MA BD LLD DD

(9) LONG SERVICE CERTIFICATES

Long Service Certificates, signed by the Moderator, are available for presentation to Elders and others in respect of not less than 30 years of service. It should be noted that the period is years of *service*, not *eg* years of ordination in the case of an Elder.

In the case of Sunday School teachers and Bible Class leaders the qualifying period is 21 years of service.

Certificates are not issued posthumously, nor is it possible to make exceptions to the rules, *eg* by recognising quality of service in order to reduce the qualifying period, or by reducing the qualifying period on compassionate grounds, such as serious illness.

A Certificate will be issued only once to any particular individual.

Applications for Long Service Certificates should be made in writing to the Principal Clerk at 121 George Street, Edinburgh EH2 4YN by the Parish Minister, or by the Session Clerk on behalf of the Kirk Session. Certificates are not issued from this office to the individual recipients, nor should individuals make application themselves.

(10) LIBRARIES OF THE CHURCH

GENERAL ASSEMBLY LIBRARY AND RECORD ROOM
Most of the books contained in the General Assembly Library have been transferred to the New College Library. Records of the General Assembly, Synods, Presbyteries and Kirk Sessions are now in H M Register House, Edinburgh. All records more than fifty years old and not in current use should be sent to the Principal Clerk.

CHURCH MUSIC
The Library of New College contains a selection of works on Church music.

(11) RECORDS OF THE CHURCH OF SCOTLAND

Church records more than 50 years old, unless still in use, should be sent or delivered to the Principal Clerk for onward transmission to the Scottish Record Office. Where Ministers or Session Clerks are approached by a local repository seeking a transfer of their records, they should inform the Principal Clerk who will take the matter up with the National Archives of Scotland.

Where a temporary re-transmission of records is sought, it is extremely helpful if notice can be given three months in advance so that appropriate procedures can be carried out satisfactorily.

SECTION 3

Church Procedure

(1) THE MINISTER AND BAPTISM

The administration of Baptism to infants is governed by Act XVII (1963). The Statement on the Doctrine of Baptism may be found in the 1991 "Blue Book", page 224.

The Act itself is as follows:

1. Baptism may be administered to a child:
    (1)   whose parents, one or both, have themselves been baptised, are in full communion with the Church, and undertake the Christian upbringing of the child;
    (2)   whose parents, one or both, having been baptised, but not in full communion, are such that the Kirk Session is satisfied that he or she is an adherent, permanently connected with the congregation and supporting the work and worship of the Church and will undertake the Christian upbringing of the child;
    (3)   whose parents, one or both, have themselves been baptised, profess the Christian faith, undertake to ensure that such child grows up in the life and worship of the Church and express the desire to seek admission to full membership of the Church. In such cases the Kirk Session shall appoint an Elder of the District in which the parents reside, or some other person, to shepherd them into full communion and to exercise pastoral care of the child concerned;
    (4)   who, being of unknown parentage, or otherwise separated from his or her parents, is in the view of the Kirk Session, under Christian care and guardianship.
2. Baptism may be administered only by Ministers authorised by the General Assembly to dispense the Sacrament of the Lord's Supper.
3. Baptism may be administered only after the parents or guardians have received such instruction in its meaning as the Minister shall deem necessary.
4. No Minister shall baptise a child resident outwith his own parish, whose parents are not members or adherents of his congregation, without consent of the Minister of that parish or of the Presbytery.
5. Without the consent of the Presbytery, no Minister may administer Baptism in a case where to his knowledge another Minister has declined to do so.
6. Baptism shall normally be administered at a diet of public worship of the congregation of which the parents or guardians are members or adherents, or of the congregation of the parish in which they normally reside. In exceptional circumstances, Baptism may be administered elsewhere (*eg* at home, in hospitals or institutions). In every case, an entry shall be made in the Register of Baptism kept by the Kirk Session of the congregation of which the parents or guardians are members or adherents, or in that of the parish in which they normally reside, as the case may be.
7. Baptism shall be administered in the Name of the Father, and of the Son, and of the Holy Ghost, with water, by sprinkling, pouring, or immersion. Other elements may not be used.
8. In all cases, a Certificate of Baptism shall be given by the Minister.
9. Nothing in this Act shall be taken to mean that the Church of Scotland rejects Baptism in the name of the Father and of the Son and of the Holy Ghost duly administered in accordance with the law and discipline of other churches.

(2) THE MINISTER AND MARRIAGE

1. BACKGROUND

Prior to 1939 every marriage in Scotland fell into one or other of two classes; regular or irregular. The former was marriage by a minister of religion after due notice of intention had been given; the latter could be effected in one of three ways: (a) declaration *de presenti,* (b) by promise *subsequente copula,* or (c) by habit and repute.

The Marriage (Scotland) Act of 1939 put an end to (a) and (b) and provided for a new classification of marriage as either religious or civil. Religious marriage, conducted by a minister of religion, might be contracted in any place at any time after due intimation. Civil marriage could take place only in the office of a Registrar, again after due intimation.

The law of marriage as it was thus established in 1939 had two important limitations to the celebration of marriage: (1) certain preliminaries had to be observed; and (2) in respect of religious marriage, the service had to be conducted according to the forms of either the Christian or the Jewish faith.

2. THE MARRIAGE (SCOTLAND) ACT 1977

These two conditions were radically altered by the Marriage (Scotland) Act 1977.

Since 1st January 1978, in conformity with the demands of a multi-racial society, the benefits of religious marriage have been extended to adherents of other faiths, the only requirements being the observance of monogamy and the satisfaction of the authorities with the forms of the vows imposed.

Since 1978 the calling of banns has also been discontinued. The couple themselves must each complete a Marriage Notice form and return this to the District Registrar for the area in which they are to be married, irrespective of where they live, at least fifteen days before the ceremony is due to take place. The papers required with the form are detailed thereon.

If everything is in order the District Registrar will issue, not more than seven days before the date of the ceremony, a Marriage Schedule. This must be in the hands of the Minister officiating at the marriage ceremony before the service begins. Under no circumstances must the minister deviate from this rule. To do so is an offence under the Act.

Ministers should note the advice given by the Procurator of the Church in 1962, that they should not officiate at any marriage until at least one day after the sixteenth birthday of the younger party.

3. PROCLAMATION OF BANNS

Proclamation of banns is no longer required in Scotland but in the Church of England marriage is governed by the provisions of the Marriage Act 1949, which requires that the parties shall have been proclaimed and which provides that in the case of a party residing in Scotland a Certificate of Proclamation given according to the law or custom prevailing in Scotland shall be sufficient for the purpose. Should a minister be requested to call banns for a person resident within the Registration District wherein his church is situated he should accede, making the proclamation only on one Sunday, if the parties are known to him and he has reason to believe that there is no impediment to the marriage; otherwise on two Sundays.

Proclamation should be made at the principal service of worship in this form:

There is a purpose of marriage between AB (Bachelor/Widower/Divorced, residing at .... in this Registration District and CD, Spinster/Widow/Divorced residing at .... in the Registration District of .... of which proclamation is hereby made for the first and only (second and last) time.

Immediately after the second reading, or not less than 48 hours after the first and only reading, a Certificate of Proclamation signed by either the Minister or the Session Clerk should be issued in the following terms:

> At .... the ...... day of ...... 20 ....
> It is hereby certified that AB, residing at .... and CD, residing at .... have been duly proclaimed in order to marriage in the Church of .... according to the custom of the Church of Scotland, and that no objections have been offered.
> Signed .... Minister or
> Signed .... Session Clerk

4. MARRIAGE OF FOREIGNERS

Marriages in Scotland of foreigners, or of foreigners with British subjects, are, if they satisfy the requirements of Scots Law, valid throughout Her Majesty's dominions; but they will not necessarily be valid in the country to which the foreigner belongs. This will be so only if the requirements of the law of his or her country have also been complied with. It is therefore most important that, before the marriage, steps should be taken to obtain from the Consul, or other diplomatic representative of the country concerned, a satisfactory assurance that the marriage will be accepted as valid in the country concerned.

5. REMARRIAGE OF DIVORCED PERSONS

By virtue of Act XXVI (1959) a Minister of the Church of Scotland may lawfully solemnise the marriage of a person whose former marriage has been dissolved on divorce and whose former spouse is still alive. The Minister however must carefully adhere to the requirements of the Act which, as slightly altered in 1985 are briefly as follows:

1. The Minister should not accede as a matter of routine to a request to solemnise such a marriage. To enable him to make his decision he should take all reasonable steps to obtain relevant information, which should normally include the following:
    (a) Adequate information concerning the life and character of the parties. The Act enjoins the greatest caution in cases where no pastoral relationship exists between the Minister and either or both of the parties concerned.
    (b) The grounds and circumstances of the divorce case.
    (c) Facts bearing upon the future well being of any children concerned.
    (d) Whether any other Minister has declined to solemnise the proposed marriage.
    (e) The denomination to which the parties belong. The Act enjoins that special care should be taken where one or more parties belong to a denomination whose discipline in this matter may differ from that of the Church of Scotland.
2. The Minister should consider whether there is danger of scandal arising if he should solemnise the re-marriage, at the same time taking into careful consideration before refusing to do so the moral and spiritual effect of his refusal on the parties concerned.
3. As a determinative factor, the Minister should do all he can to assure himself that there has been sincere repentance where guilt has existed on the part of any divorced person seeking remarriage. He should also give instruction, where needed, in the nature and requirements of a Christian marriage.
4. A Minister is not required to solemnise a re-marriage against his conscience. Every Presbytery is required to appoint certain individuals with one of whom Ministers in doubt as to the correct course of action may consult if they so desire. The final decision however rests with the Minister who has been asked to officiate.

(3) CONDUCT OF MARRIAGE SERVICES
(CODE OF GOOD PRACTICE)

1. *Marriage in the Church of Scotland is solemnised by an ordained minister in a religious ceremony wherein, before God, and in the presence of the minister and at least two competent witnesses, the parties covenant together to take each other as husband and wife as long as they both shall live and the minister declares the parties to be husband and wife. Before solemnising a marriage a minister must be assured that the necessary legal requirements are being complied with and that the parties know of no legal impediment to their marriage and he or she must afterwards ensure that the Marriage Schedule is duly completed.* (Act I 1977)

2. Any ordained minister of the Church of Scotland who is a member of Presbytery or who holds a current Ministerial Certificate may officiate at a marriage service (see Act II 1987).

3. While the marriage service should normally take place in church, a minister may, at his or her discretion, officiate at a marriage service outwith church premises. Wherever conducted the ceremony will be such as to reflect appropriately both the joy and the solemnity of the occasion. In particular a minister shall ensure that nothing is done which would bring the Church and its teaching into disrepute.

4. A minister agreeing to conduct a wedding should endeavour to establish a pastoral relationship with the couple within which adequate pre-marriage preparation and subsequent pastoral care may be given.

5. "A minister should not refuse to perform ministerial functions for a person who is resident in his or her parish without sufficient reason" (Cox, *Practice and Procedure in the Church of Scotland*, sixth edition, page 55). Where either party to the proposed marriage has been divorced and the former spouse is still alive, the minister invited to officiate may solemnise such a marriage, having regard to the guidelines in the Act anent the Re-marriage of Divorced Persons (Act XXVI 1959 as amended by Act II 1985).

6. A minister is acting as an agent of the National Church which is committed to bringing the ordinances of religion to the people of Scotland through a territorial ministry. As such he or she shall not be entitled to charge a fee or allow a fee to be charged for conducting a marriage service. When a gift is spontaneously offered to a minister as a token of appreciation, the above consideration should not be taken to mean that he or she should not accept such an unsolicited gift. The Financial Board of a congregation is at liberty to set fees to cover such costs as heat and light and in addition Organists and Church Officers are entitled to a fee in respect of their services at weddings.

7. A minister should not allow his or her name to be associated with any commercial enterprise that provides facilities for weddings.

8. A minister is not at liberty to enter the bounds of another minister's parish to perform ministerial functions without the previous consent of the minister of that parish. In terms of Act VIII 1933 a minister may "officiate at a marriage or funeral by private invitation", but, for the avoidance of doubt, an invitation conveyed through a commercial enterprise shall not be regarded as a "private invitation" within the meaning of that Act.

9. A minister invited to officiate at a Marriage Service where neither party is a member of his or her congregation or is resident within his or her own parish or has any connection with the parish within which the service is to take place should observe the following courtesies:
    (a) he or she should ascertain from the parties whether either of them has a Church of Scotland connection or has approached the appropriate parish minister(s);
    (b) if it transpires that a ministerial colleague has declined to officiate then he or she (the invited minister) should ascertain the reasons therefor and shall take these, and all other relevant factors into account in deciding whether or not to officiate.

(4) THE MINISTER AND WILLS

The Requirements of Writing (Scotland) Act of 1995, which came into force on 1st August 1995, has removed the power of a Minister to execute wills notarially. Further clarification, if required, may be obtained from the Solicitor of the Church.

---

(5) PROCEDURE IN A VACANCY
(as currently applicable)

This is regulated by Act V 1984 (as amended). The text of the Act in its current form is given here for general information. Schedules of Intimation referred to in the Act are also included.

[NOTE: Throughout this Act all masculine pronouns and titles imply the feminine equivalent.]

APPOINTMENT OF INTERIM MODERATOR
1. At the first convenient opportunity after the death or deposition of a minister the Presbytery shall appoint an Interim Moderator to act in the vacancy; at the same meeting at which it agrees to a minister's translation, accepts his demission of office as minister of a parish, or determines (or is instructed) to dissolve a pastoral tie, the Presbytery shall appoint an Interim Moderator to act in the anticipated vacancy; the person so appointed shall be a ministerial member of the Presbytery and shall not be a member of the vacant congregation. The name of the Interim Moderator shall forthwith be forwarded to the Secretaries of the Department of Ministry.

DUTIES OF INTERIM MODERATOR
2.(1)   It shall be the duty of the Interim Moderator to preside at all meetings of the Kirk Session (or of the Kirk Sessions in the case of a linked charge) and to preside at all congregational meetings in connection with the vacancy, or at which the minister would have presided had the charge been full. In the case of a congregational meeting called by the Presbytery in connection with readjustment the Interim Moderator, having constituted the meeting, shall relinquish the chair in favour of the representative of the Presbytery, but he shall be at liberty to speak at such a meeting. In consultation with the Kirk Session and the Financial Court he shall make arrangements for the supply of the vacant pulpit.

(2)   It shall be the duty of the Interim Moderator to have the charge declared vacant on the first convenient Sunday after it has actually become vacant, that is to say:
  (a)   the day of the death of the minister;
  (b)   the day when the minister's demission of office takes effect, as agreed by the Presbytery;
  (c)   the day when the minister is inducted to another charge;
  (d)   the day appointed by the Presbytery or by a superior court for the minister's deposition or for the dissolution of the pastoral tie.
When the charge consists of more than one congregation this declaration, which shall be made in terms of Schedule A hereto, shall be read in face of each congregation, and shall be duly attested.

(3)   The Interim Moderator appointed in a prospective vacancy may call and preside at meetings of the Kirk Session and of the congregation only for the transaction of business relating to the said prospective vacancy. He shall be associated with the minister until the date of the vacancy (as above defined) and after that date he shall take full charge.

QUESTION OF READJUSTMENT

3.(1)   When an Interim Moderator has been appointed in a vacancy or a prospective vacancy, the question of readjustment shall be deemed to have been raised at that point, whereupon;

    (a)   the Presbytery Clerk shall inform the Secretary of the Assembly's Committee on Parish Reappraisal of the vacancy or prospective vacancy; and

    (b)   the Presbytery shall ascertain whether the charge has current or accumulated shortfalls in contributions to central funds, and shall determine whether, and to what extent any shortfalls which exist are justified.

(2)   If the vacancy is in a charge in which

    (a)   the Presbytery has ascertained that there are no shortfalls, or

    (b)   the Presbytery has determined that such shortfalls as exist are justified,

the Presbytery shall without delay consider whether in its opinion the question of readjustment should be pursued, conferring, if thought fitting with the office-bearers of the vacant congregation. If the Presbytery resolves that the question of readjustment should be pursued it shall take appropriate action to this end and shall inform the Assembly's Committee of its decision. If the Presbytery resolves that the question of readjustment should not be pursued it shall record this decision in its minute and shall go on to grant permission, subject to the concurrence of the Assembly's Committee on Parish Reappraisal, for the congregation to call a minister without restriction, informing the said Committee accordingly. If the Assembly's Committee is not prepared to concur this shall have the effect of sisting procedure and the question shall be further pursued notwithstanding the Presbytery's decision. In so pursuing the question in such a case the Presbytery shall seek from the outset the active participation of representatives of the Assembly's Committee. Any decision to pursue the question of readjustment at this early stage shall be without prejudice to the possibility that, at a subsequent point in the negotiations, the congregation may be granted permission to call a minister without restriction. When in any case it is agreed that the question of readjustment is to be pursued the Presbytery shall direct that no steps be taken towards filling the vacancy beyond that of preparing the Electoral Register.

(3)   If the vacancy is in a charge in which the Presbytery has determined that shortfalls are to any extent unjustified, it shall pursue the question of readjustment, provided that it may not resolve to allow a call of any kind until either;

    (a)   the shortfalls have been met to the extent to which the Presbytery determined that they were unjustified; or

    (b)   the congregation has been linked to or united with another congregation or other congregations.

(4)   The Presbytery shall inform the Committee on the Maintenance of the Ministry and the Board of Stewardship and Finance of its decisions in terms of this Section.

(5)   Any appeal or dissent and complaint against any judgement made in terms of this Section shall not sist procedure in the pursuit of the question of readjustment and shall be competent only in accordance with the provisions of Act IV 1984.

PERMISSION TO CALL

4.   At the meeting of Presbytery at which it is reported that a vacancy has to be filled because the Presbytery and the Assembly's Committee on Parish Reappraisal have reached agreement, or because it has been ordained by a superior court:

    (a)   that the charge is to be allowed to call a minister (with or without restriction); or

    (b)   that some form of union or linking has been or is about to be effected resulting in the emergence of a vacant charge which is to have permission to call a minister (with or without restriction); or

    (c)   that some form of deferred union or deferred linking has been agreed which provides for the congregations involved electing a minister who will ultimately be minister of the united or linked charge but who will immediately become minister of the vacant charge; or

(d)   that an appointment is to be made under Terminable Tenure; or

(e)   that an Associate Minister is to be appointed –

the Presbytery shall appoint an *ad hoc* committee of three (of whom at least one shall be an elder) – to be known as the "Presbytery Advisory Committee" – with which the Kirk Session of the vacant charge (or the Kirk Sessions jointly in the case of a linking or of an impending union or linking or of a deferred union or linking) shall be under obligation to meet, to consider together in the light of the whole circumstances of the parish or parishes what kind of ministry would be best suited to their needs.

VACANCY SCHEDULE

5.(1)   As soon as agreement has been reached between the Presbytery and the Assembly's Committee on Parish Reappraisal as in Section 4 above there shall be issued by the Assembly's Committee on the Maintenance of the Ministry a Schedule or Schedules for completion by the responsible Financial Court of the vacant congregation (or courts of the congregations involved) in consultation with representatives of the Presbytery, setting forth the proposed arrangements for stipend and payment of ministerial expenses and for provision of a manse, and showing the amount of Aid to be given to, or to be received from, the Minimum Stipend Fund.

(2)   This Schedule (or these Schedules) shall be considered by the Presbytery and thereafter transmitted to the Assembly's Committee. The Presbytery shall not sustain an appointment and call until this Schedule has (or these Schedules have) been approved both by the Presbytery and by the Assembly's Committee.

(3)   A copy of the relevant minute of the Assembly's Committee approving the Schedule or Schedules shall be delivered by the Presbytery Clerk to the minister at the time of his induction (see section 25 (6) hereunder).

PREPARATION OF ELECTORAL REGISTER

6.   It shall be the duty of the Kirk Session of the vacant congregation, notwithstanding that the question of readjustment is being pursued, to proceed to make up the Electoral Register of the congregation. This shall contain (1) as communicants the names of those persons (a) whose names are on the communion roll of the congregation as at that date and who are not under Church discipline, (b) whose names have been added or restored to the communion roll on revision by the Kirk Session subsequently to the occurrence of the vacancy, and (c) who have given in valid Certificates of Transference by the date specified in terms of Schedule B hereto; and (2) as adherents the names of those persons who, being parishioners or regular worshippers in the congregation at the date when the vacancy occurred, being at least 18 years of age, and not being members of any other congregation in Scotland, have claimed (in writing in the form prescribed in Schedule C and within the time specified in Schedule B hereto) to be placed on the Electoral Register, the Kirk Session being satisfied that they desire to be permanently connected with the congregation and knowing of no adequate reason why they should not be admitted as communicants should they so apply.

HEARING OF CLAIMS

7.   At a meeting to be held not later than fourteen days after intimation has been made in terms of Schedule B hereto, the Kirk Session shall decide on the claims of persons to be placed on the Electoral Register, such claims to be sent to the Session Clerk before the meeting. At this meeting the Kirk Session may hear parties claiming to have an interest. The Kirk Session shall thereupon prepare the lists of names and addresses of communicants and of adherents which it is proposed shall be the Electoral Register of the congregation, the names being arranged in alphabetical order and numbered consecutively throughout. The decision of the Kirk Session in respect of any matter affecting the preparation of the Electoral Register shall be final.

INSPECTION AND FINAL ADJUSTMENT OF ELECTORAL REGISTER

8.(1)   The proposed Electoral Register having been prepared, the Interim Moderator shall cause intimation to be made on the first convenient Sunday in terms of Schedule D hereto that on that day an opportunity will be given for inspecting the Register after service, and that it will lie for inspection at such times and such places as the Kirk Session shall have determined; and further shall specify a day when the Kirk Session will meet to hear parties claiming an interest and will finally revise and adjust the Register. At this meeting, or at an adjourned meeting held later, the list having been revised and adjusted shall, on the authority of the court, be attested by the Interim Moderator and the Clerk as the Electoral Register of the congregation.

(2)   This Register, along with a duplicate copy, shall without delay be transmitted to the Presbytery Clerk who, in name of the Presbytery, shall attest and return the principal copy, retaining the duplicate copy in his own possession. For all purposes connected with the following regulations, and for all purposes connected with parish reappraisal, the congregation shall be deemed to be those persons whose names are on the Electoral Register, and no other.

(3)   If after the attestation of the Register any communicant is given a Certificate of Transference the Session Clerk shall intimate the fact to the Interim Moderator who shall delete the name from the Register and initial the deletion. Such a Certificate shall be granted only when application for it has been made in writing, and the said written application shall be retained until the vacancy is ended.

(4)   When a period of more than six months has elapsed between the Electoral Register being attested and the congregation being given permission to call, the Kirk Session shall have power, if it so desires, to revise and update the Electoral Register. Intimation of this intention shall be given in terms of Schedule E hereto. Additional names shall be added to the Register in the form of an Addendum which shall also contain authority for the deletions which have been made, and a copy of this, duly attested, shall be lodged with the Presbytery Clerk.

APPOINTMENT OF VACANCY COMMITTEE

9.   When permission to call has been given steps shall be taken to appoint a Vacancy Committee. A congregation not yet vacant may appeal to the Presbytery for permission for its Vacancy Committee to proceed with the search for a nominee, and, if satisfied that this is in the best interest of the congregation, the Presbytery may grant such permission. But such action shall not be taken without the specific approval of the Presbytery, and in no case shall a nomination be reported to the Kirk Session in terms of section 14 hereunder until the charge is actually vacant. With a view to the appointment of a Vacancy Committee the Interim Moderator shall cause intimation to be made in terms of Schedule F that a meeting of the congregation is to be held (a) to appoint a committee of its own number for the purpose of nominating one or more persons to the congregation with a view to the election and appointment of a minister and (b) to determine whether the election shall be by ballot or by open vote. On one of the two Sundays when this intimation is made there shall also be read an exhortation impressing upon the congregation the importance of their responsibilities in the election and throughout the period of the vacancy. The Interim Moderator shall preside at this meeting, and the Session Clerk, or in his absence a person appointed by the meeting, shall act as Clerk. The procedure shall be as follows:

(a) The meeting shall first determine the maximum number to serve on the Vacancy Committee. The following scale is recommended: Committee not to exceed

13 when the number on the Electoral Register is under 500
19 when the number on the Electoral Register is under 1000
25 when the number on the Electoral Register amounts to 1000 or more

When the vacancy is in a linked charge, or when a union or linking of congregations has been agreed but not yet effected, or when there is agreement to a deferred union or a deferred linking, the Presbytery shall determine the number who will act on the Vacancy Committee and how that number will be allocated among the congregations involved, unless provision for this has already been made in the Basis of Union or Basis of Linking as the case may be.

(b) The Interim Moderator shall then call for nominations. To constitute a valid nomination the name of a person on the Electoral Register has to be proposed and seconded. Only one nomination shall be made at a time. Anyone proposing the name of a person who is not present must be able to say that that person is prepared to act on the Committee. The Clerk shall take a note of all nominations in the order in which they are made.

(c) When it appears to the Interim Moderator that the nominations are complete he shall read to the meeting the list of the persons nominated. He shall then ask, first whether there are any further nominations, and, second, whether there are any withdrawals. After making any necessary adjustments he shall declare the list complete.

(d) If the number of persons nominated does not exceed the maximum, fixed in terms of sub-section (a) above there is no need for a vote, and the Interim Moderator shall declare that these persons constitute the Vacancy Committee. If the number exceeds the maximum the Interim Moderator shall submit the names one by one as they appear on the list to the vote of the congregation, each member having the right to vote for up to the maximum number fixed for the Committee, and voting being by standing up. In the event of a tie for the last place a vote shall be taken between those tying.

(e) The meeting shall then determine by standing up whether the election of a minister shall be by ballot or by open vote. In cases where the vacant charge consists of two or more congregations or where agreement has been reached on deferred union or deferred linking, the method of voting shall necessarily be by ballot.

(f) After intimating to the meeting the names of the persons elected to the Vacancy Committee, and announcing to the latter when they are to meet to appoint office-bearers (possibly immediately on the close of the congregational meeting) the Interim Moderator shall close the meeting with prayer.

The Interim Moderator shall act as an assessor to the Vacancy Committee, being available to offer guidance and advice. If the Committee so desire he may act as their Convener, but in no case shall he have a vote, either deliberative or casting.

FIRST MEETING OF VACANCY COMMITTEE
10. It shall be the duty of the Interim Moderator to summon and preside at the first meeting of the Vacancy Committee, which may be held at the close of the congregational meeting at which it is appointed. At this meeting a Convener, Vice-Convener, and Clerk shall be appointed. The Clerk, who need not be a member of the Committee, shall keep regular minutes of all proceedings. The Convener shall have both a casting and a deliberative vote (unless he be the Interim Moderator). If the Clerk is not a member of the Committee he shall have no vote.

MEETING WITH PRESBYTERY ADVISORY COMMITTEE
11.(1) The Interim Moderator shall arrange that the first regular meeting of the Vacancy Committee shall be attended by the Presbytery Advisory Committee which shall continue with the Vacancy Committee the discussion begun earlier with the Kirk Session or Sessions regarding the type of minister who could serve to greatest advantage in the situation, and the best way of proceeding in their search for such a minister.

(2) In the case of island and other remote charges it will be regarded as adequate if the Interim Moderator (accompanied, preferably, by a member of the Vacancy Committee) meets with the Presbytery Advisory Committee, or at least with its Convener, to carry on these discussions.

PROCEDURE OF VACANCY COMMITTEE
12.(1) The Vacancy Committee being charged with the duty of nominating one or more persons to the congregation with a view to the election and appointment of a minister, may proceed in any of the two ways outlined hereunder.

    (a) They may decide as a result of advertisement, recommendation, enquiry, and in other ways upon a list of candidates from which they shall in due course select one or more names for submission to the congregation.

(b)   They may decide to propose to the congregation (or congregations) that, in respect of the present vacancy only, they should restrict their right of call to the extent of electing and calling, for a period of three years only, a minister of a Church furth of Scotland which is a member of the World Alliance of Reformed Churches, or of the Church of South India, or of the Church of Pakistan. If they so decide the procedure shall be as follows:

(i)   The Interim Moderator shall cause intimation to be made on two Sundays in terms of Schedule GG that a meeting of the congregation is (or that meetings of the congregations are) to be held to determine whether they are in favour of restricting the choice of minister as proposed by the Vacancy Committee.

(ii)   If the congregation (or either or any of the congregations) vote by a majority against the proposal it shall be regarded as having fallen and the Vacancy Committee shall proceed in accordance with the other method open to them as in (a) above.

(iii)   If the congregation votes (or both or all the congregations vote) in favour of the proposal the Interim Moderator shall consult with the General Secretary of the Board of World Mission with a view to the submission of the names of not more than three ministers eligible in terms of Section 13 (11) hereunder. If none of these is accepted by the Vacancy Committee as suitable for nomination, application may be made to the Secretary of the Board for a further list of three names. Should the Vacancy Committee still be unable to recommend a sole nominee the proposal shall be regarded as having fallen and they shall proceed in accordance with the other method open to them as in (a) above.

(iv)   If the Vacancy Committee accepts one of the names for nomination procedure thereafter shall be as hereunder.

(2)   If the Vacancy Committee resolve not to have a sole nominee but to submit more than one nomination (a leet) to the congregation to be voted upon by them the Presbytery Advisory Committee shall have the right to add names up to the number submitted by the Vacancy Committee, and these too shall be heard and voted upon by the congregation.

ELIGIBILITY FOR ELECTION

13. The following categories of persons, and no others, are eligible to be nominated, elected, and called as ministers of parishes in the Church of Scotland:

(1)   A minister of a parish of the Church, a minister holding some other appointment that entitles him to a seat in Presbytery, or a minister holding a current Ministerial Certificate in terms of Sections 5-19 of Act II 1987. This is subject to the reservation that a Presbytery is not entitled to sustain a call to a minister in his first charge of a church and parish of the Church of Scotland until the expiry of at least five years from the date of his induction to that charge unless, before his nomination, a Certificate in one of the forms of Schedule G has been obtained from the Presbytery of which he is a member to the effect that there are exceptional circumstances to justify such a translation. The Interim Moderator shall be responsible for procuring this Certificate and he shall lodge it with the clerk of his own Presbytery before the nomination is reported by him to the Kirk Session in terms of section 14 (4) hereunder.

(2)   A minister of the Church of Scotland who has retired from a parish or appointment as above, provided he has not reached his seventieth birthday.

(3)   (a) A licentiate of the Church of Scotland who has satisfactorily completed, or has been granted exemption from, his period of probationary service;

(b) a graduate candidate in terms of Act V 1998, Sections 26 and 27.

(4)   A minister or licentiate or graduate candidate of the Church of Scotland who, with the approval of the Board of World Mission, has entered the courts of an indigenous Church as a full member, provided he has ceased to be such a member and has obtained from the Committee on Probationers and Transference and Admission of Ministers or its Executive a Certificate of Eligibility.

(5)   A minister or licentiate or graduate candidate of another denomination who has been admitted on petition by the General Assembly to the status of a minister or licentiate of the Church of Scotland, and who holds an extract minute of the General Assembly to that effect.

(6)   A minister or licentiate or graduate candidate of the Church of Scotland who has neither relinquished nor been judicially deprived of the status he possessed and who has become an accredited minister of the United Reformed Church in the United Kingdom, or of the Presbyterian Church in Ireland, provided he produces a Certificate from the Clerk to the General Assembly of his Church as to his status, record and character.

(7)   A minister or licentiate of the Church of Scotland who has neither relinquished nor been judicially deprived of the status he possessed and who has served, or is serving, furth of Scotland in any Church which is a member of the World Alliance of Reformed Churches, provided that prior to such nomination and call he has obtained from the Committee on Probationers and Transference and Admission of Ministers or its Executive a Certificate of Eligibility, having satisfied that body as to his status, record, and character.

(8)   A minister or licentiate of the Church of Scotland who has neither relinquished nor been judicially deprived of the status he possessed and who has undertaken employment which is not subject to the jurisdiction of any Church, provided that prior to such nomination and call (a) he has obtained from the Committee on Probationers and Transference and Admission of Ministers or its Executive a Certificate of Eligibility, having satisfied that body as to his status, record, and character, and (b) he has given a written assurance that before being admitted to a charge he shall have ceased to be so employed.

(9)   A minister of the Presbyterian Church in Ireland, provided he produces a Certificate from the Clerk to the General Assembly of that Church to the effect (a) that he was ordained by that Church, and (b) that throughout a period of not less than five years he has held one or more charges or appointments under the jurisdiction of that Church.

(10)   A minister of any regularly constituted Presbyterian Church in the United Kingdom unless eligible in terms of (9) above, of the United Reformed Church in the United Kingdom, or of any Church furth of the United Kingdom which is a member of the World Alliance of Reformed Churches, provided he holds a Certificate of Eligibility obtained from the Committee on Probationers and Transference and Admission of Ministers or its Executive, that Committee having satisfied itself (a) that he is a minister in full standing within his own Church and that throughout a period of not less than five years he has held one or more charges or appointments in that Church, (b) that he has completed a University and/or College course acceptable to the Committee on Education for the Ministry as being in accordance with the regulations of the Committee for the time being, (c) that his character and conduct are in keeping with his profession, and (d) that he is not subject to the provision of Act III 1995 Section 8 (2) (c).

(11)   A minister of a Church furth of Scotland which is a member of the World Alliance of Reformed Churches, or of the Church of South India, or of the Church of Pakistan, provided he holds a Certificate of Eligibility obtained from the Committee on Probationers and Transference and Admission of Ministers or its Executive, that Committee having satisfied itself (a) that he has fulfilled the educational requirements of his own Church, (b) that he has been ordained by that Church, (c) that he is a minister in full standing therein and has served for at least three years in a charge or appointment under its jurisdiction, and (d) that his character and conduct are in keeping with his profession. A minister in this category may be elected and called only in terms of section 12 (1) (b) above, and that for a period not exceeding three years in the first instance. With the concurrence of the Presbytery and of the Board of World Mission this period may, at the request of the congregation, be extended for one period of not more than three years.

For purposes of interpretation of Act III of 1972 it is hereby declared that ministers and licentiates in categories (6) to (10) above shall, on election to a charge, be regarded as ministers of the Church of Scotland, and, in common with those in categories (1) to (5) shall not be admitted or inducted *ad vitam aut culpam*.

NOMINATION

14.(1)   The Vacancy Committee may resolve to nominate one person only for election (a sole nominee) or they may resolve to nominate more persons than one (a leet). In the latter case they shall be subject to the provision in section 12 (2) above that the Presbytery Advisory Committee may add names to the leet. Before being asked to accept nomination a candidate shall be given adequate opportunity to see the church, the halls and the manse, and if the congregation is one where the temporal affairs are administered in accordance with a constitution peculiar to that congregation he shall be supplied with a copy of the said constitution. Before any nomination is reported in terms of subsection (4) hereunder the Secretary of the Vacancy Committee shall have secured the consent in writing of the person concerned.

(2)   Before any nomination is intimated to the Kirk Session in terms of subsection (4) hereunder it shall be the duty of the Interim Moderator to have secured and lodged with his Presbytery Clerk whichever documents are appropriate, *viz.* – in the case of:

(a)   a probationer as in Category (3) of Section 13 – a Certificate from the Committee on the Supervision of Probationers to the effect that he has satisfactorily completed, or has been exempted from, his Probationary Period;

(b)   a graduate candidate – a Certificate from the Clerk of the Presbytery within whose bounds is the congregation of which the nominee is a member to the effect that a current Exit Certificate or Graduate's Certificate exists for him in terms of Act V 1998, Sections 26 and 27;

(c)   a minister in Category (1) of Section 13 who has not completed five years in his first charge – a Certificate from the releasing Presbytery in one of the forms of Schedule G;

(d)   a minister in one of the Categories (4), (7), and (10) of Section 13 – a Certificate of Eligibility;

(e)   a minister or licentiate in Category (5) of Section 13 – an extract minute of General Assembly relative to his admission to the Church of Scotland;

(f)   a minister in Category (8) of Section 13 – a Certificate of Eligibility along with a letter from the minister giving assurance that before induction (if elected) he shall have relinquished his other employment;

(g)   a minister in Categories (6) and (9) – a Certificate from the Clerk to the General Assembly of his Church giving the assurances required in the relevant subsection;

(h)   a minister in Category (1) of Section 13 – a Certificate of Eligibility and an extract minute of the congregational meeting at which it was agreed to operate in terms of Section 12 (1) (b) above.

If the vacant charge is on the General Assembly List of Gaelic-speaking Churches a certificate of competency to preach in Gaelic should also be secured and lodged.

(3)   The Presbytery Advisory Committee shall be informed when a sole nomination or a leet is finally approved.

(4)   Immediately a final decision on nomination has been reached the Kirk Session shall be informed through intimation made to the Interim Moderator in terms of Schedule H hereto.

PREACHING BY NOMINEES

15.(1)   The Interim Moderator, on receiving notice of the Committee's nomination or nominations, shall, if it be a sole nominee, arrange that the nominee conduct public worship in the vacant church or churches on the first convenient Sunday, or, if there be a leet, that the several nominees conduct public worship in the vacant church or churches on a series of Sundays, which should if at all possible be consecutive Sundays, as soon as may conveniently be arranged. He shall then determine a day when a meeting will be held for an open vote, or, if the election is to be by ballot, for a ballot to be taken, and in so doing he shall have regard to the convenience of the electors. When a ballot is involved, time for voting shall be allowed during the day as well as in the evening, and it may be appropriate that more than one voting station be provided even when only one congregation is involved, but if there be more than one voting-station for one congregation, voting at these shall not take place concurrently.

(2)   The Interim Moderator shall thereupon cause intimation to be made on two Sundays regarding the arrangements made in connection with the preaching by the nominee or nominees concerned, and setting forth the time and place of the meeting to vote, or the details regarding the ballot, as the case may be – all in terms of Schedule 1 hereto.

THE INTERIM MODERATOR AND THE ELECTION

16.(1)   The Interim Moderator shall normally preside at all congregational meetings connected with the election and shall be in charge of the ballot if such there be. In the case of unavoidable absence from any meeting he may authorise a ministerial member of Presbytery (not being a member of the vacant congregation) to act in his place. Such authorisation shall be in writing and shall clearly specify the occasion on which the deputy is to act.

(2)   The Interim Moderator may invite one or more persons (not being persons whose names are on the Electoral Register of the vacant congregation) to assist him in the conduct of a ballot vote when he judges this desirable.

(3)   When a linking or a deferred union or deferred linking is involved the Interim Moderator shall consult and reach agreement with the minister or Interim Moderator of the other congregation regarding the arrangements for the conduct of public worship in these congregations by the candidate or candidates as in section 15 above. When a ballot is involved the Interim Moderator shall in writing appoint a ministerial member of Presbytery to take full charge of the ballot vote for the other congregation. In the case of a deferred union or deferred linking the minister of the charge which is full shall not be so appointed, nor shall he be in any way involved in the conduct of the election.

ELECTION BY OPEN VOTE

17.(1)   If the congregation have determined that the method of election is to be by open vote this will be carried through at a congregational meeting held for the purpose and presided over by the Interim Moderator. When only one person has been nominated the meeting to elect may be held at the close of the service conducted by him, and should certainly be held not later than seven days after he has preached. The question shall be put from the chair "Elect Mr X or not?" and the votes shall be counted and the result recorded. The votes For should be counted even if there are no votes Against. The Interim Moderator shall complete and attest a declaration of the result in one of the forms of Schedule J.

(2)   When more than one person has been nominated the meeting to elect shall be held not earlier than the Sunday next after that on which the last nominee preached. In this case the names shall be put and voted upon consecutively in the order in which the nominees have preached, the name having fewest votes being dropped and a fresh vote taken, and so on until only one name remains, or until one name commands more than half of the total votes cast. The Interim Moderator shall then put the question, "Elect Mr X or not?" The voting on the motion to elect or not shall be counted and the result recorded. If there is a clear majority in favour the Interim Moderator shall declare Mr X elected subject to the judgment of the courts of the Church and he shall complete and attest a declaration of the result in one of the forms of Schedule J.

(3)   If the outcome of the voting is a resolution not to elect – this is to say, if the sole nominee be rejected, or if no nominee on the leet be accepted, by the meeting – the Interim Moderator shall declare in terms of Schedule J that there has been failure to elect. Thereafter procedure shall be as in section 21 hereunder.

ELECTION BY BALLOT

18.(1)   If the congregation have determined that the method of voting shall be by ballot, or if the vacancy is in a linked charge, or in a charge where agreement has been reached on deferred union or on deferred linking the following procedure shall be followed. The Kirk Session shall arrange to have available at the time of election a sufficient supply of voting papers printed in the form of Schedule K hereto, and these shall be put into the custody of the Interim Moderator who shall preside at the election, assisted as in section 16 above. He shall issue on request to any person whose name is on the Electoral Register a voting-paper, noting on the Register that this has been done. Facilities shall be provided whereby the voter may mark the paper in secrecy, and a ballot-box shall be available wherein the paper is to be deposited when marked. The Interim Moderator may assist any person who asks for help in respect of completing the voting-paper, but no other person whatever shall communicate with the voter at this stage. The Interim Moderator, or the deputy appointed by him, shall be responsible for the safe custody of ballot-box, papers and Electoral Register.

(2)   As soon as practicable, and at latest within twenty-four hours after the close of the voting, the Interim Moderator shall constitute the Kirk Session, or the Joint Kirk Sessions when more than one congregation is involved, and in presence of the Kirk Session shall proceed with the counting of the votes, in which he may be assisted as provided in section 16 above. When more than one ballot-box has been used and when the votes of more than one congregation are involved all ballot-boxes shall be emptied and the voting-papers shall be mixed together before counting begins so that the preponderance of votes in one area or in one congregation shall not be disclosed.

(3)   When there has been a sole nomination, if the number voting For exceeds the number voting Against the nominee shall be declared appointed subject to the judgment of the courts of the Church. Otherwise it shall be declared that there has been a failure to elect.

(4)   When there has been a leet a count shall be taken of the First Choice recorded on the voting-papers. If one of the nominees receives a majority of the whole votes cast he shall be declared appointed subject to the judgment of the courts of the Church. If not, then the voting-papers for those nominees the total number of whose votes taken together does not amount to the number of votes cast for the person standing next higher on the list shall be re-examined, and they shall be counted in respect of their Second Choice, such votes being added to the total already recorded in favour of the remaining nominees. If this still does not result in any nominee having a clear majority the process shall be repeated, counting the Second or Third Choice as the case may be – and so on until a nominee emerges with a clear majority, when it shall be declared that he has been appointed subject to the judgment of the courts of the Church.

(5)   Should there be a tie between the remaining nominees, or should the votes "Against electing any of the above-named" exceed the votes cast for the remaining nominee it shall be declared that there has been failure to elect.

(6)   After the counting has been completed the Interim Moderator shall sign a declaration in one of the forms of Schedule J hereto, and this shall be recorded in the minute of the Kirk Session or of the Kirk Sessions. An extract shall be affixed to the notice-board of the church, or of each of the churches, concerned. In presence of the Kirk Session the Interim Moderator shall then seal up the voting-papers along with the marked copy of the Electoral Register, and these shall be transmitted in due course along with the other documents specified in section 22 hereunder to the Presbytery Clerk.

WITHDRAWAL OF NOMINATION

19.(1)   Should a nominee intimate withdrawal before the election-notice has been read the fact of his withdrawal shall be announced and the wording of the election-notice adjusted to suit the changed circumstances.

(2)   Should intimation of withdrawal be received after the election-notice has been read a note intimating the withdrawal shall be prominently displayed in the voting-station and the name of the nominee shall be struck from each voting-paper before it is issued, the voting proceeding otherwise as in section 17 or 18 above.

(3)   If the withdrawal is that of a sole nominee, or of the sole remaining member of a leet, declaration shall be made to the effect that there has been failure to elect (Schedule J).

(4)   In the event of there having been failure to elect the Interim Moderator shall without delay inform the Convener of the Vacancy Committee of this fact, and the Convener shall summon a meeting of his Committee as soon as conveniently possible. At this meeting the Committee may decide to make a new nomination, or to take steps towards making a new nomination, and in this case the procedure laid down in section 15 above shall be followed. Alternatively the Committee may resolve to make no further nomination and to resign, in which case the procedure shall be as in section 21 hereunder.

THE CALL

20.(1)   When the election has been by open vote the Interim Moderator may, after declaring the result of the election, invite those present to sign a Call prepared in terms of Schedule L hereunder. He shall also intimate further facilities that will be available for the call to be subscribed over a period of not fewer than eight days. When the election has been by ballot the Interim Moderator shall, along with the intimation regarding the result of the voting, intimate the arrangements made for members of the congregation over a period of not less than eight days to subscribe the call (Schedule L). Intimation shall be in the form of Schedule M hereto.

(2)   The call may be subscribed on behalf of a member not present to sign in person, provided a mandate authorising such subscription is produced as in Schedule N. All such entries shall be initialled by the Interim Moderator or by the member of the Kirk Session appending them.

(3)   A paper of concurrence in the call may be signed by regular worshippers in the congregation over 14 years of age and by adherents whose names have not been entered on the Electoral Register.

FAILURE TO NOMINATE: FAILURE TO ELECT

21.(1)   If, six calendar months after their appointment, the Vacancy Committee have not intimated a nomination it shall be in order for ten qualified electors to submit in writing a requisition for the Interim Moderator to take steps with a view to a nomination being made. On receipt of such requisition the Interim Moderator shall intimate to the Clerk of the Vacancy Committee that unless a nomination is received by him within two calendar months of writing the Committee will be regarded as having failed to nominate. If a nomination is not received within the period stipulated the Interim Moderator shall cause intimation to be made on two Sundays in terms of Schedule O (i) that the congregation is to elect a new Vacancy Committee, and the normal procedure for such election shall thereafter be followed as in section 9 above.

(2)   If there has been failure to elect as defined in sections 17 (3), 18 (3), 18 (5) and 19 (3) above and the Committee have resolved not to make a new nomination but to resign, then the same procedure shall be followed as in subsection (1) above, except that the intimation shall be in terms of Schedule O (ii).

(3)   If, after having been elected, the nominee intimates in writing that he declines the appointment this fact shall at once be intimated to the Clerk of the Vacancy Committee who shall summon a meeting of that Committee. At such meeting the Committee may resolve to take steps towards making a new nomination or they may resolve to resign. In the latter case the same procedure shall be followed as in subsection (1) above, the intimation being in terms of Schedule O (iii) hereto.

(4)   If there has been failure to elect, or if the person elected has declined to accept the appointment then notwithstanding the provisions of subsection (2) and (3) above, a requisi-

tion bearing the signature of not fewer that one-tenth of the number on the Electoral Register may be lodged with the Interim Moderator within one week after intimation of failure or declinature has been given, requiring him to call a meeting of the congregation for the purpose of determining whether the Committee shall be continued or whether a new Committee shall be appointed, and if so to appoint such a Committee. On receipt of such a requisition the Interim Moderator shall make arrangements for the holding of a congregational meeting and shall cause intimation of this to be made on two Sundays in terms of Schedule O (iv) hereto.

TRANSMISSION OF DOCUMENTS

22.(1) After an election has been made the Interim Moderator shall secure from the person appointed a letter of acceptance of the appointment, and this shall include an assurance that he has used no undue influence either by himself or by others to secure the call.

(2) The Interim Moderator shall then without delay transmit the relevant documents to the Clerk of the Presbytery. These are: the minute of nomination by the Vacancy Committee, all intimations made to the congregation thereafter, the declaration of the election and appointment, the voting-papers and marked copy of the Register in the case of a ballot, and the letter of acceptance. He shall also inform the Clerk of the steps taken in connection with the signing of the call, and shall arrange that, at the expiry of the period allowed for subscription, the call shall be transmitted by the Session Clerk to the Clerk of the Presbytery. All relevant Certificates required in the case of a probationer, or of a minister of another denomination, or of a minister who has not completed five years in his first charge, or of others requiring certification as set forth in section 14(2) above, shall have been lodged with the Presbytery Clerk at the time of that person's nomination.

(3) All of these documents shall be laid before the Presbytery at its first ordinary meeting or at an extraordinary meeting at which provision has been made for the matter to be dealt with. It shall be the duty of the Interim Moderator to cause intimation of this meeting and of the right of the congregation to attend for their interests to be made on one Sunday in terms of Schedule P hereto.

(4) After the person elected has been inducted to the charge the Presbytery Clerk shall destroy the intimations and voting-papers lodged with him in terms of subsection (2) above.

IUS DEVOLUTUM

23.(1) The exercise by a congregation of its right to call a minister shall be subject to a time-limit of six calendar months, and this period shall be calculated from the date of the Presbytery meeting referred to in section 3 above when intimation is given of the agreement to grant leave to call. If it appears that an appointment is not to be made within the allotted time the congregation may make application to the Presbytery for an extension, which will normally be for a further three months. In exceptional circumstances, and for clear cause shown, a further extension may be granted. If no election has been made and intimated to the Presbytery by the expiry of that time the permission to call shall be regarded as having lapsed. The Presbytery may thereupon look afresh at the whole question of readjustment. If the Presbytery is still satisfied that a minister should be appointed, it shall itself take steps to make such an appointment, proceeding as follows.

(2) The Presbytery shall strengthen the *ad hoc* Advisory Committee which had been involved in that case by the appointment of an additional minister and elder and shall remit to that Committee to bring forward to a subsequent meeting the name of a minister (or probationer) for appointment to the charge. If satisfied with the recommendation, and having assured itself that the person is qualified for the appointment in terms of section 13 above, the Presbytery shall thereupon make the appointment and shall record accordingly in its minutes.

(3) The Clerk of Presbytery shall thereupon intimate to the person concerned the fact of his appointment, shall request him to forward a letter of acceptance along with appropriate Certifi-

cates if these are required in terms of section 14 above, and shall arrange with him to conduct public worship in the vacant church or churches on an early Sunday.

(4)   The Clerk of Presbytery shall cause intimation to be made in terms of Schedule Q that the person appointed will conduct public worship on the day specified and that a call in the usual form will lie with the Session Clerk or other suitable person for not less than eight free days to receive the signatures of the congregation. The conditions governing the signing of the call shall be exactly as in section 20 above.

(5)   At the expiry of the time allowed, the call shall be transmitted by the Session Clerk to the Clerk of the Presbytery who shall lay it, along with the documents referred to in subsection (3) above, before the Presbytery at its first ordinary meeting or at an extraordinary meeting at which provision has been made for the matter to be dealt with.

(6)   The procedure thereafter shall be in accordance with sections 24 and 25 hereunder.

JUDGMENT OF PRESBYTERY

24.(1)   The call and other relevant documents having been laid on the table the Presbytery shall hear any person whom it considers to have an interest. In particular the Presbytery Advisory Committee shall be entitled to be heard if it so desires, or the Presbytery may ask for a report from it. The Presbytery shall then decide whether to sustain the appointment, and in doing so shall give consideration to the number of signatures on the call. It may delay reaching a decision and return the call to the Kirk Session to give further opportunity for it to be subscribed.

(2)   If the Presbytery sustain an appointment and call to a probationer, and there be no appeal tendered in due form against its judgment, it shall appoint the day and hour and place at which the ordination and induction will take place.

(3)   If the Presbytery sustain an appointment and call to a minister of the Church of Scotland not being a minister of a parish, or to a minister of another denomination, and there being no ecclesiastical impediment the Presbytery shall appoint the day and hour and place at which the induction shall take place.

(4)   If the documents lodged with the Presbytery Clerk in terms of section 22 above relate to a call addressed to a minister of a congregation within the bounds, the Clerk shall cause intimation to be made on one Sunday to that congregation in terms of Schedule R hereto, calling a meeting of the congregation to consider the situation in which they are placed and if so resolved to appoint commissioners to appear for their interests at the meeting of Presbytery at which the matter is to be considered. The Clerk shall also arrange for a ministerial member of Presbytery to preside at that meeting. If commissioners attend they shall be heard after those from the vacant congregation; if not, the congregation shall be held as concurring in the translation.

(5)   If a Presbytery sustain an appointment and call to a minister of a congregation within the bounds of another Presbytery it shall instruct its Clerk to forward to the Clerk of that other Presbytery an extract minute of Presbytery sustaining the call along with the call itself, and it may also, if it so desire, appoint commissioners to prosecute the call at the meeting of the other Presbytery. It may then go on to make provisional arrangements for the induction of the minister.

(6)   In receiving intimation in terms of subsection (5) above, a Presbytery Clerk shall intimate the call to the minister concerned and to his Session Clerk and shall cause intimation in terms of Schedule R to be made on one Sunday to the congregation concerned, calling a meeting of the congregation to consider the situation in which they are placed and if so resolved to appoint commissioners to appear for their interests at the meeting of Presbytery when the call is to be considered. The Clerk shall arrange for a ministerial member of Presbytery to preside at that meeting. If commissioners do not attend the congregation will be held as concurring in the translation.

(7)   If the Presbytery decide to place the call in the hands of the minister to whom it is addressed, and if there be no appeal or complaint, and if the minister accept the call, the Presbytery shall give judgement that it agrees to the translation, shall declare that the minister remains minister of his present charge until the date of his admission to his new charge and shall instruct

him to wait on the other Presbytery as to the time of the said admission. It shall also appoint an Interim Moderator in the prospective vacancy in terms of section 1 above.

(8) If the Presbytery resolve not to translate, the minister concerned shall have the right to appeal, as shall also the Presbytery prosecuting the call. The latter Presbytery, though it was not represented when the call was dealt with, shall have the right to intimate an appeal and to lodge reasons therefor with the Clerk of the Presbytery provided these are in his hands within ten days of judgment being given.

(9) If a minister wishes to accept a call from any congregation other than a congregation of the Church of Scotland he shall proceed by way of demission of his charge in terms of section 27 hereunder.

ADMISSION TO A CHARGE

25.(1) When the Presbytery has appointed a day for the ordination and induction of a probationer, or for the induction of a minister already ordained, the Clerk shall arrange for an edict in the form of Schedule S to be read to the congregation on the two Sundays preceding the day appointed, giving public intimation that the Presbytery intends to proceed to the ordination and induction, or the induction, of the person named unless objections to his life and doctrine be alleged and substantiated, and indicating the time and place of the Presbytery meeting to deal with objections if any; normally on the day of the induction at a slightly earlier hour and in the hall of the vacant church.

(2) At the time and place named in the edict, the Presbytery having been constituted, the Moderator shall call for the return of the edict attested as having been duly served. If the minister is being translated from another Presbytery the relevant minute agreeing to translation shall also be laid on the table. The Presbytery shall then arrange that further intimation be made by the Officer, or other person appointed for the purpose, that the Presbytery is now in session and is prepared to receive objections. Any objection to be valid at this stage, must be strictly directed to life or doctrine and must be substantiated immediately to the satisfaction of the Presbytery, in which case procedure shall be sisted and the Presbytery shall take appropriate steps to deal with the situation that has arisen. Otherwise the Presbytery shall proceed with the ordination and induction, or with the induction, as hereunder.

(3) The Presbytery shall proceed to the church where public worship shall be conducted by those appointed for the purpose. The Clerk shall read a brief narrative of the cause of the vacancy and of the steps taken for the settlement. The Moderator, having read the Preamble, shall, addressing him by name, put to the person to be inducted the questions prescribed (Schedule U (i)). Satisfactory answers having been given, the person to be inducted shall sign the Formula (Schedule U (ii)). If he has not already been ordained the person to be inducted shall then kneel, and the Moderator by prayer and the imposition of hands, in which all the ministers present join, shall ordain him to the office of the Holy Ministry. Prayer being ended, the Moderator shall say, "I now declare you to have been ordained to the office of the Holy Ministry, and in name of the Lord Jesus Christ, the King and Head of the Church, and by authority of this Presbytery, I induct you to this charge, and in token thereof we give you the right hand of fellowship". The Moderator with all other members of Presbytery present shall then give the right hand of fellowship. The Moderator shall then put the prescribed question to the members of the congregation (Schedule U (iii)). Suitable charges to the new minister and to the congregation shall then be given by the Moderator or by a minister appointed for the purpose.

(4) When an ordained minister is being inducted to a charge the act of ordination shall not be repeated and the relevant words shall be omitted from the declaration. In other respects the procedure shall be as in subsection (3) above.

(5) When the appointment is for a limited period (Terminable Tenure) the service shall proceed as in subsections (3) and (4) above except that in the declaration the Moderator shall say "I induct you to this charge on a terminable basis in terms of minute of Presbytery of date .....".

(6) After service the Presbytery shall resume its session when the name of the new minister shall be added to the Roll of Presbytery, the Clerk shall be instructed to send certified intimation of the induction to the Session Clerk to be engrossed in the minutes of the first meeting of Kirk Session thereafter, and, in the case of a translation from another Presbytery, to the Clerk of that Presbytery. The Clerk shall also furnish the new minister with an extract of the stipend arrangements (see section 5 above).

SERVICE OF INTRODUCTION

26.(1)   When a minister has been appointed to a linked charge the Presbytery shall determine in which of the churches of the linking the induction is to take place. This shall be a service of induction to the charge, in consequence of which the person inducted shall become minister of each of the congregations embraced in the linking. The edict regarding the induction, which shall be in terms of Schedule S, shall be read in all of the churches concerned. There shall be no other service of induction, but if the churches are far distant from one another, or for other good reason, the Presbytery may appoint a service of introduction to be held in the other church or churches. Intimation shall be given of such service, but not in edictal form. See subsection (6) hereunder.

(2)   When a Presbytery has resolved, with concurrence of the Assembly's Committee on Parish Reappraisal, that an Associate Ministry should be established in a parish it will in the said resolution have made provision regarding the method to be adopted in making the appointment. When an appointment to an Associateship has been made the matter shall be reported to the Presbytery, which, having satisfied itself as to the regularity of the procedure and as to the qualifications of the person appointed, shall duly ratify the appointment, and shall make arrangements for a service of introduction. If the person appointed is a probationer the Presbytery shall arrange a Service of Ordination to precede the introduction and shall cause edictal intimation of this to be made in terms of Schedule T.

(3)   When an appointment has been made to an extra-parochial office wholly or mainly under control of the Church (community ministry, full-time chaplaincy in hospital, industry, university, full-time clerkship, *etc*). the Presbytery may deem it appropriate to arrange a service of introduction to take place in a church or chapel suitable to the occasion. If ordination is involved, suitable arrangements shall be made and edictal intimation shall be given in some place or places deemed appropriate by the Presbytery, in terms of Schedule T.

(4)   In any case of deferred union or deferred linking the minister elected and appointed shall be inducted "to the vacant congregation of A in deferred union (or linking) with the congregation of B" and there shall be no need for any further act to establish his position as minister of the united congregation or of the linked congregation as the case may be. The Presbytery, however, shall in such a case arrange a service of introduction to the newly united congregation of AB or the newly linked congregation of B. Intimation shall be given of such service, but not in edictal form.

(5)   In any case of union or linking of congregations when one has a minister and it is a condition of the union or linking that he is to become minister of the united or linked charge, no induction shall take place, but the Presbytery shall arrange a service of declaration of union (or of linking) and of introduction to the united charge or to the linked charge as the case may be.

(6)   In all cases where a service of introduction is held it shall follow the lines of an induction except that instead of putting the normal questions to the minister the Moderator shall say to him, "Mr ...., on the occasion of your ordination you solemnly vowed that, believing in one God, Father, Son and Holy Spirit, and accepting His Word in Holy Scripture and the fundamental doctrines of the faith contained in the Confession of this Church, you would seek the unity and peace of the Church, and that, inspired by zeal for the glory of God, by the love of Christ, and by a desire for the salvation of men, you would lead a godly and circumspect life and would cheerfully discharge the duties of your ministry – do you now reaffirm your adherence to this vow?" In the declaration the Moderator in place of "I induct you to ....", shall say "I welcome you as ....".

DEMISSION

27.(1) A minister wishing to demit his charge for any reason must seek and obtain the permission of Presbytery so to do. If a minister departs from his parish without such permission he shall be held to be in desertion and may be deposed. Any application for permission to demit must state the grounds upon which it is based.

(2)   A minister may seek to demit his charge:
- (a)   on grounds of age or infirmity;
- (b)   to enable him to take up some other appointment under the jurisdiction of the Church of Scotland;
- (c)   to accept a call to a charge in, or to take up an appointment under the jurisdiction of, a Church other than the Church of Scotland; or
- (d)   to leave the service of the Church.

(3)   When the Clerk of Presbytery receives an application for leave to demit he shall lay it on the table at the first ordinary meeting thereafter or at an earlier meeting *pro re nata* when the Presbytery shall appoint one or more of its number to meet with the minister concerned and to confer with him regarding his reasons. The Presbytery shall also agree to deal with the application at its next ordinary meeting or at an earlier meeting *in hunc effectum* and shall instruct the Clerk to cite the congregation to appear for their interests, intimation being made in terms of Schedule V hereto. The Clerk shall also arrange for a ministerial member of Presbytery to preside at the congregational meeting.

(4)   At the Presbytery meeting at which the matter is dealt with the Clerk shall lay on the table the letter of application to demit, those who met with the applicant shall report, and parties shall be heard. If it is agreed to allow demission then if the ground be age or infirmity the minister shall retain his seat in Presbytery, unless in terms of Act VIII 1980 he elects to resign it; in other cases, unless there be special grounds for withholding it, a Presbyterial Certificate shall be issued to the minister demitting. The Presbytery shall proceed to appoint an Interim Moderator in the prospective vacancy in terms of Section 1 above.

(5)   In the case where it is a condition of some basis of readjustment that a minister shall demit his charge to facilitate union or linking, and the minister has agreed in writing in terms of the appropriate regulations governing unions and readjustments, formal application shall not be made to the Presbytery for permission to demit. The minister concerned shall be regarded as retiring in the interest of readjustment and he shall retain his seat in Presbytery unless in terms of Act VIII 1980 he elects to resign it.

(6)   A minister who demits his charge without retaining his seat in Presbytery shall, if he retains his status as a minister, remain under the supervision of the Presbytery which accepted his demission unless and until he moves into the bounds of another Presbytery, in which case he shall without delay lodge a current Presbyterial Certificate with the Clerk of that Presbytery, and he shall then come under its supervision.

SCHEDULES

Note: All pulpit intimations shall be attested in the form of Schedule W on each reading

A.   Declaration of Vacancy: Section 2(2)

To be read on the first convenient Sunday after the vacancy has actually occurred.

By order of the Presbytery of .... it is hereby declared that this Church and parish became vacant on .... by the .... of Mr/Mrs/Miss/Ms........ *It is further declared by order of the Presbytery that procedure towards filling the vacancy is meantime sisted.

....   Presbytery Clerk

*This sentence to be included where appropriate - otherwise to be deleted.

B.   Preparation of Electoral Register - Section 7
To be read on two Sundays, one of which may coincide with the reading of Schedule A.
Intimation is hereby given that, in view of the *anticipated vacancy, the Kirk Session is about to make up an Electoral Register of this congregation. Any communicant whose name is not already on the Communion Roll as a member should hand in to the Session Clerk a Certificate of Transference, and anyone wishing his or her name added to the Register as an adherent, should obtain from the Session Clerk, and complete and return to him/her, a Form of Adherent's Claim. All such papers should be in the hands of the Session Clerk not later than .... The Kirk Session will meet in .... on .... at .... to make up the Electoral Register when anyone wishing to support his or her claim in person should attend.

....   Interim Moderator

*This word to be included where appropriate - otherwise to be deleted.

C.   Form of Adherent's Claim - Section 6
I *........ of **........, being not under eighteen years of age, being a regular worshipper in the Church of .... and not being a member of any other congregation in Scotland, claim to have my name put on the Electoral Register of the parish of .... as an adherent.
Date ....   (Signed)
*   Here enter full name in block capitals   **   Here enter address in full

D.   Inspection of Electoral Register - Section 8(1)
To be read on one Sunday
Intimation is hereby given that the proposed Electoral Register of this congregation has now been prepared and that an opportunity of inspecting it will be given today in .... at the close of this service, and that it will be open for inspection at .... on .... between the hours of .... and .... each day. Any questions regarding entries in the Register should be brought to the notice of the Kirk Session which is to meet in .... on .... at .... o'clock when it will finally make up the Electoral Register.

....   Interim Moderator

E.   Revision of Electoral Register - Section 8(4)
To be read on two Sundays
Intimation is hereby given that, more than six months having elapsed since the Electoral Register of this congregation was finally made up, it is now proposed that it should be revised. An opportunity of inspecting the Register will be given in .... at the close of this service, and also at .... on .... between the hours of .... and .... each day. Anyone wishing his or her name added to the Electoral Register as a member should give in a Transference Certificate, or as an adherent should give in a Form of Adherent's Claim (copies of which may be had from the Session Clerk) not later than .... The Kirk Session will meet in .... on .... at .... o'clock when it will finally make up the Revised Register.

....   Interim Moderator

F.   Appointment of Vacancy Committee - Section 9
To be read on two Sundays, which may coincide with the reading of Schedules B and D
Intimation is hereby given that a meeting of this congregation will be held in the Church* on Sunday .... at the close of Morning Worship for the purpose of appointing a Vacancy Committee which will nominate one or more persons to the congregation with a view to the election and appointment of a minister,** and to determine whether such election shall be by ballot or by open vote. ***It is further hereby declared that, this being a congregation on the General Assembly's List of Gaelic-speaking Congregations, only a Gaelic-speaking minister or probationer is eligible for election as minister of this Church and parish.

....   Interim Moderator

*   Where other arrangements are deemed appropriate, particulars should be given here.
**   To be omitted in those cases stipulated by Section 16(I) of this Act when the election must
of necessity be by ballot.
*** Where inappropriate, to be omitted and deleted.

G.   Nomination before completion of five years - Section 13(1) and 14(2)

A Schedule in one or other of the undernoted terms must be secured before nomination.
First Schedule
We, the undersigned, declare that in our opinion there are exceptional circumstances which
would justify the translation of .... from his/her present charge of .... before the expiry of five
years from the date of his/her induction thereto.
.... Moderator of Presbytery   .... Clerk of Presbytery
.... Member of Presbytery   .... Member of Presbytery
...............Date

Second Schedule
At .... the .... day of .... 20...., the Presbytery of .... being met and constituted:
Inter alia
The Presbytery agreed that there were exceptional circumstances which would justify the translation of .... from his/her charge of .... before the expiry of five years from the date of
his/her induction thereto. The Presbytery reserved the right to deal with the question of translation if and when it arose.

Extracted by me from the records of the Presbytery of .... this .... day of .... 20.....
.... Clerk of Presbytery

GG.   Restricted choice for Call - Section 12(1)(b)

To be read on two Sundays
    As Interim Moderator I have received from the Secretary of the Vacancy Committee appointed
by this congregation on .... a notice to the effect that at a meeting of the Committee held on ....
it was resolved that the congregation be invited to restrict their right of call to the extent and in
the manner set forth in the undernoted resolution. Accordingly, intimation is hereby given that
a meeting of this congregation will be held in the Church here on Sunday the .... day of ....
20..... at the close of Morning Worship, for the purpose of considering, and if so resolved of
adopting, the following resolution: "This congregation hereby accept and adopt the proposal
of their Vacancy Committee that, in respect of the present vacancy only, they restrict their right
of call to the extent of electing and calling, for a period of three years only, a minister of a
Church furth of Scotland which is a member of the World Alliance of Reformed Churches, or of
the Church of South India, or of the Church of Pakistan"
.... Interim Moderator

H.   Minute of Nomination by Vacancy Committee - Section 14(4)

To be read on two Sundays, normally concurrently with an intimation in the form of Schedule I.
    The Committee chosen by this congregation to nominate one or more persons with a view
to the election and appointment of a minister at a meeting held at .... on .... resolved to
name and propose *........ and they accordingly do name and propose the said *........

...........Date   .... Convener of Committee

*   The name and designation of the person, or of each of the persons, should at this point be
entered in full.

I.   Intimation Regarding Election - Section 15
To be read on two Sundays
First Form (Sole Nominee: Open Vote)
Intimation is hereby given that the Vacancy Committee having, as by minute now read, named and proposed .... arrangements have been made whereby public worship will be conducted in this Church by him/her on Sunday the .... day .... of .... at .... o'clock, and that immediately at the close of that service a meeting of the congregation will be held at which a vote will be taken whether or not to elect the said .... as minister of this vacant charge. Notice is hereby further given that, if an election takes place, a Call to .... will be available for signature immediately thereafter.

.... Interim Moderator

Second Form (Sole Nominee: Ballot Vote)
Intimation is hereby given that the Vacancy Committee having, as by minute now read, named and proposed .... arrangements have been made whereby public worship will be conducted in this Church by him/her on Sunday the .... day of .... at .... o'clock, and that a vote will be taken by voting papers at .... on ...... the .... day of .... between the hours of .... and .... during the day and between the hours of .... and .... in the evening: and that electors shall vote For or Against electing and appointing the said .... as minister of this vacant charge

.... Interim Moderator

Third Form (Leet: Open Vote)
Intimation is hereby given that the Vacancy Committee having, as by minute now read, named and proposed A........B........, C........D........, and E........F........, arrangements have been made whereby public worship will be conducted in this Church by the said A........B........ on Sunday the .... day of .... at .... o'clock, by the said C........D........ on Sunday the .... day of .... at .... o'clock, and by the said E........F........ on Sunday the .... day of .... at .... o'clock, and that a meeting of the congregation will be held in the Church on .... the .... day of .... at .... o'clock when a vote will be taken to determine which, if any, of A........B........, C........D........, or E........F........ shall be elected and appointed as minister of this vacant charge. Notice is hereby further given that, if an election takes place, a Call to the successful candidate will be available for signature immediately thereafter.

.... Interim Moderator

Fourth Form (Leet: Ballot Vote)
Intimation is hereby given that the Vacancy Committee having, as by minute now read, named and proposed A........B........, C........D........, and E........F........, arrangements have been made whereby public worship will be conducted in this Church by the said A........B........ on Sunday the .... day of .... at .... o'clock, by the said C........D........ on Sunday the .... day of .... at .... o'clock, and by the said E........F........ on Sunday the .... day of .... at .... o'clock, and that a vote of the congregation will be taken by voting papers at .... on .... the .... day of .... between the hours of .... and .... during the day and between the hours of .... and .... in the evening, and the electors will be given a preferential choice among the three candidates, or against all of the three, for election and appointment of a minister in this vacant charge.

.... Interim Moderator

J.   Declaration of election result - Sections 17(1), (2), (3): 18(3), (5), (6): 19(3)
First Form (Successful Election)
I hereby declare that the following are the results of the voting for the election and appointment of a minister to the vacant charge of ...., and that the said .... has accordingly been elected and appointed subject to the judgement of the courts of the Church.
......Date   .... Interim Moderator

Second Form (Failure to elect)
I hereby declare that the following are the results of the voting for the election and appointment of a minister to the vacant charge of ...., and that in consequence of this vote there has been a failure to elect.
......Date   .... Interim Moderator

K.   Voting Paper - Section 18(1)
First Form (Sole Nominee)

	FOR Electing	....	....
	AGAINST Electing	....	....

Directions to Voters
If you are in favour of electing .... put a cross in the upper space. If you are not in favour of electing .... put a cross in the lower space. Do not put any other mark upon the paper or it will be regarded as spoilt and will not be counted.
Note: The Directions to Voters must be printed prominently on the face of the voting-paper.

Second Form (Leet)

FOR Electing A.................. B..................	....
FOR Electing C.................. D..................	....
FOR Electing E.................. F..................	....
AGAINST Electing any of the above named	....

Directions to Voters
You are asked to vote for the candidates in the order of your preference by marking 1, 2 and 3 in the spaces opposite their names. In this way, should your first choice not be successful, your second vote will be counted. If you put a cross opposite a name, that will be counted as a first choice, but if you put a cross opposite more names than one, that will be counted as a spoilt paper. If you do not favour any of the candidates, you should put a cross in the bottom space.
Note: The Directions to Voters must be printed prominently on the face of the voting-paper.

L.   The Call - Section 20(1)
Form of Call
We, members of the Church of Scotland and of the congregation known as ...., being without a minister, address this Call to be our minister to you .... of whose gifts and qualities we have been assured, and we warmly invite you to accept this Call, promising that we shall devote ourselves with you to worship, witness, mission and service in this parish, and also to the further-ance of these in the world, to the glory of God and for the advancement of His Kingdom.

Paper of Concurrence
We, regular worshippers in the congregation of the Church of Scotland known as .... concur in the Call addressed by that congregation to .... to be their minister.
NB The Call and Paper of Concurrence should be dated and attested by the Interim Moder-ator before they are transmitted to the Clerk of the Presbytery.

M.   Subscribing the call - Section 20(1)
To be read on at least one Sunday
Intimation is hereby given that this congregation, having elected .... to be their minister, a Call to the said .... has been prepared and will lie in .... on .... the .... day of .... between the hours of .... and .... when members may sign in person or by means of mandates. Forms of mandate may be obtained from the Session Clerk. A Paper of Concurrence will also be available for signature by persons of fourteen years of age or over who are connected with the congregation but are not communicant members.
.... Interim Moderator

N.   Mandate to sign Call - Section 20(2)

I, ... of .... being a person whose name is on the Electoral Register of the congregation, hereby authorise the Session Clerk, or other member of Session, to adhibit my name to the Call addressed to .... to be our minister.

..........Date   .... (Signed)

O. Meeting to elect a new Committee - Section 21
To be read on two Sundays

(i) Intimation is hereby given that a Committee having on .... been appointed by this congregation to nominate one or more persons to the congregation with a view to the election and appointment of a minister, the said Committee has failed so to nominate. Accordingly a meeting of the congregation will be held in the Church on .... the .... day of .... at .... o'clock when they will proceed to elect a new Committee.

.... Interim Moderator

(ii) Intimation is hereby given that a Committee having on .... been appointed by this congregation to nominate one or more persons to the congregation with a view to the election and appointment of a minister, and the congregation having failed to elect, the said Committee has resigned. Accordingly a meeting of the congregation will be held in the Church on .... the .... day of .... at .... o'clock when they will proceed to elect a new Committee.

.... Interim Moderator

(iii) Intimation is hereby given that a Committee having on .... been appointed by this congregation to nominate one or more persons to the congregation with a view to the election and appointment of a minister, and the *person so nominated having withdrawn, the said Committee has resigned. Accordingly a meeting of the congregation will be held in the Church on .... the .... day of .... at .... o'clock when they will proceed to elect a new Committee.

.... Interim Moderator

*   or 'the persons so nominated having all withdrawn'
      or 'the person so nominated having been elected but having subsequently withdrawn'
      or 'the nominee who was elected having subsequently withdrawn''

(iv) Intimation is hereby given that, a requisition to that effect having been made to me as Interim Moderator by the required number of qualified electors, a meeting of this congregation will be held in the Church on .... the .... day of .... at .... o'clock to determine whether or not the present Vacancy Committee should be continued in office, and so to continue them or to appoint a new Committee as may be resolved.

.... Interim Moderator

P.   Citation in pursuance of call - Section 22(3)
To be read on one Sunday

Intimation is hereby given that the Presbytery of .... will meet to deal with the appointment and Call addressed by this congregation to .... at .... on .... the .... day of .... at .... o'clock, and that the congregation are hereby cited to attend for their interests.

.... Presbytery Clerk

Q.   Citation in case of Ius Devolutum - Section 23(4)
To be read on one Sunday

Intimation is hereby given that .... whom the Presbytery has appointed to be minister of this congregation will conduct public worship in the Church on Sunday the .... day of .... at .... o'clock.

Intimation is hereby further given that a Call addressed to the said .... will lie in .... on .... the .... day of .... between the hours of .... and .... during the day and between the hours of .... and .... in the evening, when members may sign in person or by means of mandates, forms of which may be had from the Session Clerk.

Intimation is hereby further given that the Presbytery will meet to deal with the appointment and Call at .... on .... the .... day of .... at .... o'clock and that the congregation are hereby cited to attend for their interests.

.... Presbytery Clerk

R. Citation in case of translation - Section 24(4) and (6)
To be read on one Sunday

The congregation of .... having addressed a Call to .... minister of this congregation, to be their minister, and the said Call having been sustained by the Presbytery of .... as a Call regularly proceeded in:

Notice is hereby given that a meeting of this congregation will be held here on Sunday the .... day of .... at the close of Morning Worship for the purpose of considering the circumstances in which the congregation is placed by the Call addressed to their minister, and of taking such steps thereanent as may be resolved upon.

Notice is hereby further given that the Presbytery will meet at .... on .... the .... day of .... at .... o'clock to deal with this Call, and that if no commissioners appear to represent the congregation they will be held as consenting to the translation.

.... Presbytery Clerk

S. Edictal intimation of admission - Section 25(1) and 26(1)
To be read on two Sundays

Whereas the Presbytery of .... has received a Call from this congregation addressed to .... *Probationer, to be their minister, and the said Call has been sustained as a regular Call, and has been accepted by him/her**:

And whereas the said Presbytery, having judged the said .... qualified ***for the ministry of the Gospel and for this Charge, has resolved to proceed to his/her ****ordination and induction on .... the .... day of .... at .... o'clock unless something occurs which may reasonably impede it:

Notice is hereby given to all concerned that if they, or any of them, have anything to object to in the life or doctrine of the said .... they may appear at the Presbytery which is to meet at .... on .... the .... day of .... at .... o'clock, with certification that if no relevant objection be then made and immediately substantiated, the Presbytery will proceed without further delay.

By order of the Presbytery   .... Presbytery Clerk

```
*      or "Minister of the Gospel"
**     add "and his/her translation has been agreed to by the Presbytery of ........"
***    omit "for the ministry of the Gospel" and
****   omit "ordination and"
```

T. Edictal intimation of ordination in case of introduction - Section 26(2)
To be read on two Sundays

Whereas the Presbytery of .... has agreed that an Associate Ministry be *established in this charge, and **the congregation has, in terms of said agreement made choice of ...., Probationer, to be Associate Minister***,

And whereas the Presbytery, having found the said .... to have been regularly appointed and to be qualified for the ministry of the Gospel and for the said appointment has resolved to proceed to his/her ordination to the Holy Ministry and to his/her introduction as

****Associate Minister on .... the .... day of .... at .... o'clock unless something occurs which may reasonably impede it:

Notice is hereby given to all concerned that if they, or any of them, have anything to object to in the life or doctrine of the said .... they may appear at the Presbytery which is to meet at .... on .... the .... day of .... at .... o'clock, with certification that if no relevant objection be then made and immediately substantiated, the Presbytery will proceed without further delay.

By order of the Presbytery   .... Presbytery Clerk

*   or "be continued"
**   or "the congregations have"
***   or "Whereas the Presbytery of .... has been notified that ...., Probationer, has been appointed to the position of Hospital Chaplain (or Industrial Chaplain, or University Chaplain, or ....) within the bounds of the Presbytery"
****   or Hospital Chaplain etc.

U.   Service of induction - Section 25(3)

(i)   Questions to Minister
1.   Do you believe in one God - Father, Son, and Holy Spirit: and do you confess anew the Lord Jesus Christ as your Saviour and Lord?
2.   Do you believe the Word of God, which is contained in the Scriptures of the Old and New Testaments, to be the supreme rule of faith and life?
3.   Do you believe the fundamental doctrines of the Christian faith contained in the Confession of Faith of this Church?
4.   Do you acknowledge the Presbyterian Government of this Church to be agreeable to the Word of God: and do you promise to be subject in the Lord to this Presbytery and to the superior Courts of the Church, and to take your due part in the administration of its affairs?
5.   Do you promise to seek the unity and peace of this Church: to uphold the doctrine, worship, government, and discipline thereof: and to cherish a spirit of love towards all your brothers and sisters in the Lord?
6.   Are not zeal for the glory of God, love to the Lord Jesus Christ, and a desire for the salvation of all people, so far as you know your own heart, your great motive and chief inducement to enter into the office of the Holy Ministry?*
7.   Do you engage in the strength of the Lord Jesus Christ to live a godly and circumspect life: and faithfully, diligently, and cheerfully to discharge the duties of your ministry, seeking in all things the advancement of the Kingdom of God?
8.   Do you accept and close with the call to be Pastor of this charge, and promise through grace to study to approve yourself a faithful Minister of the Gospel among this people?**

*   Read "into this ministry" when only induction is involved.
**   Omit this question in cases where induction is not involved.

(ii) The Formula
I believe the fundamental doctrines of the Christian faith contained in the Confession of Faith of this Church.

I acknowledge the Presbyterian government of this Church to be agreeable to the Word of God, and promise that I will submit thereto and concur therewith.

I promise to observe the order of worship and the administration of all public ordinances as the same are or may be allowed in this Church.

(iii) Question to Congregation

Do you, the members and adherents of this congregation, in receiving .... whom you have called to be your minister, promise him/her all due honour and support in the Lord: and in view of the pastoral and missionary obligations of this congregation, do you each now agree to share with your minister the responsibility for Christian witness and Christian service, and will you give of your means, as the Lord shall prosper you, for the maintenance of the Christian Ministry and the furtherance of the Gospel?

Will you signify your assent by rising and standing in your places.

V.   Citation in case of application to demit - Section 27(3)

To be read on one Sunday

The Presbytery of ...., having received a letter from .... asking leave to demit his/her office as minister of this charge, and having resolved to deal with the said application at its meeting to be held at .... on .... the .... day of .... at .... o'clock, hereby cites the congregation to attend there for their interests, with certification that if they do not so attend they will be held as consenting to the demission of the said ....

.... Presbytery Clerk

W.   Form of attestation

At the Church of .... the .... day of .... 20....

The above intimation was duly made by me this day in face of the congregation.

.... Preacher

SECTION 4

The
General Assembly
of 2000

(1) OFFICIALS OF THE GENERAL ASSEMBLY

The Lord High Commissioner:	His Royal Highness the Prince Charles
Moderator:	Right Rev Andrew R.C. McLellan
	MA BD STM
Chaplains to the Moderator:	Rev John P. Chalmers
	Rev. Isabel H. Whyte
Principal Clerk:	Rev. Dr Finlay A.J. Macdonald
Depute Clerk:	Rev. Marjory A. MacLean
Procurator:	Mr Patrick S. Hodge Q.C.
Procurator *pro tem*:	Mr James W. McNeill QC
Law Agent:	Mrs Janette S. Wilson
Convener of the Business Committee:	Mrs Ann I McCarter
Vice-Convener of the Business Committee:	Rev. David W. Lacy
Precentor:	Rev. Douglas Galbraith
Assembly Officer:	Mr George Stephenson
Assistant Assembly Officer	Mr David McColl

(2) THE MODERATOR

The Right Reverend Andrew R.C. McLellan MA BD STM

Andrew McLellan was born on 16th June, 1944, the son of a Church of Scotland minister. His grandfather was also a minister, as were several other members of his family. He has an MA from the University of St. Andrews with Honours in English Language and Literature, a BD from Glasgow University with Honours in New Testament Language and Literature, and an STM from Union Theological Seminary, New York. At Glasgow University his principal supervisor was Professor William Barclay: he won the Gold Medal in Professor Barclay's class, and was also prize-winner in the Practical Theology class of Professor Murdo Ewen Macdonald. At Union Seminary he studied with John Macquarrie and Paul Lehmann and did further work in homiletics under Edmund Steimle.

After two years as assistant minister in St. George's West Church in Edinburgh he was, for nine years, parish minister in Greenock, an industrial town on the west coast of Scotland. The congregation was set in the middle of a huge parish of considerable poverty and accompanying social problems. As part of his ministry there, Andrew McLellan ran for office for the City Council and was elected. This experience of political involvement was a powerful influence on his ministry in those early days.

For six years, from 1980 to 1986, he was minister of Viewfield Church in Stirling. This was a congregation of 750 people which sought to be creative in ecumenical relationships, in serving this ancient Scottish town, and in new forms of worship. During this ministry Andrew served as chaplain to the only prison for women in Scotland and also taught in Glasgow University's Department of New Testament.

Since 1986 he has been minister of St. Andrew's and St. George's in Edinburgh. This church is in the very centre of the city and has developed a lively ministry to the business community around it. At the same time it has sustained a remarkable commitment to the world's poor and to the artistic community in Edinburgh. Sunday worship is central to the life of the congregation and throughout its two hundred year history it has always placed a very high value on preaching.

From 1992 to 1996 Andrew McLellan was the Convener of the Church and Nation Committee of the General Assembly of the Church of Scotland. This highly influential and often controversial Committee has responsibility for a huge range of social and political concerns, and the annual presentation of its report is always one of the highlights of the General Assembly. The Committee's Convener has both the opportunity and the responsibility to interpret and proclaim the Gospel in the public life of the nation, involving the Convener in a great variety of contact with a large range of Scottish life and opinion. Andrew McLellan has been Moderator of the Presbytery of Edinburgh.

In addition to ministry in his city centre and parish and his commitment to the public witness of the Gospel, Andrew McLellan has been for many years involved in religious broadcasting. The senior producer for Scotland said of him recently, "As a religious broadcaster he is always excellent and often exceptional". He is the Chairman of the Scottish Religious Advisory Committee of the BBC. A book of his sermons was published in 1997 with the title "Preaching for these People". The reviewer in "Theology in Scotland" spoke of its "encouragement, hope and good theology": in "The Expository Times" it was "fresh, lively, relevant". Andrew McLellan delivered the 2000 Warrack Lectures on Preaching: "Preaching as Public Business".

His wife, Irene, is Principal Teacher of Home Economics in Holyrood High School, Edinburgh, a Roman Catholic school. They have twin sons, Andi and Ian, both of whom are students.

(Information supplied by the Media Relations Unit)

Andrew R. C. McLellan brings to the Moderatorial Chair a vast wealth of experience of the Church of Scotland. A third generation minister, his father and grandfather would be proud of the respect in which he is held by the whole Church.

His conduct of worship at the General Assembly set the tone for the year ahead. He brought a new dimension of reality to the idea that the Assembly is not just a place for doing business, but it is a place where the people of God worship God. He brought to each of the acts of worship the same clarity and vitality that he has brought to worship in all of the Parishes he has served.

Andrew stated at the outset of his Moderatorial Year that he wanted to be a "political Moderator". At the General Assembly, he urged the Church to "do harm" to the causes of poverty and injustice. It is not surprising, therefore, that he has set as the priorities of his Moderatorial Year concern for the poor, both in the developing world and here at home in Scotland. His work as a parish minister in Edinburgh has been punctuated by enormous bursts of energy which have been devoted to the work of Christian Aid. St. Andrew's and St. George's now hosts Christian Aid's single biggest fundraiser in the United Kingdom.

Another theme of the Moderatorial Year will be a concern about prisons and prisoners. Andrew McLellan was at one time chaplain to Scotland's only female prison at Corntonvale, and ever since his involvement there he has continued to maintain an interest in a prison service which cares about the rehabilitation of offenders. During his year as Moderator he will visit all of Scotland's prisons. This will be a major undertaking, but the staff and inmates of our prisons will undoubtedly gain from the benefit of his pastoral skills, sensitivity and experience.

While Andrew McLellan has a wide-ranging interest in the life of the Church and has convened its Church and Nation Committee with distinction, he is above and beyond all else a parish minister. He has extraordinary gifts, both as a pastor and a preacher. It will not surprise anyone to know that the third priority of his Moderatorial Year will be the promotion of preaching as "the living voice of a person proclaiming what he or she believes about the world". He recently delivered the Warrack Lectures at Glasgow University and he wants to do all that he possibly can to encourage an interest in preaching and the development of this very precious gift which is at the very centre of the Church's life.

Andrew McLellan is married to Irene and together they have set out on this Moderatorial Year with excitement and enthusiasm. Together they will give the Church of Scotland their total commitment and during this time they will have, and they deserve to have, great fun. Their twin sons, Andi and Ian, are also proud to be at their father's side during this important time.

Andrew McLellan has wide-ranging interests which include reading, Robert Burns, music and golf. He has a wonderful sense of humour which, together with a tangible faith, will sustain him throughout a year in which there will be little time to pursue his extra curricular activities.

(John P. Chalmers)

(3) DIGEST OF ASSEMBLY DECISIONS

The following, in the opinion of the Editor, are the decisions of the General Assembly of 2000 which are of most interest and concern. The full volume of "Acts and Deliverances" may be obtained from the Principal Clerk.

ACTS

II   Consolidating Act anent **Ministry**: Reports p1/15
III   Consolidating Act anent **Church Courts**: Reports p1/20
IV   Act amending Act XIX 1956: Section 3 now reads, "A minister, **deacon** or elder shall be eligible for election as Moderator of the General Assembly....." Daily Papers p36
V   Consolidating Act anent **the Sacraments**: Reports p1/27
VI   Consolidating Act anent **Communion Rolls**: Reports p1/29
VII   Act amending Act X 1932 as amended: Act anent **election and admission of elders and deacons**: Reports p1/31
VIII   Act amending Act II 1987 as amended: Act anent **ordination and functions of the Ministry**: *inter alia* **Ministerial Certificates** are replaced by **Practising Certificates** and changes are introduced regarding the application for, the issuing of, and the renewal of such Certificates. Reports p 1/33
XIII   Act anent **New Charge Development**: Reports p20/24

REGULATIONS

I   Regulation amending Regulations anent **Long Service Certificates**: Section 22 of the Deliverance on the Report of the Board of Practice and Procedure
II   Revised Regulations anent **Ministerial staffing in the Presbytery of Shetland**: Appendix VIII: Report of the Board of Ministry
III   Revised Regulations anent **Pulpit Supply**: Appendix VI: Report of Board of Ministry
IV   Amendment of Regulations anent **Further Endowment**: Reports p17/37
VI   Regulations anent the **deployment of TA Chaplains in voluntary mobilisation**: Reports p18/5

REMITS TO PRESBYTERIES

1.   **Overture anent Ministers and Deacons in Public Office:** transmitted to Presbyteries under the Barrier Act with returns to be sent to the Principal Clerk by 31st December, 2000.

2.   **Overture anent Discipline of Ministers, Licentiates, Graduate Candidates and Deacons:** transmitted to Presbyteries under the Barrier Act with returns to be sent to the Principal Clerk by 31st December, 2000.

RESOLUTIONS ("DELIVERANCES") OF GENERAL INTEREST

ASSEMBLY COUNCIL
•   Presbyteries, Kirk Sessions and congregations were encouraged to discuss the paper and questions in Appendix I ("Change or Decay?") to the Council's Report and to send responses to the Council by 31st January, 2001.

BOARD OF COMMUNICATION
•   The Assembly welcomed the proposed revision of the Barclay Daily Study Bible: New Testament Series, together with the associated marketing and promotional initiative.
•   The Church of Scotland's new Internet Site was welcomed as was the Board's plan to market vigorously Life and Work, building on the findings of a survey of readers and non-readers.

BOARD OF MINISTRY
•   The Assembly affirmed the developmental and creative role of Interim Ministry in the Church of Scotland and encouraged the Interim Ministry team in its ongoing endeavours.
•   Ministers who have not attended training in the Protection of Children and Young People were reminded of the instructions of the General Assembly of 1998. Presbyteries were instructed to meet with such ministers and to take steps to ensure that they did comply with those instructions.

BOARD OF NATIONAL MISSION
•   Congregations were urged to join the Eco-Congregation scheme for environmental auditing of church life and premises, beginning in Autumn 2000.
•   The Board's decision to close St. Ninian's Centre, Crieff was resisted. A Special Commission of seven persons was appointed to review the management, purpose and future of St. Ninian's. It will report to the General Assembly of 2001. The Centre will meantime continue in operation.

BOARD OF NOMINATION TO CHURCH CHAIRS
•   The Board was discharged. A Board of Nomination to Theological Chairs was appointed in its place.

BOARD OF PARISH EDUCATION
•   The Assembly noted with approval the establishment of a West of Scotland base for the Board of Parish Education. It is in the International Christian College in Glasgow.
•   The Assembly affirmed the place of the National Youth Assembly in the life of the Church of Scotland and welcomed the intention of the Board of Parish Education to organise such an Assembly annually, beginning in 2001.

BOARD OF PRACTICE AND PROCEDURE
- Mr Patrick S. Hodge QC was appointed Procurator in succession to Mr R. Alastair Dunlop QC who had been appointed Sheriff Principal of Tayside, Central and Fife.
- Volume XI of the Fasti Ecclesiae Scoticanae has been published.
- The Clerks of Assembly were authorised to republish the Acts and Regulations of the General Assembly, incorporating appropriate amendments and corrections, removing or rewording all unnecessary gender-references, all without changing the meaning or legal force of any Act or Regulation.
- The Board was encouraged to develop its work in regard to marketing the Assembly Hall as a conference and concert venue.
- Mr George Stephenson was thanked for his services over twenty-one years as Assembly Officer. Mr David McColl was appointed as his successor.
- The Board of Stewardship and Finance was instructed to consider including financial provision in the future budget of the Church for child care during attendance at meetings of Boards and Committees.
- The number of ministers serving in charges (1143) comprises 977 male and 166 female. The total number of students completing their course in 2000 (23) comprises 12 male and 11 female.

BOARD OF SOCIAL RESPONSIBILITY
- The Assembly noted with satisfaction the major contribution the Board of Social Responsibility makes as an employer of 2262 staff.
- The Assembly noted with serious concern the continuing under-funding of residential care of older people, noted the Board's efforts to secure the implementation of all the recommendations made in the Royal Commission for Long Term Care, instructed the Principal Clerk to write to the Prime Minister urging the early implementation of the financial recommendations of the Royal Commission and stressing that failure so to implement would amount to gross dereliction of duty, and recognised that the Board's continuing involvement in residential care for older people will require to be subject to a fundamental review in the coming year. Presbyteries and congregations were urged to write to their MPs and local political parties asking them to commit themselves to do all in their power to ensure the earliest possible implementation of all the recommendations of the Royal Commission.

BOARD OF SOCIAL RESPONSIBILITY with THE COMMITTEE ON EDUCATION
- The Assembly affirmed anew that marriage is the normative context for heterosexual, permanent relationships and the appropriate environment in which to raise and nurture children.
- The Scottish Executive was urged to fund in-service training so that teaching staff are well equipped to provide good sex education.

BOARD OF STEWARDSHIP AND FINANCE
- Individual members were thanked for the 5.8 per cent increase in per capita offerings in 1999: it was, however, noted that, primarily because of the fall in membership, the increase in total congregational offerings was limited to 2.8 per cent.
- The Board will be arranging area meetings to assist in the promotion and administration of giving by Gift Aid. All congregations were urged to send representatives to these meetings.
- There was agreement that deficit budgeting, together with the use of reserves, by Boards and Committees was acceptable as a short term expedient, pending the establishment of strategic planning to allow changes to the Church's budget priorities to be implemented.

BOARD OF WORLD MISSION

- The Assembly congratulated the Uniting Presbyterian Church of Southern Africa on the successful Union Assembly held in September 1999 and assured the new Church of the prayerful support of the Church of Scotland as it seeks to witness to the reconciling love of Christ in the South Africa situation.
- The development and expansion of the Faithshare Programme was commended. Presbyteries were encouraged to take up the opportunities that the Programme offered. Ministers and others planning study leave were urged to consider spending such leave overseas and to contact the Faithshare Group for guidance and support.
- Funding arrangements for the development of the Sea of Galilee Centre, up to a maximum project cost of £9.5m, had been agreed by all parties.
- HMG was congratulated on its decision to cancel the debts owed to the UK by the world's poorest countries and was urged to do everything in its power to achieve total multilateral debt relief at the G7 summit.

CHURCH OF SCOTLAND GUILD

- The Assembly encouraged the Guild in its involvement with agencies working to combat violence against women.
- Ministers and Kirk Sessions were urged actively to encourage appropriate new and existing congregational groups to affiliate to the Guild.

CHURCH OF SCOTLAND PENSION TRUSTEES

- The Assembly supported the concept of not-for-profit mutual life assurance companies based on returning any surpluses to the members, noted with approval the intention of the Trustees of the Church of Scotland Pension funds to use their one vote at the Special General Meeting of Standard Life to continue as a mutual life assurance company and urged all church members eligible to vote to do the same.

COMMITTEE ON CHURCH AND NATION

- In consultation with the Church and Nation Committee, the Board of Practice and Procedure was instructed to investigate ways in which Church practice can reflect the standards of openness enshrined in the proposed Freedom of Information legislation.
- The Assembly welcomed the decision of the five nuclear powers on the United Nations Security Council to eliminate their nuclear arsenals and urged HMG to use every endeavour to implement this decision in the earliest possible agreed timescale and to use their influence to persuade all other nuclear powers to commit themselves to nuclear disarmament now.
- The Assembly encouraged the Church, both on local and national levels, and individual church members to continue to support the Jubilee 2000 Campaign which is still striving to cancel all Third World debt.

COMMITTEE ON ECUMENICAL RELATIONS

- Presbyteries, seeking views of Kirk Sessions, and all Boards and Committees of the Church were instructed to study the Second Interim Report of the Scottish Church Initiative for Union (SCIFU), with responses to be sent to the Ecumenical Relations Committee by 30th April 2001. The Report was also commended to Kirk Sessions and local Churches Together groups for study, with comments requested by the same date.
- There was a welcome for the setting up of a new Joint Commission on Doctrine with the Roman Catholic Church.
- The Assembly welcomed the setting up of an Ecumenical Youth Assembly in 2001 so that young people could engage fully in the ecumenical relations process.

COMMITTEE ON EDUCATION
- Concern was expressed at the proposal of the Scottish Consultative Council on the Curriculum that Religious and Moral Education, Health Education and Personal and Social Development might become one curricular area in the 5 - 14 programme with the consequent possible erosion of the time allocated to Religious and Moral Education.
- The Committee on Education was instructed to write to the Minister for Children and Education and to the Directors of Education seeking reassurances that the time presently allocated to Religious and Moral Education would be protected.
- The Committee on Education was not permitted to seek at once a successor to its General Secretary, the Rev. John Stevenson, who was retiring. A Special Commission of seven persons was appointed to examine how the work of the Education Department might best be delivered within the current organisational structures of the Church and to report to the General Assembly of 2001. The short-term appointment of a temporary Secretary was authorised.

COMMITTEE ON THE PRIORITY AREAS FUND
- The Assembly noted with approval the finalising of plans for the Scottish Churches Community Trust (SCCT) and the distribution of grants to local inter-church projects tackling poverty and disadvantage. The official launch of the Trust is to take place during Advent 2000. Congregations and members are urged to remember this work in their prayers.

COMMITTEE TO REVISE THE HYMNARY
- Presbyteries were encouraged to arrange presbytery or regional gatherings with a member or members of the Committee present.

CONSULTATIVE COMMITTEE ON ARTISTIC MATTERS
- Attention was drawn to the exhibition, "The World of Worship", which was on tour throughout the country.

GENERAL TRUSTEES
- Financial Boards were encouraged to work glebes for the benefit of the Church.
- The setting up of the Millennium Project Fund administered by the General Trustees was noted. The aim is to see financial provision made to help replace or modify radically church buildings which are no longer suitable for the work of a modern congregation.

IONA COMMUNITY BOARD
- There was a welcome for the progress made and the agreement reached concerning Historic Scotland's taking over responsibility for the management and maintenance of Iona Abbey. The Iona Cathedral Trustees and Historic Scotland were urged to ensure the continuance of the Iona Community's witness and activities on Iona.

JOINT COMMITTEE ON THE PROTECTION OF CHILDREN AND YOUNG PEOPLE IN THE CHURCH
- The Scottish Executive was urged to affirm that the costs of criminal records checks on voluntary workers be borne by government income, and not by either voluntary organisations or the individual concerned.

PANEL ON DOCTRINE
- There was a welcome for the proposed reconstitution of the Joint Commission on Doctrine.

SECTION 5

Presbytery Lists

SECTION 5 – PRESBYTERY LISTS

In each Presbytery list the congregations are listed in alphabetical order. Under the name of the congregation will be found the name of the minister and, where applicable, that of an Associate Minister, Auxiliary Minister, and member of the Diaconate. In a linked charge the names appear under the first named congregation. The years indicated after a minister's name in the congregational section of each Presbytery list are the Year of Ordination (Col 1) and the Year of current Appointment (Col 2). Where only one date is given, it is both the year of Ordination and the Year of Appointment.

In the second part of each Presbytery list those listed are listed alphabetically. The first date is the Year of Ordination and the following date is the Year of Appointment or Retirement. If the person concerned is retired, then the appointment last held will be shown in brackets.

KEY TO ABBREVIATIONS

(E)   Indicates a Church Extension charge. New Charge Developments are separately indicated.
(GD) Indicates a charge where it is desirable that the minister should have a knowledge of Gaelic.
(GE) Indicates a charge where public worship must be regularly conducted in Gaelic.
(H)   Indicates that a Hearing Aid Loop system has been installed. In Linked charges the (H) is placed beside the appropriate building as far as possible.
(L)   Indicates that a Chair Lift has been installed.
(T)   Indicates that the minister has been appointed on the basis of Terminable Tenure.

PRESBYTERY NUMBERS

1	Edinburgh	18	Dumbarton
2	West Lothian	19	South Argyll
3	Lothian	20	Dunoon
4	Melrose and Peebles	21	Lorn and Mull
5	Duns	22	Falkirk
6	Jedburgh	23	Stirling
7	Annandale and Eskdale	24	Dunfermline
8	Dumfries and Kirkcudbright	25	Kirkcaldy
9	Wigtown and Stranraer	26	St Andrews
10	Ayr	27	Dunkeld and Meigle
11	Irvine and Kilmarnock	28	Perth
12	Ardrossan	29	Dundee
13	Lanark	30	Angus
14	Paisley	31	Aberdeen
15	Greenock	32	Kincardine and Deeside
16	Glasgow	33	Gordon
17	Hamilton	34	Buchan

35	Moray	43	Uist
36	Abernethy	44	Lewis
37	Inverness	45	Orkney
38	Lochaber	46	Shetland
39	Ross	47	England
40	Sutherland	48	Europe
41	Caithness	49	Jerusalem
42	Lochcarron – Skye		

(1) EDINBURGH

Meets at Palmerston Place Church, Edinburgh, on the first Tuesday of October, November, December, February, April and May and on the second Tuesday in September and on the last Tuesday of June. When the first Tuesday of April falls in Holy Week the meeting is on the second Tuesday.

Clerk: REV. W. PETER GRAHAM MA BD   10 Palmerston Place, Edinburgh EH12 5AA [e-mail: peter.graham@dial.pipex.com]   0131 225 9137

No.	Name / Charge	Year	Address	Telephone
1	**Abercorn linked with Dalmeny (T)** James Brown BA BD DipHSW DipPsychol 1973	1995	Dalmeny, South Queensferry EH30 9TT	0131 331 1869
2	**Edinburgh: Albany Deaf Church of Edinburgh (H) (0131 556 3128)** Alistair F. Kelly BL (Locum)	1961	34/1 Shore Road, South Queensferry EH30 9SG	0131 319 1841
3	**Edinburgh: Balerno (H)** Vacant Charles Barrington MA BD (Assoc)	1997	3 Johnsburn Road, Balerno, Midlothian EH14 7DN 3 Newmills Road, Balerno, Midlothian EH14 5AG	0131 449 3830 0131 449 4249
4	**Edinburgh: Barclay (0131 229 6810)** D. Graham Leitch MA BD 1974	1980	38 Cluny Gardens EH10 6BN	0131 447 8702
5	**Edinburgh: Blackhall St Columba (0131 332 4431)** Alexander B. Douglas BD 1979	1991	5 Blinkbonny Crescent EH4 3NB	0131 343 3708
6	**Edinburgh: Bristo Memorial Craigmillar** Angus L. Bayne LTh BEd MTh 1969 Agnes M. Rennie (Miss) DCS	1994	72 Blackchapel Close, Bramley Park EH15 3SL 3/1 Craigmillar Court EH16 4AD	0131 657 4151 0131 661 8475
7	**Edinburgh: Broughton St Mary's (H) (0131 556 4786)** I. Alasdair Elders MA BD 1964	1973	103 East Claremont Street EH7 4JA [e-mail: alelders@msn.com]	0131 556 7313 (Tel) 0131 558 7313 (Fax)
8	**Edinburgh: Canongate (H)** Charles Robertson MA 1965	1978	Manse of Canongate EH8 8BN [e-mail: canongate1@aol.com]	0131 556 3515
9	**Edinburgh: Carrick Knowe (H) (0131 334 1505)** Vacant			
10	**Edinburgh: Cluny (H) (0131 447 6745)** Vacant		20 Braidburn Crescent EH10 6EN	0131 447 1617
11	**Edinburgh: Colinton (H) (0131 441 2232)** George J. Whyte BSc BD 1981 Mark Evans DCS	1992	The Manse, Colinton EH13 0JR 13 East Drylaw Drive EH4 2QA	0131 441 2315

No.	Congregation / Minister	Date	Address	Telephone
12	**Edinburgh: Colinton Mains (H)**			
	Ian A. McQuarrie BD	1993	17 Swanston Green EH10 7EW	0131 445 3451
13	**Edinburgh: Corstorphine Craigsbank (H) (0131 334 6365)**			
	George D.W. Grubb BA BD BPhil DMin	1962 1971	22 Belgrave Road EH12 6NF	0131 334 3557
	Ann Inglis (Mrs) LLB BD (Assoc)	1986	4 Sycamore Gardens EH12 7JJ	0131 334 8882
14	**Edinburgh: Corstorphine Old (H) (0131 334 7864)**			
	Ian D. Brady BSc ARCST BD	1967 1976	23 Manse Road EH12 7SW	0131 334 5425
	Lynn Brady (Miss) BD DipMin (Assist)	1996 2000	21 Traquair Park West EH12 7AN	0131 334 9774
15	**Edinburgh: Corstorphine St Anne's (0131 316 4740)**			
	J. William Hill BA BD	1967 1976	23 Belgrave Road EH12 6NG	0131 334 3188
16	**Edinburgh: Corstorphine St Ninian's (H)**			
	Alexander T. Stewart BD	1975 1995	17 Templeland Road EH12 8RZ	0131 334 2978
17	**Edinburgh: Craigentinny St Christopher's**			
	Lilly C. Easton (Mrs)	1999	61 Milton Crescent EH15 3PQ	0131 669 2429
18	**Edinburgh: Craiglockhart (H)**			
	Andrew Ritchie BD DipMin	1984 1991	202 Colinton Road EH14 1BP	0131 443 2020
19	**Edinburgh: Craigmillar Park (T) (H) (0131 667 5862)**			
	Sarah E.C. Nicol (Mrs) BSc BD	1985 1994	14 Hallhead Road EH16 5QJ	0131 667 1623
20	**Edinburgh: Cramond (H)**			
	G. Russell Barr BA BD MTh DMin	1979 1993	Manse of Cramond EH4 6NS [e-mail: rev.r.barr@dial.pipex.com]	0131 336 2036
	I. Maxwell Homewood MSc BD (Assoc)	1997	5 Essex Brae EH4 6LN	0131 339 3554
21	**Currie (H) (0131 451 5141)**			
	Vacant		43 Lanark Road West, Currie EH14 5JX	0131 449 4719
	Margaret Gordon (Mrs) DCS		92 Lanark Road West, Currie, Midlothian EH14	0131 449 2554
22	**Dalmeny** see Abercorn			
23	**Edinburgh: Davidson's Mains (H) (0131 312 6282)**			
	J.R.H. Middleton LLB BD	1981 1988	1 Hillpark Terrace EH4 7SX	0131 336 3078
24	**Edinburgh: Dean**			
	Mark M. Foster BSc BD	1998	1 Ravelston Terrace EH4 3EF	0131 332 5736

No.	Congregation / Minister	Year	Address	Telephone
25	**Edinburgh: Drylaw (0131 343 6643)**			
	Adrian J.T. Rennie BA BD	1987	15 House o' Hill Gardens EH4 2AR [e-mail: adrian@drylawmanse.freeserve.co.uk]	0131 332 3785
26	**Edinburgh: Duddingston**			
	Vacant		Manse of Duddingston EH15 3PX	0131 661 4240
27	**Edinburgh: Fairmilehead (H) (0131 445 2374)**			
	John R. Munro BD	1976	40 Frogston Road West EH10 7AJ	0131 445 1789
28	**Edinburgh: Gilmerton (H)**			
	Vacant		43 Ravenscroft Street EH17 8QJ	0131 664 2147
29	**Edinburgh: Gorgie (H) (0131 337 7936)**			
	Peter I. Barber MA BD	1984	90 Myreside Road EH10 5BZ [e-mail: pibarber@supanet.com]	0131 337 2284
30	**Edinburgh: Granton (H) (0131 552 3033)**			
	Lynne MacMurchie (Miss) LLB BD	1998	8 Wardie Crescent EH5 1AG	0131 551 2159
	Marilynn Steele (Mrs) DCS		2 Northfield Gardens, Prestonpans EH32 9LQ	01875 811497
31	**Edinburgh: Greenbank (H) (0131 447 9969)**			
	Ian G. Scott BSc BD STM	1965	112 Greenbank Crescent EH10 5SZ [e-mail: iangscott@greenbankmanse.u-net.com]	0131 447 4032
32	**Edinburgh: Greenside (H) (0131 556 5588)**			
	Andrew F. Anderson MA BD	1981	80 Pilrig Street EH6 5AS [e-mail: afanderson@compuserve.com]	0131 554 3277 (Tel/Fax)
33	**Edinburgh: Greyfriars Tolbooth and Highland Kirk (G)(H) (0131 225 1900)**			
	David M. Beckett BA BD	1964	12 Tantallon Place EH9 1NZ	0131 667 8671
34	**Edinburgh: High (St Giles') (0131 225 4363)**			
	Gilleasbuig I. Macmillan CVO MA BD DrHc	1969	St Giles' Cathedral EH1 1RE	0131 225 4363
	Karen K. Watson (Mrs) BD (Assist)	1997	64 Inchview Terrace EH7 6TH	0131 657 3145
	Paul Middleton	2000	1F2, 1 Cranston Street EH8 8BE	0131 557 1497
35	**Edinburgh: Holyrood Abbey (H) (0131 661 4883)**			
	Philip R. Hair BD	1980	100 Willowbrae Avenue EH8 7HU	0131 652 0640
36	**Edinburgh: Holy Trinity (H) (0131 442 3304)**			
	Stanley A. Brook BD	1977	16 Thorburn Road EH13 0BQ	0131 441 7167
	Michael S. Dawson BTech BD (Assoc)	1979	12 Sighthill Crescent EH11 4QE	0131 453 6279
	Joyce Mitchell (Mrs) DCS		16/4 Murrayburn Place EH14 2RR	0131 453 6548

No.	Charge / Minister			Address	Tel.
37	**Edinburgh: Inverleith (H)**				
	D. Hugh Davidson MA	1965	1975	43 Inverleith Gardens EH3 5PR [e-mail: hdavidson@freeuk.com]	0131 552 3874
38	**Edinburgh: Juniper Green (H)**				
	James S. Dewar MA BD	1983	2000	476 Lanark Road, Juniper Green EH14 5BQ	0131 453 3494
39	**Edinburgh: Kaimes Lockhart Memorial**				
	Iain D. Penman BD	1977	1995	76 Lasswade Road EH16 6SF	0131 664 2287
40	**Edinburgh: Kirkliston**				
	Glenda Keating (Mrs) MTh	1996		14 Kirklands Park Crescent, Kirkliston EH29 9EP	0131 333 3298
41	**Edinburgh: Kirk o' Field (T)(H)**				
	Ian D. Maxwell MA BD PhD	1977	1996	31 Hatton Place EH9 1UA	0131 667 7954
42	**Edinburgh: Leith North (H) (0131 553 7378)**				
	Alistair G.C. McGregor QC BD	1987		22 Primrose Bank Road EH5 3JG	0131 551 2802
43	**Edinburgh: Leith St Andrew's (H)**				
	John Cook MA BD	1967	1984	13 Claremont Park EH6 7PJ	0131 554 7695
44	**Edinburgh: Leith St Serf's (T)(H)**				
	Sara R. Embleton (Mrs) BA BD	1977	1999	20 Wilton Road EH16 5NX	0131 478 1624
45	**Edinburgh: Leith St Thomas' Junction Road (T)**				
	Shirley Blair (Miss) BD DipMin	1990	1991	28 Summerside Street EH6 4NU	0131 554 5039
46	**Edinburgh: Leith South (H) (0131 554 2578)**				
	Ian Y. Gilmour BD	1985	1995	37 Claremont Road EH6 7NN [e-mail: ianyg@aol.com]	0131 554 3062
	Jennifer Booth (Mrs) BD (Assoc)	1996		39 Lilyhill Terrace EH8 7DR	0131 661 3813
47	**Edinburgh: Leith Wardie (H) (0131 551 3847)**				
	Brian C. Hilsley LLB BD	1990		35 Lomond Road EH5 3JN	0131 552 3328
48	**Edinburgh: Liberton (H)**				
	John N. Young MA BD PhD	1996		7 Kirk Park EH16 6HZ	0131 664 3067
49	**Edinburgh: Liberton Northfield (H) (0131 551 3847)**				
	John M. McPake LTh	2000		9 Claverhouse Drive EH16 6BR	0131 658 1754

No.	Congregation / Minister	Ord. years	Address	Phone
50	**Edinburgh: London Road (H) (0131 661 1149)** William L. Armitage BSc BD	1976 1991	26 Inchview Terrace EH7 6TQ [e-mail: billarm@cableinet.co.uk]	0131 669 5311
51	**Edinburgh: Marchmont St Giles' (H) (0131 447 4359)** Donald M. Stephen TD MA BD ThM Elspeth G. Dougall (Mrs) MA BD	1962 1974 1989 1991	19 Hope Terrace EH9 2AP 60B Craigmillar Park EH16 5PU	0131 447 2834 0131 668 1342
52	**Edinburgh: Mayfield Salisbury (0131 667 1522)** Vacant		26 Seton Place EH9 2JT	0131 667 1286
53	**Edinburgh: Morningside Braid (0131 447 9430)** John R. Wells BD DipMin	1991	5 Cluny Avenue EH10 4RN	0131 447 4647
54	**Edinburgh: Morningside United (H) (0131 447 3152)** John R. Smith MA BD	1973 1998	1 Midmar Avenue EH10 6BS [e-mail: jsmith4772@aol.com]	0131 447 8724
55	**Edinburgh: Muirhouse St Andrew's (E)** Frederick D.F. Shewan MA BD	1970 1980	35 Silverknowes Road EH4 5LL	0131 336 4546
56	**Edinburgh: Murrayfield (H) (0131 337 1091)** Vacant		45 Murrayfield Gardens EH12 6DH	0131 337 5431
57	**Edinburgh: Newhaven (H)** Grant MacLaughlan BA BD	1998	11 Laverockbank Terrace EH5 3BL	0131 552 8906
58	**Edinburgh: New Restalrig (H) (0131 661 5676)** David L. Court BSc BD	1989 2000	19 Abercorn Road EH8 7DP	0131 661 4045
59	**Edinburgh: Old Kirk (H)** Thomas Preston BD	1978 1992	24 Pennywell Road EH4 4HD	0131 332 4354
60	**Edinburgh: Palmerston Place (H) (0131 220 1690)** Colin A.M. Sinclair BA BD	1981 1996	30B Cluny Gardens EH10 6BJ	0131 447 9598 0131 225 3312 (Fax)
61	**Edinburgh: Pilrig St Paul's (0131 553 1876)** John M. Tait BSc BD	1985 1999	78 Pilrig Street EH6 5AS [e-mail: john.m.tait@btinternet.com]	0131 554 1842
62	**Edinburgh: Polwarth (H) (0131 346 2711)** John K.S. McMahon MA BD	1998	9 Merchiston Bank Gardens EH10 5EB [e-mail: jksmcmahon@hotmail.com]	0131 447 2741

No.	Congregation / Minister	Date	Address	Telephone
63	**Edinburgh: Portobello Old (H)** Neil Buchanan BD	1991	6 Hamilton Terrace EH15 1NB	0131 669 5312
64	**Edinburgh: Portobello St James' (H)** Malcolm M. McDougall BD	1981	34 Brighton Place EH15 1LT	0131 669 1767
65	**Edinburgh: Portobello St Philip's Joppa (H) (0131 669 3641)** John Weir Cook MA BD Alison M. Jack (Mrs) MA BD PhD (Assist)	1962 1998	6 St Mary's Place EH15 2QF 7/2 Marchhall Crescent EH16 7HL	0131 669 2410 0131 662 0433
66	**Edinburgh: Priestfield (H) (0131 667 5644)** Thomas N. Johnston LTh	1972	13 Lady Road EH16 5PA	0131 668 1620
67	**Edinburgh: Queensferry (H)** John G. Carrie BSc BD	1971	1 Station Road, South Queensferry EH30 9HY [e-mail: john.carrie@virgin.net]	0131 331 1100
68	**Edinburgh: Ratho** Ian J. Wells BD	1999	Ratho, Newbridge EH28 8NP	0131 333 1346
69	**Edinburgh: Reid Memorial (H) (0131 662 1203)** Brian M. Embleton BD	1976	20 Wilton Road EH16 5NX	0131 667 3981
70	**Edinburgh: Richmond Craigmillar (H) (0131 661 6561)** Elizabeth M. Henderson (Miss) MA BD	1985 1997	13 Wisp Green EH15 3QX	0131 669 1133
71	**Edinburgh: St Andrew's and St George's (H) (0131 225 3847)** Andrew R.C. McLellan MA BD STM	1970 1986	25 Comely Bank EH4 1AJ	0131 332 5324
72	**Edinburgh: St Andrew's Clermiston** Alistair H. Keil BD DipMin	1989	87 Drum Brae South EH12 8TD [e-mail: alistair.h.keil@talk.21.com]	0131 339 4149
73	**Edinburgh: St Catherine's Argyle (H) (0131 667 7220)** Victor W.N. Laidlaw BD	1975	5 Palmerston Road EH9 1TL	0131 667 6855
74	**Edinburgh: St Colm's (T)(H)** Stewart M. McPherson BD CertMin Mary Gargrave (Mrs) DCS	1991	1 Merchiston Gardens EH10 5DD 229/2 Calder Road EH11 4RG	0131 337 1107 0131 476 3493

No.	Name		Address	Tel
75	**Edinburgh: St Cuthbert's (H) (0131 229 1142)**			
	Tom C. Cuthell MA BD MTh	1965 1976	22 Learmonth Terrace EH4 1PG	0131 332 6138
	Peter Neilson MA BD MTh (Assoc)	1975 1997	12 Strathalmond Court EH4 8AE	0131 339 4536
76	**Edinburgh: St David's Broomhouse (H) (0131 443 9851)**			
	Neil J. Dougall BD	1991	33 Traquair Park West EH12 7AN [e-mail: neild3344@aol.com]	0131 334 1730
77	**Edinburgh: St George's West (H) (0131 225 7001)**			
	Peter J. MacDonald BD DipMin	1986 1998	6 Wardie Avenue EH5 2AB [e-mail: pjmacdon@aol.com]	0131 552 4333
78	**Edinburgh: St John's Oxgangs**			
	Yvonne E.S. Atkins (Mrs) BD	1997	2 Caiystane Terrace EH10 6SR	0131 445 1688
79	**Edinburgh: St Margaret's (H) (0131 554 7400)**			
	Ewan R. Aitken BA BD	1992 1995	43 Moira Terrace EH7 6TD	0131 669 7329
	Liz Crocker (Mrs) DCS		77C Craigcrook Road EH4 3PH	0131 332 0227
	Marion Buchanan (Mrs) DCS		6 Hamilton Terrace EH15 1NB	0131 669 5312
80	**Edinburgh: St Martin's**			
	Elizabeth B. Ross (Ms) BD	1996 1999	5 Duddingston Crescent EH15 3AS	0131 657 9894
81	**Edinburgh: St Michael's (H)**			
	Margaret R. Forrester (Mrs) MA BD	1974 1980	25 Kingsburgh Road EH12 6DZ	0131 337 5646
82	**Edinburgh: St Nicholas' Sighthill**			
	Kenneth J. Mackay MA BD	1971 1976	122 Sighthill Loan EH11 4NT	0131 453 6921
83	**Edinburgh: St Stephen's Comely Bank (0131 315 4616)**			
	Graham T. Dickson MA BD	1985 1996	8 Blinkbonny Crescent EH4 3NB [e-mail: graham@dickson22.fsnet.co.uk]	0131 332 3364 (Tel/Fax)
84	**Edinburgh: Slateford Longstone**			
	Gordon R. Palmer MA BD STM	1986 1994	50 Kingsknowe Road South EH14 2JW [e-mail: gordonrp@aol.com]	0131 443 2960
85	**Edinburgh: Stenhouse St Aidan's**			
	Vacant		65 Balgreen Road EH12 5UA	0131 337 7711
	Mary Gargrave (Mrs) DCS		229/3 Calder Road EH11 4RG	0131 476 3493
86	**Edinburgh: Stockbridge (H) (0131 332 0122)**			
	Anne T. Logan (Mrs) MA BD	1981 1993	19 Eildon Street EH3 5JU	0131 557 6052
87	**Edinburgh: Tron Kirk Moredun**			
	Stephen Manners MA BD	1989	467 Gilmerton Road EH17 7JG	0131 666 2584

88   Edinburgh: Viewforth (T)(H) (0131 229 1917)
Anthony P. Thornthwaite MTh   1995   91 Morningside Drive EH10 5NN   0131 447 6684

Name	Dates	Position	Address	Telephone
Aitken, Alexander R. MA	1965 1997	(Newhaven)	36 King's Meadow EH16 5JW	0131 667 1404
Alexander, Ian W. BA BD STM	1990 1995	Board of World Mission	c/o 121 George Street EH2 4YN	0131 225 5722
Anderson, David J.B. MA BD	1974 1994	General Secretary: Evangelical Alliance (Scot)	46 Elliot Road EH14 1DZ	0131 441 7399
Anderson, Hugh MA BD PhD DD	1951 1985	(University of Edinburgh)	23/13 Maxwell Street EH10 5HT	0131 447 1401
Auld, A. Graeme MA BD PhD	1973 1973	University of Edinburgh	Nether Swanshiel, Hobkirk, Bonchester Bridge, Hawick TD9 8JU	
Baigrie, R.A. MA	1945 1985	(Kirkurd with Newlands)	32 Inchcolm Terrace, South Queensferry EH30 9NA	0131 331 4311
Baxter, Richard F. OBE MA BD	1954 1990	(Assistant at St Andrew's and St George's)	138 Braid Road, Edinburgh EH10 6JB	0131 447 7735
Blakey, Ronald S. MA BD MTh	1962 2000	Editor: The Year Book	61 Orchard Brae Avenue, Edinburgh EH4 2UR	0131 343 6039
Brown, William D. MA	1963 1989	(Wishaw Thornlie)	121 Dalkeith Road EH16 5AJ	0131 667 1124
Cameron, G. Gordon MA BD STM	1957 1997	(Juniper Green)	4 Ladywell Grove, Clackmannan FK10 4JQ	01259 723769
Cameron, John W.M. MA BD	1957 1996	(Liberton)	10 Plewlands Gardens EH10 5JP	0131 447 1277
Cattanach, William D. DD	1951 1990	(Geneva)	145 Craigleith Road EH4 2ED	0131 332 4503
Chalmers, John P. BD	1979 1995	Department of Ministry	10 Liggars Place, Dunfermline KY12 7XZ	01383 739130
Chalmers, Murray MA	1965 1991	Hospital Chaplain	25 Greenbank Road EH10 5RX	0131 447 3387
Cheyne, Alexander C. MA BD BLitt DLitt	1958 1986	(University of Edinburgh)	12 Crossland Crescent, Peebles EH45 8LF	01721 722288
Clinkenbeard, William W. BSc BD STM	1966 2000	(Edinburgh: Carrick Knowe)	107 The Moorings, St. David's Harbour, Dalgety Bay KY11 5GP	01383 824011
Cobain, Alan R. BD	2000	Army Chaplain	54 Cowan Road, EH11 1RJ	0131 337 4529
Cowie, James M. BD	1976 1996	Community Minister at Craigmillar	c/o Thistle Foundation, Niddrie Mains Road EH16 4AE [e-mail: jim@jimcowie.demon.co.uk]	0131 661 3366
Cross, Brian F. MA	1961 1998	(Coalburn)	23 Broomlee Court, Broomlee Crescent, West Linton EH46 7EY	01968 660705
Currie, David E. P. BSc BD	1983 2000	Adviser in Evangelism	5 Eriskay Avenue, Hamilton ML3 8QB	
Davidson, Ian M.P. MA BD	1957 1994	(Stirling: Allan Park South with Church of the Holy Rude)	13/8 Craigend Park EH16 5XX	0131 664 0074
Doyle, Ian B. MA BD PhD	1946 1991	(Department of National Mission)	21 Lygon Road EH16 5QD	0131 667 2697
Drummond, R. Hugh	1953 1991	(Balmaclellan with Kells)	19 Winton Park EH10 7EX	0131 445 3634
Drummond, Rhoda (Miss) DCS		(Deaconess)	Flat K, 23 Grange Loan EH9 2ER	0131 668 3631
Dunn, W. Iain C. DA LTh	1983 1998	(Pilrig and Dalmeny Street)	10 Fox Covert Avenue EH12 6UQ	0131 334 1665
Elliot, George MA BD STM	1958 1989	(Board of Stewardship and Finance)	28 Pentland Gardens EH10 6NW	0131 447 4017
Faulds, Norman L. MA BD FSAScot	1968 2000	(Aberlady with Gullane)	Wellwood, 8 Juniper Place, Juniper Green EH14 5TX	0131 453 4984
Finlayson, J. Clarence MA	1930 1972	(Grange)	52 Falcon Avenue EH10 4AW	0131 447 6550
Forrester, Duncan B. MA BD DPhil DD	1962 1978	University of Edinburgh	25 Kingsburgh Road EH12 6DZ	0131 337 5646
Galbraith, Douglas MA BD BMus MPhil ARSCM	1965 1995	Office for Worship, Doctrine and Artistic Matters	c/o 121 George Street EH2 4YN	0131 240 2233
Gibson, John C.L. MA BD DPhil	1959 1994	(University of Edinburgh)	Cairnbank, Morton Street South EH15 2NB	0131 669 3635

Name			Role	Address	Telephone
Gillon, J. Blair MA	1935	1980	(Borthwick with Heriot)	15D Cramond Green, Cramond Road North EH4 6NH	0131 336 2551
Glass, Irene (Miss) DCS			(Deaconess)	3E Falcon Road West EH10 4AA	0131 447 6554
Gordon, Tom MA BD	1974	1994	Chaplain: Fairmile Marie Curie Centre	7 Buckstone Row EH10 6TW	0131 445 3566
Graham, W. Peter MA BD	1967	1993	Presbytery Clerk	23/6 East Comiston EH10 6RZ	0131 445 5763
Hardy, Basil G. MA BD	1946	1984	(Dundee Meadowside St Paul's)	14 Elliot Place EH14 1DR	0131 441 3449
Harkness, James CB OBE QHC MA LB DD	1961	1995	(Chaplain General: Army)	13 Saxe Coburg Place EH3 5BR	0131 343 1297
Henderson, Charlotte (Mrs)	1986	1994	(Hospital Chaplain)	89 West Savile Terrace EH9 3DP	0131 667 7123
Hepburn, James L. MA BD	1950	1991	(Ardoch with Blackford)	16 Marchmont Road. EH9 1HZ	0131 229 6170
Houston, Graham R. BSc BD MTh PhD	1978	1990	National Bible Society of Scotland	3 Ramsay Place, Penicuick EH26 9JS [e-mail: ghouston@aol.com]	01968 672752
Hutchison, Maureen (Mrs) DCS	1974	2000	(Deaconess)	23 Drylaw Crescent EH4 2AU	0131 332 8020
Jamieson, Gordon D. MA BD	1954	1994	Director of Stewardship	41 Goldpark Place, Livingston EH54 6LW	01506 412020
Jeffrey, Eric W.S. JP MA			(Edinburgh Bristo Memorial)	18 Gillespie Crescent, Edinburgh EH10 4HT	0131 229 7815
Johnston, William B. MA BD DD DLitt	1945	1991	(Colinton)	15 Elliot Road EH14 1DU	0131 441 3387
Kant, Everard FVCM MTh	1953	1988	(Kinghorn)	38 Redford Loan EH13 0AX	0131 441 3853
Kelly, Alastair F. BL	1961		Board of National Mission	34/1 Shore Road, South Queensferry EH30 9SG	0131 319 1841
Kelly, Ewan MB ChB BD	1994	1998	Chaplain: Edinburgh Royal Infirmary	29 Buckstone Crescent EH10 6RJ	
Kesting, Sheilagh M. (Miss) BA BD	1980	1993	Ecumenical Relations	12 Glenview Drive, Falkirk FK1 5JU	01324 671489
Kingston, David V.F. BD	1993	1993	Army Chaplain	1 Rawlinson Road, Catterick Garrison, North Yorks DL9 3AR	01875 822026
Lamont, A. Donald BSc BD	1941	1975	(Nakuru)	36 St Clair Terrace EH10 5PS	0131 447 4665
Lawson, Kenneth C. MA BD	1963	1984	(Adviser in Adult Education)	56 Easter Drylaw View EH4 2QP	0131 539 3311
Lyall, David BSc BD STM PhD	1965	1990	University of Edinburgh	1 North Meggetland EH14 1XG	0131 443 7640
Lyon, D.H.S. MA BD STM	1952	1986	(Board of World Mission and Unity)	30 Mansfield Road, Balerno EH14 7IZ	0131 449 5031
Macdonald, Donald M. MA BD	1940	1985	(Kippen)	1 Cargil Court, Cargil Terrace EH5 3NE	0131 552 4046
Macdonald, Finlay A.J. MA BD PhD	1971	1996	Principal Clerk	c/o 121 George Street EH2 4YN	0131 225 5722
McDonald, James I.H. MA BD MTh PhD	1958	1980	(University of Edinburgh)	23 Ravelston House Road EH4 3LP	0131 332 2172
Macdonald, William J. BD	1976	1999	Board of National Mission: New Charge Development	21 Ormidale Terrace EH12 6DY	0131 337 3441
McDonald, William J.G. DD	1953	1992	(Mayfield)	7 Blacket Place EH9 1RN	0131 667 2100
McDowell, Brian		1999	Chaplain: Fettes College	6 West Woods, Fettes College EH4 1RA	0131 332 9510
McGillivray, A. Gordon MA BD STM	1951	1993	(Presbytery Clerk)	7 Greenfield Crescent, Balerno, Midlothian EH14 7HD	0131 449 4747
MacGregor, Margaret S. (Miss) MA BD DipEd	1985	1994	(Calcutta)	16 Learmonth Court EH4 1PB	0131 332 1089
McGregor, T. Stewart MBE MA BD	1957	1998	(Chaplain: Edinburgh Royal Infirmary)	19 Lonsdale Terrace EH3 9HL [e-mail: cetsm@dir.con.uk]	0131 229 5332
McIntosh, Hamish MC MA BD	1943	1983	(Auchterarder St Andrew's and West)	19 Falcon Gardens EH10 4AP	0131 447 3516
McIntyre, John CVO DLitt DD Drhc FRSE	1941	1986	(University of Edinburgh)	22/4 Minto Street EH9 1RQ	0131 667 1203
McKean, David MA STM	1942	1982	(Paris)	79 Baberton Mains Drive EH14 3DA	0131 442 2128
Maclean, Ailsa G. (Mrs) BD DipCE	1979	1988	Chaplain: George Heriot's School	28 Swan Spring Avenue EH10 6NJ	0131 445 1320
McLean, Campbell M. MA	1949	1992	(Cramond)	16 West Terrace, South Queensferry EH30 9LL	0131 319 1320

Name	Ord.	Ind.	Position	Address	Telephone
MacLean, Marjory (Miss) LLB BD	1991	1998	Board of Practice and Procedure	121 George Street, Edinburgh EH2 4YN	0131 225 5722
McLeod, Roderick MA BD	1951	1990	(Lochwinnoch)	2 East Savile Road EH16 5ND	0131 667 1475
Macmillan, W.B.R. LLD DD	1954	1993	(Dundee: St Mary's)	Flat 5, 3 Craigend Park EH16 5XY	0131 672 1832
McPheat, Elspeth DCS			Deaconess: Social Responsibility	11/5 New Orchardfield, Leith EH6 5ET	0131 554 4143
McPhee, Duncan C. MA BD	1953	1993	(Department of National Mission)	94 Balgreen Road EH12 5UB	0131 337 5230
Macpherson, Allan S. MA	1967	1993	Chaplain: Merchiston Castle School	The Fairway, Merchiston Castle School EH13 0PU	0131 667 1456
Macpherson, Colin C.R. MA BD	1958	1996	(Dunfermline St Margaret's)	7 Eva Place EH9 3ET	
Macpherson, Fergus MA PhD	1946	1988	(British Council of Churches)	The Cottages, the Gables, Carlton Road, Barnsley S71 3JD	
Mackie, Steven G. MA BD	1956	1994	(University of St Andrews)	38 Grange Loan EH9 2NR	0131 667 9532
Mathieson, Angus R MA BD	1988	1998	Department of Ministry	2nd Floor, 7 Novar Drive, Glasgow G12 9PX [e-mail: angus.mathieson@which.net]	0141 334 4665
Mechie, William M.	1946	1984	(Kirknewton and East Calder)	Flat 62, 77 Barnton Park View EH4 6EL	0131 339 1644
Mickelson, May B. (Miss) DCS			(Deaconess)	81 Milton Road East EH15 2NL	0131 669 0482
Miller, I David OBE MA	1992	1999	Prison Chaplain (PT)	146 Craigleith Road EH4 2EQ	0131 332 6378
Miller, J. Stewart MA BD STM	1954	1997	(Morningside United)	54 Mayfield, East Craigs EH12 8UH	0131 339 0537
Moir, Ian A MA BD	1962	2000	(Adviser for Urban Priority Areas)	28/6 Comely Bank Avenue, Edinburgh EH4 1EL	0131 332 2748
Morrice, William G. MA BD STM PhD	1957	1991	(St John's College Durham)	Flat 37, The Cedars, 2 Manse Road, Corstorphine EH12 7SN [e-mail: w.g.morrice@btinternet.com]	0131 316 4845
Morrison, Mary B. (Mrs) MA BD DipEd	1978	2000	(Edinburgh: Stenhouse St. Aidan's)	14 Eildon Terrace EH3 5LU	0131 332 6592
Morton, Andrew R. MA BD DD	1956	1994	(Board of World Mission and Unity)	11 Oxford Terrace EH4 1PX	0131 449 7359
Morton, R. Colin BA BD	1960	1998	(Jerusalem)	313 Lanark Road West, Currie EH14 5RS	0131 551 1731
Moyes, Sheila A. (Miss) DCS			(Deaconess)	158 Pilton Avenue EH5 2JZ	0131 346 7092
Mulligan, Anne (Miss) DCS			Deaconess: Hospital Chaplain's Assistant	1/6 Coxfield, Gorgie EH11 2SY	
Munro, George A. M.	1968	2000	(Edinburgh: Cluny)	108 Cayside EH10 7HR	0131 441 2460
Murison, William G.	1951	1990	(Department of World Mission and Unity)	21 Hailes Gardens EH13 0JL	01506 852 464
Murrie, John BD	1953	1996	(Kirkliston)	31 Nicol Road, The Whins, Broxburn EH52 6JJ	
Newell, Alison M. (Mrs) BD	1986	2000	Director: Ecumenical Spirituality Prog.	1A Inverleith Terrace EH3 5NS	0131 336 1965
Nicol, Douglas A.O. MA BD	1974	1991	National Mission Secretary	24 Corbiehill Avenue EH4 5DR	0131 229 6070
O'Neill, John C. BA BD PhD	1960	1996	(University of Edinburgh)	9 Lonsdale Terrace EH3 9HN	0131 445 2876
Orr, John F. MA	1949	1987	(St John's Oxgangs)	2/34 Pentland Drive EH10 6PX	0131 662 4564
Page, Ruth MA BD DPhil	1976	2000	(University of Edinburgh)	7 Seton Place EH9 2JT	0131 332 9735
Paterson, Ian M. MA	1947	1985	(Eccles with Greenlaw)	45/15 Maidencraig Crescent EH4 2UU	0131 332 5876
Paterson, J.M.K. MA ACII BD DD	1964	1987	(Milngavie St Paul's)	58 Orchard Drive EH4 2DZ	0131 337 0095
Paterson, John M.	1976	1987	(Blackbraes and Shieldhill)	9 Saughtonhall Circus EH12 5RG	0131 653 2310
Philip, James MA	1948	1997	(Holyrood Abbey)	3 Ferguson Gardens, Musselburgh EH21 6XF	0131 661 3124
Philip, Connie (Miss) BD	1980	1995	(Arbuthnott with Bervie)	22/5 South Elixa Place, Baronscourt View EH8 7PG	0131 447 4632
Porteous, Norman W. DD	1929	1968	(University of Edinburgh)	3 Hermitage Gardens EH10 6DL	0131 557 2144
Potts, Jean (Miss) DCS			(Deaconess)	28B East Claremont Street EH7 4JP	0131 447 6855
Reid, J.K.S. CBE TD MA DD	1939	1976	(University of Aberdeen)	8 Abbotsford Court, 18 Colinton Road EH10 5EH	0131 447 7642
Reid, W. Scott BD MA DipPS PhD	1950	1990	(London Road)	14/37 Ethel Terrace EH10 5NA	
Renton, Ian P.	1976	2000	(St Colm's)	98 Homeross House, Strathearn Road, Edinburgh EH9 2QY	0131 228 1008
Ronald, Norma A. (Miss) MBE DCS	1958	1990	(Deaconess)	43/26 Gillespie Crescent EH10 4HY	0131 447 5987
Ross, Andrew C. MA BD STM PhD	1958	1998	(University of Edinburgh)	27 Colinton Road EH10 5DR	

Name			Position	Address	Tel
Ross, Kenneth R. BD	1982	1999	General Secretary, Board of World Mission	121 George Street EH2 4YN	0131 225 5722
Sandilands, Ian S.	1986	1999	(Black Mount)	51 Little Road, Edinburgh EH16 6SH	0131 664 6924
Schofield, Melville F. MA	1960	1988	Chaplain: Western General Hospitals	25 Rowantree Grove, Currie EH14 5AT	0131 449 4745
Searle, David C. MA DipTh	1965	1993	Warden: Rutherford House	38 Rosslyn Crescent, Edinburgh EH6 5AX	0131 554 5713
Sim, John G. MA	1946	1987	(Kirkcaldy Old)	7 Grosvenor Crescent EH12 5EP	0131 226 3190
Skinner, Donald M MBE JP FIES	1962	2000	(Edinburgh: Gilmerton)	12 Straid a Cnoc, Clynder G84 0QX	
Sloan, Elma C. (Miss) DCS			(Deaconess)	7 Dunedin Street, Edinburgh EH7 4JB	0131 556 3496
Steel, David MA BD DD LLD	1936	1976	(Linlithgow St Michael's)	39 Newbattle Terrace EH10 4SF	0131 447 2180
Stevenson, John MA BD	1963	1993	Department of Education	12 Swanston Gardens, Edinburgh EH10 7DL	0131 445 3960
Stiven, Iain K. MA BD	1960	1997	(Strachur and Strathlachlan)	3 Gloucester Place EH3 6EE	0131 225 8177
Taylor, Howard G. BSc BD MTh	1971	1998	Chaplain: Heriot Watt University Board of Ministry	The Chaplaincy, Heriot Watt University EH14 4AS	0131 449 5111 (ext 4508)
Teague, Yvonne (Mrs) DCS			(Deaconess)	46 Craigcrook Avenue EH4 3PX	0131 536 3113
Thom, Helen (Miss) DCS			(Wigtown)	84 Great King Street EH3 6QU	0131 556 5687
Thomson, J.G.S.S. MA BD BA PhD	1951	1981	(Leith Wardie)	4 Drum Brae South EH12 8SJ	0131 334 6035
Thomson, Thomas MA	1954	1990	(University of Aberdeen)	8/7 Craigend Park EH16 5XX	0131 672 3585
Torrance, James B. MA BD	1954	1989	(University of Edinburgh)	3 Greenbank Crescent, Edinburgh EH10 5TE	0131 447 3230
Torrance, Thomas F. MBE DLitt DD DSc DrTheol DrTeol FBA FRSE	1940	1979	(Lesmahagow Abbeygreen)	37 Braid Farm Road EH10 6LE	
Walker, R.W. MB ChB	1941	1981	(Dean)	16 Cumin Place EH9 2JX	0131 667 0578
Webster, W. Thoms MA	1944	1986	Assistant Chaplain General	3 Columba Road EH4 3QU	0131 343 2071
Whitton, John P.	1977	1999	(Chaplain: University of Edinburgh)	HQ Army Scotland, Craigiehall, South Queensferry EH30 9TN	
Whyte, Iain A. BA BD STM	1968	2000	(St Andrew's College, Selly Oak)	34 Shandon Crescent EH11 1QF	0131 337 3559
Wigglesworth, J. Christopher MBE BSc PhD BD	1967	1999	(Board of World Mission)	12 Leven Terrace EH3 9LW	
Wilkie, James L. MA BD	1959	1998	(Kikuyu)	7 Comely Bank Avenue EH4 1EW [e-mail:jl.wilkie@btinternet.com]	0131 228 6335 0131 343 1552
Wilkinson, John BD MD FRCP DTM&H	1946	1975	Christian Fellowship of Healing	70 Craigleith Hill Gardens EH4 2JH	0131 332 2994
Williams, Jenny (Miss) BSc CQSW BD	1996	1997		3 Milton Mill, Milton Bridge, Penicuik EH26 0NS	
Young, Alexander W. BD DipMin	1988	1999	Chaplain: Western General Hospitals	48 Whitelock Avenue, Macmerry, Tranent EH31 1PG	01875 612359

EDINBURGH ADDRESSES

Church	Address
Albany	Albany Street
Balerno	Johnsburn Road, Balerno
Barclay	Barclay Place
Blackhall St Columba	Queensferry Road
Bristo Memorial	Peffermill Road, Craigmillar
Broughton St Mary's	Bellevue Crescent
Canongate	Canongate
Carrick Knowe	North Saughton Road
Cluny	Cluny Gardens
Colinton	Dell Road
Colinton Mains	Oxgangs Road North
Corstorphine	
Craigsbank	Craig's Crescent
Old	Kirk Loan
St Anne's	Kaimes Road
St Ninian's	St John's Road
Craigentinny	Craigentinny Road
Craiglockhart	Craiglockhart Avenue
Craigmillar Park	Craigmillar Park
Cramond	Cramond Glebe Road
Currie	Kirkgate, Currie
Davidson's Mains	Quality Street
Dean	Dean Path
Drylaw	Groathill Road North
Duddingston	Old Church Lane, Duddingston
Fairmilehead	Frogston Road West, Fairmilehead
Gilmerton	Ravenscroft Street
Gorgie	Gorgie Road
Granton	Boswall Parkway
Greenbank	Braidburn Terrace
Greenside	Royal Terrace
Greyfriars	Greyfriars Place
Tolbooth Highland Kirk	High Street
High (St Giles')	Dalziel Place x London Road
Holyrood Abbey	Hailesland Place
Holy Trinity	Wester Hailes
Inverleith	Inverleith Gardens
Juniper Green	Lanark Road, Juniper Green
Kaimes Lockhart M'l	Gracemount Drive
Kirkliston	The Square, Kirkliston
Kirk o' Field	Pleasance
Leith	
North	Madeira Street off Ferry Road
St Andrew's	Easter Road
St Serf's	Ferry Road
St Thomas'	Great Junction Street
Junction Road	
South	Kirkgate
Wardie	Primrosebank Road
Liberton	Liberton
Northfield	Gilmerton Road, Liberton
London Road	London Road
Marchmont St Giles'	Kilgraston Road
Mayfield/Salisbury	Mayfield Road x W. Mayfield.
Morningside Braid	Nile Grove
Morningside United	Bruntsfield Place x Chamberlain Road
Muirhouse St Andrew's	Pennywell Gardens
Murrayfield	Abinger Gardens
Newhaven	Craighall Road
New Restalrig	Willowbrae Road
Old Kirk	Pennywell Road
Palmerston Place	Palmerston Place
Pilrig St Paul's	Pilrig Street
Polwarth	Polwarth Terrace x Harrison Road
Portobello	
Old	Bellfield Street
St James'	Rosefield Place
St Philip's, Joppa	Abercorn Terrace
Priestfield	Dalkeith Road x Marchall Place
Queensferry	The Loan, South Queensferry
Ratho	Baird Road, Ratho
Reid Memorial	West Savile Terrace
Richmond Craigmillar	Niddrie Mains Road
St Andrew's and St George's	George Street
St Andrew's Clermiston	Clermiston View
St Catherine's-Argyle	Grange Road x Chalmers Crescent
St Colm's	Dalry Road x Cathcart Place
St Cuthbert's	Lothian Road
St David's Broomhouse	Broomhouse Crescent
St George's West	Shandwick Place
St John's Oxgangs	Oxgangs Road
St Margaret's	Restalrig Road South
St Martin's	Magdalene Drive
St Michael's	Slateford Road
St Nicholas' Sighthill	Calder Road
St Stephen's Comely Bank	Comely Bank
Slateford-Longstone	Kingsknowe Road North
Stenhouse St Aidan's	Chesser Avenue
Stockbridge	Saxe Coburg Street
Tron Moredun	Fernieside Drive
Viewforth	Gilmore Place

(2) WEST LOTHIAN

Meets in St John's Church Hall, Bathgate on the first Tuesday of every month except December when the meeting is on the second Tuesday and January, July and August when there is no meeting.

Clerk: REV. DUNCAN SHAW BD MTh   St John's Manse, Mid Street, Bathgate EH48 1QD   01506 653146
[e-mail: duncanshaw@dial.pipex.com]

Armadale (H)
Geoffrey H. Smart LTh   1994   70 Mount Pleasant, Armadale EH48 3HB   01501 730358

Avonbridge linked with Torphichen
Clifford Acklam BD MTh   1997 2000   Torphichen, Bathgate EH48 4LT   01506 652794

Bathgate: Boghall (H)
John McLean MA BD — 1967 — 1 Manse Place, Ash Grove, Bathgate EH48 1NJ — 01506 652940

Bathgate: High (H)
Ronald G. Greig MA BD — 1987 — 1998 — 19 Hunter Grove, Bathgate EH48 1NN — 01506 652654

Bathgate: St David's
Elliot G.S. Wardlaw BA BD DipMin — 1984 — Marjoribanks Street, Bathgate EH48 1AH — 01506 653177

Bathgate: St John's (H)
Duncan Shaw BD MTh — 1975 — 1978 — Mid Street, Bathgate EH48 1QD — 01506 653146

Blackburn
Robert A. Anderson MA BD DPhil — 1980 — 1998 — Blackburn, Bathgate EH47 7QR — 01506 652825
[e-mail: robertaland@supanet.com]

Blackridge linked with Harthill St Andrew's
H. Warner Hardie BD — 1979 — Harthill, Shots ML7 5QW — 01501 751239

Breich Valley
Vacant — Stoneyburn, Bathgate EH47 8AU — 01501 762018
New Charge formed by the union of Addiewell linked with Longridge and Breich linked with Stoneyburn

Broxburn (H)
Richard T. Corbett BSc MSc PhD BD — 1992 — 2 Church Street, Broxburn EH52 5EL — 01506 852825

Fauldhouse: St Andrew's
Elizabeth Smith (Mrs) BD — 1996 — 2000 — 7 Glebe Court, Fauldhouse EH47 9DX — 01501 771190

Harthill St Andrew's See Blackridge

Kirknewton and East Calder
Ann M. Ballentine (Miss) MA BD — 1981 — 1993 — 8 Manse Court, East Calder EH53 0HF — 01506 880802

Kirk of Calder (H)
John M. Povey MA BD — 1981 — 19 Maryfield Park, Mid Calder EH53 0SB — 01506 882495

Linlithgow: St Michael's (H)
John L. Paterson MA BD STM — 1964 — 1977 — Linlithgow EH49 7AL — 01506 842195
Thomas S. Riddell BSc (Aux) — 1993 — 1994 — 4 The Maltings, Linlithgow EH49 6DS — 01506 843251
Alan Miller BA MA BD (Assoc) — 2000 — Crosshouse, The Cross, Linlithgow EH49 7AL — 01506 842665

Linlithgow: St Ninian's Craigmailen (H)
Iain C. Morrison BA BD — 1990 — 29 Philip Avenue, Linlithgow EH49 7BH — 01506 845535
[e-mail: cmo2@dial.pipcx.com]

Livingston Ecumenical Parish
Incorporating the Worship Centres at:
Carmondean and Craigshill (St Columba's)
Gillean P. Maclean (Mrs) BD | 1994 | 2000 | 53 Garry Walk, Craigshill, Livingston EH54 5AS | 01506 434536

Knightsridge and Ladywell (St Paul's)
Colin R. Douglas MA BD STM | 1969 | 1987 | 27 Heatherbank, Ladywell, Livingston EH54 6EE | 01506 432326

Dedridge (The Lanthorn)
Marion Keston MB ChB MTh
(Scottish Episcopal Church) | | | 12B Carrick Gardens, Murieston, Livingston EH54 9ET | 01506 410668

Livingston: Old (H)
Graham W. Smith BA BD FSAScot | 1995 | | Manse of Livingston, Charlesfield Lane, Livingston EH54 7AJ | 01506 420227

Pardovan, Kingscavil and Winchburgh
A. Scott Marshall DipComm BD | 1984 | 1998 | The Manse, Winchburgh EH52 6TT | 01506 890919

Polbeth Harwood
William McLaren MA BD | 1990 | 1994 | 150 Chapelton Drive, Polbeth EH55 8SG | 01506 871247

Strathbrock
David W. Black BSc BD | 1968 | 1984 | Manse Park, Uphall, Broxburn EH52 6JR | 01506 852550

Torphichen See Avonbridge

Uphall South (H)
Margaret Steele (Miss) BSc BD | 2000 | | 8 Fernlea, Uphall, Broxburn EH52 6DF | 01506 852788

West Kirk of Calder (H)
Mary D. Dilbey (Miss) BD | 1997 | | 27 Learmonth Crescent, West Calder EH55 8AF | 01506 870460

Whitburn: Brucefield (H)
Robin Brough BA | 1968 | 1977 | Whitburn, Bathgate EH47 8NU | 01501 740263

Whitburn: South (H)
Gordon A. McCracken BD | 1988 | | 5 Mansewood Crescent, Whitburn EH47 8HA | 01501 740333

Name			Position	Address	Phone
Cameron, Ian MA BD	1953	1981	(Kilbrandon and Kilchattan)	37 Burghmuir Court, Linlithgow EH49 7LJ	01506 847987
Crichton, Thomas JP ChStJ MA	1965	1989	Hospital Chaplain	18 Carlton Terrace, Edinburgh EH7 5DD	0131 557 0009
Dickson, A. Stuart	1963	1995	(Glasgow: Govan Old – Assoc)	74 Netherwood Park, Deans, Livingston EH54 8RW	01506 420167
Dundas, Thomas B.S. LTh	1969	1996	(West Kirk of Calder)	35 Cookill, Sandyford, Dublin 18	00353 12953061
McDonald, Alexander BA CMIWSC DUNIV	1968	1988	Department of Ministry	95 Glasgow Road, Bathgate EH48 2AN	01506 635129
Manson, Robert L. MA DPS	1956	1991	(Chaplain: Royal Edinburgh Hospital)	4 Murieston Drive, Livingston EH54 9AU	01506 434746
Moore, J.W. MA	1950	1983	(Daviot with Rayne)	31 Lennox Gardens, Linlithgow EH49 7PZ	01506 842534
Morrice, Charles S. MA BD PhD	1959	1997	(Kenya)	104 Baron's Hill Avenue, Linlithgow EH49 7JG	01506 847167
Moyes, Andrew	1959	1992	(Broxburn)	5 Grange Road, Broxburn EH52 5HL	01506 858203
Murray, Ronald N.G. MA	1946	1986	(Pardovan and Kingscavil with Winchburgh)	42 Lennox Gardens, Linlithgow EH49 7QA	01506 845680
Nelson, Georgina (Mrs) MA BD PhD DipEd	1990	1995	Hospital Chaplain	6 Pentland Park, Craigshill, Livingston EH54 5NR	01506 434874
Robertson, Emmanuel ThM ThD	1953	1993	(Armadale)	39 Drumcross Road, Bathgate EH48 4HF	01506 654766
Russell, Archibald MA	1949	1991	(Duror with Glencoe)	4 Bonnytoun Avenue, Linlithgow EH49 7JS	01506 842530
Smith, W. Ewing BSc	1962	1994	(Livingston: Old)	8 Hardy Gardens, Bathgate EH48 1NH	01506 652028
Stirling, A. Douglas BSc	1956	1994	(Rhu and Shandon)	162 Avontoun Park, Linlithgow EH49 6QH	01506 845021
Trimble, Robert DCS			(Deacon)	5 Temple Rise, Dedridge, Livingston EH54 6PJ	01506 412504
Walker, Ian BD MEd DipMS	1943	1984	Parish Education	92 Carse Knowe, Linlithgow EH49 7LG	01506 844412

(3) LOTHIAN

Meets at Musselburgh: St Andrew's High Parish Church on the last Thursday of January and June and the first Thursday of March, April, May, Sepember, October, November and December.

Clerk:	MR JOHN D. McCULLOCH CA DL	Auchindinny House, Penicuik EH26 8PE [e-mail: lothianpresbytery@dial.pipex.com]	01968 676300 (Tel/Fax)

Aberlady (H) linked with Gullane (H)
Vacant | Hummel Road, Gullane EH31 2BG | 01620 843192

Athelstaneford linked with Whitekirk and Tyninghame
Kenneth D.F. Walker MA BD   1976 | Athelstaneford, North Berwick EH39 5BE [e-mail: kandv-walker@connectfree.co.uk] | 01620 880378

Belhaven (H) linked with Spott
Laurence H. Twaddle MA BD MTh   1977 1978 | Belhaven Road, Dunbar EH42 1NH [e-mail: revtwaddle@aol.com] | 01368 863098

Bolton and Saltoun linked with Humbie linked with Yester (H)
Donald Pirie LTh   1975   1999   Tweeddale Avenue, Gifford, Haddington EH41 4QN   01620 810515

Bonnyrigg (H)
John Mitchell LTh CMin   1991   9 Viewbank View, Bonnyrigg EH19 2HU   0131 663 8287 (Tel/Fax)
[e-mail: rev.j.mitchell@lineone.net]

Borthwick (H) linked with Newtongrange (H)
Vacant   7 Maesterton Place, Newtongrange, Dalkeith EH22 4UF   01875 822772

Cockenzie and Port Seton: Chalmers Memorial (H)
Robert L. Glover BMus BD ARCO   1971   1997   Braemar Villa, 2 Links Road, Port Seton, Prestonpans EH32 0HA   01875 812481
[e-mail: elizabeth@glovere.swinternet.co.uk]

Cockenzie and Port Seton: Old (H)
Vacant   1 Links Road, Port Seton, Prestonpans EH32 0HA   01875 812310

Cockpen and Carrington (H) linked with Rosewell (H)
Wendy F. Drake (Mrs) BD   1978   1992   11 Pendreich Terrace, Bonnyrigg EH19 2DT   0131 663 6884

Cranstoun, Crichton and Ford (H) linked with Fala and Soutra (H)
Peter M. Gardner MA BD   1988   1989   Cranstoun Cottage, Ford, Pathhead EH37 5RE   01875 320314
[e-mail: pgardner@cranstouncottage.freeserve.co.uk]

Dalkeith: St John's and King's Park (H)
Alistair K. Ridland MA BD   1982   1988   13 Weir Crescent, Dalkeith EH22 3JN   0131 663 3114 (Tel)
[e-mail: akridland@aol.com]   0131 454 0206 (Fax)

Dalkeith: St Nicholas' Buccleuch (H)
J. Edward Andrews MA BD DipCG   1985   1991   116 Bonnyrigg Road, Dalkeith EH22 3HZ   0131 663 3036
[e-mail: edward.andrews@btinternet.com]

Dirleton (H) linked with North Berwick: Abbey (H) (01620 890110)
David J. Graham BSc BD PhD   1982   1998   20 Westgate, North Berwick EH39 4AF   01620 892410
[e-mail: davidjohn@grahams.fsbusiness.co.uk]

Dunbar (H)
Vacant   Bayswell Road, Dunbar EH42 1AB   01368 863749

Dunglass
Anne R. Lithgow (Mrs) MA BD   1992   1994   The Manse, Cockburnspath, TD13 5XZ   01368 830713
[e-mail: anne.lithgow@btinternet.com]

Fala and Soutra See Cranstoun, Crichton and Ford

Garvald and Morham linked with Haddington: West (H)
Cameron Mackenzie BD   1997   15 West Road, Haddington EH41 3RD   01620 822213

Gladsmuir linked with Longniddry (H)
A. Graham Black MA   1964   1973   The Manse, Elcho Road, Longniddry EH32 0LB   01875 853195
                                             [e-mail: grablack@aol.com]
Florence A. Underwood (Mrs) BD (Assist) 1992   The Sheiling, Main Street, Stenton, Dunbar EH42 1TE   01368 850629

Glencorse (H) linked with Roslin (H)
James A. Manson LTh   1981   38 Penicuik Road, Roslin EH25 9LH   0131 440 2012

Gorebridge (H)
Mark S. Nicholas MA BD   1999   100 Hunterfield Road, Gorebridge EH23 4TT   01875 820387
                                             [e-mail: mark.nicholas@ukgateway.net]

Gullane See Aberlady

Haddington: St Mary's (H)
Clifford E. Hughes MA BD   1993   21 Sidegate, Haddington EH41 4BZ   01620 823109

Haddington: West See Garvald and Morham

Howgate (H) linked with Penicuik: South (H)
Frank Ribbons MA BD DipEd   1985   18 Broomhill Avenue, Penicuik EH26 9EG   01968 674692

Humbie See Bolton and Saltoun
Lasswade See Cockpen and Carrington

Loanhead
Vacant   120 The Loan, Loanhead EH20 9AS   0131 440 0182

Longniddry See Gladsmuir

Musselburgh: Northesk (H)
Alison P. Matheson (Mrs) MA BD   1991   1998   16 New Street, Musselburgh EH21 6JP   0131 665 2128

Musselburgh: St Andrew's High (H) (0131 665 7239)
Violet C.C. McKay (Mrs) BD   1988   1999   8 Ferguson Drive, Musselburgh EH21 6XA   0131 665 5583

Musselburgh: St Clement's and St Ninian's
Moira McDonald (Ms) MA BD   1997   Wallyford Loan Road, Wallyford, Musselburgh EH21 8BU   0131 653 6588
                                             [e-mail: moira.mc@tesco.net]

Musselburgh: St Michael's Inveresk Andrew B. Dick BD DipMin	1986	1999	8 Hope Place, Musselburgh EH21 7QE [e-mail: dixbit@aol.com]	0131 665 0545
Newbattle (H) Jared W. Hay BA MTh DipMin	1987	1989	70 Newbattle Abbey Crescent, Dalkeith EH22 3LW [e-mail: jared.hay@virgin.net]	0131 663 3245 (Tel/Fax) 07050 216433 (Mbl)
Newton Vacant			Newton, Dalkeith EH22 1SR	0131 663 3845
Newtongrange See Borthwick **North Berwick: Abbey** See Dirleton				
North Berwick: St Andrew Blackadder (H) Edward C. McKenna BD DFS	1989		7 Marine Parade, North Berwick EH39 4LD [e-mail: eddiemckenna@compuserve.com]	01620 892132 (Tel/Fax)
Ormiston linked with Pencaitland Mark Malcolm MA BD	1999		Pencaitland, Tranent EH34 5DL [e-mail: markmalcolm.pencaitland@virgin.net]	01875 340208
Pencaitland See Ormiston				
Penicuik: North (H) John W. Fraser MA BD	1974	1982	93 John Street, Penicuik EH26 8AG [e-mail: office@pnk3.freeserve.co.uk]	01968 672213
Penicuik: St Mungo's (H) William D. Irving LTh	1985		31a Kirkhill Road, Penicuik EH26 8JB	01968 672916
Penicuik: South See Howgate				
Prestonpans: Prestongrange Robert R. Simpson BA BD	1994		East Loan, Prestonpans EH32 9ED	01875 810308
Rosewell See Cockpen and Carrington **Roslin** See Glencorse **Spott** See Belhaven				
Tranent Thomas M. Hogg BD	1986		244 Church Street, Tranent EH33 1BW [e-mail:tom@hoggtran.freeserve.co.uk]	01875 610210

Traprain
Howard J. Haslett BA BD   1972   2000   Preston Road, East Linton EH40 3DS   01620 860227 (Tel/Fax)
[e-mail: howard-haslett@beeb.net]

(This Charge formed by the union of Prestonkirk, Stenton and Whittingehame)

Whitekirk and Tyninghame See Athelstaneford
Yester See Bolton and Saltoun

Name			(Charge)	Address	Tel.
Adamson, T. Sidney S. MA BD	1937	1985	(Musselburgh: St Michael's Inveresk)	48 Hailes Gardens, Edinburgh EH13 OJH	0131 441 2471
Brown, Ronald H.	1974	1998	(Musselburgh: Northesk)	6 Monktonhall Farm Cottages, Musselburgh EH21 6RZ	0131 653 2531
Brown, William BD	1972	1997	(Edinburgh: Polwarth)	13 Thornyhall, Dalkeith EH22 2ND	(Tel/Fax) 0131 654 0929
Chalmers, William R. MA BD STM	1953	1992	(Dunbar)	c/o 62 Mayne Road, Elgin IV30 1PD	01343 547620
Day, Colin T. MA	1947	1984	(Warden, Carberry Tower)	20 Hadfast Road, Cousland, Dalkeith EH22 2NU	0131 660 5777
Donaldson, Colin V.	1981	1998	(Ormiston with Pencaitland)	3A Playfair Terrace, St Andrews KY16 9HX	01334 472889
Faulds, Norman L. MA BD FSScot	1968	2000	(Aberlady with Gullane)	8 Juniper Place, Juniper Green, Edinburgh EH14 5TX	0131 453 4984
Fraser, John W. BEM MA BD PhD	1950	1983	(Farnell)	12 Quarryfoot Green, Bonnyrigg EH19 2EJ	0131 663 8037
Gilfillan, James LTh	1967	1997	(East Kilbride: Old)	15 Long Cram, Haddington EH41 4NS	01620 824843
Hill, Arthur T.	1940	1981	(Ormiston with Prestonpans: Grange)	8A Hamilton Road, North Berwick EH39 4NA	01620 893961
Hutchison, Alan E.W.			(Deacon)	132 Lochbridge Road, North Berwick EH39 4DR	01620 894077
Levison, L. David MA BD	1943	1981	(Ormiston with Pencaitland)	Westdene Conservatory Flat 2, 50B Perth Road, Dundee DD2 1LJ	
Macdonell, Alasdair W. MA BD	1955	1992	(Haddington: St Mary's)	St Andrews Cottage, Duns Road, Gifford, Haddington EH41 4QW	01620 810341
MacLeod, Roderick N. MA BD	1986	1992	(Chaplain, Army)	Army Training Regiment, Glencorse Barracks, Penicuik EH26 0NP	0131 310 3300
Macrae, Norman C. MA DipEd	1942	1985	(Loanhead)	6 Lonsdale Terrace, Edinburgh EH3 9HN	0131 228 6283
Maule-Brown, Robert MA	1949	1985	(Strathy and Halladale)	5 Acredales Walk, Haddington EH41 4RR	01620 824959
Ritchie, James McL. MA BD	1950	1985	(Coalsnaughton)	46 St James's Gardens, Penicuik EH26 9DU [e-mail: ritchjm@aol.com]	01968 676123
Robertson, James LTh	1970	2000	(Newton)	11 Southfield Square, Edinburgh EH15 1QS	
Sanderson, W. Roy DD	1933	1973	(Stenton with Whittingehame)	1A York Road, North Berwick EH39 4LS	01620 892780
Sawers, E.A.H. VRD	1950	1989	(Cranstoun Crichton and Ford with Fala and Soutra)		
Swan, Andrew F. BD	1983	2000	(Loanhead)	18 Lydgait Gardens, Haddington EH41 3DB	01620 825830
Thomson, William H	1964	1999	(Edinburgh Liberton Northfield)	3 Mackenzie Gardens, Dolphinton EH46 7HS	
Torrance, David W. MA BD	1955	1991	(Earlston)	3 Baird's Way, The Grange, Bonnyrigg EH19 3NS	0131 654 9799
				38 Forth Street, North Berwick EH39 4JQ [e-mail:dwtmet@connectfree.co.uk]	(Tel/Fax) 01620 895109
Turner, Duncan M. MBE MA	1940	1977	(Innerwick with Spott)	1 Main Street, Spott, Dunbar EH42 1RJ	01368 862668
Underwood, Geoffrey H. BD DipTh FPhS	1964	1992	(Cockenzie and Port Seton: Chalmers Memorial)	The Sheiling, Main Street, Stenton, Dunbar EH42 1TE	01368 850629
Whiteford, David H. CBE MA BD PhD	1943	1985	(Gullane)	3 Old Dean Road, Longniddry EH32 OQY	01875 852980

(4) MELROSE AND PEEBLES

Meets at Innerleithen, on the first Tuesday of February, March, May, October, November, December, and on the fourth Tuesday of June, and in places to be appointed on the first Tuesday of September.

Clerk:	REV. JACK M. BROWN BSc BD		High Road, Galashiels TD1 2BD [e-mail: brownstaidan@dial.pipex.com]	01896 752420 (Tel/Fax)

Ashkirk linked with Selkirk (H)

| James W. Campbell BD | 1995 | 1 Loanside, Selkirk TD7 4DJ | 01750 22833 |
| George McD. McCann BSc ATI (Aux) | 1994 | Rosbeg, Parsonage Road, Galashiels TD1 3HS | 01896 752055 |

Bowden (H) linked with Newtown

| Vacant | | Newtown St Boswells TD6 0PL | 01835 822106 |

Broughton, Glenholm and Kilbucho linked with Skirling linked with Stobo and Drumelzier linked with Tweedsmuir

| Rachel J.W. Dobie (Mrs) LTh | 1991 1996 | Broughton, Biggar ML12 6HQ
[e-mail: racheldobie@compuserve.com] | 01899 830331 |

Caddonfoot (H) linked with Galashiels St Ninian's (H)

| Hilary W. Smith (Miss) BD DipMin MTh PhD | 1999 | Mossilee Road, Galashiels TD1 1NF | 01896 752058 |

Carlops linked with Kirkurd and Newlands (H) linked with West Linton St Andrew's (H)

| Thomas W. Burt BD | 1985 | West Linton, Peeblesshire EH46 7EN | 01968 660221 |

Channelkirk linked with Lauder Old

| John M. Shields MBE LTh | 1972 | Lauder, Berwickshire TD2 6QD | 01578 722320 |

Earlston

| Michael D. Scouler MBE BSc BD | 1988 | Earlston, Berwickshire TD4 6DE | 01896 849236 |

Eddleston (H) linked with Peebles Old (H)

| James B. MacLean MTheol DipPTheol | 1986 | Innerleithen Road, Peebles EH45 8BD | 01721 720568 |

Ettrick linked with Yarrow

| Bruce B. Lawrie BD | 1974 | Yarrow, Selkirk TD7 5LA | 01750 82219 |

Galashiels: Old and St Paul's (H)

| Leslie M. Steele MA BD | 1973 | Barr Road, Galashiels TD1 3HX
[e-mail: lms@gala.prestel.co.uk] | 01896 752320 |

Galashiels: St Aidan's (H)
Jack M. Brown BSc BD — 1977 1981 — High Road, Galashiels TD1 2BD — 01896 752420 (Tel/Fax)

Galashiels: St John's (H)
Stephen F. Clipston MA BD — 1982 — Hawthorn Road, Galashiels TD1 2JZ. — 01896 752573 (Tel) / 01896 758561 (Fax)

Galashiels: St Ninian's See Caddonfoot

Innerleithen (H) linked with Traquair linked with Walkerburn
Vacant — Innerleithen, Peeblesshire EH44 6HL — 01896 830309

Kirkurd and Newlands See Carlops
Lauder: Old See Channelkirk

Lyne and Manor
Nancy M. Norman (Miss) BA MDiv MTh — 1988 1998 — 25 March Street, Peebles EH45 8EP — 01721 721699

Maxton and Mertoun linked with St Boswells
Bruce F. Neill MA BD — 1966 1996 — St Boswells, Roxburghshire TD6 0BB — 01835 822255

Melrose (H)
Alistair G. Bennett BSc BD — 1978 1984 — Melrose, Roxburghshire TD6 9ST — 01896 822217

Newtown See Bowden
Peebles: Old See Eddleston

Peebles: St Andrew's Leckie (H)
James H. Wallace MA BD — 1973 1983 — Mansefield, Innerleithen Road, Peebles EH45 8BE — 01721 721749 (Tel/Fax)

St Boswells See Maxton and Mertoun
Selkirk See Ashkirk
Skirling See Broughton, Glenholm and Kilbucho
Stobo and Drumelzier See Broughton, Glenholm and Kilbucho

Stow: St Mary of Wedale and Heriot
Stanley Kennon BA BD — 1992 — Stow, Galashiels TD1 2RE — 01578 730237

Traquair See Innerleithen
Tweedsmuir See Broughton, Glenholm and Kilbucho
Walkerburn See Innerleithen
West Linton St Andrew's See Carlops
Yarrow See Ettrick

Name			Description	Address	Tel
Brown, Robert BSc	1962	1997	(Kilbrandon and Kilchattan)	11 Thornfield Terrace, Selkirk TD7 4DU	01750 20311
Cashman, P. Hamilton BSc	1985	1998	(Dirleton with North Berwick: Abbey)	38 Abbotsford Road, Galashiels TD1 3HR	01896 752711
Dick, J. Ronald BD	1973	1996	Hospital Chaplain	5 Georgefield Farm Cottages, Earlston TD4 6BH	01896 848956
Donald, Thomas W. LTh CA	1977	1987	(Bowden with Lilliesleaf)	The Quest, Huntly Road, Melrose TD6 9SB	01896 822345
Duncan, Charles A. MA	1956	1992	(Heriot with Stow St Mary of Wedale)	10 Elm Grove, Galashiels TD1 3JA	01896 753261
Kellet, John M. MA	1962	1995	(Leith: South)	4 High Cottages, Walkerburn, Peebles-shire EH43 6QW	01896 870351
Laing, William F. DSC VRD MA	1952	1986	(Selkirk: St Mary's West)	10 The Glebe, Selkirk TD7 5AB	01750 21210
MacFarlane, David C. MA	1957	1997	(Eddleston with Peebles Old)	61 Viewlands Road, Perth PH1 1ND	01738 624996
Moore, W. Haisley MA	1966	1996	(Secretary: The Boys' Brigade)	26 Tweedbank Avenue, Galashiels TD1 3SP	01896 668577
Morton, Alasdair J. MA BD DipEd FEIS	1960	2000	(Bowden with Newtown)	8 Ormiston Grove, Melrose TD6 9SR	01896 822033
Morton, Gillian M. (Mrs) MA BD PGCE	1983	1996	(Hospital Chaplain)	8 Ormiston Grove, Melrose TD6 9SR	01896 822033
Rae, Andrew W.	1951	1987	(Annan: St Andrew's Greenknowe Erskine)	Roseneuk, Tweedside Road, Newtown St Boswells TD6 OPQ	01835 823783
Slack, J.W.	1968	1985	(Ashkirk with Selkirk Lawson Memorial)	17 Grenville Avenue, St Anne's-on-Sea, Fylde FY8 2RR	01253 728863
Taverner, Glyn R. MA BD	1957	1995	(Maxton and Mertoun with St Boswells)	Woodcot Cottage, Waverley Road, Innerleithen EH44 6QW	01896 830156
Thomson, G.F.M. MA	1956	1988	(Dollar Associate)	49 High Cross Avenue, Melrose TD6 9SX	01896 823112

(5) DUNS

Meets at Duns, in the Old Parish Church Hall, normally on the first Tuesday of February, March, April, May, October, November, December, on the last Tuesday in June, and in places to be appointed on the first Tuesday of September.

Clerk: REV. JAMES S.H. CUTLER, BD CEng MIStructE   The Manse, Duns Road, Coldstream TD12 4DP   01890 882537

Ayton (H) and Burnmouth linked with Grantshouse and Houndwood and Reston
David J. Hebenton MA BD   1958   1983   Grey Gables, Beanburn, Ayton, Eyemouth TD14 5QY   018907 81333

Berwick-upon-Tweed: St Andrew's Wallace Green (H) and Lowick
Alison A. Meikle (Mrs) BD   1999   3 Meadow Grange, Berwick-upon-Tweed TD15 1NW   01289 303304

Bonkyl and Preston linked with Chirnside (H) linked with Edrom Allanton (H)
William Paterson BD   1977   1993   Chirnside, Duns TD11 3XL   01890 818269

Chirnside See Bonkyl and Preston

Coldingham and St. Abb's linked with Eyemouth
Daniel G. Lindsay BD   1978   1979   Victoria Road, Eyemouth TD14 5JD   018907 50327

Coldstream (H) linked with Eccles   1986   1995   Duns Road, Coldstream TD12 4DP   01890 882537
James S.H. Cutler BD CEng MIStructE

Duns (H)   1999   The Manse, Duns, Berwickshire TD11 3DP   01361 883755
Andrew Morrice MA BD

Eccles See Coldstream
Edrom Allanton See Bonkyl and Preston
Eyemouth See Coldingham and St. Abb's

Fogo and Swinton linked with Ladykirk linked with Leitholm linked with Whitsome (H)
Alan C.D. Cartwright BSc BD   1976   Swinton, Duns TD11 3JJ   01890 860228

Foulden and Mordington linked with Hutton and Fishwick and Paxton
Geraldine H. Hope (Mrs) MA BD   1986   Hutton, Berwick upon Tweed TD15 1TS   01289 386396

Gordon: St Michael's linked with Greenlaw (H) linked with Legerwood linked with Westruther
Thomas S. Nicholson BD DPS   1982   1995   The Manse, Todholes, Greenlaw, Berwickshire TD10 6XD   01361 810316

Grantshouse and Houndwood and Reston See Ayton and Burnmouth
Greenlaw See Gordon St Michael's
Hutton and Fishwick and Paxton See Foulden and Mordington

Kirk of Lammermuir linked with Langton and Polwarth
Alexander Slorach CA BD   1970   1983   Cranshaws, Duns TD11 3SJ   01361 890289

Ladykirk See Fogo and Swinton
Langton and Polwarth See Kirk of Lammermuir
Legerwood See Gordon St Michael's
Leitholm See Fogo and Swinton
Lowick See Berwick-on-Tweed St Andrew's Wallace Green
Westruther See Gordon St Michael's
Whitsome See Fogo and Swinton

Name			Notes	Address	Phone
Dunnett, W. Gavin MBE	1968	1985	(Foulden and Mordington with Hutton and Fishwick and Paxton)	Old Smithy Cottage, Hutton, Berwick-on-Tweed TD15 1TS	01289 86225
Gaddes, Donald R.	1961	1994	(Kelso North and Ednam)	35 Winterfield Gardens, Duns TD11 3EZ	01361 883172
Gale, Ronald A.A. LTh	1982	1995	(Dunoon Old and St Cuthbert's)	55 Lennel Mount, Coldstream TD12 4NS	01890 883699
Hay, Bruce J.L.	1957	1997	(Makerstoun and Smailholm with Stichill, Hume and Nenthorn)	Tweed House, Tweed Street, Berwick-upon-Tweed TD15 1NG	01289 303171
Jackson, John MA	1958	1990	(Bonnybridge)	2 Milne Graden West, Coldstream TD12 4HE	01890 883435
Kerr, Andrew MA BLitt	1948	1991	(Kilbarchan West)	Meikle Harelaw, Westruther, Berwickshire TD10 6XT	01578 740263
Macleod, Allan M. MA	1945	1985	(Gordon St Michael's with Legerwood with Westruther)	Silverlea, Machrihanish, Argyll PA28 6PZ	
Prentice, Donald K. BSc BD	1989	1992	Chaplain: Army	RDMC, Fort Blockhouse, Gosport PO12 2AB	01705 765272

(6) JEDBURGH

Meets at Jedburgh on the first Wednesday of February, March, May, October, November and December and on the last Wednesday of June. Meets in the Moderator's church on the first Wednesday of September.

Clerk   REV. ALAN D. REID MA BD   23 Langholm Street, Newcastleton TD9 0QX   013873 75242
[e-mail: ad@reid63.freeserve.co.uk]

Ancrum linked with Crailing and Eckford with Lilliesleaf (T)
W. Frank Campbell BA BD   1989 1991   22 The Glebe, Ancrum, Jedburgh TD8 6UX   01835 830318

Bedrule linked with Denholm (H) linked with Minto
William Longmuir LTh   1984 1992   Denholm, Hawick TD9 8NB   01450 870268

Cavers and Kirkton linked with Hawick St Mary's and Old
William R. Taylor MA BD   1983 1998   Braid Road, Hawick TD9 9LZ   01450 377865

Crailing and Eckford See Ancrum

Denholm See Bedrule

Hawick: Burnfoot
Charles J. Finnie LTh DPS   1991 1997   29 Wilton Hill, Hawick TD9 8BA   01450 373181
[e-mail: charles@finnierev.freeserve.co.uk]
Ronald M. Mackinnon DCS   70 Eildon Road, Hawick TD9 8ES   01450 374816 (Tel)   07808 117538 (Mbl)

Hawick: Teviot (H) and Roberton
Neil R. Combe BSc MSc BD   1984   Buccleuch Road, Hawick TD9 0EL   01450 372150
[e-mail: neil.combe@btinternet.com]

Hawick: St Mary's and Old H) See Cavers and Kirkton

Hawick: Trinity (H)
E.P. Lindsay Thomson MA   1964 1972   Fenwick Park, Hawick TD9 9PA   01450 372705

Hawick: Wilton linked with Teviothead
John Shedden BD   1971 1998   4 Wilton Hill Terrace, Hawick TD9 8BE   01450 370744

Hobkirk and Southdean
Continued Vacancy

Jedburgh: Old and Edgerston
Bruce McNicol JP BL BD   1967   1992   Honeyfield Drive, Jedburgh TD8 6LQ   01835 863417

Jedburgh: Trinity
John A. Riddell MA BD   1967   42 High Street, Jedburgh TD8 6DQ   01835 863223

Kelso: North (H) and Ednam (H) (01573 224154)
Tom McDonald BD   1994   20 Forestfield, Kelso TD5 7BX   01573 224677
[e-mail: revtom@20thepearlygates.fsnet.co.uk]

Kelso: Old (H) and Sprouston
Marion E. Dodd (Miss) MA BD LRAM   1988   1989   Glebe Lane, Kelso, Roxburghshire TD5 7AU   01573 226254
[e-mail: mariondodd@scottishborders.co.uk]

Liddesdale (H)
Alan D. Reid MA BD   1989   23 Langholm Street, Newcastleton TD9 0QX   013873 75242
[e-mail: ad@reid63.freeserve.co.uk]

Lilliesleaf See Ancrum

Linton linked with Morebattle and Hownam linked with Yetholm (H)
Robin D. McHaffie BD   1979   1991   Kirk Yetholm, Kelso TD5 8RD   01573 420308

Makerstoun and Smailholm linked with Stichill, Hume and Nenthorn
Vacant

Minto See Bedrule
Morebattle and Hownam See Linton

Oxnam
Continued Vacancy

Roxburgh
Vacant

Teviothead See Hawick: Wilton
Yetholm See Linton

Bowie, Adam McC.	1976	1996	(Cavers and Kirkton with Hobkirk and Southdean)	Glenbield, Redpath, nr Earlston TD4 6AD 01896 848173
Brown, Joseph MA	1954	1991	(Linton with Hownam and Morebattle with Yetholm)	The Orchard, Hermitage Lane, Kelso TD5 7AN 01573 223481
Fox, G. Dudley A.	1972	1988	(Kelso Old)	14 Pinnacle Hill Farm, Kelso TD5 8HD 01573 223335
Hamilton, Robert MA BD	1938	1979	(Kelso Old)	Ridge Cottage, 391 Totnes Road, Collaton St. Mary, Paignton TQ4 7PW 01803 526440

Leadbeater, Dennis TD	1946	1999	(The Glens)	Flat 30, Douglas Haig Court, Linden Crescent, Hawick TD9 9PW	01450 370816
McConnell, Robert	1959	1983	(Hawick St Margaret's and Wilton South with Roberton)		
Ritchie, Garden W.M.	1961	1995	(Ardersier with Petty)	Flat 9, Queensfort Court, Carryduff, Belfast BT8 8NF	01573 224419
Thompson, W.M.D. MA	1950	1997	(Crailing and Eckford with Oxnam with Roxburgh)	23 Croft Road, Kelso TD5 7EP	01835 862492
				The Old Manse, Oxnam, Jedburgh TD8 6RD	
Watson, Valerie G. C. (Miss) MA BD STM	1987	1999	University of Glasgow	1 Duke Street, Hawick TD9 9PY	01450 377122

HAWICK ADDRESSES

Burnfoot	Fraser Avenue		
	St Mary's and Old	Kirk Wynd	Princes Street
	Teviot	off Buccleuch Road	
	Trinity	Central Square	
	Wilton		

(7) ANNANDALE AND ESKDALE

Meets on the first Tuesday of February, May, September and December and the third Tuesday of March, June and October in a venue to be determined by Presbytery.

| Clerk: | REV. C. BRYAN HASTON LTh | | | The Manse, Gretna Green DG16 5DU [e-mail: cbhaston@cofs.demon.co.uk] | 01461 338313 (Tel) |
| | | | | | 0870 1640 119 (Fax) |

Annan: Old (H)

| Duncan J. Macpherson BSc BD | 1993 | 1997 | 12 Plumdon Park Avenue, Annan DG12 6EY [e-mail: duncan.macpherson@ukonline.co.uk] | 01461 201405 (Tel) |
| | | | | 01461 201408 (Fax) |

Annan: St Andrew's Greenknowe Erskine (H)

| George K. Lind BD MCIBS | 1998 | 1 Annerley Road, Annan DG12 6HE [e-mail: gklind@bosinternet.com] | 01461 202626 |

Applegarth and Sibbaldbie (H) linked with Lochmaben (H)

| John J.C. Owen LTh | 1967 | 1980 | Lochmaben, Lockerbie DG11 1QF [e-mail: jjowen@appleonline.net] | 01387 810590 (Tel/Fax) |

Brydekirk linked with Hoddam

| S. Edwin P. Beveridge BA | 1959 | 1993 | Ecclefechan, Lockerbie DG11 3BU | 01576 300357 |

Canonbie (H) Linda J. Williams (Mrs) BD	1993	1999	Kirtlebridge, Lockerbie DG11 3LY	01461 500882
Carlisle: Chapel Street linked with Longtown: St Andrew's William D. Brown BD CQSW		1987	197 Brampton Road, Carlisle CA3 9AX	01228 401655
Dalton linked with Hightae linked with St Mungo Vacant			Hightae, Lockerbie DG11 1JL	01387 811499
Dornock Ronald S. Seaman MA	1967		Dornock, Annan DG12 6NR	01461 40268
Eskdalemuir linked with Hutton and Corrie linked with Tundergarth Vacant			Hutton Manse, Boreland, Lockerbie DG11 2PB	01576 610213
Gretna: Old (H), Gretna: St Andrew's and Half Morton and Kirkpatrick Fleming C. Bryan Haston LTh		1975	Gretna Green DG16 5DU [e-mail: cbhaston@cofs.demon.co.uk]	01461 338313 (Tel) 08701 640119 (Fax)
Hightae See Dalton				
Hoddam See Brydekirk				
Hutton and Corrie See Eskdalemuir				
Johnstone linked with Kirkpatrick Juxta (H) John M. Stewart MA BD	1964	1986	Beattock, Moffat DG10 9RF	01683 300349
Kirkpatrick Juxta See Johnstone				
Kirtle-Eaglesfield linked with Middlebie linked with Waterbeck Trevor C. Williams LTh	1990	1999	Kirtlebridge, Lockerbie DG11 3LY	01461 500378
Langholm, Ewes and Westerkirk Robert B. Milne	1999	1999	Langholm DG13 0BL [e-mail: rbmilne@aol.com]	01387 380252
Lochmaben See Applegarth and Sibbaldbie				
Lockerbie: Dryfesdale David M. Almond BD		1996	The Manse, 5 Carlisle Road, Lockerbie DG11 2DW	01576 202361
Longtown St Andrew's See Carlisle Chapel Street				
Middlebie See Kirtle-Eaglesfield				

Moffat St Andrew's (H) linked with Wamphray

| Vacant | | | Moffat DG10 9EJ | 01683 220128 (Tel) |
| | | | | 01683 220758 (Fax) |

St Mungo See Dalton
Tundergarth See Eskdalemuir
Wamphray See Moffat St Andrew's
Waterbeck See Kirtle-Eaglesfield

Annand, James M. MA BD	1955	1995	(Lockerbie Dryfesdale)	48 Main Street, Newstead, Melrose TD6 9DX	
Baillie, David R.	1979	1990	(Crawford with Lowther)	1 Preston Court, Annan DG12 5HS	01461 201486
				[e-mail: annan@baillie.abcl.co.uk]	
Byers, Alan J	1959	1992	(Gamrie with King Edward)	Meadowbank, Plumdon Road, Annan DG12 6SJ	01461 206512
Byers, Mairi (Mrs) BTh CPS	1992	1998	(Jura)	Meadowbank, Plumdon Road, Annan DG12 6SJ	01461 206512
Fisher, D. Noel MA BD	1939	1979	(Glasgow Sherbrooke St Gilbert's)	Sheraig Cottage, Killochries Fold, Kilmacolm PA13 4TE	
Kirk, W. Logan MA BD MTh	1988	2000	(Dalton with Hightae with St. Mungo)	2 Firpark Cottages, Lockerbie DG11 1BL	01576 204653
McLean, Margaret G. BD	1978	1991	(Community Minister: Annandale and Eskdale)		
MacMillan, William M. LTh	1980	1998	(Kilmory with Lamlash)	84 Union Road, Gretna DG16 5JT	01461 338491
Rennie, John D. MA	1962	1996	(Broughton, Glenholm and Kilbucho with Skirling with Stobo and Drumelzier with Tweedsmuir)	Balskia, 61 Queen Street, Lochmaben DG11 1PP	01387 811528
				Dundoran, Ballplay Road, Moffat DG10 9JX	01683 220223
				[e-mail: rennies@dundoran96.freeserve.co.uk]	
Ross, Alan C. CA BD	1988	1997	(Annan: St Andrew's Greenknowe) Erskine	Yarra, Ettrickbridge, Selkirk TD7 5JN	01750 52324
				[e-mail: alkaross@aol.com]	
Swinburne, Norman BA	1960	1993	(Sauchie)	Damerosehay, Birch Hill Lane, Kirkbride, Carlisle CA5 5HZ	01697 351497

(8) DUMFRIES AND KIRKCUDBRIGHT

Meets at Dumfries, on the first Wednesday of February, March, April, May, September, October, November, December, and the last Wednesday of June.

| Clerk: | REV. GORDON M.A. SAVAGE MA BD | 11 Laurieknowe, Dumfries DG2 7AH | 01387 252929 |

Anwoth and Girthon linked with Borgue

| Austin U. Erskine | 1986 | 1990 | Gatehouse of Fleet, Castle Douglas DG7 2EQ | 01557 814233 |

Auchencairn and Rerrick linked with Buittle and Kelton

| James H. Sinclair MA BD | 1966 | 1992 | Auchencairn, Castle Douglas DG7 1QS | 01556 640288 |

Balmaclellan and Kells (H) linked with Carsphairn linked with Dalry (H)
David S. Bartholomew BSc MSc PhD BD   1994
Dalry, Castle Douglas DG7 3PJ
01644 430380

Balmaghie linked with Tarff and Twynholm (H)
Christopher Wallace BD   1988
Twynholm, Kirkcudbright DG6 4NY
01557 860381

Borgue See Anwoth and Girthon
Buittle and Kelton See Auchencairn and Rerrick

Caerlaverock
Continued Vacancy

Carsphairn See Balmaclellan and Kells

Castle Douglas (H)
Vacant
1 Castle View, Castle Douglas DG7 1BG
01556 502171

Closeburn linked with Durisdeer
James W. Scott MA CDA   1952   1953
Durisdeer, Thornhill, Dumfriesshire DG3 5BJ
01848 500231

Colvend, Southwick and Kirkbean
Barry Knight BD   1991   1996
Colvend, Dalbeattie DG5 4QN
[e-mail: barryknight@hotmail.com]
01556 630255

Corsock and Kirkpatrick Durham linked with Crossmichael and Parton
James A. Guthrie   1969   1999
Knockdrocket, Clarebrand, Castle Douglas DG7 3AH
01556 503645

Crossmichael and Parton See Corsock and Kirkpatrick Durham

Cummertrees linked with Mouswald linked with Ruthwell (H)
James Williamson BA BD   1986   1991
Ruthwell, Dumfries DG1 4NP
01387 870217

Dalbeattie (H) linked with Urr (H)
Norman M. Hutcheson MA BD   1973   1988
36 Mill Street, Dalbeattie DG5 4HE
01556 610029

Dalry See Balmaclellan

Dumfries: Greyfriars (T) (H)
W.C. Campbell-Jack BD MTh PhD   1979   1999
4 Georgetown Crescent, Dumfries DG1 4EQ
01387 257045

Dumfries: Lincluden linked with Holywood (T)
John Spencer MA BD   1962   1995
96 Glasgow Road, Dumfries DG2 9DE
01387 264298

Dumfries: Lochside
Thomas M. Bryson BD   1997
27 St Anne's Road, Dumfries DG2 9HZ
01387 252912

Dumfries: Maxwelltown West (H) Gordon M.A. Savage MA BD	1977	1984	11 Laurieknowe, Dumfries DG2 7AH	01387 252929
Dumfries: St George's (H) Donald Campbell BD	1997		9 Nunholm Park, Dumfries DG1 1JP	01387 252965
Dumfries: St Mary's (H) Graham D.S. Deans MA BD MTh	1978	1987	47 Moffat Road, Dumfries DG1 1NN	01387 254873
Dumfries: St Michael's and South Maurice S. Bond MTh BA DipEd PhD	1981	1999	39 Cardoness Street, Dumfries DG1 3AL	01387 253849
Dumfries: Troqueer (H) William W. Kelly BSc BD	1994		Troqueer Road, Dumfries DG2 7DF [e-mail: 100410.3003@compuserve.com]	01387 253043
Dunscore linked with Glencairn and Moniaive Christine Sime BSc BD	1994		Wallaceton, Auldgirth, Dumfries DG2 0TJ	01387 820245
Durisdeer See Closeburn **Glencairn and Moniaive** See Dunscore **Holywood** See Dumfries: Lincluden				
Kirkconnel (H) David Deas Melville BD	1989	1999	Kingsway, Kirkconnel, Sanquhar DG4 6PN	01659 67241
Kirkcudbright (H) Douglas R. Irving LLB BD WS	1984	1998	6 Bourtree Avenue, Kirkcudbright DG6 4AU	01557 330489
Kirkgunzeon Continued Vacancy				
Kirkmahoe Dennis S. Rose LTh	1996		Kirkmahoe, Dumfries DG1 1ST	01387 710572
Kirkmichael linked with Tinwald linked with Torthorwald Vacant			Tinwald, Dumfries DG1 3PL	01387 710246
Elizabeth A. Mack (Miss) DipPEd (Aux)	1994	1999	24 Roberts Crescent, Dumfries DG2 7RS	01387 264847
Kirkpatrick Irongray linked with Lochrutton linked with Terregles David K.P. Bennett BA	1974	1987	Irongray Manse, Dumfries DG2 9TR	01387 720227
Lochend linked with New Abbey William Holland MA	1967	1971	New Abbey, Dumfries DG2 8BY	01387 850232

Lochrutton See Kirkpatrick Irongray
Mouswald See Cummertrees
New Abbey See Lochend

Penpont, Keir and Tynron (T)
Robert Gehrke BSc BD CEng MIEE   1994   Penpont, Thornhill DG3 4BH   01848 330430

Rerrick See Auchencairn
Ruthwell (H) See Cummertrees

Sanquhar: St Bride's (H)
William T. Hogg MA BD   1979   2000   Glasgow Road, Sanquhar DG4 6BS   01659 50247

Tarff and Twynholm See Balmaghie
Terregles See Kirkpatrick Irongray

Thornhill (T)(H)
John E. Gisbey MA BD MSc   1964   1997   Thornhill, Dumfriesshire DG3 5ER   01848 331191

Tinwald See Kirkmichael
Torthorwald See Kirkmichael
Urr See Dalbeattie

Name			(Charge)	Address	Tel
Calderwood, Walter M. MA BD	1934	1974	(Leven Forman)	Flat 10, Duar Lodge, 6 St. Mary Street, Kirkcudbright DG6 4AQ	01557 330330
Craig, N. Douglas MA BD	1947	1987	(Dalbeattie Craignair with Urr)	33 Albert Road, Dumfries DG2 9DN	01387 252187
Elder, Albert B. MA	1960	1998	(Dumfries: St Michael's & South)	87 Glasgow Street, Dumfries DG2 9AG	01387 249811
Geddes, Alexander J. MA BD	1960	1998	(Stewarton: St Columba's)	166 Georgetown Road, Dumfries DG1 4DT	01387 252287
Gillespie, Ann M. (Miss) DCS			(Deaconess)	Barlochan House, Palnackie, Castle Douglas DG7 1PF	01556 600378
Grant, G.V.R. MA	1948	1982	(Urray and Kilchrist)	Lynedoch, Schair Drive, Bearsden, Glasgow G61 3BS	01848 330829
Grant, James BA	1961	1987	(Penpont Keir and Tynron)	147A Drumlanrig Street, Thornhill DG3 5LJ	
Greer, A. David C. LLB DMin DipAdultEd	1956	1996	(Barra)	10 Watling Street, Dumfries DG1 1HF	01387 256113
Hamill, Robert BA	1956	1989	(Castle Douglas St Ringan's)	11 St Andrew Drive, Castle Douglas DG7 1EW	01556 502962
Hutchison, Mary L. (Mrs) BD	1982	1995	(Dumfries Lincluden with Holywood)	Monzie, 25 Twiname Way, Heathhall, Dumfries DG1 3ST	01387 250610
Johnston, John MA BD	1963	1999	(Hospital Chaplain)	Near Bye, Amisfield, Dumfries DG1 3LN	01387 710254
Leishman, James S LTh BD MA(Div)			(Kirkmichael with Tinwald with Torthorwald)	11 Hunter Avenue, Heathhall, Dumfries DG1 3UX	01387 249241
Mackay, Donald MBE FCP FSAScot	1951	1986	(Ardrossan: St John's)	8 Urquhart Crescent, Dumfries DG1 8XF	01387 259132
McKenzie, William M. DA	1958	1993	(Dumfries: Troqueer)	41 Kingholm Road, Dumfries DG1 4SR	01387 253688
Miller, John R. MA BD	1958	1992	(Carsphairn with Dalry)	4 Fairgreen Court, Rhonehouse, Castle Douglas DG7 1SA	01556 680428
Robertson, Ian W. MA BD	1956	1995	(Colvend, Southwick and Kirkbean)	10 Marjoriebanks, Lochmaben, Lockerbie DG11 1QH	01387 810541
Robertson, Thomas R. MA BD	1934	1976	(Broughton, Glenholm and Kilbucho with Skirling)	1 Church Row, Kirkcudbright DG6 4AP	01557 330795
Smith, Richmond OBE MA BD	1952	1983	(World Alliance of Reformed Churches)	Aignish, Merse Way, Kippford, Dalbeattie DG5 4LH	01556 620624

Strachan, Alexander E MA BD	1974 1999	Dumfries Health Care Chaplain (Stonehouse)	2 Leafield Road, Dumfries DG1 2DS	01387 279460
Vincent, C. Raymond MA FSAScot	1952 1992		Rosebank, Newton Stewart Road, New Galloway, Castle Douglas DG7 3RT	01644 420451
Wortherspoon, Robert C. LTh	1976 1998	(Corsock and Kirkpatrick Durham with Crossmichael and Parton)	7 Hillowton Drive, Castle Douglas, DG7 1LL	01556 502267
Wilkie, James R. MA MTh	1957 1993	(Penpont, Keir and Tynron)	31 West Morton Street, Thornhill, Dumfriesshire DG3 5NF	01848 331028
Young, John MTh DipMin	1963 1999	(Airdrie: Broomknoll)	Craigview, North Street, Moniaive, Thornhill DG3 4HR	01848 200318

DUMFRIES ADDRESSES

Greyfriars	Church Crescent	Maxwelltown West	Laurieknowe	St Michael's and South	St Michael's Street
Lincluden	Stewartry Road	St George's	George Street	Troqueer	Troqueer Road
Lochside	Lochside Road	St Mary's	St Mary's Street		

(9) WIGTOWN AND STRANRAER

Meets at Glenluce, in Old Luce Parish Church on the first Tuesday of each month except, January, April, July and August, when there is no meeting; June, when it meets on the fourth Tuesday and October, when it meets in the Moderator's Church.

Clerk: REV. D.W. DUTTON BA   High Kirk Manse, Leswalt High Road, Stranraer DG9 0AA   01776 703268

Bargrennan (H) linked with Newton Stewart: Penninghame St John's (H)
Neil G. Campbell BA BD | 1988 1989 | Newton Stewart DG8 6HH | 01671 402259

Ervie Kirkcolm linked with Leswalt
Michael J. Sheppard BD | 1997 | Ervie Manse, Stranraer DG9 0QZ | 01776 854225
[e-mail: michael@erviecos.freeserve.co.uk]

Glasserton and Isle of Whithorn linked with Whithorn: St Ninian's Priory
Alexander I. Currie BD CPS | 1990 | Whithorn, Newton Stewart DG8 8PY | 01988 500267

Inch linked with Stranraer: St Andrew's (H)
John H. Burns BSc BD | 1985 1988 | Bay View Road, Stranraer DG9 8BE | 01776 702383

Kirkcowan (H) linked with Wigtown (H)
Martin Thomson BSc DipEd BD | 1988 | Harbour Road, Wigtown, Newton Stewart DG8 9AL | 01988 402242
[e-mail: martin@thomsonm40.freeserve.co.uk]

Kirkinner linked with Sorbie (H)
Jeffrey M. Mead BD — 1978 1986 — Kirkinner, Newton Stewart DG8 9AL — 01988 840643

Kirkmabreck linked with Monigaff (H)
Hugh D. Steele LTh DipMin — 1994 — Cree Bridge, Newton Stewart DG8 6NR — 01671 403361

Kirkmaiden (H) linked with Stoneykirk
Ian McIlroy BSS BD — 1996 — Church Street, Sandhead, Stranraer DG9 9JJ — 01776 830337
Mary Munro (Mrs) BA (Aux) — 1993 — High Barbeth, Leswalt DG9 0QS — 01776 870250

Leswalt See Ervie Kirkcolm

Mochrum (H)
Roger A.F. Dean LTh — 1983 1995 — Port William, Newton Stewart DG8 9QP — 01988 700257

Monigaff (H) See Kirkmabreck

New Luce (H) linked with Old Luce (H)
Thomas M. McWhirter MA MSc BD — 1992 1997 — Glenluce, Newton Stewart DG8 0PU — 01581 300319

Newton Stewart: Penninghame St John's See Bargrennan
Old Luce See New Luce

Portpatrick linked with Stranraer: St Ninian's (H)
Gordon Kennedy BSc BD — 1993 2000 — London Road, Stranraer DG9 9AB — 01776 702443

Sorbie See Kirkinner
Stoneykirk See Kirkmaiden

Stranraer: High Kirk (H)
David W. Dutton BA — 1973 1986 — Leswalt High Road, Stranraer DG9 0AA — 01776 703268

Stranraer: Old (H)
Samuel McC. Harris BA BD — 1974 1990 — Linden, Leswalt High Road, Stranraer DG9 0AA — 01776 706387

Stranraer St Andrew's See Inch
Stranraer St Ninian's See Portpatrick
Whithorn: St Ninian's Priory See Glasserton and Isle of Whithorn
Wigtown See Kirkcowan

Cairns, Alexander B. MA	1957 1997	(Ervie Kirkcolm with Leswalt)	Beechwood, Main Street, Sandhead, Stranraer DG9 9JG	01776 830389
Cordiner, John	1950 1986	(Portpatrick)	Tara, Fellview Road, Stranraer DG9 8BK	01776 704720
Harkes, George	1962 1988	(Cumbernauld Old)	11 Main Street, Sorbie, Newton Stewart DG8 8EG	01988 850255
Jesson, W.J.M.	1971 1984	(Mochrum)	4 Mote Brae, Mochrum, Newton Stewart DG8 9LZ	01988 700257

McCreadie, David W.	1961 1995	(Kirkmabreck)	77 St John Street, Creetown, Newton Stewart DG8 7JB	01671 820390
McGill, Thomas W.	1972 1990	(Portpatrick with Stranraer St Ninian's)	Ravenstone Moor, Dramrae. Whithorn. Newton Stewart DG8 8DS	01988 0X449
Ogilvy, Oliver M.	1959 1985	(Leswalt)	8 Dale Crescent, Stranraer DG9 OHG	01776 706285

(10) AYR

Meets in Ayr, in Alloway Church Hall, on the first Tuesday of every month from September to May, excluding January; and on the fourth Tuesday of June.

Clerk: REV. JAMES CRICHTON MA BD MTh   30 Garden Street, Dalrymple KA6 6DG   01292 560263 (Tel)

Alloway (H)
Neil A. McNaught BD MA   1987   1999   1A Parkview, Alloway, Ayr KA7 4QG   01292 441252

Annbank (H)
Kenneth L. Johnston BA LTh   1969   1989   57 Annbank Road, Annbank, Ayr KA6 5AG   01292 520257
[e-mail: Klindjay@hotmail.com.]

Arnsheen Barrhill linked with Colmonell
John S. Lochrie BSc BD MTh PhD   1967   1999   Colmonell, Girvan KA26 0SA   01465 881224

Auchinleck (H)
Vacant   28 Mauchline Road, Auchinleck KA18 2BN   01290 421108

Ayr: Auld Kirk of Ayr (St John the Baptist) (H)
David R. Gemmell MA BD   1991   1999   58 Monument Road, Ayr KA7 2UB   01292 262580 (Tel/Fax)
[e-mail: drgemmell@aol.com.]

Ayr: Castlehill (H)
Ian R. Stirling BSc BD   1990   1994   3 Old Hillfoot Road, Ayr KA7 3LF   01292 267332
[e-mail: Astirling@aol.com.]

Ayr: Newton on Ayr (H)
G. Stewart Birse CA BD BSc   1980   1989   5 Montgomerie Terrace, Ayr KA7 1JL   01292 264251

Ayr: St Andrew's (H)
Harry B. Mealyea BArch BD   1984   2000   31 Bellevue Crescent, Ayr KA7 2DP   01292 261126

Ayr: St Columba (H)
Fraser R. Aitken MA BD   1978   1991   2 Hazelwood Road, Ayr KA7 2PY   01292 283125

Ayr: St James' Gillian Weighton (Mrs) BD STM	1992	1 Prestwick Road, Ayr KA8 8LD	01292 262420
Ayr: St Leonard's (H) Robert Lynn MA BD	1984	1989	7 Shawfield Avenue, Ayr KA7 4RE	01292 442109
Ayr: St Quivox (H) David T. Ness LTh	1972	1988	11 Springfield Avenue, Prestwick KA9 2HA	01292 478306
Ayr: Wallacetown (H) A.M. McPhail BA	1968	87 Forehill Road, Ayr KA7 3JR	01292 269161
Ballantrae (H) Robert P. Bell BSc	1968	1998	Ballantrae, Girvan KA26 0NH [e-mail: RevBobBell@aol.com]	01465 831252 (Tel) 01465 831260 (Fax)
Barr linked with Dailly linked with Girvan South Ian K. Mclachlan MA BD	1999	30 Henrietta Street, Girvan KA26 9AL [e-mail; iankmclachlan@yetiville.freeserve.co.uk]	01465 713370
Catrine linked with Sorn George A. Chalmers MA BD MLitt	1962	1994	Catrine, Mauchline KA5 6NA	01290 553057
Colmonell See Arnsheen Barnhill			
Coylton linked with Drongan: The Schaw Kirk Paul R. Russell MA BD	1984	1991	4 Hamilton Place, Coylton, Ayr KA6 6JQ	01292 570272
Craigie linked with Symington Vacant		16 Kerrix Road, Symington, Kilmarnock KA1 5QD	01563 830205
Crosshill linked with Dalrymple James Crichton MA BD MTh	1969	30 Garden Street, Dalrymple KA6 6DG	01292 560263 (Tel) 01292 560574 (Fax)
Dailly See Barr			
Dalmellington Kenneth B. Yorke BD DipEd	1982	1999	4 Carsphairn Road, Dalmellington, Ayr KA6 7RE	01292 550353
Dalrymple See Crosshill **Drongan: The Schaw Kirk** See Coylton			
Dundonald (H) Robert Mayes BD	1982	1988	Dundonald, Kilmarnock KA2 9HG	01563 850243

Fisherton (H) linked with Maybole: West
Thomas C. Bogle BD — 1983 — 1996 — Maybole, Ayrshire KA19 7EB — 01655 883102

Girvan: North (Old and St Andrew's) (H)
Douglas G. McNab BA BD — 1999 — 38 The Avenue, Girvan KA26 9DS — 01465 713203

Girvan: South: See Barr linked with Dailly

Kirkmichael linked with Straiton: St Cuthbert's
W. Gerald Jones MA BD MTh — 1984 — 1985 — Kirkmichael, Maybole KA19 7PJ — 01655 750286

Kirkoswald (H)
Arrick D. Wilkinson — 2000 — 2000 — Kirkoswald, Maybole KA19 8JA — 01655 760210

Lugar linked with Old Cumnock: Old (H)
John W. Paterson BSc BD DipEd — 1994 — 33 Barrhill Road, Cumnock KA18 1PJ [e-mail: ocochurchwow@hotmail.com] — 01290 420769

Mauchline (H)
Alan B. Telfer BA BD — 1983 — 1991 — 4 Westside Gardens, Mauchline KA5 5DJ — 01290 550386

Maybole: Old
David Whiteman BD — 1998 — 64 Culzean Road, Maybole KA19 8AH [e-mail: davesoo@aol.com] — 01655 889456

Maybole: West See Fisherton

Monkton and Prestwick: North (H)
Arthur A. Christie BD — 1997 — 2000 — 40 Monkton Road, Prestwick KA9 1AR [e-mail: revaac@compuserve.com] — 01292 477499

Muirkirk (H)
William Hannah BD MCAM MIPR — 1987 — 2 Smallburn Road, Muirkirk, Cumnock KA18 3RF [e-mail: wbillrev@aol.com] — 01290 661157 (Tel/Fax)

New Cumnock (H)
Vacant — New Cumnock, Cumnock KA18 4AG — 01290 338296

Ochiltree linked with Stair
Carolyn M. Baker (Mrs) BD — 1997 — 10 Mauchline Road, Ochiltree, Cumnock KA18 2PZ — 01290 700365

Old Cumnock: Crichton West linked with St Ninian's
Vacant — 46 Ayr Road KA18 1DW — 01290 420119

Old Cumnock: Old See Lugar
Old Cumnock: St Ninian's See Old Cumnock Crichton West

Patna Waterside
Vacant

Prestwick: Kingcase (H)
T. David Watson BSc BD 1988 1997 15 Bellrock Avenue, Prestwick KA9 1SQ   01292 479571
[e-mail: tdwatson@tesco.net]

Prestwick: St Nicholas' (H)
George R. Fiddes BD 1979 1985 3 Bellevue Road KA9 1NW   01292 477613
[e-mail: George@gfiddes.freeserve.co.uk]

Prestwick: South (H)
Kenneth C. Elliott BD CertMin 1989 68 St Quivox Road KA9 1JF   01292 478788
[e-mail: kenneth@revelliott.freeserve.co.uk]

Sorn See Catrine
Stair See Ochiltree
Straiton St Cuthbert's See Kirkmichael
Symington See Craigie

Tarbolton
Mary C. McLauchlan (Mrs) LTh 1997 1999 1 Kirkport, Tarbolton, Mauchline KA5 5QJ   01292 541236
[e-mail: mary.shaw@ntlworld.com]

Troon: Old (H)
Alastair H. Symington MA BD 1972 1998 85 Bentinck Drive, Troon KA10 6HZ   01292 313644
[e-mail: revahs@care4free.net]

Troon: Portland (H)
Ronald M.H. Boyd BD DipTh 1995 1999 89 South Beach, Troon KA10 6EQ   01292 313285

Troon: St Meddan's (H)
David L. Harper BSc BD 1972 1979 27 Bentinck Drive, Troon KA10 6HX   01292 311784
[e-mail: d.l.harper@btinternet.com]

Andrew, R.J.M. MA	1955	1994	(Uddingston Old)	6A Ronaldshaw Park, Ayr KA7 2TS	01292 263430
Banks, John BD	1968	1988	Hospital Chaplain, Ailsa	19 Victoria Drive, Troon KA10 6JF	01292 317758
Bird, John W.	1965	1997	(Bathgate High)	14 Springfield Avenue, Prestwick KA9 2HA	01292 476037
Blyth, James G.S. BSc BD	1963	1986	(Glenmuick)	40 Robsland Avenue, Ayr KA7 2RW	01292 261276
Campbell, Effie C. (Mrs) BD	1981	1991	(Old Cumnock Crichton West with St Ninian's)	7 Landsowne Road, Ayr KA8 8LS	01292 264282

Name			(Charge)	Address	Tel.
Dickie, Michael M. BSc	1955	1994	(Ayr Castlehill)	8 Noltmire Road, Ayr KA8 9ES	01292 317097
Garrity, T. Alan W. BSc BD MTh	1969	1999	(Christ Church, Warwick, Bermuda)	PO Box PG88, Paget PG BX, Bermuda	
Glencross, William M. LTh	1968	1999	(Bellshill: Macdonald Memorial)	1 Lochay Place, Troon KA10 7HH	01292 311852
Grant, J. Gordon MA BD	1957	1997	(Edinburgh: Dean)	33 Fullarton Drive, Troon KA10 6LE	
Helon, George G. BA BD	1984	2000	(Barr linked with Dailly)	9 Park Road, Maxwellton, Dumfries DG2 7PW	01387 259255
Hollins, Roger M. BSc DipEd FEIS	1957	1988	(Lecturer in Religious Education)	Smithy Cottage, Dunure, Ayr KA7 4LH	01292 500273
Kent, Arthur F.S.	1966	1999	(Monkton and Prestwick: North)	17 St David's Drive, Evesham, Worcs WR11 6AS	01386 421562
Macdonald, Ian U.	1960	1997	(Tarbolton)	18 Belmont Road, Ayr KA7 2PF	01292 283085
McNidder, Roderick H. BD	1987	1997	Chaplain, South Ayrshire Hospitals Trust	6 Hollow Park, Alloway KA7 4SR	01292 442554
Phillips, John S. MA	1939	1978	(Ayr Lochside)		
Robertson, Daniel M. MA	1960	2000	(Auchinleck)	14 Corrie Place, Drongan, Ayrshire KA6 7DU	
Saunders, Campbell M. MA BD	1952	1989	(Ayr St Leonard's)	42 Marle Park, Ayr KA7 4RN	01292 441673
Sutherland, Alexander S.	1952	1987	(Symington with Craigie)	8 Phillips Avenue, Largs KA30 9EP	01475 674846
Whitelaw, William D.	1984	1998	(Bothkennar and Carronshore)	10 Leslie Crescent, Ayr KA7 3BW	01292 267067

AYR ADDRESSES

Ayr

Auld Kirk	Kirkport (116 High Street)
Castlehill	Castlehill Road x Hillfoot Road
Lochside	Lochside Road x Murray Street
Newton-on-Ayr	Main Street
St Andrew's	Park Circus
St Columba	Midton Road x Carrick Park
St James'	Prestwick Road x Falkland Park Road
St Leonard's	St Leonard's Road x Monument Road
Wallacetown	John Street x Church Street

Girvan

North	Montgomerie Street
South	Stair Park

Maybole

Old	Centre of Cassillis Road
West	Foot of Coral Glen

Prestwick

Kingcase	Waterloo Road
Monkton and Prestwick North	Monkton Road
St Nicholas	Main Street

South	Main Street

Troon

Old	Ayr Street
Portland	St Meddan's Street
St Meddan's	St Meddan's Street

(11) IRVINE AND KILMARNOCK

The Presbytery meets ordinarily at 6.30pm in the Hall of Howard St Andrew's Church, Kilmarnock, on the first Tuesday of each month from September to May; (except January when it meets on the second Tuesday) for the celebration of Holy Communion and in conference or socially) and on the fourth Tuesday in June.

Clerk:	REV. COLIN G.F. BROCKIE BSc(Eng) BD	51 Portland Road Kilmarnock KA1 2EQ [e-mail: revcol@revcol.demon.co.uk]	01563 525311
Depute Clerk:	REV. ROBERT TRAVERS BA BD	23 Kirk Vennel, Irvine KA12 0DQ [e-mail:robert@travers46.freeserve.co.uk]	01294 279265
Treasurer:	JAMES McINTOSH BA CA	15 Dundonald Rd, Kilmarnock	01563 523552

Crosshouse Rona M. Young (Mrs) BD DipEd	1991		27 Kilmarnock Road, Crosshouse KA2 0EZ	01563 521035
Darvel Vacant			46 West Main Street, Darvel KA17 4AQ [e-mail: robert@travers46.freeserve.co.uk]	01560 320484
Dreghorn and Springside Gary E. Horsburgh BA	1976	1983	96A Townfoot, Dreghorn KA11 4EZ	01294 217770
Dunlop Maureen M. Duncan (Mrs) BD	1996		4 Dampark, Dunlop KA3 4BZ	01560 484083
Fenwick (H) Geoffrey Redmayne BSc BD MPhil	2000		2 Kirkton Place, Fenwick KA3 6DW	01560 600217
Galston (H) T.J. Loudon Blair MA BD	1965	1980	Galston Ayrshire KA4 8DX [e-mail: louden.blair@virgin.net]	01563 820246
John H.B. Taylor MA BD DipEd (Assoc)	1952	1990	62 Woodlands Grove, Kilmarnock KA3 1TZ	01563 526698
Hurlford James D. McCulloch BD MIOP	1996		12 Main Road, Crookedholm KA3 6JT	01563 535673
Irvine: Fullarton Neil Urquhart BD DipMin	1989		48 Waterside, Irvine KA12 8QJ [e-mail: neil.urquhart@btinternet.com]	01294 279909
Irvine: Girdle Toll (E) Clare B. Sutcliffe BSc BD	2000		2 Littlestane Rise, Irvine KA11 2BJ	01294 213565
Irvine: Mure (H) Hugh M. Adamson BD	1976		West Road, Irvine KA12 8RE	01294 279916

Irvine: Old (H) (01294 273503)
Robert Travers BA BD — 1993 — 1999 — 23 Kirk Vennel, Irvine, Ayrshire KA12 0DQ
[e-mail: robert@travers46.freeserve.co.uk] — 01294 279265

Irvine: Relief Bourtreehill (H)
Robert A. Hamilton BA BD — 1995 — 4 Kames Court, Irvine KA11 1RT
[e-mail: rabbie@thegirdle.freeserve.co.uk] — 01294 216939

Irvine: St Andrew's (H) (01294 276051)
Vacant — 206 Bank Street, Irvine KA12 0YB — 01294 211403

Kilmarnock: Grange (H) (01563 534490)
Colin G.F. Brockie BSc(Eng) BD — 1967 — 1978 — 51 Portland Road, Kilmarnock KA1 2EQ
[e-mail: revcol@revcol.demon.co.uk] — 01563 525311

Kilmarnock: Henderson (H) (01563 541302)
David W. Lacy BA BD — 1976 — 1989 — 52 London Road, Kilmarnock KA3 7AJ
[e-mail: thelacys@tingword.co.uk] — 01563 523113

Kilmarnock: Howard St Andrew's (H)
Malcolm MacLeod BA BD — 1979 — 1989 — 1 Evelyn Villas, Holehouse Road, Kilmarnock KA3 7AX
[e-mail: calum@calum.freeserve.co.uk] — 01563 522278

Kilmarnock: Laigh (H)
Vacant — 1 Holmes Farm Road, Kilmarnock KA1 1TP — 01563 525416

Kilmarnock: Old High Kirk (H)
William M. Hall BD — 1972 — 1979 — 107 Dundonald Road, Kilmarnock KA1 1UP — 01563 525608

Kilmarnock: Riccarton
Thomas W. Jarvie BD — 1953 — 1968 — 2 Jasmine Road, Kilmarnock KA1 2HD — 01563 525694

Kilmarnock: St Andrew's Glencairn
R.A.K. Martin MA — 1957 — 1970 — 19 Holehouse Rd. Kilmarnock KA3 7AU — 01563 525023

Kilmarnock: St John's Onthank
Susan M. Anderson (Mrs) — 1997 — 84 Wardneuk Drive, Kilmarnock KA3 2EX — 01563 521815
Catherine A.M. Shaw MA (Aux) — 1998 — 40 Merrygreen Place, Stewarton KA3 5EP — 01560 483352

Kilmarnock: St Kentigern's
S. Grant Barclay LLB BD — 1995 — 89 Mure Avenue, Kilmarnock KA3 1TT
[e-mail: grant.barclay@bigfoot.com] — 01563 571280

Kilmarnock: St Marnock's (H) (01563 541337)
James McNaughtan BD DipMin — 1983 — 1989 — 35 South Gargieston Drive, Kilmarnock KA1 1TB — [e-mail: jmcnaughton@mcmail.com] — 01563 521665

Kilmarnock: St Ninian's Bellfield (T) (01563 524705)
Vacant — 186 Whatriggs Road, Kilmarnock KA1 3TJ — 01563 525480

Kilmarnock: Shortlees (T)
Rolf H. Billes BD — 1996 — 14 McLelland Drive, Kilmarnock KA1 1SE — [e-mail: rbilles@aol.com] — 01563 529920

Kilmarnock: West High
Robert S. Christie MA BD ThM — 1964 — 1973 — 69 Dundonald Road, Kilmarnock KA1 1TJ — 01563 525302

Kilmaurs: St Maur's Glencairn
John A. Urquhart — 1993 — 9 Standalane, Kilmaurs KA3 2NB — 01563 538289

Newmilns: Loudoun (H)
John Macleod MA BD — 2000 — Newmilns, Ayrshire KA16 9HH — 01560 320174

Stewarton: John Knox
Samuel Hosain BD MTh — 1979 — 1993 — 27 Avenue St Stewarton KA3 5AP — 01560 482418

Stewarton: St Columba's (H)
Elizabeth A. Waddell — 1999 — 1 Kirk Glebe, Stewarton KA3 5BJ — 01560 482453

Ayrshire Mission to the Deaf
S. Grant Barclay LLB BD (Chaplain) — 1991 — 1998 — 89 Mure Avenue, Kilmarnock KA3 1TT — [e-mail: grant.barclay@bigfoot.com] — 01563 571280

Boath, Gibson K. BA	1951 1989	(Kilmarnock Howard St Andrew's)	6 Woodlands Place, Kilmarnock KA3 1UA	01563 571170
Campbell, George H.	1957 1992	(Stewarton: John Knox)	20 Woodlands Grove, Kilmarnock KA3 1TZ	01563 536365
Campbell, John A. JP FIEM	1984 1998	(Irvine St. Andrew's)	Flowerdale, Balmoral Lane, Blairgowrie PH10 7AF	01250 872795
Crawford, Robert MA	1933 1972	(Annan Erskine)	11 Glencraig Terrace, Fenwick KA3 6DE	01560 600458
Downie, Andrew A. BD	1994 1999	(Prison Chaplain)	HMP Bowhouse, Mauchline Road, Kilmarnock KA1	
Goudie, Stuart M. MA BD	1951 1988	(Perceton and Dreghorn)	6 Charles Drive, Troon KA10 7AG	01292 311610
Greig, James	1966 1999	(Irvine: Old)	127A Ayr Road, Prestwick KA9 1TW	
Hare, Malcolm M.W. BA BD	1956 1994	(Kilmarnock St Kintigern's)	21 Raith Road, Fenwick KA3 6DB	01560 600388
Hay, W.J.R. MA BD	1959 1995	(Buchanan with Drymen)	18 Jamieson Place, Stewarton KA3 3AY	01560 482799
Huggett, Judith A. (Miss) BA BD	1990 1998	Hospital Chaplain	4 Westmoor Crescent, Kilmarnock KA1 1TX	
Jamieson, Robert C. MA	1943 1980	(Galston Old)	20 Brewland Street, Galston KA4 8DR	01563 820304
MacDonald, James M. BD	1983 1999	(Irvine: Girdle Toll)	5 Carters Place, Irvine KA12 0BU	
McGarva, Sarah (Miss) DCS	1964 1987	(Kilmarnock St John's Onthank)	29 Carmel Place, Kilmarnock, Kilmarnock KA3 2QU	01563 525254
		(Deaconess)	87 Hunter Drive, Irvine KA12 9BS	01294 271257

Patience, Donald MA	1954 1993	(Kilmaurs)	Kirkhill, 42 Fenwick Road, Kilmaurs KA3 2TD	01563 544447
Roy, James BA	1967 1982	(Irvine Girdle Toll)	23 Bowes Rigg, Stewarton I..A3 5EL	01560 482185
			[e-mail: jroy@dougtr-globalnet.co.uk]	
Scott, Thomas T.	1968 1989	(Kilmarnock St Marnock's)	6 North Hamilton Place, Kilmarnock KA1 2QN	01563 531415
			[e-mail: 101725.216@compuserve.com]	
Urquhart, Barbara (Mrs) DCS		Deaconess, Part-time Hospital Chaplain and Presbytery S.S. Adviser	9 Standalane, Kilmaurs, Kilmarnock KA3 2NB	01563 538289

IRVINE and KILMARNOCK ADDRESSES

Irvine

Dreghorn and Springside	Townfoot x Station Brae
Fullarton	Marress Road x Church Street
Girdle Toll	Bryce Knox Court
Mure	West Road
Old Parish	Kirkgate
Relief	Crofthead, Bourtreehill
St Andrew's	Caldon Road x Oaklands Ave

Kilmarnock

Ayrshire Mission to the Deaf	10 Clark Street	Riccarton	Old Street
Grange	Woodstock Street	St Andrew's	St Andrew's Street
Henderson	London Road	Glencairn	84 Wardneuk Street
Howard	5 Portland Road	St John's Onthank	St Marnock's Street
Laigh	John Dickie Street	St Marnock's	Whatriggs Road
Old High	Church Street x Soulis Street	St Ninian's Bellfield	Central Avenue
		Shortlees	Portland Street
		West High	

(12) ARDROSSAN

Meets at Saltcoats: New Trinity, on the first Tuesday of February, March, April, May, September, October, November and December, and on the second Tuesday of January and June

Clerk: REV. DAVID BROSTER   BA DipTh CPS   Manse of St Columba's, Kilbirnie KA25 7JU   01505 683342 (Tel)
[e-mail: pres@davbros.demon.co.uk]   01505 684024 (Fax)
07836 380383 (Mbl)
07669 036762 (24hr pager)

Ardrossan: Barony St John's (H) (01294 465009)

Colin Alexander Sutherland LTh	1995	1999	10 Seafield Drive, Ardrossan KA22 8NU 01294 463868

Ardrossan: Park (01294 463711)

William Johnston BD	1998	35 Ardneil Court, Ardrossan KA22 7NQ 01294 471808
Marion L.K. Howie (Mrs) MA ACRS (Aux)	1992	51 High Road, Stevenston KA20 3DY 01294 466571

[e-mail: marion.howie@ndirect.co.uk]

Beith: High (H) (01505 502686) linked with Beith: Trinity (H)

Andrew R. Black BD DipMin	1987	2 Glebe Court, Beith KA15 1ET	01505 503858
Fiona C. Ross BD DipMin (Assoc)	1996	16 Spiers Avenue, Beith KA15 1JD	01505 502131

Beith: Trinity (H) See Beith: High

Brodick linked with Corrie

Ian MacLeod LTh BA MTh PhD	1969 1974	4 Manse Crescent, Brodick, Isle of Arran KA27 8AS	01770 302334

Corrie See Brodick

Cumbrae

Marjory H. Mackay BD DipEd CCE	1998	Millport, Isle of Cumbrae KA28 0ED	01475 530416

Dalry: St Margaret's

A. Douglas Lamb MA	1964 1973	Dalry, Ayrshire KA24 4DA [e-mail: A.D.Lamb@lamb.junglelink.co.uk]	01294 832234

Dalry: Trinity (H)

David I.M. Grant MA BD	1969	Dalry, Ayrshire KA24 5DX	01294 832363

Fairlie (H)

Robert J. Thorburn BD	1978 1980	14 Fairlieburne Gardens, Fairlie, Largs KA29 0ER [e-mail: rjthorburn@aol.com]	01475 568342

Fergushill linked with Kilwinning Erskine

Vacant		14 McLuckie Drive, Kilwinning KA13 6DL	01294 551565

Kilbirnie: Auld Kirk (H)

Ian W. Benzie BD	1999	49 Holmhead, Kilbirnie KA25 6BS [e-mail: revian@ibenzie.freeserve.co.uk]	01505 682348

Kilbirnie: St Columba's (H) (01505 685239)

David Broster BA DipTh CPS	1969 1983	Kilbirnie, Ayrshire KA25 7JU [e-mail: pres@davbros. demon.co.uk]	01505 683342 (Tel) 01505 684024 (Fax) 07836 380383 (Mbl) 07669 036762 (24 hr pager)

Kilmory linked with Lamlash

Vacant		Lamlash, Brodick, Isle of Arran KA27 8LE	01770 600318

Kilwinning: Abbey (H)

William Buchan DipTheol BD	1987	54 Dalry Road, Kilwinning KA13 7HE [e-mail: wbuchan3@aol.com]	01294 552606

Kilwinning: Erskine (01294 552188) See Fergushill

Kilwinning: Mansefield Trinity (E) (01294 550746)
Douglas S. Paterson   1976

Lamlash See Kilmory

Largs: Clark Memorial (H) (01475 675186)
Stephen J. Smith BSc BD   1993   27 Treesbank, Kilwinning KA13 6LY   1999   01294 552453

Largs: St Columba's (01475 686212)
David M. McKay MA BD   1979   31 Douglas Street, Largs KA30 8PT   1998   01475 672370

Largs: St John's (H) (01475 674468)
Andrew F. McGurk BD   1983   17 Beachway, Largs KA30 8QH   1992   01475 673107
                                                  [e-mail: demacmin@ukgateway.net]

Lochranza and Pirnmill linked with Shiskine (H)
Vacant   1 Newhaven Grove, Largs KA30 8NS   1993   01475 676123
                                                  [e-mail: afmcg.largs@talk21.com]

Saltcoats: New Trinity (H) (01294 472001)
Alexander D. McCallum BD   1987   Shiskine, Brodick, Isle of Arran KA27 8EP   01770 860380

Saltcoats: North (01294 464679)
Calum D. Macdonald BD   1993   1 Montgomerie Crescent, Saltcoats KA21 5BR 1994   01294 461143
                                                  [e-mail: sandy@newtrinity.co.uk]

Saltcoats: St Cuthbert's (H)
Brian H. Oxburgh BSc BD   1980   25 Longfield Avenue, Saltcoats KA21 6DR   1993   01294 604923
                                                  [e-mail: calummacdonald@saltcoats50.freeserve.co.uk]

Shiskine See Lochranza and Pirnmill

Stevenston: Ardeer
G. Gray Fletcher BSc BD   1989   10 Kennedy Road, Saltcoats KA21 5SF   1988   01294 602674

Stevenston: High (H)
Ann C. McCool (Mrs) BD DSD IPA ALCM   1989   40 Shore Road, Stevenston KA20 3LA   1989   01294 463814

Stevenston: Livingstone (H)
John M.M. Lafferty   1999   Stevenston, Ayrshire KA20 3DL   01294 463356

                                                  32 High Road, Stevenston KA20 3DR   1999   01294 464180

West Kilbride: Overton (H)
Norman Cruickshank BA BD 1983 Goldenberry Avenue, West Kilbride KA23 9LJ 01294 823186

West Kilbride: St Andrew's (H) (01294 829902)
D. Ross Mitchell BA BD 1972 1980 7 Overton Drive, West Kilbride KA23 9LQ 01294 823142
[e-mail: ross.mitchell@virgin.net]

Whiting Bay and Kildonan
Elizabeth R.L. Watson (Miss) BA BD 1981 1982 Whiting Bay, Isle of Arran KA27 8RE 01770 700289
[e-mail: elizabeth@rlwatson.freeserve.co.uk]

Dailly, J.R. BD DipPS	1979	1979	Staff Chaplain: Army	DACG, HQ 42 (NW) Bde, Fulwood Barracks, Preston PR2 8AA	
Downie, Alexander S.	1975	1997	(Ardrossan: Park)	14 Korsankel Wynd, Saltcoats KA21	01294 464097
Ewing, James MA BD	1948	1987	(Ardrossan Barony)	8 Semple Crescent, Fairlie, Largs KA29 0EN	01475 568115
Fisher, Kenneth H.	1969	1994	(Stronsay with Eday)	33 Halfway Street, West Kilbride KA23 9EQ	01294 829973
Harbison, David J.H.	1958	1998	(Beith: High with Beith: Trinity)	42 Mill Park, Dalry KA24 1BB	01294 834092
Kirkwood, Hugh BA BD	1942	1981	(Saltcoats Erskine)	2 Alton Way, West Kilbride KA23 9JJ	01294 823932
McIlroy, Alexander M. LTh	1972	1987	(Darvel Irvinebank and Easton Memorial)	16A Hawkhill Drive, Stevenston KA20 3DF	01294 601609
McKay, Johnston R. MA BA	1969	1987	Religious Broadcasting (BBC)	41 Stakehill, Largs KA30 9PH	01475 672960
MacKenzie, Andrew H.	1963	1969	(Acharacle with Ardnamurchan)	Avonpark Nursing Home, Strathaven ML10 6BZ	
Maclagan, David W. MA ThD	1965	1991	(Largs: St John's)	Flat C, 1 Greenock Road, Largs KA30 8PQ	01475 673258
Paterson, John H. BD	1977	2000	(Kirkintilloch: St. David's Memorial Park)	Creag Bhan, Golf Course Road, Whiting Bay, Arran KA27 8QT	01770 700569
Reid, Agnes A. (Miss)	1985	1994	(Auchindoir and Kildrummy)	91 New Street, Dalry KA24 5BY	01294 835362
Roy, Iain M. MA BD	1960	1997	(Stevenston: Livingstone)	2 The Fieldings, Dunlop, Kilmarnock KA3 4AU	01560 483072
Taylor, Andrew S. BTh FPhS	1959	1992	(Greenock Union)	9 Raillies Avenue, Largs KA30 8QY	01475 674709
Thomson, Margaret (Mrs)	1988	1993	(Saltcoats: Erskine)	72 Knockrivoch Place, Ardrossan KA22 7PZ	01294 468685
Walker, David S. MA	1939	1978	(Markerstoun with Smailholm with Stichill, Hume and Nenthorn)	6 Stuirlie Crescent, West Kilbride KA23 9BT	01294 823061
Weir, D. Gordon	1949	1992	(Saltcoats Landsborough and Trinity)	Flat 4, Lauriston Court, 2 South Beach Road, Ardrossan KA22 8AU	01294 462969

(13) LANARK

Meets at Lanark on the first Tuesday of February, March, April, May, September, October, November and December, and on the third Tuesday of June

Clerk: REV. IAIN D. CUNNINGHAM MA BD

9 Station Road, Carluke ML8 5AA
[e-mail: Lanark.Presbytery@dial.pipex.com]
[http://www.biggar.net.co.uk/lanark]

01555 771262 (Tel/Fax)

Biggar (H)
Gavin J. Elliott MA BD

1976   1995   61 High Street, Biggar ML12 6DA
[e-mail: 100541.1325@compuserve.com]

01899 220227 (Tel/Fax)

Black Mount linked with Culter linked with Libberton and Quothquan
Stephen A. Pacitti MA

1963   1997   6 Cardon Drive, Biggar ML12 6EZ

01899 220625

Cairngryffe linked with Symington
John Brown MA BD

1995   16 Abington Road, Symington, Biggar ML12 6JX

01899 308838 (Tel/Fax)

Carluke: Kirkton (H)
Iain D. Cunningham MA BD

1979   1987   9 Station Road, Carluke ML8 5AA
[e-mail: IainDC@dial.pipex.com]

01555 771262 (Tel/Fax)

Carluke: St Andrew's (H)
Helen E. Jamieson (Mrs) BD DipED

1989   120 Clyde Street, Carluke ML8 5BG

01555 771218

Carluke: St John's (H)
Michael W. Frew BSc BD

1978   1991   18 Old Bridgend, Carluke ML8 4HN
[e-mail: mwfrew@aol.com]

01555 772259

Carnwath (H)
Beverly G.D.D. Gauld MA BD

1972   1978   The Manse, Carnwath, Lanark ML11 8JY

01555 840259

(Auchengray Tarbrax and Woolfords)

Carstairs linked with Carstairs Junction
J. Melvyn Coogan LTh

1992   1996   80 Lanark Road, Carstairs ML11 8QH

01555 870250

Carstairs Junction See Carstairs

Charge	Minister	Year(s)	Address	Telephone
Coalburn linked with Lesmahagow: Old Sheila M. Mitchell (Miss) BD MTh		1995	Calsay Cottage, 103 New Trows Road, Lesmahagow ML11 0ER [e-mail: sheila@smitchell.dabsol.co.uk]	01555 892425
Crossford linked with Kirkfieldbank Steven Reid BAcc CA BD		1989 1997	The Manse, Crossford,Carluke ML8 5RE	01555 860415
Culter linked with Libberton and Quothquan See Black Mount				
Douglas: St Bride's linked with Douglas Water and Rigside Lawrie I. Lennox MA BD		1991 1991	The Manse, Douglas, Lanark ML11 0RB	01555 851213
Forth: St Paul's (H) James Bain BD DipMin		1996	22 Lea-Rig, Forth, Lanark ML11 8EA [e-mail: jimbain@compuserve.com]	01555 811748
Glencaple linked with Lowther Vacant			66 Carlisle Road, Crawford, Biggar ML12 6TW	01864 502625
Kirkfieldbank See Crossford				
Kirkmuirhill (H) David A. Young		1972 1974	2 Lanark Road, Kirkmuirhill, Lanark ML11 9RB [e-mail: DavidKCS @ aol.com]	01555 892409 (Tel/Fax)
Lanark: Greyfriars Catherine E.E. Collins (Mrs) MA BD David A. Collins BSc BD		1993 1993	2 Friarsdene, Lanark ML11 9EJ [e-mail: greyfriars@mcmail.com]	01555 663363
Lanark: St Nicholas' John M.A. Thomson BD ThM		1978 1988	32 Braxfield Road, Lanark ML11 9BS [e-mail: JohnT@lanark.demon.co.uk]	01555 662600 (Tel) 01555 665905 (Fax)
Law Vacant			53 Lawhill Road, Law, Carluke ML8 5EZ	01698 373180
Lesmahagow: Abbeygreen David S. Carmichael		1982	Abbeygreen Manse, Lesmahagow, Lanark ML11 0DB	01555 893384
Lesmahagow: Old (H) See Coalburn				
Libberton and Quothquan See Black Mount				
Lowther See Glencaple				
Symington See Cairngryffe				

Craig, William BA LTh	1974	1997	(Cambusbarron: The Bruce Memorial)	31 Heathfield Drive, Blackwood, Lanark ML11 9SR	01555 893710
Jones, Philip H.	1968	1987	(Bishopbriggs Kenmure)	81 Vere Road, Kirkmuirhill, Lanark ML11 9RP	01555 894326
Kennedy, David A. LTCL	1959	1983	(Lanark Cairns)	63 Hall Road, Nemphlar, Lanark ML11 9JE	01555 664484
McCormick, W. Cadzow MA BD	1943	1983	(Glasgow Maryhill Old)	82 Main Street, Symington, Biggar ML12 6LJ	01899 308221
McMahon, Robert J. BD	1959	1997	(Crossford with Kirkfieldbank)	7 Ridgepark Drive, Lanark ML11 9PG	01555 663844
Seath, Thomas J.G.	1980	1992	(Motherwell: Manse Road)	1 Allan Avenue, Carluke ML8 5UA	01555 771644
Thomson, John S. MA	1934	1972	(Covington and Thankerton with Libberton and Quothquan)	20 Whitehouse Loan, Edinburgh EH9 2EZ	0131 447 9455

(14) PAISLEY

Meets at Paisley, in St James' Church Hall, on the second Tuesday of each month, except January, July and August.

| Clerk: | REV. DAVID KAY BA BD MTh | | | 6 Southfield Avenue, Paisley PA2 8BY [e-mail: gmw86@dial.pipex.com] | 0141 884 3600 (Tel/Fax) |

Barrhead: Arthurlie (H) (0141 881 8442)

| James S.A. Cowan BD | 1986 | 1998 | 10 Arthurlie Avenue, Barrhead G78 2BU [e-mail: revjcowan@aol.com] | 0141 881 3457 |

Barrhead: Bourock (H) (0141 881 9813)

| Maureen Leitch (Mrs) BA BD | 1995 | 14 Maxton Avenue, Barrhead G78 1DY | 0141 881 1462 |

Barrhead: South and Levern (H) (0141 881 7825)

| R.M. Hetherington MA BD | 1966 | 1977 | 3 Colinbar Circle, Barrhead G78 2BE | 0141 571 4059 |

Bishopton (H)

| Vacant | Newton Road, Bishopton PA7 5JP | 01505 862161 |

Bridge of Weir: Freeland (H) (01505 612610)

| Kenneth N. Gray BA BD | 1988 | 15 Lawmarnock Crescent, Bridge of Weir PA11 3AS | 01505 690919 |

Bridge of Weir: St Machar's Ranfurly (01505 614364)

| Suzanne Dunleavy (Miss) BD DipEd | 1990 | 1992 | 9 Glen Brae PA11 3BH | 01505 612975 |

Caldwell John Campbell MA BD BSc	1973	2000	Uplawmoor, Glasgow G78 4AL [e-mail: campbelljohn@iname.com]	01505 850215
Elderslie Kirk (H) (01505 323348) David N. McLachlan BD	1985	1994	282 Main Road, Elderslie PA5 9EF	01505 321767
Houston and Killellan (H) Georgina M. Baxendale (Mrs) BD	1981	1989	The Manse, Main Street, Houston PA6 7EL	01505 612569
Howwood Benjamin J.A. Abelado BTh DipTh PTh	1991	1995	The Manse, Beith Road, Howwood PA9 1AS	01505 703678
Inchinnan (H) (0141 812 1263) Marilyn MacLaine (Mrs) LTh	1995		Inchinnan PA4 9PH	0141 812 1688
Johnstone: High (H) (01505 336303) Vacant			76 North Road, Johnstone PA5 8NF	01505 320006
Johnstone: St Andrew's Trinity J.C. MacColl BSc BD	1966	1974	The Grange, Park Road, Johnstone PA5 8LS	01505 320142
Johnstone: St Paul's (H) (01505 321632) James A.S. Boag BD Linda Black (Miss) BSc DCS	1992		61 Auchenlodement Road, Elderslie PA5 9PA 127B Spateston Road, Johnstone PA5 0SY	01505 320060 01505 345735
Kilbarchan: East Alister W. Bull BD DipMin	1994		Church Street, Kilbarchan PA10 2JQ	01505 702621
Kilbarchan: West Arthur Sherratt BD	1994		West Manse, Shuttle Street, Kilbarchan PA10 2JR	01505 342930
Linwood (H) (01505 328802) T. Edward Marshall BD Margaret McBain (Miss) DCS	1987		Linwood PA3 3DL 33 Quarry Road, Paisley PA2 7RD	01505 325131 0141 884 2920
Lochwinnoch (T) Robin N. Allison BD DipMin	1994	1999	Riverside, Burnfoot Road, Lochwinnoch PA12 4AN	01505 843484
Neilston (0141 881 9445) Alexander Macdonald MA BD	1966	1984	Neilston, Glasgow G78 3NP	014 881 1958
New Erskine (0141 812 4620) Ian W. Bell LTh Morag Erskine (Miss) DCS	1990	1998	7 Leven Place, Linburn, Erskine PA8 6AS 111 Main Drive, Erskine PA8 7JJ	0141 812 2439 0141 581 0955

Paisley: Abbey (H) (Tel: 0141 889 7654   Fax: 0141 887 3929)
Alan D. Birss MA BD   1979   1988   15 Main Road, Castlehead, Paisley PA2 6AJ   0141 889 3587

Paisley: Castlehead (T)
Esther J. Ninian MA BD   1993   1998   28 Fulbar Crescent, Paisley PA2 9AS   01505 812304

Paisley: Glenburn (0141 884 2602)
George C. MacKay BD CertMin   1994   10 Hawick Avenue, Paisley PA2 9LD   0141 884 4903
Greta Gray (Miss) DCS   67 Crags Avenue, Paisley PA3 6SG   0141 884 6178

Paisley: Laigh Kirk (H) (0141 889 7700)
Thomas M. Cant MA BD   1964   1972   18 Oldhall Road, Paisley PA1 3HL   0141 882 2277

Paisley: Lylesland (H) (0141 561 7139)
Andrew W. Bradley BD   1975   1998   36 Potterhill Avenue, Paisley PA2 8BA   0141 884 2882

Paisley: Martyrs (0141 889 6603)
Alison Davidge (Mrs) MA BD   1990   1997   12 Low Road, Paisley PA2 6AG   0141 889 2182

Paisley: Oakshaw Trinity (H) (Tel: 0141 887 4647: Fax: 0141 848 5139: e-mail: iancurrie@hawkhead.freeserve.co.uk)
Ian S. Currie MBE BD   1975   1980   9 Hawkhead Road, Paisley PA1 3ND   0141 887 0884
Christopher L. Levison MA BD   1972   1983   178 Glasgow Road, Paisley PA1 3LT   0141 889 3316

Paisley: St Columba Foxbar (H) (01505 812377)
Anthony J.R. Fowler BSc BD   1982   1985   13 Corsebar Drive, Paisley PA2 9QD   0141 889 9988
Mary Johnston (Miss) DCS   19 Lounsdale Drive, Paisley PA2 9ED   0141 849 1615

Paisley: St James' (0141 889 2422)
Eleanor J. McMahon (Miss) BEd BD   1994   38 Woodland Avenue, Paisley PA2 8BH
[e-mail: eleanormcmahon@classic.msa.com]   0141 884 3246

Paisley: St Luke's (H)
D. Ritchie M. Gillon BD DipMin   1994   31 Southfield Avenue, Paisley PA2 8BX
[e-mail: revgillon@aol.com]   0141 884 6215

Paisley: St Mark's Oldhall (H) (0141 882 2755)
Alistair H. Morrison BTh DipYCS   1985   1989   36 Newtyle Road, Paisley PA1 3JX   0141 889 4279

Paisley: St Ninian's Ferguslie (E) (0141 887 9436)
Archibald Speirs BD   1995   10 Stanely Drive, Paisley PA2 6HE
[e-mail: 100412.124@compuserve.com]   0141 884 3875

Paisley: Sandyford (Thread Street) (0141 889 5078)

Minister			Address	Phone
David Kay BA BD MTh	1974	1980	6 Southfield Avenue, Paisley PA2 8BY [e-mail: revdkay@hotmail.com]	0141 884 3600

Paisley: Sherwood Greenlaw (H) (0141 889 7060)

Minister			Address	Phone
Alasdair F. Cameron BD CA	1986	1993	5 Greenlaw Drive, Paisley PA1 3RX [e-mail: alcamron@lineone.net]	0141 889 3057
May Bell (Mrs) (Assistant)		1998	7 Leven Place, Linburn, Erskine PA8 6AS	0141 581 0955

Paisley: Wallneuk North (Tel: 0141 889 9265 Fax: 0141 887 6670)

Minister			Address	Phone
Thomas Macintyre MA BD	1972	1988	27 Mansionhouse Road, Paisley PA1 3RG	0141 581 1505
John Cathcart DCS	1989	1996	Flat 2/1, 39 Broomlands Street, Paisley PA1 2NQ	0141 848 5163

Renfrew: North (0141 885 2154)

Minister			Address	Phone
E. Lorna Hood (Mrs) MA BD	1978	1979	1 Alexandra Drive, Renfrew PA4 8UB	0141 886 2074

Renfrew: Old (Tel/Fax: 0141 886 6913)

Minister			Address	Phone
Alexander C. Wark MA BD STM	1982	1998	31 Gibson Road, Renfrew PA4 0RH	0141 886 2005

Renfrew: Trinity (H) (0141 885 2129)

Minister			Address	Phone
Stuart C. Steell BD		1992	25 Paisley Road, Renfrew PA4 8JH	0141 886 2131

Alexander, Douglas N. MA BD	1961	1999	(Bishopton)	West Morningside, Main Road, Langbank PA4 6XP	0141 840 2479
Cameron, Margaret (Miss) DCS	1961	1999	(Deaconess)	2 Rowans Gate, Paisley PA2 6RD	01334 474708
Cubie, John P. MA BD			(Caldwell)	36 Winram Place, St Andrews KY16 8XH	0141 889 7497
Low, Nan (Mrs) DCS			(Chaplain's Assistant: RAF)	46 Benmore Drive, Paisley PA2 7NH	0141 580 5726
Lowe, Edwin MA BD	1950	1988	(Caldwell)	45 Duncarnock Crescent, Neilston, Glasgow G78 3HH	0141 882 6353
McLachlan, Duncan MA BD ThM	1955	1992	(Paisley: Sherwood)	27 Penilee Road, Paisley PA1 3EU	01505 850294
Marr, E.R. MA	1933	1977	(Buttle)	Firwood, Uplawmoor, Glasgow G78	0141 812 3210
Mathers, J. Allan C.	1950	1989	(Inchinnan)	19 Braemar Road, Inchinnan PA4 9QB	01674 677289
Moffet, James R. BA	1942	1979	(Paisley: St Matthew's)	21 Paton's Lane, Montrose DD10 8JA	01505 615280
O'Leary, Thomas BD	1983	1998	(Lochwinnoch)	1 Carters Place, Irvine KA12 0BU	0141 842 1585
Palmer, S.W. BD	1980	1991	(Kilbarchan: East)	4 Bream Place, Houston PA6 7ZJ	0141 886 2896
Prentice, George BA BTh	1964	1997	(Paisley: Martyrs)	46 Victoria Gardens, Corsebar Road, Paisley PA2 9AQ	0141 889 9512
Rule, James A.	1952	1991	(Renfrew: Moorpark)	6 St Andrew's Road, Renfrew PA4 0SN	
Steele, Jean (Miss) DCS			(Deaconess)	93 George Street, Paisley PA1 2JX	

PAISLEY ADDRESSES

Abbey	Town Centre	Oakshaw: Trinity	Churchill
Castlehead	Canal Street	St Columba Foxbar	Amochrie Road, Foxbar
Glenburn	Nethercraigs Drive off Glenburn Road	St James'	Underwood Road
Laigh	Causeyside Street	St Luke's	Neilston Road
Lylesland	Rowan Street off Neilston Road	St Mark's Oldhall	Glasgow Road, Ralston
Martyrs'	Broomlands	St Ninian's Ferguslie	Blackstoun Road

Sandyford (Thread St)	Gallowhill
Sherwood Greenlaw	Glasgow Road
Wallneuk North	off Renfrew Rd

(15) GREENOCK

Meets at Greenock, in Ardgowan Parish Church Hall, on the second Tuesday of December, February and May, on the fourth Tuesday of October and March, on the third Tuesday of June, and in the Moderator's Church on the second Tuesday of September.

Clerk: REV. DAVID MILL KSJ MA BD   105 Newark Street, Greenock PA16 7TW   01475 639602
[e-mail: Greenock.Presbytery@dial.pipex.com]

Gourock: Old Gourock and Ashton (H)
Frank J. Gardner MA   1966   1979   90 Albert Road, Gourock PA19 1NN   01475 631516

Gourock: St John's (H)
P. Jill Gibson (Miss) BD   2000   6 Barrhill Road, Gourock PA19 1JX   01475 632143

Greenock: Ardgowan
W. John Harvey BA BD (Interim Minister)   1965   2000   72 Forsyth Street, Greenock PA16 8SX   01475 790849

Greenock: Cartsdyke
Peter Webster BD   1977   1981   84 Forsyth Street, Greenock PA16 8QY   01475 721439

Greenock: Finnart St Paul's (H)
David Mill KSJ MA BD   1978   1979   105 Newark Street, Greenock PA16 7TW   01475 639602

Greenock: Mount Kirk
James H. Simpson BD LLB   1964   1965   76 Finnart Street, Greenock PA16 8HJ   01475 722338

Greenock: Old West Kirk
C. Ian W. Johnson MA BD   1997   39 Fox Street, Greenock PA16 8PD   01475 888277
Eileen Manson (Mrs) DipCE (Aux)   1994   1 Cambridge Avenue, Gourock PA19 1XT   01475 632401

Greenock: St George's North W. Douglas Hamilton BD	1975	1986	67 Forsyth Street, Greenock PA16 8SX	01475 724003
Greenock: St Luke's (H) William C. Hewitt BD DipPS	1977	1994	50 Ardgowan Street, Greenock PA16 8EP	01475 721048
Greenock: St Margaret's (01475 781953) Isobel J.M. Kelly (Miss) MA BD DipEd	1974	1998	105 Finnart Street, Greenock PA16 8HN	01475 786590
Greenock: St Ninian's Allan G. McIntyre BD Joyce Nicol (Mrs) DCS	1985		5 Auchmead Road, Greenock PA16 OPY 93 Brisbane Street, Greenock PA16 8NY	01475 631878 01475 723235
Greenock: Wellpark Mid Kirk Alan K. Sorensen BD MTh DipMin FSAScot	1983	2000	101 Brisbane Street, Greenock PA16 8PA	01475 721741
Inverkip (H) Janet E. Gillies (Mrs) BD	1998		Inverkip, Greenock PA16 OBJ	01475 521207
Kilmacolm: Old (H) Gordon D. Irving BD	1994	1998	Glencairn Road, Kilmacolm, Renfrewshire PA13 4NJ	01505 873174
Kilmacolm: St Columba (H) R. Douglas Cranston MA BD	1986	1992	6 Churchill Road, Kilmacolm PA13 4LH	01505 873271
Langbank (T) Anna S. Rodwell (Mrs) BD DipMin	1998		Langbank, Port Glasgow PA14 6XB	01475 540252
Port Glasgow: Hamilton Bardrainney Vacant			80 Bardrainney Avenue, Port Glasgow PA14 6HD	01475 706551
Port Glasgow: St Andrew's (H) Andrew T. MacLean BA BD	1980	1993	Barr's Brae, Port Glasgow PA14 5QA	01475 741486
Port Glasgow: St Martin's John G. Miller BEd BD MTh	1983	1998	Clunebraehead, Clune Brae, Port Glasgow PA14 5SL	01475 704115
Skelmorlie and Wemyss Bay William R. Armstrong BD	1979		8 Eglinton Gardens, Skelmorlie PA17 5DW	01475 520703

Bruce, A. William MA	1942	1981	(Fortingall and Glenlyon)	75 Union Street, Greenock PA16 8BG	01475 787534
Chestnut, Alexander MBE BA	1948	1987	(Greenock St Mark's Greenbank)	5 Douglas Street, Largs KA30 8PS	01475 674168
Copland, Agnes M. (Mrs) MBE DCS			(Deacon)	3 Craigmuschat Road, Gourock PA19 1SE	01475 631870

Name		Position	Address	Telephone
Crumlish, Elizabeth A. (Mrs) BD	1995 1996	Hospital Chaplain	146 South Street, Greenock PA16 8TD	01475 727750
McCully, M. Isobel (Miss) DCS		(Deacon)	10 Broadstone Avenue, Port Glasgow PA14 5BB	01475 742240
MacQuien, Duncan DCS		(Deacon)	2 Manor Crescent, Gourock PA19 1UY	01475 633407
Marshall, Fred J. BA		(Bermuda)	Flat 4, Varrich House, 7 Church Hill, Edinburgh EH10 4BG	0131 446 0205
Montgomery, Robert A. MA	1946 1992	(Quarrier's Village: Mount Zion)	11 Myreton Avenue, Kilmacolm PA13 4LJ	01505 872028
Porteous, Alexander MA BD	1955 1992	(Greenock Mid Kirk)	Strathmore, Golf Road, Millport KA28 0HB	01475 530460
Pyper, J. Stewart BA	1965 1987	(Greenock St George's North)	39 Brisbane Street, Greenock PA16 8NR	01475 793234
Scot, Ernest M. MA	1951 1986	(Port Glasgow St Andrew's)	17 Brueacre Road, Wemyss Bay PA18 6ER	01475 522267
Stevenson, Alex	1959 1992	(Greenock St Andrew's)	34E St John's Road, Gourock PA19 1PQ	01475 631834
Stone, W. Vernon MA BD	1951 1976	(Langbank)	Santis, Finlaystone Road, Kilmacolm PA13 4RE	01505 872644
Swan, Andrew MA	1949 1985	(Greenock: St Margaret's)	11 The Terrace, Ardbeg, Rothesay, Isle of Bute PA20 0NE	01700 502138
Whyte, John H. MA	1941 1983 / 1946 1986	(Gourock: Ashton)	6 Castle Levan Manor, Cloch Road, Gourock PA19 1AY	01475 636788

GREENOCK ADDRESSES

Gourock
Old Gourock and Ashton — 41 Royal Street
St John's — Bath Street x St John's Road

Greenock
Ardgowan — 31 Union Street
Cartsdyke — 14 Crescent Street

Finnart St Paul's — Newark Street x Bentinck Street
Mount Kirk — Dempster Sreet at Murdieston Park
Old West Kirk — Esplanade x Campbell Street
St George's North — George Square
St Margaret's — Finch Road x Kestrel Crescent
St Ninian's — Warwick Road, Larkfield
St Luke's — 9 Nelson Street
Wellpark Mid Kirk — Cathcart Square

Port Glasgow
Hamilton-Bardrainney — Bardrainney Avenue x Auchenbothie Road
St Andrew's — Princes Street
St Martin's — Mansion Avenue

(16) GLASGOW

Meets at New Govan Church, Govan Cross, Glasgow, on the second Tuesday of each month, except June when the meeting takes place on the third Tuesday. In January, July and August there is no meeting

Clerk:	REV. ALEXANDER CUNNINGHAM MA BD	260 Bath Street, Glasgow G2 4JP	0141 332 6606 (Tel/Fax)
Hon. Treasurer:	T.G. FIELDING Esq	[e-mail: cofs.glasgow.presbytery@dial.pipex.com]	

1 Banton linked with Twechar
Jean R.M. Blackley (Mrs) BD   1989   Manse of Banton, Kilsyth G65 OQL   01236 826129

2 Bishopbriggs: Kenmure
Iain A. Laing MA BD   1971 1992   5 Marchfield. Bishopbriggs, Glasgow G64 3PP   0141 772 1468

No.	Charge / Minister	Year	Year	Address	Telephone
3	**Bishopbriggs: Springfield** William Ewart BSc BD	1972		39 Springfield Road, Bishopbriggs Glasgow G64 1PL	0141 772 1540
4	**Blairbeth Rodger Memorial (T)** Brian S. Sheret MA BD DPhil	1982	1990	4 Milrig Road, Rutherglen, Glasgow G73 2NH	0141 647 6762
5	**Broom (0141 639 3528)** James Whyte BD	1981	1987	3 Laigh Road, Newton Mearns G77 5EX	0141 639 2916 0141 639 3528 (Fax) 0141 639 6853
	Margaret McLelland (Mrs) DCS			5 Kinloch Road, Newton Mearns G77 6LY	
6	**Burnside (0141 634 4130)** David J.C. Easton MA BD	1965	1977	59 Blairbeth Road, Burnside, Glasgow G73 4JD	0141 634 1233 (Tel) 0141 634 7383 (Fax)
7	**Busby (0141 644 2073)** Jeremy Eve BSc BD	1998		17A Carmunnock Road, Busby G76 8SZ	0141 644 3670
8	**Cadder (0141 772 7436)** Graham S. Finch MA BD	1977	1999	6 Balmuildy Road, Bishopbriggs Glasgow G64 3BS	0141 772 1363
9	**Cambuslang: Flemington Hallside** R. David Currie BSc BD	1984		103 Overton Road, Cambuslang, Glasgow G72 7XA	0141 641 2097
10	**Cambuslang: Old** Alan H. Ward MA BD	1978	1985	74 Stewarton Drive, Cambuslang, Glasgow G72 8DG [e-mail: alanhward@ntlworld.com]	0141 641 3261
11	**Cambuslang: St Andrew's** John Stevenson LTh	1998		37 Brownside Road, Cambuslang, Glasgow G72 8NH [e-mail: john@stevensonj.fsnet.co.uk]	0141 641 3847 (Tel) 0141 641 0773 (Fax)
12	**Cambuslang: Trinity St Paul's** David Stewart MA DipEd BD MTh	1977	1989	4 Glasgow Road, Cambuslang, Glasgow G72 7BW [e-mail: Revdavidst@aol.com]	0141 641 3414 (Tel) 0141 646 1260 (Fax)
13	**Campsie (01360 310939)** David J. Torrance BD DipMin	1993		19 Redhills View, Lennoxtown Glasgow G65 7BL	01360 312527
14	**Chryston (H)** Martin A.W. Allen MA BD ThM David J. McAdam BSc BD (Assoc)	1977	1990	Main Street, Chryston Glasgow G69 9LA 12 Dunellan Crescent, Moodiesburn, Glasgow G69 0GE	0141 779 1436 01236 870472

#	Congregation / Minister			Address	Telephone
15	**Eaglesham (01355 302047)** W. Douglas Lindsay BD CPS	1978	1988	East Kilbride Road, Eaglesham Glasgow G76 ONS	01355 303495
16	**Fernhill and Cathkin** Douglas W. Wallace MA BD	1981	1990	82 Blairbeth Road, Rutherglen, Glasgow G73 4JA	0141 634 1508
17	**Gartcosh (H) (01236 873770) linked with Glenboig (01236 875625)** Alexander M. Fraser BD DipMin	1985		26 Inchknock Avenue, Gartcosh G69 8EA [e-mail: Sandy@revfraser.freeserve.co.uk]	01236 872274
18	**Giffnock: Orchardhill (0141 638 3604)** John M. Spiers LTh MTh	1972	1977	23 Huntly Avenue, Giffnock G46 6LW	0141 571 7675 (Tel/Fax)
19	**Giffnock: South (0141 638 2599)** Edward V. Simpson BSc BD	1972	1983	5 Langtree Avenue, Whitecraigs, Glasgow G46 7LN	0141 638 8767 (Tel) 0141 620 0605 (Fax)
20	**Giffnock: The Park** Michael Gibson BD STM	1974		41 Rouken Glen Road, Thornliebank Glasgow G46 7JD	0141 638 3023
21	**Glenboig** See Gartcosh				
22	**Greenbank (H) (0141 644 1891)** Alistair N. Shaw MA BD	1982	1999	Greenbank Manse, Clarkston, Glasgow G76 7DJ [e-mail: alistairn@shaw98.freeserve.co.uk]	0141 644 1395 (Tel) 0141 644 4804 (Fax)
23	**Kilsyth: Anderson** Charles M. MacKinnon BD	1989	1999	Anderson Manse, Kilsyth, Glasgow G65 0HR	01236 822345
24	**Kilsyth: Burns and Old** T.A. McLachlan BSc	1972	1983	The Grange, Glasgow Road, Kilsyth G65 9AE	01236 823116
25	**Kirkintilloch: Hillhead** Vacant			81 Hillhead Road, Kirkintilloch G66 2HY	0141 776 1198
26	**Kirkintilloch: St Columba's (H)** David M. White BA BD	1988	1992	14 Crossdykes, Kirkintilloch G66 3EU	0141 578 4357
27	**Kirkintilloch: St David's Memorial Park (H)** Vacant			2 Roman Road, Kirkintilloch G66 1EA	0141 776 1434
28	**Kirkintilloch: St Mary's** Vacant			The Manse, Union Road, Kirkintilloch G66 1DH	0141 776 1252

#	Name			Address	Telephone
29	**Lenzie: Old (H)** Douglas W. Clark LTh	1993	2000	41 Kirkintilloch Road, Lenzie, Glasgow G66 4LB	0141 776 2184
30	**Lenzie: Union (H)** James B. Ferguson LTh	1972		1 Larch Avenue, Lenzie, Glasgow G66 4HX	0141 776 3831
31	**Maxwell Mearns Castle (0141 639 5169)** David C. Cameron BD CertMin	1993		122 Broomfield Avenue, Newton Mearns G77 5JR	0141 616 0642
32	**Mearns (H) (0141 639 6555)** Joseph A. Kavanagh BD DipPTh Anne M. MacFadyen (Mrs) BSc BD (Aux)	1992 1995	1998 2000	Manse of Mearns, Newton Mearns G77 5BU 295 Mearns Road, Newton Mearns G77 5LT	0141 616 2410 0141 639 3605
33	**Milton of Campsie (H)** Diane E. Stewart BD	1988		33 Birdstone Road, Milton of Campsie G65 8BX	01360 310548 (Tel/Fax)
34	**Netherlee (H)** Ian R. Boyd MA BD PhD	1989	1997	532 Clarkston Road, Glasgow G44 3RT [e-mail: ianboyd@lineone.net]	0141 585 7545
35	**Newton Mearns (H) (0141 639 7373)** Angus Kerr BD CertMin ThM	1983	1994	28 Waterside Avenue, Newton Mearns G77 6TJ	0141 616 2079
36	**Rutherglen: Old** Alexander Thomson BSc BD MPhil PhD	1973	1985	31 Highburgh Drive, Rutherglen, Glasgow G73 3RR	0141 647 6178
37	**Rutherglen: Stonelaw (0141 647 5113)** Alastair M. Morrice MA BD	1968	1987	80 Blairbeth Road, Rutherglen, Glasgow G73 4JA [e-mail: Alastair@amorrice.freeserve.co.uk]	0141 583 9923 (Tel/Fax)
38	**Rutherglen: Wardlawhill** George Cranston BD	1976	1983	26 Parkhill Drive, Rutherglen, Glasgow G73 2PW	0141 563 9590
39	**Rutherglen: West** John W. Drummond MA BD	1971	1986	12 Albert Drive, Rutherglen, Glasgow G73 3RT	0141 569 8547
40	**Stamperland (0141 637 4999) (H)** Alastair J. Cherry BA BD	1982	1987	109 Ormonde Avenue, Glasgow G44 3SN [e-mail: a.j.cherry@btinternet.com]	0141 637 4976 (Tel/Fax)
41	**Stepps (H)** Kenneth S. Baird MSc PhD BD CEng MIMarE	1998		2 Lenzie Road, Stepps, Glasgow G33 6DX	0141 779 9556

42	**Thornliebank (H)** Robert M. Silver BD	1995		19 Arthurlie Drive, Giffnock G46 6UR	0141 620 2133
43	**Torrance (T)** Nigel L. Barge BSc BD	1991		27 Campbell Place, Meadow Rise, Torrance G64 4HR [e-mail: nigel@nbarge.freeserve.co.uk]	01360 622379
44	**Twechar** See Banton				
45	**Williamwood** G. Hutton B. Steel MA BD	1982	1990	125 Greenwood Road, Clarkston, Glasgow G76 7LL	0141 571 7949
46	**Glasgow: Anderston Kelvingrove (0141 221 9408)** Gordon Kirkwood BSc BD	1987	1997	16 Royal Terrace G3 7NY	0141 332 3136
47	**Glasgow: Baillieston Mure Memorial (0141 773 1216)** Allan S. Vint BSc BD	1989	1996	28 Beech Avenue, Baillieston, Glasgow G69 6LF [e-mail: allan@vint.co.uk]	0141 771 1217
48	**Glasgow: Baillieston St Andrew's (0141 771 6629)** Vacant			12 Oakhill Avenue, Baillieston, Glasgow G69 7ES	0141 771 1791
49	**Glasgow: Balshagray Victoria Park** Vacant			20 St Kilda Drive G14 9JN	0141 954 9780
50	**Glasgow: Barlanark Greyfriars** Vacant			4 Rhindmuir Grove, Glasgow G69 6NE	0141 771 1240
51	**Glasgow: Battlefield East (H) (0141 632 4206)** Alan C. Raeburn MA BD	1977		110 Mount Annan Drive G44 4RZ	0141 632 1514
52	**Glasgow: Blawarthill** Ian M.S. McInnes BD DipMin	1995	1997	46 Earlbank Avenue G14 9HL	0141 579 6521
53	**Glasgow: Bridgeton St Francis in the East (H): Church House: telephone 0141 554 8095)** Howard R. Hudson MA BD	1982	1984	10 Albany Drive, Rutherglen, Glasgow G73 3QN	0141 647 9973
	Alex Mair DCS			53 Gardenside Grove, Fernlee Meadows, Carmyle G32 8DS	0141 646 2165
	Margaret S. Beaton (Miss) DCS			64 Gardenside Grove, Fernlee Meadows, Carmyle G32 8DS	0141 646 2297
54	**Glasgow: Broomhill (0141 334 2540)** William B. Ferguson BA BD	1971	1987	27 St Kilda Drive G14 9LN	0141 959 3204

No.	Charge / Ministers	Year	Address	Telephone
55	**Glasgow: Calton Parkhead (0141 554 3866)** Ronald Anderson BD DipTh Karen Hamilton (Mrs) DCS	1992	98 Drumover Drive G31 5RP 6 Beckfield Gate, Robroyston, Glasgow G33 1SW	0141 556 2520
56	**Glasgow: Cardonald (0141 882 1051)** Eric McLachlan BD	1978 1983	133 Newtyle Road, Paisley PA1 3LB	0141 561 1891
57	**Glasgow: Carmunnock** Robert J.M. Anderson BD	1993	The Manse, 161 Waterside Road, Carmunnock G76 9AJ [e-mail: robert@carmanse.freeserve.co.uk]	0141 644 1578 (Tel/Fax)
58	**Glasgow: Carmyle linked with Kenmuir Mount Vernon** Murdo Maclean BD CertMin	1997 1999	3 Meryon Road, Glasgow G32 9NW	0141 778 2625
59	**Glasgow: Carntyne Old linked with Eastbank** Ronald A.S. Craig BACC BD	1983	211 Sandyhills Road G32 9NB	0141 778 1286
60	**Glasgow: Carnwadric (E)** Graeme K. Bell BA BD Christine M. McVean (Miss) DCS	1983	62 Loganswell Road G46 8AX 38 Cruachan St Glasgow G46 8LY	0141 638 5884 0141 638 9035
61	**Glasgow: Castlemilk: East (H) (0141 634 2444)** John D. Miller BA BD Ann Lyall (Miss) DCS	1971	15 Castlemilk Drive G45 9TL 117 Barlia Drive, Glasgow G45 0AY	0141 631 1244 0141 631 3643
62	**Glasgow: Castlemilk: West (H) (0141 634 1480)** Charles Cameron BA BD PhD	1980	156 Old Castle Road G44 5TW	0141 637 5451
63	**Glasgow: Cathcart Old** Neil W. Galbraith BD CertMin	1987	21 Courthill Avenue, Cathcart G44 5AA	0141 633 5248 (Tel/Fax)
64	**Glasgow: Cathcart South (H) (0141 637 6658)** Andrew M. Smillie LTh	1990	82 Merrylee Road G43 2QZ	0141 633 3744
65	**Glasgow: Cathedral (High or St Mungo's)** William Morris KCVO DD PhD LLD JP	1951	1 Whitehill Grove, Newton Mearns G77 5DH	0141 639 6327
66	**Glasgow: Colston Milton (0141 772 1922)** Christopher D. Park BSc BD	1977	118 Birsay Road G22 7QP	0141 772 1958
67	**Glasgow: Colston Wellpark (H)** Christine M. Goldie (Miss) LLB BD	1984 1999	16 Bishop's Gate Gardens, Colston G21 1XS	0141 402 4002

68 **Glasgow: Cranhill (H) (0141 774 5593)**
James A. Trevorrow LTh — 1971 1994 — 31 Lethamhill Crescent G33 2SH [e-mail: csmillie@netcomuk.co.uk] — 0141 770 6873
J.B. MacPherson DCS — 13 Leslie Street, Glasgow G41 2LQ — 0141 423 6868

69 **Glasgow: Croftfoot (H) (0141 637 3913)**
John M. Lloyd BD CertMin — 1984 1986 — 20 Victoria Road, Burnside, Rutherglen G73 3QG [e-mail: JohnMLloyd@compuserve.com] — 0141 647 5524

70 **Glasgow: Dennistoun Blackfriars (H)**
Vacant — 41 Broompark Drive G31 2JB — 0141 554 8667

71 **Glasgow: Dennistoun Central (H)**
Ada Younger (Mrs) BD — 1978 1996 — 45 Broompark Drive G31 2JB [adah@younger31.prestel.co.uk] — 0141 550 4487

72 **Glasgow: Drumchapel Drumry St Mary's (0141 944 1998)**
Hilda C. Smith (Miss) MA BD — 1992 — 8 Fruin Road G15 6SQ — 0141 944 4493
Senga Nicol (Miss) DCS — 2/1, 160 Tollcross Road, Glasgow G31 4OZ — 0141 554 3028

73 **Glasgow: Drumchapel St Andrew's (0141 944 3758)**
John S. Purves LLB BD — 1983 1984 — 6 Firdon Crescent G15 6QQ — 0141 944 4566
Allan McKenzie BSc BD (Assoc) — 1988 2000 — 17 Summerhill Gardens, Glasgow G15 7JD — 0141 944 6856
Elizabeth Gregson (Mrs) BD (Assist) — 1996 — 17 Westfields, Bishopbriggs G64 3PL — 0141 563 1918

74 **Glasgow: Drumchapel St Mark's**
Vacant — 146 Garscadden Road G15 6PR — 0141 944 5440

75 **Glasgow Eastbank** See Carntyne Old

76 **Glasgow: Easterhouse St George's and St Peter's (E) (0141 781 0800)**
Malcolm Cuthbertson BA BD — 1984 — 3 Barony Gardens, Baillieston G69 6TS [e-mail: malcuth@aol.com] — 0141 573 8200 (Tel) / 0141 773 4878 (Fax)

77 **Glasgow: Eastwood**
Moyna McGlynn (Mrs) BD PhD — 1999 — 54 Mansewood Road G43 1TL — 0141 632 0724

78 **Glasgow: Gairbraid (H)**
Ian C. MacKenzie MA BD — 1970 1971 — 1515 Maryhill Road G20 7XL — 0141 946 1568

79 **Glasgow: Gardner Street (GE)**
Roderick Morrison MA BD — 1974 1994 — 148 Beechwood Drive G11 7DX — 0141 563 2638

No.	Charge / Minister	Year(s)	Address	Telephone
80	**Glasgow: Garthamlock and Craigend East (E)**			
	Valerie J. Duff (Miss) DMin	1993	175 Tillycairn Drive, Garthamlock G33 5HS	0141 774 6364
	James Hamilton DCS		6 Beckfield Gate, Robroyston G33 1SW	0141 558 3195
81	**Glasgow: Gorbals**			
	Ian F. Galloway BA BD	1976	44 Riverside Road G43 2EF	0141 649 5250
82	**Glasgow: Govan Old (0141 445 1941)**			
	T.A. Davidson Kelly MA BD FSAScot	1975	4 Dalziel Quadrant, Pollokshields G41 4NR	0141 427 0321
	Michael S. Edwards BD (Assoc)	1982	108 Cleveden Road, G12 0JT	0141 579 7115
83	**Glasgow: Govanhill Trinity**			
	Sigrid Marten (Mrs) BD	1997	143 Albert Road G42 8UE	0141 422 1293
			[e-mail: smarten@gn.apc.org]	
84	**Glasgow: High Carntyne (0141 778 4186)**			
	Peter W. Nimmo BD ThM	1996	165 Smithycroft Road G33 2RD	0141 770 6464
85	**Glasgow: Hillington Park (H)**			
	Ian Morrison BD	1991	61 Ralston Avenue G52 3NB	0141 882 7000
			[e-mail: Iain@mor77.freeserve.co.uk]	
86	**Glasgow: Househillwood St Christopher's**			
	Vacant		29 Torridon Avenue G41 5AT	0141 427 2596
87	**Glasgow: Hyndland (H) (0141 339 1804)**			
	John C. Christie BSc BD	1990	24 Hughenden Gardens G12 9YH	0141 334 1002
88	**Glasgow: Ibrox (H) (0141 427 0896)**			
	C. Blair Gillon BD	1975 1980	3 Dargarvel Avenue G41 5LD	0141 427 1282 (Tel/Fax)
			[e-mail: cb@gillon3.freeserve.co.uk]	0370 660 123 (mbl)
89	**Glasgow John Ross Memorial Church for Deaf People**			
	(Voice Text: 0141 420 1759 Text Only: 0141 429 6682 Fax: 0141 429 6860 ISDN Video Phone: 0141 418 0579)			
	Richard C. Durno DSW CQSW	1989 1998	31 Springfield Road, Bishopbriggs G64 1PJ	(Voice/Text) 0141 772 1052
			[e-mail: richard@deafconnections.co.uk]	
			[www.deafconnections.co.uk]	
90	**Glasgow: Jordanhill (0141 959 2496 Tel/Fax))**			
	Colin C. Renwick BMus BD	1989 1996	96 Southbrae Drive G13 1TZ	0141 959 1310 (Tel)
				0141 959 2496 (Fax)
91	**Glasgow: Kelvin Stevenson Memorial (0141 339 1750)**			
	William McAreavey BA	1950 1956	94 Hyndland Road G12 9PZ	0141 334 5352

No.	Congregation / Minister	Ord.	Ind.	Address	Telephone
92	**Glasgow: Kelvinside Hillhead** Jennifer Macrae (Mrs) BD	1998	2000	39 Athole Gardens G12 9BQ	0141 339 2865
93	**Glasgow: Kenmuir Mount Vernon** See Carmyle				
94	**Glasgow: King's Park (H) (0141 632 1131)** G. Stewart Smith MA BD STM	1966	1979	1101 Aikenhead Road G44 5SL	0141 637 2803 (Tel/Fax)
95	**Glasgow: Kinning Park (0141 427 3063)** Margaret H. Johnston (Miss) BD	1988	2000	168 Arbroath Avenue, G52 HH	0141 570 0642
96	**Glasgow: Knightswood St Margaret's (H)** Andrew P. Lees BD	1984	1989	26 Airthrey Avenue G14 9LJ	0141 959 1094
97	**Glasgow: Langside (0141 632 7520)** John Owain Jones MA BD FSAScot	1981	1998	36 Madison Avenue G44 5AQ	0141 637 0797
98	**Glasgow: Lansdowne** Roy J.M. Henderson MA BD DipMin Helen M. Hughes (Miss) DCS	1987	1992	18 Woodlands Drive G4 9EH Flat 2/2, 43 Burnbank Terrace G20 6UQ	0141 339 2794 0141 333 9459
99	**Glasgow: Linthouse St Kenneth's** James Macfarlane PhD	1991		51 Morriston Crescent, Deanpark, Renfrew PA4 0XU	0141 885 2597
100	**Glasgow: Lochwood (H) (0141 771 2649)** Stuart M. Duff BA	1997		42 Rhindmuir Road, Swinton G69 6AZ [e-mail: Stuart@duff58.freeserve.co.uk]	0141 773 2756
101	**Glasgow: Martyrs', The** Ewen MacLean BA BD	1995		30 Louden Hill Road, Robroyston, Glasgow G33 1GA	0141 558 7451
102	**Glasgow: Maryhill (H) (0141 946 3512)** Anthony J.D. Craig BD	1987		111 Maxwell Avenue G61 1HT [e-mail: craig.glasgow@auroranova.net]	0141 570 0642
103	**Glasgow: Merrylea (0141 637 2009)** Sidney H. Coleman BA BD MTh	1961	1982	37 Burnhead Road, Newlands G43 2SU [e-mail: sidney.coleman@dtn.ntl.com]	0141 637 6700 0141 571 2410 (Fax and Voice Mail)
104	**Glasgow: Mosspark (H) (0141 882 2240)** D. Muir McLaren MA BD MTh PhD	1971	1984	396 Kilmarnock Road G43 2DJ [e-mail: cellmuir@breathemail.net]	0141 632 1247 0378 480 514 (Mbl)

105 Glasgow: Mount Florida (H) Hugh M. Wallace MA BD	1981	1987	90 Mount Annan Drive G44 4RZ	0141 632 8868
106 Glasgow: New Cathcart (H) Richard S. Campbell LTh	2000		"Kilrenny", 30 Elmore Avenue, Old Cathcart G44 5AD	0141 637 7373
107 Glasgow: New Govan (H) Vacant			19 Dumbreck Road G41 5LJ	0141 427 3197
108 Glasgow: Newlands South (H) (0141 632 3055) John D. Whiteford MA BD	1989	1997	24 Monreith Road G43 2NY	0141 632 2588
109 Glasgow: North Kelvinside William G. Alston	1961	1971	41 Mitre Road G14 9LE	0141 954 8250
110 Glasgow: Partick South Alan L. Dunnett LLB BD	1994	1997	17 Munro Road G13 1SQ [e-mail: dustydunnett@prtck.freeserve.co.uk]	0141 959 3732
111 Glasgow Partick Trinity (H) Stuart J. Smith BEng BD	1994		99 Balshagray Avenue, Glasgow	0141 576 7149
112 Glasgow: Penilee St Andrew (H) (0141 882 2691) Esther M.M. Jamieson (Mrs) BD	1984		80 Tweedsmuir Road G52 2RX	0141 882 3432
113 Glasgow: Pollokshaws Margaret Whyte (Mrs) BA BD	1988		33 Mannering Road G41 3SW	0141 649 4981
114 Glasgow: Pollokshields (H) David R. Black MA BD Anne MacDonald (Miss) BA DCS	1986	1997	36 Glencairn Drive G41 4PW 81 Arbroath Avenue G52 3HJ	0141 423 4000 0141 883 5618
115 Glasgow: Possilpark Martin R. Forrest BA MA BD	1988		11E 231 Westercommon Road G22 5ND	0141 336 3127
116 Glasgow: Priesthill and Nitshill Douglas M. Nicol BD CA Thomas C. Houston BA (Assoc)	1987 1975	1996 2000	36 Springkell Drive G41 4EZ	0141 427 7877
117 Glasgow: Queen's Park (0141 423 3654) Vacant				

(New Charge formed by the union of Crosshill Queen's Park and Strathbungo Queen's Park)

118 Glasgow: Renfield St Stephen's (Tel: 0141 332 4293   Fax: 0141 332 8482)
David W. Lunan MA BD   1970   1987   101 Hill Street G3 6TY   0141 353 3395

119 Glasgow: Robroyston (New Charge Development)
Keith McKillop MB ChB BD   1999   7 Beckfield Drive, Robroyston G33 1SR   0141 558 8414

120 Glasgow: Ruchazie (0141 774 2759)
William F. Hunter MA BD   1986   1999   18 Borthwick Street G33 3UU   0141 774 6860
[e-mail: bhunter@tesco.net]
Janet Anderson (Miss) DCS   322 Gartcraig Road G33 2TB   0141 774 5329

121 Glasgow: Ruchill (0141 946 0466)
John C. Matthews MA BD   1992   9 Kirklee Road G12 ORQ   0141 357 3249

122 Glasgow: St Andrew's East (0141 554 1485)
Janette G. Reid (Miss) BD   1991   43 Broompark Drive G31 2JB   0141 554 3620

123 Glasgow: St Columba (GE) (0141 221 3305)
Vacant

124 Glasgow: St David's Knightswood (0141 959 1024) [e-mail: DrInglis@stdavidschurch.freeserve.co.uk]
Graham M. Thain LLB BD   1988   1999   60 Southbrae Drive G13 1QD   0141 959 2904

125 Glasgow: St Enoch's Hogganfield (H) (0141 770 5694) [e-mail: church@st-enoch.org.uk] (www.st-enoch.org.uk)
Andrew J. Philip BSc BD   1996   43 Smithycroft Road G33 2RH   0141 770 7595
[e-mail: andrewphilip@minister.com]   0870 284 (Fax)]

126 Glasgow: St George's Tron (0141 221 2141)
Sinclair B. Ferguson MA BD PhD   1972   1998   29 Vancouver Drive G14 9HR   0141 959 2535
John Rushton BVMS BD (Assoc)   1983   2000   29 Brent Avenue, Thornliebank G46 8IU   0141 638 0837
[e-mail: JohnSusanRushton@talk21.com]

127 Glasgow: St James' (Pollok) (0141 882 4984)
Helen Hamilton (Miss) BD   1991   30 Ralston Avenue G52 3NA   0141 883 7405
Ann Merrilees (Miss) DCS   0/1 15 Crookston Grove G52 3PN   0141 883 2488

128 Glasgow: St John's Renfield (0141 339 7021) (www.stjohns-renfield.org.uk)
Dugald J.R. Cameron BD DipMin MTh   1990   1999   26 Leicester Avenue G12 OLU   0141 339 4637
[e-mail: dugald.cameron@tinyworld.co.uk]

129 Glasgow: St Luke's and St Andrew's
Ian C. Fraser BA BD   1982   1995   10 Chalmers Street G40 2HA   0141 556 3883
[e-mail: stluke@cqm.co.uk]

130 Glasgow: St Margaret's Tollcross Park
George M. Murray LTh — 1995 — 31 Kenmuir Avenue, Sandyhills G32 9LE — 0141 778 5060

131 Glasgow: St Nicholas' Cardonald
Roderick I.T. MacDonald BD — 1992 — 104 Lamington Road G52 2SE — 0141 882 2065

132 Glasgow: St Paul's Provanmill (0141 770 8559)
R. Russell McLarty BD — 1985 — 38 Lochview Drive G33 1QF — 0141 770 9611

133 Glasgow: St Rollox
E. Gwynfai Jones BA — 1964 1967 — 42 Melville Gardens, Bishopbriggs, Glasgow G64 3DE — 0141 772 2848

134 Glasgow: St Thomas' Gallowgate
Irene A. Bristow (Mrs) BD — 1989 1997 — 8 Helenvale Court G31 4LH — 0141 554 0997

135 Glasgow: Sandyford Henderson Memorial
C. Peter White BVMS BD MRCVS — 1974 1997 — 66 Woodend Drive G13 1TG — 0141 954 9013

136 Glasgow: Sandyhills
John P.F. Martindale BD — 1994 — 60 Wester Road G32 9JJ — 0141 778 2174

137 Glasgow: Scotstoun (T)
Richard Cameron BD — — 15 Northland Drive G14 9BE — 0141 959 4637

138 Glasgow: Shawlands (0141 649 2012)
Alastair M. Sanderson BA LTh — 1971 1976 — 29 St Ronan's Drive G41 3SQ — 0141 632 9046
Alastair D. McLay BSc BD (Assoc) — 1989 1990 — 47 Dinmont Road G41 3UJ — 0141 649 2034
[e-mail: alastair@mclay79.freeserve.co.uk]

139 Glasgow: Sherbrooke St Gilbert's (H) (0141 427 1968)
Donald Macleod BD LRAM DRSAM — 1987 — 9 Springkell Gate G41 4BY — 0141 423 3912
[e-mail: dml@d-macleod.prestel.co.uk]

140 Glasgow: Shettleston Old (T) (0141 778 2484)
David K. Speed LTh — 1969 1999 — 57 Mansionhouse Road, North Mount Vernon G32 0RP — 0141 778 8904

141 Glasgow: South Carntyne (H) (0141 778 1343)
Vacant — — 47 Broompark Drive G31 2JB — 0141 554 5930

142 Glasgow: South Shawlands (T) (0141 649 4656)
Fiona Gardner (Mrs) BD — 1997 2000 — 391 Kilmarnock Road G43 2NU — 0141 632 0013

143 Glasgow: Springburn (H) (0141 557 2345)
Alan A. Ford BD AIBScotland — 1977 2000 — 3 Tofthill Avenue, Bishopbriggs, Glasgow G64 3PA — 0141 762 1844
[e-mail: alanford@springburnchurch.freeserve.co.uk]

144 Glasgow: Temple Anniesland (0141 959 1814)
John Wilson BD — 1985 — 76 Victoria Park Drive North G14 9PJ [e-mail: jwilson@crowroad0.freeserve.co.uk] — 0141 959 5835

145 Glasgow: Toryglen (H)
Keith W. Ross MA BD — 1984 1991 — 28 Snuffmill Road, Cathcart G44 5TR — 0141 569 6892

146 Glasgow: Townhead Blochairn
William P. Finlay MA BD — 1969 1988 — 35 Lansdowne Crescent G20 6NH — 0141 339 0301

147 Glasgow: Trinity Possil and Henry Drummond
Richard G. Buckley BD MTh — 1990 1995 — 50 Highfield Drive G12 0HL — 0141 339 2870

148 Glasgow: Tron St Mary's
William Wilson BSc BD — 1999 — 3 Hurly Hawkin', Bishopbriggs G64 1YL — 0141 772 8555

149 Glasgow: Victoria Tollcross
Richard Coley LTh — 1971 — 228 Hamilton Road G32 9QU — 0141 778 2413

150 Glasgow: Wallacewell
John McGregor BD — 1999 — 54 Etive Crescent, Bishopbriggs G64 1ES — 0141 772 1453
Joanna Love (Mrs) DCS — Flat 2R, 11 Grantley Gardens G41 3PY — 0141 401 8066

151 Glasgow: Wellington (H) (0141 339 0454)
M. Leith Fisher MA BD — 1967 1990 — 27 Kingsborough Gardens G12 9NH — 0141 339 3627

152 Glasgow: Whiteinch (New Charge Development)
Alan McWilliam BD — 1993 2000 — 65 Victoria Park Drive South G14 9NX [e-mail: alanmcwilliam@netscape.net] — 0141 576 9020

153 Glasgow: Yoker Old linked with Yoker St Matthew's (T)
Neil A. Simpson BA BD PhD — 1992 — 15 Coldingham Avenue G14 0PX [e-mail: neilsimpson@easynet.co.uk] — 0141 952 3620

154 Glasgow: Yoker St Matthew's　See Yoker Old

Name			Charge	Address	Phone
Aiken, Andrew J. BD APhS MTh PhD	1951	1981	(Tollcross Central with Park)	18 Dorchester Avenue G12 0EE	0141 357 1617
Alexander, Eric J MA BD	1958	1997	(St George's Tron)	PO Box 14725, St Andrews KY16 8WB	ex-directory
Allan, A.G.	1959	1989	(Candlish Polmadie)	30 Dalrymple Drive, East Mains, East Kilbride G74 4LF	01355 226190
Barr, Alexander C. MA BD	1950	1992	(St Nicholas' Cardonald)	25 Fisher Drive, Phoenix Park, Paisley PA1 2TP	0141 848 5941
Beattie, John A.	1951	1984	(Dalmuir Overtoun)	0/1, 15 Kelvindale Gardens, Kelvindale Road G20 8DW	0141 946 5978

Name	Years	Role	Address	Tel/Fax
Beautyman, Paul H. MA BD	1993 1998	Mission Co-ordinator	59 Elmbank Street G2 4PQ	0141 352 6946 (Tel/Fax)
Bell, John L. MA BD FRSCM	1978 1988	Iona Community	Flat 2/1, 31 Lansdowne Crescent G20 6NH	0141 334 0688
Black, Sandra (Mrs) BSc BD	1988 1997	Hospital Chaplain	36 Glencairn Drive G41 4PW	0141 423 4000
Brain, Ernest J.	1955 1985	(Liverpool St Andrew's)	14 Chesterfield Court, 1240 Great Western Road G12 0BJ	0141 357 2249
Brain, Isobel J. (Mrs) MA	1987 1997	(Ballantrae)	14 Chesterfield Court, 1240 Great Western Road G12 0BJ	0141 357 2249
Brice, Dennis G. BSc BD	1981	(Taiwan)	18 Hermitage Avenue, Thundsley, Benfleet, Essex SS7 1TQ	01702 555333
Bryden, William A. BD	1977 1984	(Yoker Old with St Matthew's)	145 Bearsden Road G13 1BS	0141 959 5213
Campbell, A. Iain MA DipEd	1961 1997	(Busby)	430 Clarkston Road G44 3QF	0141 637 7460
Campbell, Colin MA BD	1940 1989	(Williamwood)	4 Golf Road, Clarkston G76 7LZ	0141 638 1215
Carmont, Robert	1958 1994	(Sandyhills)	11 Mossgeil Gardens, Uddingston G71 6EP	01698 329109
Cartlidge, G.R.G. MA BD STM	1977 1993	Religious Education	5 Briar Grove, Newlands G43 2TD	0141 637 3228
Chester, Stephen	1999	RE Teacher, International Christian College		
Clark, David M. MA BD	1989 1996	General Director, Scripture Union	Flat 1/2, 7 Craighouse Street, Ruchazie, Glasgow G33 3RU	(Tel) 0141 634 4256
			39 Blairbeth Road G73 4JF	(Fax) 0141 332 5925
Cooke, John M. MA BD PhD	1950 1982	(Fowlis Wester with Monzie)	2 Wellfield Court, Giffnock G46 7QJ	0141 638 4749
Cullen, William T. BA LTh	1984 1996	(Kilmarnock: St John's Onthank)	71 Fenwick Road, Giffnock G46 6AX	0141 637 8244
Cunningham, Alexander MA BD	1961 1980	Presbytery Clerk	The Glen, 103 Glenmavis Road, Airdrie ML6 OPQ	01236 763012
Cunningham, James S. A. MA BD BLitt PhD	1992 2000	(Glasgow: Barlanark Greyfriars)	"Kirkland", 5 Inveresk Place, Coatbridge ML5 2OA	01236 421541
Currie, Robert MA	1955 1990	(Community Minister)	Flat 3/2, 13 Redlands Road G12 0SJ	0141 334 5111
Dunnet, Linda (Mrs) DCS		Frontier Youth Trust, West of Scotland Development Officer	759B Argyle Street, Glasgow G3 8DS	(Off) 0141 204 4800
			17 Munro Road G13 1SQ	0141 959 3732
Fairweather, Ian C.M. MA BD	1945 1985	(Jordanhill College of Education)	86 Whittinghame Court, Glasgow G12 0BH	0141 334 7577
Fenton, Robert J. MA	1940 1976	(St Kiaran's Dean Park)	Eastwoodhill, 238 Fenwick Road, Glasgow G46 6UU	0141 638 5127
Forbes, George A. R. BD	1971 2000	(Kirkintilloch Hillhead)	28 Murrayfield, Bishopbriggs G46 3OS	0141 762 0272
Forrest, Gavin W. MA BD	1984 1987	(Whitburn South)	12 Vancouver Road G14 9HJ	0141 954 9110
Galloway, Allan D. MA BD STM PhD FRSE	1948 1982	(University of Glasgow)	5 Straid Bheag, Barrcmman, Clynder, Helensburgh G84 OQX	01436 83432
Gibson, H. Marshall MA BD	1957 1996	(St Thomas' Gallowgate)	39 Buralbroom Drive G69 7XG	0141 771 0749
Gilchrist, George R. MA BD DD	1940 1980	(Dalrymple)	53 Alexander Avenue, Eaglesham G76 ODP	01355 32272
Goss, Alister BD		Industrial Mission Organiser	79 Weymouth Crescent, Gourock PA19 1HR	01475 638944
Grimstone, A. Frank MA	1949 1986	(Calton Parkhead)	144C Howth Drive, Parkview Estate, Anniesland G13 1RL	0141 954 1009
Haley, Derek BD DPS	1960 1999	(Chaplain, Gartnavel Royal)	9 Kinnaird Crescent, Bearsden, Glasgow G61 2BN	0141 942 9281
Harper, Anne J.M. (Miss) BD STM MTh CertSocPsych	1979 1990	Hospital Chaplain	122 Greenock Road, Bishopton PA7 5AS	01505 862466
Haughton, Frank MA BD	1942 1947	(Kirkintilloch: St. Mary's)	Union Road, Parkview Estate, Kirkintilloch	
Herron, Andrew DD LLD	1934 1981	(Presbytery Clerk)	Eastwoodhill, 238 Fenwick Road, G46 6UU	0141 638 6893
Hope, Evelyn P. (Miss) BA BD	1990 1998	(Wishaw: Thornlie)	Flat 0/1, 48 Moss-side Road, Glasgow G41 3UA	0141 649 1522
Hunter, Alastair G. MSc BD	1976 1980	University of Glasgow	487 Shields Road G41 2RG	0141 429 1687
Hunter, George	1950 1987	(Scotstoun West)	Flat 1C, 256 Great Western Road G4 9EJ	0141 332 7228
Hutcheson, J. Murray MA	1943 1987	(Possilpark)	88 Ainslie Road, Kildrum, Cumbernauld G67 2ED	01236 729378
Hutchison, Henry MA BEd BD MLitt PhD LLCM	1948 1993	(Cumnock)	4A Briar Grove, Newlands, Glasgow G43 2TG	0141 637 2766

Name	Charge / Appointment			Address	Tel.
Irvine, Euphemia H.C. (Mrs) BD	(Milton of Campsie)	1972	1988	32 Baird Drive, Bargarran, Erskine PA8 6BB	0141 812 2777
Johnston, Robert W.M. MA BD STM	(Temple Anniesland)	1964	1999	13 Kilmardinny Crescent, Bearsden, Glasgow G61 3ND	0141 931 5862
Johnstone, David MC MA BD	(Belhaven Westbourne)	1951	1987	140 Hyndland Road G12 9PN	0141 339 5896
Johnstone, H. Martin J. MA BD	Urban Priority Areas Adviser	1989	2000	3 Herries Road, Glasgow G41 4DE	
Jolly, John BA	(Old Partick)	1950	1990	10 Kensington Court, 20 Kensington Road G12 9NX	0141 339 8815
Jones, John D. BA	(Kirkconnel St Mark's)	1935	1972	50 Melville Gardens, Bishopbriggs G64 3DD	0141 772 4776
Langlands, Cameron H. BD MTh ThM	Hospital Chaplain	1995	1999	Flat G/1, Plantation Park Gardens, Glasgow G51 1NW	0141 620 3492
Levison, C. L. MA BD	Hospital Chaplain	1972	1998	5 Deaconsbank Avenue, Stewarton Road, Glasgow G46 7UN	0141 334 5411
Lewis, E.M.H. MA	(Drumchapel St Andrew's)	1962	1994	7 Cleveden Place, Glasgow G12 0HG	0141 810 3776
Liddell, Matthew MA BD	(St Paul's (Outer High) and (St David's (Ramshorn))	1943	1982	17 Traquair Drive G52 2TB	
Lindsay, James A. MC MA	(Burnside)	1936	1976	113 Rosslyn Avenue, Rutherglen, Glasgow G73 3EZ	0141 647 5053
Macarthur, J.M.M.	(St Columba)	1966	1996	5 Polquhap Gardens, Thorncroft Park, Crookston G53 7FW [e-mail: Polquhap@quista.net]	0141 891 5385
Macaskill, Donald MA BD PhD	Board of Parish Education	1994	1994	44 Forfar Avenue, Cardonald, Glasgow G52 3JQ	0141 883 5956
Macaskill, Marjory (Mrs) LLB BD	Chaplain: University of Strathclyde	1990	1998	44 Forfar Avenue, Cardonald, Glasgow G52 3JQ	0141 883 5956
MacBain, Iain W.	(Coatbridge: Coatdyke)	1971	1993	24 Thornyburn Drive, Baillieston G69 7ER	0141 771 7030
Macdonald, Murdo Ewen DD	(University of Glasgow) Director/Chaplain, Lodging House Mission	1939	1984	Eastwoodhill, 238 Fenwick Road, Glasgow G46 6UU	0141 638 5127
McDonald, Ross J. BA BD ThM	(South Shawlands)	1998		35 East Campbell Street, Glasgow G1 5DT	0141 552 0285
Macfarlane, Thomas G. BSc PhD BD	(Edinburgh Richmond Craigmillar)	1956	1992	Flat 0/2, 19 Corrour Road G43 2DY	0141 632 7966
McKenzie, Mary O. (Miss)	(St Andrew's Plantation)	1976	1996	4 Dunellan Avenue, Moodiesburn, Glasgow G69 0GB	01236 870180
McLean, John MA	Chaplain Army	1948	1977	18 Pelham Road, Droitwich, Worcester WR9 8NT	
MacLeod, Charles Angus BD	(Kirkintilloch St David's Memorial)	1996		1 KOSB, Dreghorn Barracks, Edinburgh EH13 9QM	
MacLeod, Willliam J. DipTh	Chaplain: Southern General Hospital	1963	1988	42 Hawthorn Drive, Banknock, Bonnybridge FK4 1LF	01324 840667
MacMahon, Janet P.H. (Mrs) MSc BD	(Summertown)	1992	1992	6 Jubilee Gardens, Bearsden G61 2RT	0141 942 3671
McMurtrie, D.W. MA ATCL ARPS	(Hyndland)	1939	1965	9 Iain Drive, Bearsden, Glasgow G61 4PD	0141 942 0293
Macnaughton, J.A. MA BD	Chaplain: University of Glasgow	1949	1989	62 Lauderdale Gardens G12 9QW	0141 339 1294
Mathieson, Fiona C. (Mrs) BEd BD	(Glasgow University)	1988	1995	11 The Square G12 8QQ	0141 339 8855
Millar, David A.R. MA	(Shawlands Old)	1956	1989	310A Albert Drive G41 5RS	0141 429 2249
Millar, James	Chaplain: Marie Curie Hospice, Glasgow	1949	1989	9 Glenbank Court G46 7EJ	0141 638 6250
Mitchell, David BD DipPTheol		1988	1998	48 Leglin Wood Drive, Wallacewell Park, Glasgow G21 [e-mail: DavidMitchell@chaplain48.freeserve.co.uk]	0141 558 4679
Morton, Thomas MA BD LGSM	(Rutherglen Stonelaw)	1945	1986	54 Greystone Avenue, Burnside, Rutherglen G73 3SW	0141 647 2682
Muir, Fred C. MA BD ThM ARCM	(Stepps)	1961	1997	20 Alexandra Avenue, Stepps G33 6BP	0141 779 2504
Murray, Douglas M. MA BD PhD	University of Glasgow	1976	1989	28 Sherbrooke Drive G41 5PA [e-mail: D.Murray@arts.gla.ac.uk]	0141 427 9524
Myers, Frank BA	(Springburn)	1952	1978	18 Birmingham Close, Grantham NG31 8SD	01476 594430
Newlands, George M. MA BD PhD	University of Glasgow	1970	1986	29 Clermiston Road, Edinburgh EH12 6XD	0131 476 9377
Peterkin, W. Neilson MA	(Broom)	1945	1986	7 Craigie Drive, Newton Mearns G77 5DA	0141 639 2329
Philip, George M. MA	(Sandyford Henderson Memorial)	1953	1996	44 Beech Avenue, Bearsden G61 3EX	0141 942 1327
Philip, Robert A. BA BD	(Stepps St Andrew's)	1937	1981	2 Hockley Court, Weston Park West, Bath BA1 4AR	01225 333041
Porter, Richard MA	(Govanhill)	1953	1988	58 Hillend Road G76 7XT	0141 639 4169

Rae, D.L.	1955	1990	(Kolhapur)	29 Falcon Avenue, Edinburgh EH10 4AL	0131 447 3158
Ramsay, W.G.	1967	1999	(Springburn)	53 Kelvinvale, Kirkintilloch G66 1RD	0141 776 2915
Robertson, Archibald MA BD	1957	1999	(Eastwood)	19 Canberra Court, Briadpark Drive, Glasgow G46 6NS	0141 637 7572
Robertson, Blair MA BD ThM	1990	1998	Chaplain: Southern General Hospital	c/o Chaplain's Office, Southern General Hospital, Glasgow	0141 201 2156
Ross, Donald M. MA	1953	1994	(Industrial Mission Organiser)	14 Cartsbridge Road, Busby G76 8DH	0141 644 2220
Ross, James MA BD	1968	1998	(Kilsyth: Anderson)	53 Turnberry Gardens, Westerwood, Cumbernauld G68 0AY	01236 730501
Saunders, Keith BD	1983	1999	Hospital Chaplain	Gartnavel Hospital, Glasgow G12 0YN	0141 211 3000
Scrimgeour, Alice M. (Miss) DCS			(Deaconess)	265 Golfhill Drive G31 2PB	0141 564 9602
Shackleton, William	1960	1996	(Greenock: Wellpark West)	3 Tynwald Avenue, Burnside, Glasgow G73 4RN	0141 569 9407
Shanks, Norman J. MA BD	1983	1988	Iona Community	1 Marchmont Terrace G12 9LT	0141 339 4421
Smith, A. McLaren	1971	1997	(Cumbrae)	27 Fenwick Road, Glasgow G46 6AU	
Smith, J. Rankine MA BD	1945	1982	(Barmulloch)	44 Middlemuir Road, Lenzie G66 4ND	0141 776 0870
Smith, James S.A.	1956	1991	(Drongan, The Schaw Kirk)	146 Aros Drive, Glasgow G52 1TJ	0141 883 9666
Spence, Elisabeth G.B. (Miss) BD	1995	2000	Industrial Missioner: Glasgow Area	45 Selvieland Road, Glasgow G52 4AS	0141 883 8973
Stewart, Norma D. (Miss) MA MEd BD	1977	2000	(Glasgow: Strathbungo Queens Park)	127 Nether Auldhouse Road, Glasgow G43 2YS	07714 112424
Storrar, William F.	1984	1996	University of Glasgow	35 Strathalmond Park, Edinburgh EH4 8AH	
Sutherland, Denis I.	1963	1995	(Hutchesontown)	19 Boyd Orr Crescent, Kilmaurs KA3 2QB	01563 520641
Sutherland, Elizabeth W. (Miss) BD	1972	1996	(Balornock North with Barmulloch)	20 Kirkland Avenue, Blanefield, Glasgow G63 9BZ	01360 770154
Tait, Alexander	1967	1995	(St Enoch's Hogganfield)	8 Mossbank Drive, Hogganfield, Glasgow G33 1LS	0141 779 3370
Turner, Angus BD	1976	1990	Industrial Chaplain	46 Keir Street, Pollokshields, Glasgow G41 2LA	0141 424 0493
Tuton, Robert M. MA	1957	1995	(Shettleston: Old)	6 Holmwood Gardens, Uddingston G71 7BH	01698 321108
Walker, A.L.	1955	1988	(Trinity Possil and Henry Drummond)	11 Dundas Avenue, Torrance G64 4BD	01360 622281
Webster, John G. BSc	1964	1998	(St John's Renfield)	Plane Tree, King's Cross, Isle of Arran KA27 8RG	01770 700747
White, Elizabeth (Miss) DCS			(Deaconess)	17 Clincarthill Road, Rutherglen G73 2LF	0141 647 2683

GLASGOW ADDRESSES

Banton		Kelvinhead Road, Banton
Bishopbriggs		
Kenmure		Viewfield Road, Bishopbriggs
Springfield		Springfield Road
Blairbeth Rodger		
Memorial		Kirkcriggs Gardens
Broom		Mearns Road, Newton Mearns
Burnside		Church Avenue, Burnside
Busby		Church Road, Busby
Cadder		Cadder Road, Glasgow
Cambuslang		
Flemington Hallside		
Old		265 Hamilton Road
St Andrew's		Cairns Road
Trinity St Paul's		Main Street x Clydeford Road
Campsie		Main Street, Lennoxtown
Chryston		Main Street, Chryston
Eaglesham		Montgomery Street, Eaglesham
Gartcosh		113 Lochend Road, Gartcosh
Glenboig		138 Main Street, Glenboig
Giffnock		
Orchardhill		Church Road
South		Eastwood Toll
The Park		Ravenscliffe Drive
Greenbank		Eaglesham Road, Clarkston
Kilsyth		
Anderson		Kingston Road
Burns and Old		Church Street
Kirkintilloch		
Hillhead		Newdyke Road
St Columba's		Waterside Road nr Old Aisle Road
St Davids Mem Pk		Alexander Street
St Mary's		High Street
Lenzie		
Old		Kikintilloch Road x Garngaber Avenue
Union		Moncrieff Ave x Kirkintilloch Road
Maxwell		
Mearns Castle		Waterfoot Road
Mearns		Mearns Road, Newton Mearns
Milton of Campsie		Antermony Road, Milton of Campsie
Netherlee		Ormonde Drive x Ormonde Avenue
Newton Mearns		Ayr Road, Newton Mearns
Rutherglen		
Old		Main Street at Queen Street
Stonelaw		Stonelaw Road x Dryburgh Avenue
Wardlawhill		Hamilton Road
West		Glasgow Road nr Main Street
Stamperland		Stamperland Gardens, Clarkston
Stepps		Whitehill Avenue
Thornliebank		Woodlands Road
Torrance		School Road, Torrance
Twechar		Main Street, Twechar
Williamwood		Vardar Avenue x Seres Ave, Clarkston

Glasgow

Congregation	Address
Anderston Kelvingrove	Argyle Street x Elderslie Street
Baillieston	
Mure Memorial	Beech Avenue, Garrowhill
St Andrew's	Church Street
Balshagray Victoria Pk	Broomhill Cross
Barlanark Greyfriars	Edinburgh Road x Hallhill Road
Battlefield East	1216 Cathcart Road
Blawarthill	Millbrix Avenue
Bridgeton St Francis in the East	Queen Mary Street x Bernard Street
Broomhill	Randolph Rd x Marlborough Ave
Calton Parkhead	122 Helenvale Street
Cardonald	2141 Paisley Road West
Carmunnock	Kirk Road, Carmunnock
Carmyle	South Carmyle Avenue
Carntyne Old	862 Shettleston Road
Carnwadric	556 Boydstone Road, Thornliebank
Castlemilk	
East	Barlia Terrace
West	Carmunnock Road
Cathcart	
Old	119 Carmunnock Road
South	92 Clarkston Road
Cathedral	Cathedral Square
Colston Milton	Egilsay Crescent
Colston Wellpark	1378 Springburn Road
Cranhill	Bellrock Crescent x Bellrock Street
Croftfoot	Croftpark Ave x Crofthill Road
Dennistoun	
Blackfriars	Whitehill Street
Central	Armadale Street
Drumchapel	
Drumry St Mary's	Drumry Road East
St Andrew's	Garscadden Road
St Mark's	Kinfauns Drive
Eastbank	679 Old Shettleston Road
Easterhouse St George's and St Peter's	Boyndie Street
Eastwood	Mansewood Road
Fernhill and Cathkin	Neilvaig Drive
Gairbraid	1517 Maryhill Road
Gardner Street	Gardner Street x Muirpark Street
Garthamlock and Craigend East	Porchester Street x Balveny Street
Gorbals	Eglinton Street x Cumberland Street
Govan Old	866 Govan Road
Govanhill Trinity	Daisy Street nr Allison Street
High Carntyne	358 Carntynehall Road
Hillington Park	24 Berryknowes Road
Househillwood St Christopher's	Meikle Road
Hyndland	Hyndland Road, opp Novar Drive
Ibrox	Carillon Road x Clifford Street
John Ross Memorial	100 Norfolk Street G5 9EJ
Jordanhill	Woodend Drive x Munro Road
Kelvin Stevenson Mem	Belmont Street at Belmont Bridge
Kelvinside Hillhead	Huntly Gardens
Kenmuir Mount Vernon	London Road, Mount Vernon
King's Park	242 Castlemilk Road
Kinning Park	Eaglesham Place
Knightswood St Margaret's	Knightswood Cross
Langside	Ledard Road x Lochleven Road
Lansdowne	Gt Western Road at Kelvin Bridge
Linthouse St Kenneth's	9 Skipness Drive
Lochwood	Lochend Road x Liff Place
Martyrs', The	St Mungo Avenue
Maryhill	1990 Maryhill Road
Merrylea	78 Merrylee Road
Mosspark	149 Ashkirk Drive
Mount Florida	1123 Cathcart Road
New Cathcart	Newlands Road nr Clarkston Road
New Govan	Govan Cross
Newlands South	Riverside Road x Langside Drive
North Kelvinside	153 Queen Margaret Drive
Partick South	Dumbarton Road
Trinity	20 Lawrence Street
Penilee St Andrew	Bowfield Cres x Bowfield Avenue
Pollokshaws	223 Shawbridge Street
Pollokshields	Albert Drive x Shields Road
Possilpark	124 Saracen Street
Priesthill and Nitshill	Freeland Drive x Muirshiel Cres
Queen's Park	170 Queen's Drive
Renfield St Stephen's	260 Bath Street
Robroyston	
Ruchazie	Elibank Street x Milncroft Road
Ruchill	Shakespeare Street nr Maryhill Rd.
St Andrew's East	681 Alexandra Parade
St Columba	300 St Vincent Street
St David's	
Knightswood	Boreland Drive nr Lincoln Avenue
St Enoch's Hogganfield	860 Cumbernauld Road
St George's Tron	163 Buchanan Street
St James' (Pollok)	Lyoncross Rd x Byrebush Road
St John's Renfield	22 Beaconsfield Road
St Luke's and St Andrew's	Well Street at Bain Square
St Margaret's Tollcross Pk	179 Braidfauld Street
St Nicholas' Cardonald	Hartlaw Crescent nr Gladsmuir Road
St Paul's Provanmill	Langdale Street x Greenrig Street
St Rollox	Fountainwell Road
St Thomas Gallowgate	Gallowgate opp Bluevale Street
Sandyford-Henderson Memorial	Kelvinhaugh Street at Argyle Street
Sandyhills	28 Baillieston Rd nr Sandyhills Rd
Scotstoun	Earlbank Avenue x Ormiston Avenue
Shawlands	Shawlands Cross
Sherbrooke St Gilbert's	Nithsdale Rd x Sherbrooke Avenue
Shettleston Old	111 Killin Street
South Carntyne	538 Carntyne Road
South Shawlands	Regwood Street x Deanston Drive
Springburn	Springburn Road x Atlas Street
Temple Anniesland	869 Crow Road
Toryglen	Glenmore Ave nr Prospecthill Road
Townhead Blochairn	178 Roystonhill
Trinity Possil and Henry Drummond	Crowhill Street x Broadholm Street
Tron St Mary's	128 Red Road
Victoria Tollcross	1134 Tollcross Road
Wallacewell	57 Northgate Road
	Ryehill Road x Quarrywood Road
Wellington	University Ave x Southpark Avenue
Whiteinch	Whiteinch Neighbourhood Centre, Dumbarton Road
Yoker Old	Dumbarton Road
St Matthew's	Hawick Street

(17) HAMILTON

Meets at Motherwell: Dalziel St Andrew's Parish Church Halls, on the first Tuesday of February, March, May, September, October, November, December and on the third Tuesday of June

		(Tel) / (Fax)
Presbytery Office:	**18 Haddow Street, Hamilton ML3 7HX** [e-mail: hamilton.presbytery@dial.pipex.com]	01698 286837 (Tel) 01698 457258 (Fax)
Clerk:	**REV. JAMES H. WILSON LTH**	01698 457042
Treasurer:	**MR DAVID FORRESTER CA** Belmont, Lefroy Street, Coatbridge ML5 1PN	01236 421892

1 **Airdrie Broomknoll (H) (01236 762101) [e-mail: airdrie-broomknoll@presbyteryofhamilton.co.uk]**
   linked with Calderbank [e-mail: calderbank@presbyteryofhamilton.co.uk]
   Andrew Thomson BA   1976   2000   38 Commonhead Street, Airdrie ML6 6NS   01236 602538

2 **Airdrie Clarkston [e-mail: airdrie-clarkston@presbyteryofhamilton.co.uk]**
   Thomas L. Pollock
   JP BA BD MTh FSAScot   1982   1992   Forrest Street, Airdrie ML6 7BE   01236 769676
                                                      [e-mail: tom.pollock@totalise.co.uk]

3 **Airdrie: Flowerhill (H) [e-mail: airdrie-flowerhill@presbyteryofhamilton.co.uk]**
   Andrew Gardner BSc BD PhD   1997   31 Victoria Place, Airdrie ML6 9BX   01236 763025

4 **Airdrie: High [e-mail: airdrie-high@presbyteryofhamilton.co.uk]**
   W. Richard Houston BSc BD   1998   17 Etive Drive, Airdrie ML6 9QL   01236 762010
                                                      [e-mail: richard.houston@virgin.net]

5 **Airdrie: Jackson (01236 733508) [e-mail: airdrie-jackson@presbyteryofhamilton.co.uk]**
   Sharon E.F. Colvin (Mrs)
   BD LRAM LTCL   1985   1998   48 Dunrobin Road, Airdrie ML6 8LR   01236 763154

6 **Airdrie: New Monkland (H) [e-mail: airdrie-newmonkland@presbyteryofhamilton.co.uk]**
   linked with Greeengairs [e-mail: greeengairs@presbyteryofhamilton.co.uk]
   Vacant   Glenmavis, Airdrie ML6 0NW   01236 763286 (Tel/Fax)

7 **Airdrie: St Columba's [e-mail: airdrie-stcolumbas@presbyteryofhamilton.co.uk]**
   Margaret F. Currie BEd BD   1980   1987   52 Kennedy Drive, Airdrie ML6 9AW   01236 763173

8 **Airdrie: The New Wellwynd [e-mail: airdrie-newwellwynd@presbyteryofhamilton.co.uk]**
   R. Fraser Penny BA BD   1984   1995   20 Arthur Avenue, Airdrie ML6 9EZ   01236 763022
                                                      [e-mail: FraserPenn@aol.com]

9 **Bargeddie (H) [e-mail: bargeddie@presbyteryofhamilton.co.uk]**
Vacant   Bargeddie, Baillieston, Glasgow G69 6UB   0141 771 1322

10 **Bellshill: Macdonald Memorial [e-mail: bellshill-macdonald@presbyteryofhamilton.co.uk]**
Vacant   32 Adamson Street, Bellshill ML4 1DT   01698 843176

11 **Bellshill: Orbiston [e-mail: bellshill-orbiston@presbyteryofhamilton.co.uk]**
linked with Bellshill: St Andrew's [e-mail: bellshill-standrews@presbyteryofhamilton.co.uk]
Vacant   65 Crossgates, Bellshill ML4 2EE   01698 841912

12 **Bellshill: St Andrew's** See Bellshill: Orbiston

13 **Bellshill: West (H) (01698 747581) [e-mail: bellshill-west@presbyteryofhamilton.co.uk]**
Quintin A. Blane BSc BD   1979   1994   16 Croftpark Street, Bellshill ML4 1EY   01698 842877
                              [e-mail: qablane@surfaid.org]

14 **Blantyre: Livingstone Memorial [e-mail: blantyre-livingstone@presbyteryofhamilton.co.uk]**
Vacant   286 Glasgow Road, Blantyre G72 9DB   01698 823794

15 **Blantyre: Old (H) [e-mail: blantyre-old@presbyteryofhamilton.co.uk]**
Rosemary A. Smith (Ms) BD   1997   High Blantyre G72 9UA   01698 823130

16 **Blantyre: St Andrew's [e-mail: blantyre-standrews@presbyteryofhamilton.co.uk]**
Ian Meredith BA MTh   1980   1993   332 Glasgow Road, Blantyre, Glasgow G72 9LQ   01698 827982

17 **Bothwell (H) [e-mail: bothwell@presbyteryofhamilton.co.uk]**
James M. Gibson TD LTh LRAM   1978   1989   Manse Avenue, Bothwell, Glasgow G71 8PQ   01698 853189 (Tel)
                              [e-mail: james gibson1@compuserve.com]   01698 853229 (Fax)

18. **Calderbank** See Airdrie Broomknoll

19 **Caldercruix Longriggend and Meadowfield (H) [e-mail: caldercruix@presbyteryofhamilton.co.uk]**
Ian M. Watson LLB DipLP BD   1998   Main Street, Caldercruix, Airdrie ML6 7RF   01236 842279
                              [e-mail: ikwatson@aol.com]

20 **Carfin [e-mail: carfin@presbyteryofhamilton.co.uk] linked with Newarthill [e-mail: newarthill@presbyteryofhamilton.co.uk]**
Vacant   Church Street, Newarthill ML1 5HS   01698 860316

21 **Chapelhall (H) [e-mail: chapelhall@presbyteryofhamilton.co.uk]**
James R. Nelson BD DipTheol   1986   Chapelhall, Airdrie ML6 8SG   01236 763439

22 **Chapelton [e-mail: chapelton@presbyteryofhamilton.co.uk]
linked with Strathaven: Rankin (H) [e-mail: strathaven-rankin@presbyteryofhamilton.co.uk]**
Shaw J. Paterson BSc BD   1991   15 Lethame Road, Strathaven ML10 6AD   01357 520019 (Tel)
                                                       [e-mail: Shaw@Patersonsj.freeserve.co.uk]   01357 529316 (Fax)

23 **Cleland (H) [e-mail: cleland@presbyteryofhamilton.co.uk]**
John A. Jackson BD   1997   Bellside Road, Cleland ML1 5NP   01698 860260

24 **Coatbridge: Blairhill Dundyvan (H) [e-mail: coatbridge-blairhill@presbyteryofhamilton.co.uk]**
John M. Black MA BD   1963   1991   18 Blairhill Street, Coatbridge ML5 1PG   01236 432304

25 **Coatbridge: Calder (H) [e-mail: coatbridge-calder@presbyteryofhamilton.co.uk]**
Randolph Scott MA BD   1991   2000   26 Bute Street, Coatbridge ML5 4HF   01236 421516
                                                       [e-mail: rev.rs@tinyworld.co.uk]

26 **Coatbridge: Clifton (H) [e-mail: coatbridge-clifton@presbyteryofhamilton.co.uk]**
Leslie W. Thorne BA LTh   1987   1992   132 Muiryhall Street, Coatbridge ML5 3NH   01236 421181

27 **Coatbridge: Middle [e-mail: coatbridge-middle@presbyteryofhamilton.co.uk]**
James Grier BD   1991   1996   47 Blair Road, Coatbridge ML5 1JQ   01236 432427

28 **Coatbridge: Old Monkland [e-mail: coatbridge-oldmonkland@presbyteryofhamilton.co.uk]**
James G. Munton BA   1969   Old Monkland Manse, Coatbridge ML5 5QT   01236 423788 (Tel)
                                                       [e-mail:jgmunton@oldmonkland.fsnet.co.uk]   01236 423788 (Fax)

29 **Coatbridge: St Andrew's [e-mail: coatbridge-standrews@presbyteryofhamilton.co.uk]**
Ian G. Wotherspoon BA LTh   1967   1994   77 Eglinton Street, Coatbridge ML5 3JF   01236 437271

30 **Coatbridge: Townhead (H) [e-mail: coatbridge-townhead@presbyteryofhamilton.co.uk]**
David Hood BD Cert Min   1997   Crinan Crescent, Coatbridge ML5 2LH   01236 423150

31 **Dalserf [e-mail: dalserf@presbyteryofhamilton.co.uk]**
D. Cameron McPherson BSc BD   1982   Dalserf, Larkhall ML9 3BN   01698 882195

32 **East Kilbride: Claremont (H) (01335 238088) [e-mail: ek-claremont@presbyteryofhamilton.co.uk]**
John K. Collard MA BD   1986   1991   17 Deveron Road, East Kilbride G74 2HR   01355 248526

33 **East Kilbride: Greenhills (E) (01355 221746) [e-mail: ek-greenhills@presbyteryofhamilton.co.uk]**
John Brewster MA BD DipEd   1988   21 Turnberry Place, East Kilbride G75 8TB   01355 242564

34 **East Kilbride: Moncreiff (H) (01355 223328) [e-mail: ek-moncreiff@presbyteryofhamilton.co.uk]**
Alastair S. Lusk BD   1974   1983   16 Almond Drive, East Kilbride G74 2HX   01355 238639

35 **East Kilbride: Mossneuk (E) (01355 260954) [e-mail: ek-mossneuk@presbyteryofhamilton.co.uk]**
John L. McPake BA BD PhD   1986   2000   30 Eden Grove, Mossneuk, East Kilbride G75 8XU 01355 234196

36 East Kilbride: Old (H) [e-mail: ek-old@presbyteryofhamilton.co.uk]
Vacant
40 Maxwell Drive, East Kilbride G74 4NG — 01355 220732

37 East Kilbride: South (H) [e-mail: ek-south@presbyteryofhamilton.co.uk]
John C. Sharp BSc BD PhD   1980
7 Clamps Wood, East Kilbride G74 2HB — 01355 247993

38 East Kilbride: West (H) [e-mail: ek-west@presbyteryofhamilton.co.uk]
Vacant
1 Barr Terrace, East Kilbride G74 1AP — 01355 220753

39 East Kilbride: Westwood (H) (01355 245657) [e-mail: ek-westwood@presbyteryofhamilton.co.uk]
Kevin Mackenzie BD DPS   1989 1996
16 Inglewood Crescent, East Kilbride G75 8QD — 01355 223992

40 Glasford [e-mail: glassford@presbyteryofhamilton.co.uk] linked with Strathaven East [e-mail: strathaven-east@presbyteryofhamilton.co.uk]
William T. Stewart BD   1980
68 Townhead Street, Strathaven ML10 6BA — 01357 521138

41 Greengairs See Airdrie New Monkland

42 Hamilton: Burnbank [e-mail: hamilton-burnbank@presbyteryofhamilton.co.uk] linked with Hamilton North (H) [e-mail: hamilton-north@presbyteryofhamilton.co.uk]
Raymond D. McKenzie BD   1978 1987
9 South Park Road, Hamilton ML3 6PJ — 01698 424609

43 Hamilton: Cadzow (H) (01698 428695) [e-mail: hamilton-cadzow@presbyteryofhamilton.co.uk]
Arthur P. Barrie LTh   1973 1979
3 Carlisle Road, Hamilton ML3 7BZ — 01698 421664 (Tel) / 01698 891126 (Fax)

44 Hamilton: Gilmour and Whitehill (H) [e-mail: hamilton-gilmourwhitehill@presbyteryofhamilton.co.uk]
Ronald J. Maxwell Stitt   1977 2000
LTh BA ThM BREd DMin FSAScot
86 Burnbank Centre, Burnbank ML3 ONA — 01698 284201
[e-mail: rev.rjmstitt@hotmail.com]

45 Hamilton: Hillhouse [e-mail: hamilton-hillhouse@presbyteryofhamilton.co.uk]
David W.G. Burt BD DipMin   1989 1998
66 Wellhall Road, Hamilton ML3 9BY — 01698 422300
William Wishart DCS
17 Swift Bank, Earrock, Hamilton ML3 8PX — 01698 429371
[e-mail: bill@wwishart.freeserve.co.uk]

46 Hamilton: North See Hamilton Burnbank

47 Hamilton: Old (H) (01698 281905) [e-mail: hamilton-old@presbyteryofhamilton.co.uk]
Vacant

48 Hamilton: St Andrew's (T) [e-mail: hamilton-standrews@presbyteryofhamilton.co.uk]
Norma Moore MA BD   1995
15 Bent Road, Hamilton ML3 6QB — 01698 891361
[e-mail: norma.moore@cablenet.co.uk]

49 Hamilton: St John's (H) (01698 283492) [e-mail: hamilton-stjohns@presbyteryofhamilton.co.uk]
Robert M. Kent MA BD   1973   1981   12 Castlehill Crescent, Hamilton ML3 7DG   01698 425002

**50 Hamilton: South (H) (01698 281014) [e-mail: hamilton-south@presbyteryofhamilton.co.uk]
linked with Quarter [e-mail: quarter@presbyteryofhamilton.co.uk]**
Fraser K. Turner LTh   1994   Quarter, Hamilton ML3 7XA   01698 424511

51 Hamilton: Trinity (01698 284254) [e-mail: hamilton-trinity@presbyteryofhamilton.co.uk]
Karen E. Harbison (Mrs) MA BD   1991   69 Buchan Street, Hamilton ML3 8JY   01698 425326

52 Hamilton: West (H) (01698 284670) [e-mail: hamilton-west@presbyteryofhamilton.co.uk]
J. Stanley Cook BD DipPSS   1974   43 Bothwell Road, Hamilton ML3 0BB   01698 458770
        [e-mail: stan.cook@virgin.net]

53 Holytown [e-mail: holytown@presbyteryofhamilton.co.uk]
James S. Salmond BA BD MTh ThD   1979   Holytown, Motherwell ML1 5RU   01698 832622

54 Kirk o' Shotts (H) [e-mail: kirk-o-shotts@presbyteryofhamilton.co.uk]
Sheila M. Spence (Mrs) MA BD   1979   Salsburgh, Shotts ML7 4NS   01698 870208

55 Larkhall: Chalmers (H) [e-mail: larkhall-chalmers@presbyteryofhamilton.co.uk]
James S.G. Hastie CA BD   1990   Quarry Road, Larkhall ML9 1HH   01698 882238
        [e-mail: JHastie@chalmers.demon.co.uk]   0870 056 2133 (Fax)

56 Larkhall: St Machan's (H) [e-mail: larkhall-stmachans@presbyteryofhamilton.co.uk]
Iain M. Greenshields   1985   1993   2 Orchard Gate, Larkhall ML9 1HG   01698 882457
BD DipRS ACMA MTh   [e-mail: machan@cableinet.co.uk]

57 Larkhall: Trinity [e-mail: larkhall-trinity@presbyteryofhamilton.co.uk]
Lindsay Schluter (Miss) ThE CertMin   1995   13 Machan Avenue, Larkhall ML9 2HE   01698 881401

58 Motherwell: Crosshill (H) [e-mail: mwell-crosshill@presbyteryofhamilton.co.uk]
W. Stuart Dunn LTh   1970   1982   15 Orchard Street, Motherwell ML1 3JE   01698 263410

59 Motherwell: Dalziel St Andrew's (H) (01698 264097) [e-mail: mwell-dalzielstandrews@presbyteryofhamilton.co.uk]
Derek W. Hughes BSc BD DipEd   1990   1996   4 Pollock Street, Motherwell ML1 1LP   0870 085 2564 (Tel/Fax)
        [e-mail: derek@hughes04.freeserve.co.uk]
Colin M. Brough BSc BD (Assoc)   1998   5 Bredin Way, Motherwell ML1 3PD   01698 252527
        [e-mail: Colin.Brough@btinternet.com]   0870 284 1587 (Fax)

60 Motherwell: Manse Road [e-mail: mwell-manseroad@presbyteryofhamilton.co.uk]
Vacant   10 Hamilton Drive, Motherwell ML1 2QA   01698 267345

61 Motherwell: North [e-mail: mwell-north@presbyteryofhamilton.co.uk]
Derek H.N. Pope BD   1987   1995   Kirkland Street, Motherwell ML1 3JW   01698 266716

62 **Motherwell: St Margaret's [e-mail: mwell-stmargarets@presbyteryofhamilton.co.uk]**
Andrew M. Campbell BD   1984   70 Baron's Road, Motherwell ML1 2NB   01698 263803

63 **Motherwell: St Mary's (H) [e-mail: mwell-stmarys@presbyteryofhamilton.co.uk]**
David W. Doyle MA BD   1977   1987   19 Orchard Street, Motherwell ML1 3JE   01698 263472

64 **Motherwell: South Dalziel (H) [e-mail: mwell-southdalziel@presbyteryofhamilton.co.uk]**
Phyllis M. Wilson (Mrs) DipCom DipRE   1985   1994   62 Manse Road, Motherwell ML1 2PT   01698 263054

65 **Newarthill** See Carfin

66 **Newmains: Bonkle (H) [e-mail: bonkle@presbyteryofhamilton.co.uk]**
linked with **Newmains: Coltness Memorial (H) [e-mail: coltness@presbyteryofhamilton.co.uk]**
Graham L. Duffin BSc BD DipEd   1989   5 Kirkgate, Newmains, Wishaw ML2 9BT   01698 383858 (Tel/Fax)
[e-mail: GLDuffin@CofSNewmains.freeserve.co.uk]
John McAlpine BSc (Aux)   1998   201 Bonkle Road, Newmains, Wishaw ML2 9AA   01698 384610

67 **Newmains: Coltness Memorial** See Newmains: Bonkle

68 **New Stevenston: Wrangholm Kirk [e-mail: wrangholml@presbyteryofhamilton.co.uk]**
Vacant   222 Clydesdale Street, New Stevenston ML1 4IQ   01698 832533

69 **Overtown [e-mail: overtown@presbyteryofhamilton.co.uk]**
Vacant   Overtown, Wishaw ML2 OQP   01698 372330

70 **Quarter** See Hamilton South

71 **Shotts: Calderhead Erskine [e-mail: calderhead-erskine@presbyteryofhamilton.co.uk]**
Ian G. Thom BSc PhD BD   1985   2000   The Manse, Kirk Road, Shotts ML1 5ET   01501 820042
James Zambonini LlA Dip (Aux)   1997   100 Old Manse Road, Netherton, Wishaw ML2 0EP   01698 350889
(office)   0141 204 6301

72 **Stonehouse: St Ninian's (H) [e-mail: stonehouse@presbyteryofhamilton.co.uk]**
Thomas Nelson BSc BD   1992   4 Hamilton Way, Stonehouse ML9 3PU   01698 792364

73 **Strathaven: Avendale Old and Drumclog (H) (01357 529748) [e-mail: strathaven-avendaleold@presbyteryofhamilton.co.uk] and**
[e-mail: drumclog@presbyteryofhamilton.co.uk]
Vacant   Strathaven, Lanarkshire ML10 6BA   01357 520077

74 **Strathaven: East** See Glasford
75 **Strathaven: Rankin** See Chapelton

76 Strathaven: West [e-mail: strathaven-west@presbyteryofhamilton.co.uk]
Stuart D. Rogerson BSc BD   1980   1996   6 Avenel Crescent, Strathaven ML10 6JF   01357 529086 (Tel/Fax)
[e-mail: s.rogerson@cnetwork.co.uk]

77 Uddingston: Burnhead (H) [e-mail: uddingston-burnhead@presbyteryofhamilton.co.uk]
Robert A. Mackenzie LLB BD   1993   90 Laburnum Road, Uddingston G71 5DB   01698 813716
Raymond Deans DCS   22 Garrowhill Drive, Garrowhill, Glasgow G69 6HL   0141 771 6847

78 Uddingston: Old (H) (01698 814015) [e-mail: uddingston-old@presbyteryofhamilton.co.uk]
Norman B. McKee BD   1987   1994   1 Belmont Avenue, Uddingston G71 7AX   01698 814757
[e-mail: normanb.mckee@belmont89.freeserve.co.uk]

79 Uddingston: Park (T)(H) [e-mail: uddingston-park@presbyteryofhamilton.co.uk]
W. Bruce McDowall BA BD   1989   1999   25 Douglas Gardens, Uddingston G71 7HB   01698 817256

80 Uddingston: Viewpark (H) [e-mail: uddingston-viewpark@presbyteryofhamilton.co.uk]
Scott McKenna BA BD   1994   14 Holmbrae Road, Uddingston G71 6AP   01698 813113
[e-mail: scottsmckenna@aol.com]

81 Wishaw: Cambusnethan North (H) [e-mail: wishaw-cambusnethannorth@presbyteryofhamilton.co.uk]
Mhorag Macdonald (Ms) MA BD   1989   350 Kirk Road, Wishaw ML2 8LH   01698 381305
[e-mail: mhorag@mhorag force9.co.uk]

82 Wishaw: Cambusnethan Old [e-mail: wishaw-cambusnethanold@presbyteryofhamilton.co.uk]
and Morningside [e-mail: wishaw-morningside@presbyteryofhamilton.co.uk]
Iain C. Murdoch MA LLB DipEd BD   1995   22 Coronation Street, Wishaw ML2 8LF   01698 384235

83 Wishaw: Chalmers (H) (01698 375306) [e-mail: wishaw-chalmers@presbyteryofhamilton.co.uk]
Ian O. Coltart CA BD   1988   161 Kirk Road, Wishaw ML2 7BZ   01698 372464

84 Wishaw: Craigneuk and Belhaven (H) [e-mail: wishaw-craigneukbelhaven@presbyteryofhamilton.co.uk]
Scott Raby LTh   1991   100 Glen Road, Wishaw ML2 7NP   01698 372495
[e-mail: revscott@rabyfamily28.freeserve.co.uk]

85 Wishaw: Old (H) (01698 376080) [e-mail: wishaw-old@presbyteryofhamilton.co.uk]
James Davidson BD Dip AFH   1989   130 Glen Road, Wishaw ML2 7NP   01698 375134 (Tel/Fax)
[e-mail:revjamesdavidson@clergy.net]   07788 747808 (Mbl)

86 Wishaw: St Mark's [e-mail: wishaw-stmarks@presbyteryofhamilton.co.uk]
Henry J.W. Findlay MA BD   1965   1967   Coltness Road, Wishaw ML2 7EX   01698 384596 (Tel)
01698 386025 (Fax)

87 Wishaw: Thornlie (H) [e-mail: wishaw-thornlie@presbyteryofhamilton.co.uk]
Klaus O.F. Buwert LLB BD   1984   1999   West Thornlie Street, Wishaw ML2 7AR   01698 372356
[e-mail: RevKlausB@aol.com]   07801 533548 (Mbl)

Allan, James B. BA	1965	1993	(Motherwell: South Dalziel)	42 Catherine Street, Motherwell ML1 2RN	01698 264756
Anderson, Catherine B. (Mrs) DCS	1944	1984	(Deaconess)	13 Mosshill Road, Bellshill ML4 1NQ	01698 745907
Baird, George W. MA	1951	1986	(Crimond with St Fergus)	42 Neilsland Drive, Motherwell ML1 3EB	01698 262088
Beattie, William G. BD BSc	1947	1983	(Hamilton St Andrew's)	33 Dungavel Gardens, Hamilton ML3 7PE	01698 423804
Cowper, Macknight C. MA BD STM	1937	1978	(East Kilbride West)	17 Manor Place, Edinburgh EH3 7DH	0131 225 6214
Douglas, Andrew M. MA	1959	1993	(Hamilton Cadzow)	21 Allanshaw Street, Hamilton ML3 6NZ	01698 429176
Dunn, James F.	1951	1988	(Coatbridge: Dunbeth)	167 Silvertonhill Avenue, Hamilton ML3 7PP	01698 426043
Fraser, James P.	1954	1993	(Strathaven Avendale Old and Drumclog)	26 Hamilton Road, Strathaven ML10 6JA	01357 522758
Handley, John	1951	1979	(Motherwell: Clason Memorial)	12 Airbles Crescent, Motherwell ML1 3AR	01698 262733
Heron, John			(Ochiltree)	Flat 7, Malin Court, Turnberry, Ayrshire KA26 9PB	
Hunter, James E. LTh	1974	1997	(Blantyre: Livingstone Memorial)	57 Dalwhinnie Avenue, Blantyre G72 9NQ	01698 826177
King, Crawford S. MA	1958	1984	(Glenboig)	77 Faskine Avenue, Airdrie ML6 9EA	01236 761753
Learmonth, Adam J.	1966	1993	(Airdrie: Wellwynd)	13 Drumbathie Terrace, Airdrie ML6 7EU	01236 763248
McCabe, George	1963	1996	(Airdrie: High)	Flat 8, Park Court, 2 Craighouse Park, Edinburgh EH10 5LD	0131 447 9522
McCance, Andrew BSc	1986	1995	(Coatbridge: Middle)	6a Manse Road, Bearsden, Glasgow G61 3PT	0141 942 2373
Martin, James MA BD DD	1946	1987	(Glasgow: High Carntyne)	9 Magnolia Street, Wishaw ML2 7EQ	01698 385825
Melrose, J.H. Loudon MA BD MEd	1955	1996	(Gourock: Old Gourock & Ashton [Assoc])	24 Avonbridge Drive, Hamilton ML3 7EJ	01698 891033
Niven, William LTCL	1955	1994	(Lesmahagow: Old)	92 Linden Lea, Hamilton ML3 9AG	01698 420653
Price, Peter O. CBE QHC BA FPhS	1960	1996	(Blantyre Old)	20A Old Bothwell Road, Bothwell G71 8AW	01698 854032
Walker, R. Forbes BSc BD ThM	1987	2000	School Chaplain	2 Holmleigh, Priory Road, Ascot, Berkshire SL5 8EA [e-mail: RevFW@hotmail.com]	01344 883272
Wilson, James H.	1970	1996	(Cleland)	21 Austine Drive, Hamilton ML3 7YE	01698 457042
Wylie, Hugh R. MA DD FCIBS	1962	2000	(Hamilton Old)	18 Chantinghall Road, Hamilton ML3 8PN	01698 420002

HAMILTON ADDRESSES

Airdrie

Congregation	Address
Broomknoll	Broomknoll Street
Clarkston	Forrest Street
Flowerhill	89 Graham Street
High	North Bridge Street
Jackson	Glen Road
New Monkland	Glenmavis
St Columba's	Thrashbush Road
The New Wellwynd	Wellwynd

Coatbridge

Congregation	Address
Blairhill Dundyvan	Blairhill Street
Calder	Calder Street
Clifton	Muiryhall Street x Jackson Street
Middle	Bank Street
Old Monkland	Woodside Street
St Andrew's	Church Street
Townhead	Crinan Crescent

East Kilbride

Congregation	Address
Claremont	High Common Road, St Leonard's
Greenhills	Greenhills Centre
Moncreiff	Calderwood Road
Mossneuk	Eden Drive
Old	Montgomery Street
South	Baird Hill, Murray
West	Kittoch Street
Westwood	Belmont Drive, Westwood

Hamilton

Congregation	Address
Burnbank	High Blantyre Road
Cadzow	Woodside Walk
Gilmour and Whitehill	Glasgow Road, Burnbank
Hillhouse	Abbotsford Road, Whitehill
North	Clerkwell Road
Old	Windmill Road
St Andrew's	Leechlee Road
St John's	Avon Street
South	Duke Street
	Strathaven Road
Trinity	
West	

Motherwell

Congregation	Address
Crosshill	Neilsland Square off North Road
	Burnbank Road
Dalziel St Andrew's	Manse Road
North	Windmillhill Street x Airbles Street
St Margaret's	Merry Street and Muir Street
St Mary's	Gavin Street
South Dalziel	Chesters Crescent
	Shields Road
	Avon Street
	504 Windmillhill Street

Uddingston

Congregation	Address
Burnhead	Laburnum Road
Old	Old Glasgow Road.
Park	Main Street
Viewpark	Old Edinburgh Road

Wishaw

Congregation	Address
Cambusnethan	

Wishaw (cont)

North	Kirk Road
Old	Kirk Road
Chalmers	East Academy Street
Craigneuk and Belhaven	
Old	Craigneuk Street
St Mark's	Main Street
Thornlie	Coltness Road
	West Thornlie Street

(18) DUMBARTON

Meets at Dumbarton in Riverside Church Halls, on the first Tuesday of February, March, April, May, October, November, December, and on the second Tuesday of June and September (and April when the first Tuesday falls in Holy Week).

Clerk:	REV. DAVID P. MUNRO MA BD STM		14 Birch Road, Killearn, Glasgow G63 9SQ [e-mail: dmunro@dial.pipex.com]	01360 550098 (Tel) 01360 551198 (Fax) 07710 866982 (Mbl)

Alexandria				
Elizabeth W. Houston (Miss) MA BD DipEd	1985	1995	32 Ledrish Avenue, Balloch G83 8JB	01389 751933
Archibald M. Ferguson MSc PhD CEng FRINA (Aux)	1989	1997	The Whins, Barrowfield, Cardross G82 5NL	01389 841517
Arrochar linked with Luss				
H. Dane Sherrard BD	1971	1998	Luss, Alexandria G83 8NZ [e-mail: dane@cadder.demon.co.uk]	01436 860240 07801 939138 (Mbl)
Baldernock (H)				
Harold A.M. Steven LTh	1970	1994	Bardowie, Milngavie G62 6ES	01360 620471
Bearsden: Killermont (H)				
G. Fraser H. Macnaughton MA BD	1982	1997	8 Clathic Avenue, Bearsden, Glasgow G61 2HF [e-mail: fraser.macnaughton@dial.pipex.com]	0141 942 0021
Bearsden: New Kilpatrick (H) (0141 942 8827)				
David D. Scott BSc BD	1981	1999	51 Manse Road, Bearsden, Glasgow G61 3PN	0141 942 0035
Bearsden: North (H) (0141 942 2818)				
Keith T. Blackwood BD Dip Min		1997	5 Fintry Gardens, Bearsden, Glasgow G61 4RJ [e-mail: kblackwood@totalise.co.uk]	0141 942 0366 07961 442972 (Mbl)

Bearsden: South (H)
John W.F. Harris MA — 1967, 1987 — 61 Drymen Road, Bearsden, Glasgow G61 2SU [e-mail: jwfh@globalnet.co.uk] — 0141 942 0507 / 07711 573877 (Mbl)

Bearsden: Westerton Fairlie Memorial (H) (0141 942 6960)
Eric V. Hudson LTh — 1971, 1990 — 3 Canniesburn Road, Bearsden G61 1PW [e-mail: evhudson@aol.com] — 0141 942 2672
Alistair E. Ramage BA ADB CertEd (Aux) — 1996 — 16 Claremont Gardens, Milngavie G62 6PG [e-mail: A.Ramage@gcal.ac.uk] — 0141 956 2897

Bonhill (H) (01389 756516)
Ian H. Miller BD — 1975 — 1 Glebe Gardens, Bonhill, Alexandria G83 9NZ — 01389 753039

Cardross (H) (01389 841322)
Andrew J. Scobie MA BD — 1963, 1965 — Cardross, Dumbarton G82 5LB [e-mail: ascobie55@netscapeonline.co.uk] — 01389 841289 / 07889 670252 (Mbl)

Clydebank: Abbotsford [e-mail: abbotsford@lineone.net] (www.lineone.net/-abbotsford)
Roderick G. Hamilton MA BD — 1992, 1996 — 35 Montrose Street, Clydebank G81 2PA [e-mail: rghamilton@lineone.net] — 0141 952 5151

Clydebank: Faifley
Gregor McIntyre BSc BD — 1991 — Kirklea, Cochno Road, Hardgate Clydebank G81 6PT [e-mail: mail@gregormcintyre.com] — 01389 876836
Agnes Tait (Mrs) DCS — 2 Lennox Drive, Faifley, Clydebank G81 5JU — 01389 873196

Clydebank: Kilbowie St Andrew's
Roderick P. Grahame BD CPS — 1991 — 5 Melfort Avenue, Clydebank G81 2HX — 0141 951 2455 / 07778 488232 (Mbl)

Clydebank: Radnor Park
Margaret J.B. Yule (Mrs) BD — 1992 — Spencer Street, Clydebank G81 3AS [e-mail: mjbyule@tinyworld.co.uk] — 0141 951 1007

Clydebank: St Cuthbert's (T)
Ian A. Manson BA BD — 1989, 1992 — 1 Peterson Drive, Glasgow G13 4JY [e-mail: imanson@iname.com] — 0141 941 3469
Roy Wilson DA ARIBA ARIAS — 1986, 1997 — 20 William Ure Place, Bishopbriggs G64 3BH — 0141 563 1829

Craigrownie linked with Rosneath St Modan's (H)
Malcolm Wright LTh — 1970, 1984 — Edenkiln, Argyll Road, Kilcreggan G84 OJW [e-mail: malcolm_wright@compuserve.com] — 01436 842274

Dalmuir Barclay (0141 941 3988) James F. Gatherer BD	1984	Parkhall Road, Dalmuir, Clydebank G81 3RJ	0141 941 3317
Dumbarton: Riverside (H) (01389 742551) John B. Cairns LTh LLB	1974	5 Kirkton Road, Dumbarton G82 4AS	01389 762512 07713 195084 (Mbl)
Dumbarton: St Andrew's (H) Leslie G. Donaghy BD DipMin PGCE FSAScot	1990	17 Mansewood Drive, Dumbarton G82 3EU [e-mail: info@bellsmyre.co.uk]	01389 604259 07654 555473 (Pager)
Dumbarton: West Kirk (H) Christine Liddell (Miss) BD	1999	3 Havoc Road, Dumbarton G82 4JW [e-mail: christine.liddell@nationwideisp.net]	01389 604840
Duntocher (H) Vacant		Roman Road, Duntocher, Clydebank G81 6BT	01389 878846
Garelochhead (01436 810589) Alastair S. Duncan MA BD	1989	Old School Road, Garelochhead Helensburgh G84 0AT [e-mail: alastair@arduncan.freeserve.co.uk]	01436 810022
Helensburgh: Park (H) (01436 671714) James H. Brown BD	1977	35 East Argyle Street, Helensburgh G84 7EL [e-mail: jh@jhbrown.freeserve.co.uk]	01436 672209 07639 575624 (Pager)
Helensburgh: St Columba (H) Frederick M. Booth LTh	1970	46 Suffolk Street, Helensburgh G84 9QZ	01436 672054
Helensburgh: The West Kirk (H) (01436 676880) David W. Clark MA BD	1975	37 Campbell Street, Helensburgh G84 9NH	01436 674063
Jamestown (H) Kenneth G. Russell BD CCE	1986	Appin House, Drymen Road, Balloch, Alexandria G83 8HT	01389 752734
Kilmaronock Gartocharn Andrew S. Mitchell BA BD HDipREd AdvDipEd(Open)	1965	Kilmaronock Manse, Alexandria G83 8SB	01360 660295
Luss See Arrochar			
Milngavie: Cairns (H) (0141 956 4868) Andrew Frater BA BD	1987	4 Cairns Drive, Milngavie, Glasgow G62 8AJ	0141 956 1717

Milngavie: St Luke's (0141 956 4226)
Ramsay B. Shields BA BD — 1990 1997 — 70 Hunter Road, Milngavie, Glasgow G62 7BY — 0141 577 9171 (Tel)
[e-mail: rbshields@iname.com] — 0141 577 9181 (Fax)

Milngavie: St Paul's (H) (0141 956 4405)
Fergus C. Buchanan MA BD — 1982 1988 — 8 Buchanan Street, Milngavie, Glasgow G62 8DD — 0141 956 1043

Old Kilpatrick Bowling
Alistair J. MacKichan MA BD — 1984 — Old Kilpatrick, Glasgow G60 5JQ — 01389 873130

Renton Trinity (H)
Vacant — 38 Main Street, Renton, Dumbarton G82 4PU — 01389 752017

Rhu and Shandon (H)
Alison Paul (Miss) MA BD DipTheol — 1986 1994 — Ardenconnel Way, Rhu, Helensburgh G84 8LX — 01436 820213

Rosneath St Modan's See Craigrownie

Crombie, W.M.D. MA BD	1947	1987	(Calton New with St Andrew's)	32 Westbourne Drive, Bearsden G61 4BH	0141 943 0235
Davidson, Professor Robert MA BD DD FRSE	1956	1991	(University of Glasgow)	30 Dumgoyne Drive, Bearsden G61 3AP	0141 942 1810
Easton, I.A.G. MA FIPM	1945	1988	Lecturer	6 Edgehill Road, Bearsden G61 3AD	0141 942 4214
Hamilton, David S.M. MA BD STM	1958	1996	(University of Glasgow)	2 Roselea Drive, Milngavie, Glasgow G62 8HQ	0141 956 1839
Houston, Peter M. FPhS	1952	1997	(Renfrew Old)	25 Honeysuckle Lane, Jamestown, Alexandria G83 8PL	01389 721165
Hunter, G. Lindsay BD PhD APhS	1949	1990	(Teacher: Religious Education)	16 Restway Wall, Chepstow, Mon NP6 5EF	01291 629445
Jack, Robert MA BD	1950	1996	(Bearsden: Killermont)	142 Turnhill Drive, Erskine PA8 7AH	0141 812 8370
Keddie, David A. MA BD	1966	1983	Teacher: Religious Education	21 Ilay Road, Bearsden G61 1QG	0141 942 1408
Lawson, Alexander H. ThM ThD FPhS	1950	1988	(Clydebank Kilbowie)	1 Glebe Park, Mansewood, Dumbarton G82 3HE	01389 742030
McFadzean, Iain MA BD	1989	1999	Chaplain: Royal Navy	HMS Neptune, Faslane, Helensburgh G84 8HL	01436 674321
Macfarlane, William J.E. MA BD	1953	1987	(Alexandria St Andrew's)	3 Inchfad Road, Balloch G83 8SY	01389 758185
McIntyre, J. Ainslie MA BD	1963	1984	(University of Glasgow)	60 Bonnaughton Road, Bearsden G61 4DB	0141 942 5143
Mackenzie, Ian M. MA	1967	1989	(BBC)	1 Glennan Gardens, Helensburgh G84 8XT	01436 673429
Morton, Andrew Q. MA BSc BD FRSE	1949	1987	(Culross and Torryburn)	4 Upper Adelaide Street, Helensburgh G84 7HT	01436 675152
Munro, David P. MA BD STM	1953	1996	(Bearsden North)	14 Birch Road, Killearn, Glasgow G63 9SQ	01360 550098
Spence, C.K.O. MC TD MA BD	1949	1983	(Craigrownie)	8B Cairndhu Gardens, Helensburgh G84 8PG	01436 678838

DUMBARTON ADDRESSES

Clydebank		Dumbarton		Helensburgh	
Abbotsford	Town Centre	Riverside	High Street	Park	Charlotte Street
Faifley	Faifley Road	St Andrew's	Off Bonhill Road	St Columba	Sinclair Street
Kilbowie St Andrew's	Kilbowie Road	West Kirk	West Bridgend	The West Kirk	Colquhoun Square
Radnor Park	Radnor Street				
St Cuthbert's	Linnvale				

(19) SOUTH ARGYLL

Meets on first Wednesday of February (at Clachan), March (at Tarbert), June (island), November and December (at Tarbert) and first Tuesday of May (in Mid-Argyll) and September (in Tarbert).

Clerk: MR MICHAEL A.J. GOSSIP OBE JP BL   Tigh-na-Coille, Ardrishaig, Argyll PA30 8EP   **01546 603454   (Tel/Fax)**
[e-mail: gossip@dial.pipex.com]

Ardrishaig (H) linked with South Knapdale		
David Carruthers BD	1998	Ardrishaig, Argyll PA30 8HD 01546 603269
Campbeltown: Highland (H)		
Michael J. Lind LLB BD	1984 1997	Kirk Street, Campbeltown, Argyll PA28 6BN 01586 551146
Campbeltown: Lorne and Lowland (H)		
John Oswald BSc PhD BD	1997	Castlehill, Campbeltown, Argyll PA28 6AN 01586 552468
		[e-mail: revdocoz@bigfoot.com]
Craignish linked with Kilninver and Kilmelford		
Michael J. Erskine MA BD	1985 1992	Kilmelford, by Oban, Argyll PA34 4XA 01852 200373
Cumlodden, Lochfyneside and Lochgair		
Roderick MacLeod		
MA BD PhD(Edin) PhD(Open)	1966 1985	Furnace, Inveraray, Argyll PA32 8XU 01499 500288
Gigha and Cara (H)(GD)		
Continuing Vacancy		Gigha, Argyll PA41 7AA 01583 505245
Glassary and Kilmartin and Ford		
Alison J. Ross (Mrs) BD	1995 1999	Kilmichael Glassary, Lochgilphead, Argyll PA31 8QA 01546 606926

Glenaray and Inveraray W. Brian Wilkinson MA BD	1968	1993	Inveraray, Argyll PA32 8XT	01499 302060
Jura (GD) [Dwin Capstick]		1999	Craighouse, Isle of Jura PA60 7XG	01496 820384
Kilarrow (H) linked with Kilmeny Anne McIvor (Miss) SRD BD	1996		Bowmore, Isle of Islay PA43 7LH	01496 810271
Kilberry linked with Tarbert (H) Jane C. Taylor (Miss) BD DipMin	1990	1995	Tarbert, Argyll PA29 6TY	01880 820288
Kilcalmonell linked with Skipness Charles R. Wood LTh DipYL FRGS	1993		Whitehouse, Tarbert, Argyll PA29 6XS	01880 730224
Kilchoman (GD) linked with Portnahaven (GD) Bernard P. Lodge BD	1967	2000	Port Charlotte, Isle of Islay PA48 7TX	01496 850241
Kildalton and Oa (GD)(H) Norman MacLeod BTh	1999		Port Ellen, Isle of Islay PA42 7DB	01496 302447
Killean and Kilchenzie (H) John H. Paton JP BSc BD	1983	1984	Muasdale, by Tarbert, Argyll PA29 6XD	01583 421249
Kilmeny See Kilarrow				
Kilninver and Kilmelford See Craignish				
Lochgilphead Alastair H. Gray MA BD	1978	1996	Manse Brae, Lochgilphead, Argyll PA31 8QZ [e-mail: a.gray1@tinyworld.co.uk]	01546 602238
North Knapdale Robert J. Malloch BD	1987	1997	Tayvallich, by Lochgilphead, Argyll PA31 8PG [e-mail: robert@scotnish.freeserve.co.uk]	01546 870611
Portnahaven See Kilchoman				
Saddell and Carradale (H) Alistair J. Dunlop MA FSAScot	1965	1979	Carradale, by Campbeltown, Argyll PA28 6QG	01583 431253
Skipness See Kilcalmonell				

Southend (H)   01586 830274
Callum T. O'Donnell MA BD   1984   1997   Southend, Campbeltown, Argyll PA28 6RQ

South Knapdale See Ardrishaig
Tarbert See Kilberry

Name			Position	Address	Phone
Bristow W.H.G. BEd HDipRE DipSpecEd	1951	1970	Part time Hospital Chaplain: Campbeltown (Deaconess)	The Manse, Isle of Gigha PA41 7AA	01583 505245
Campbell, Margaret M. (Miss) DCS	1948	1991	(Craignish with Kilninver and Kilmelford)	Tigh-an-Rudha, Pier Road, Port Ellen, Islay PA42 7DJ	01496 302006
Carmichael, Robert C.M. MA	1941	1981	(Campbeltown Lowland)	13 The Glebe, Kilmelford, Argyll PA34 4AF	01852 200346
Cormack, John R.H. MA BD	1987	1998	Moderator's Chaplain	21 Dell Road, Campbeltown PA28	01586 554265
Davidson David W (Aux)				Grainail, Glenegeadale, Port Ellen, Isle of Islay PA42 7AS	01496 302194
Gibson, Frank S. BL BD STM DSWA DD	1963	1995	(Kilarrow with Kilmeny)	163 Gilbertstoun, Edinburgh EH15 2RG	0131 657 5208
Gordon, David C.	1953	1988	(Gigha and Cara)	16 Braeside Avenue, Largs KA30 8HD	
Henderson, Charles M.	1952	1989	(Campbeltown Highland)	Springbank House, Askomill Walk, Campbeltown PA28 6EP	01586 552759
Hood, H. Stanley C. MA BD	1966	2000	(London: Crown Court)		
Hosie, James MA BD MTh	1959	1998	(Ardrishaig with South Knapdale)	Hibre, Strachur, Cairndow, by Dunoon, Argyll PA27 8BY	01369 860634
Montgomery, David	1961	1996	(North Knapdale)	15 Avongrove, Hamilton ML3 7UP	01698 200029
Morrison, Angus W MA BD	1959	1999	(Kildalton and Oa)	1 Livingstone Way, Port Ellen, Isle of Islay PA42 7EP	01496 300043
Ritchie, Malcolm A.	1955	1990	(Kilbrandon and Kilchattan)	Roadside Cottage, Tayvallich, Argyll PA31 8PN	01546 870616
Stewart, Jean E. (Mrs)	1983	1989	(Kildalton and Oa)	Tigh-na-Truain, Port Ellen, Isle of Islay PA42 7AH	01496 302068

SOUTH ARGYLL
Communion Sundays

Ardrishaig	4 Ap., 1 Nv.	Glenaray and Inveraray	1 Ap., Jl., Oc., Dc.
Campbeltown – Highland	1 My., Nv.	Jura	Passion Sun. 2 Jl. 3 Nv.
Lorne and Lowland	1 My., Nv.	Kilarrow	1 Mr., Je., Sp., Dc.
Craignish	1 Je., Nv.	Kilberry with Tarbert	1 My., Oc.
Cumlodden, Lochfyneside and and Lochgair	1 My., 3 Nv.	Kilcalmonell	1 Jl., 3 Nv.
Gigha and Cara	1 My., Nv.	Kilchoman	1 Jl., 2 Dec. E.
Glassary, Kilmartin and Ford	1 Ap., Sp.	Kildalton	Lst Ja., Je., Oc., E.
		Killean and Kilchenzie	1 Mr., Jl., Dc.
		Kilmeny	2 My., 3 Nv.
		Kilninver and Kilmelford	2 Je., Oc.
		Lochgair	2 Oct (Gaelic)
		Lochgilphead	1 Ap., Nv.0

North Knapdale	3 Oc., 2 My.
Inverlussa and Bellanoch	2 My., Nv.
Tayvallich	2 My., Nv.
Portnahaven	3 Jl.
Saddell and Carradale	2 My., 1 Nv.
Skipness	2 My., Nv.
Southend	1 Je., Dc.
South Knapdale	4 Ap., 1 Nv.

(20) DUNOON

Meets at Dunoon St John's, on the first Tuesday of February, April, June and November; at Rothesay Trinity on the first Tuesday of March, October and December; and at the Moderator's Church on the first Tuesday of September.

| Clerk: | REV. RONALD SAMUEL TD BSc BD STM | 9 Bishop Terrace, Rothesay, Isle of Bute PA20 9HF
[e-mail:ronald.samuel@ukgateway.net] | 01700 504378 (Tel/Fax) |

Bute United

| John Murning BD | 1988 | 2000 | 10 Bishop Terrace, Rothesay PA20 9HF | |
| (The union of North Bute, Ascog linked with Rothesay: Craigmore St. Brendan's, and Kingarth and Kilchattan Bay linked with Rothesay: the High Kirk) | | | | |

Dunoon: Old and St Cuthbert's (H)

| I. Pat Lang (Miss) BSc | 1996 | | 1 Royal Crescent, Dunoon PA23 7AH | 01369 701291 |

Dunoon: St John's linked with Sandbank (H)

| Joseph Stewart LTh | 1979 | 1989 | 23 Bullwood Road, Dunoon, Argyll PA23 7QJ | 01369 702128 |

Innellan (H) linked with Inverchaolain and Toward (H)

| Hugh Conkey BSc BD | 1987 | | 7A Matheson Lane, Innellan, Argyll PA23 7SH
[e-mail: conkey@tesco.net] | 01369 830276 |

Inverchaolain and Toward (H) See Innellan

Kilfinan linked with Kyles (H)

| David J. Kellas BD | 1966 | 1998 | Tighnabruaich, Argyll PA21 2DX | 01700 811887 (Tel/Fax) |

Kilmodan and Colintraive

| Robert M. Donald BA | 1969 | 1998 | Glendaruel, Colintraive, Argyll PA22 3AA
[e-mail: robdon@colglen. freeserve.co.uk] | 01369 820232 (Tel/Fax) |

Kilmun (St Munn's) (H) linked with Strone (H) and Ardentinny

| Evelyn M. Young (Mrs) BSc BD | 1984 | 1997 | Blairmore, Dunoon PA23 8TE | 01369 840313 |

Kirn (H)

| May M. Allison (Mrs) BD | 1988 | | Stewart Street, Kirn, Dunoon PA23 8DS
[e-mail: revmay@kirnpc.freeserve.co.uk] | 01369 702220 |

Kyles See Kilfinnan

Lochgoilhead (H) and Kilmorich
Vacant   Lochgoilhead, Argyll PA24 8AA   01301 703369

Rothesay: Trinity (H)
Vacant   12 Crichton Road, Rothesay PA20 9JR   01700 502797 (Tel/Fax)

Sandbank See Dunoon St John's

Strachur and Strathlachlan
Robert K. Mackenzie MA BD PhD   1976   1998   Strachur, Argyll PA27 8DG   01369 860246

Strone and Ardentinny See Kilmun

Name			Former charge	Address	Telephone
Cumming, David P.L. MA	1957	1997	(Kilmodan and Colintraive)	Shillong, Tarbat Ness Road, Portmahomack, Ross-shire IV20 1YA	01862 871794
Fenemore, John H.C.	1980	1993	(Edinburgh Colinton Mains)	Seaford Cottage, 74e Shore Rd, Innellan PA23 7TR	01369 830678
Forrest, Alan B. MA	1956	1993	(Uphall: South)	126 Shore Road, Innellan, Dunoon PA23 7SX	01369 830424
Gray, John A.	1950	1986	(Glasgow Baillieston Mure Memorial)	Holyns, Ardentinny, Dunoon PA23 8TR	01369 810243
Hamilton, Patrick J.R. MA	1948	1979	(East Kilbride South)	La Madrugada, Tighnabruaich PA21 2BE	01700 811586
Inglis, Donald B. C. MA MEd BD	1975	2000	(Turriff St. Andrew's)	"Lindores", 11 Bullwood Road, Dunoon PA23 7QJ	
Marshall, James S. BA BD FFA MDiv	1986	1989	(Lochgoilhead and Kilmorich)	12 Manse Gardens, Strachur, Cairndow PA27 8DS	01369 860544
Miller, Harry Galbraith MA BD	1941	1985	(Iona and Ross of Mull)	An Cala Ciatach, Bannatyne Mains Road, Port Bannatyne, Rothesay PA20 OPH	01700 502920
Samuel, Ronald TD BSc BD STM	1960	2000	(Rothesay Trinity)	9 Bishop Terrace, Rothesay PA20 9HF [e-mail: ronald.samuel@ukgateway.net]	(Tel/Fax) 01700 504378
Stewart, Donald MA	1944	1984	(Fenwick)	Seafield, Toward, Dunoon PA23 7UG	01369 870206
Watson, James LTh	1968	1994	(Bowden with Lilliesleaf)	7 Lochan Avenue, Kirn, Dunoon PA23 8HT	01369 702851

DUNOON
Communion Sundays

Dunoon			
Old and St Cuthbert's	1Fb., Je. Oc.	Kilmodan and Colintraive	1Ap., Sp.
St John's	1Mr., Je.., Nv.	Kilmun	Lst Je.. Nv.
Inellan	1Mr., Je., Sp., Dc.	Kirn	Lst Fb., Je.., Oc.
Inverchaolain and Toward	Lst Fb., My., Au., Nv.	Kyles	1My., Nv.
Kilfinan	Lst Ap., Oc	Lochgoilhead and Kilmorich	2 Mr., Je.. Sp., Nv 1Au.. E.
		Rothesay Trinity	1Fb., My., Nv.
		Sandbank	1Ja., My., Nv.
		Strachur and Strathlachlan	1Mr., Je., Nv.
		Strone and Ardentinny	Lst Fb., Je., Oc.

(21) LORN AND MULL

Meets at Oban, in the Church of Scotland Centre, Glencruitten Rd., on the first Wednesday of March and December and on the first Tuesday of September and June.

Clerk: REV. JEFFREY A. McCORMICK BD			The Manse, Ardchattan, Connel, Argyll PA37 1QZ	01631 710364
Treasurer: DONALD J.F. MACDONALD			4 William Street, Oban	01631 564191

Appin linked with Lismore				
Douglas R. Robertson BSc BD	1991	1995	Appin, Argyll PA38 4DD [e-mail: douglas@appinmanse.freeserve.co.uk]	01631 730206
Ardchattan (H)				
Jeffrey A. McCormick BD	1984		Ardchattan, Connel, Argyll PA37 1QZ	01631 710364
Coll				
Continuing Vacancy			Arinagour, Isle of Coll PA78 6SY	01879 230366
Colonsay and Oronsay linked with Kilbrandon and Kilchattan	1993	1997		
Freda Marshall (Mrs) BD FCII			The Manse, Winterton Road, Balvicar, Argyll PA34 4TF [e-mail: f.marshall@ukonline.co.uk]	01852 300240
Connel				
Ronald Gall BSc BD	1985	1991	St Oran's Manse, Connel, Argyll PA37 1PJ [e-mail: ronniegall@aol.com]	01631 710242
Glenorchy and Innishael linked with Strathfillan				
Vacant			The Manse, Tyndrum, Crianlarich FK20 8RY [e-mail:wthogg@easynet.co.uk]	01838 400240
Iona linked with Kilfinichen and Kilvickeon and the Ross of Mull	1982	1993		
David J. Taylor MA BD			Bunessan, Isle of Mull PA67 6DW	01681 700227
Kilbrandon and Kilchattan See Colonsay and Oronsay				
Kilchrenan and Dalavich linked with Muckairn				
Margaret R.M. Millar (Miss) BTh	1977	1996	Taynuilt, Argyll PA35 1HW [e-mail: macoje@aol.com]	01866 822204

Kilfinichen and Kilvickeon and the Ross of Mull See Iona

Kilmore (GD) and Oban
Andrew B. Campbell BD DPS   1979   Strathearn, Breadalbane Street, Oban PA34 5PA   01631 562322
[e-mail: revabc@obancofs.freeserve.co.uk]

**Mull, Isle of, Kilninian and Kilmore linked with Salen (H) and Ulva
linked with Tobermory (GD) (H) linked with Torosay (H) and Kinlochspelvie**
Alan T. Taylor BD   1980   Tobermory, Isle of Mull PA75 6PS   01688 302226
01688 302037 (Fax)

William Pollock MA BD PhD (Assoc)   1987   Salen, Aros, Isle of Mull PA72 6JF   01680 300359
[e-mail: wpollock@salen.freeserve.co.uk]

Lismore See Appin
Muckairn See Kilchrenan
Salen and Ulva See Mull
Strathfillan See Glenorchy

Tiree (GD)
Robert D. Higham BD   1985   1996   Isle of Tiree PA77 6TN   01879 220377

Tobermory See Mull
Torosay and Kinlochspelvie See Mull

Galbraith, David O. MA BD   1940 1980   Achnameadhonach, Balindeor, Taynuilt, Taynuilt, Argyll PA35 1JS
Lamont, Archibald   1952 1994   (Kilcalmonell with Skipness)   8 Achlonan, Taynuilt, Argyll PA35 1JJ   01866 822385
MacKechnie, J.M. MBE MA   1938 1978   (Kilchrenan and Dalavich)   Eastwing, Manton Grounds, Windermere, Cumbria
Troup, Harold J.G. MA   1951 1980   (Garelochhead))   Tighshee, Isle of Iona PA76 6SP   01681 700309

(22) FALKIRK

Meets at St Andrew's West, Falkirk on the first Tuesday of September, October, November, December and March, and on the fourth Tuesday of January and
June; and in one of the Cumbernauld churches by rotation on the first Tuesday in May.

Clerk: REV. IAN W. BLACK MA BD   Zetland Manse, Ronaldshay Crescent, Grangemouth FK3 9JH   01324 472868
[e-mail: iwblack@dial.pipex.com]   01324 471656 (Presby)
[Internet: http://www.falkirkp.dabsol.co.uk]

Treasurer: MR. I. MACDONALD   1 Jones Avenue, Larbert FK5 3ER   01324 553603

Name	Year(s)	Address	Telephone
Airth (H)			
John Fairful BD	1994	Airth, Falkirk FK2 8JQ	01324 831474
Blackbraes and Shieldhill			
James H. Drysdale LTh	1987 1997	Shieldhill, Falkirk FK1 2EG [e-mail: 106412.2152@compuserve.com]	01324 621938
Bo'ness: Old			
William McPherson BD DipEd	1994	10 Dundas Street, Bo'ness EH51 ODG	01506 822206
Bo'ness: St Andrew's			
Albert O. Bogle BD MTh	1981	Bo'ness EH51 9DT [e-mail:a.bogle@cableinet.co.uk] [Internet: www.standrewsparishchurch.organisation.uk]	01506 822195
Bonnybridge St Helen's (H) (01324 815756)			
Vacant			
David Wandrum (Aux)	1993 1998	133 Falkirk Road, Bonnybridge FK4 1BA 42C Clouden Road, Kildrum, Cumbernauld G67 2EW	01324 812621 (Tel/Fax) 01236 723288
Bothkennar and Carronshore			
Patricia A. Carruth (Mrs) BD	1998	11 Hunter's Place, Greenmount Park, Carronshore FK2 8QS	01324 570525
Brightons (H)			
Scott R. McL. Kirkland BD MAR	1996	The Manse, Maddiston Road, Brightons, Falkirk FK2 OJP [e-mail: scott@kirkland46.freeserve.co.uk]	01324 712062 01324 713855 (2nd num)
Carriden			
R. Gordon Reid BSc BD AMIEE	1993	Carriden, Bo'ness EH51 9LW	01506 822141
John Jenkinson LTCL ALCM DipEd (Aux)	1991	8 Rosehall Terrace, Falkirk FK1 1PY	01324 625498
Cumbernauld: Abronhill (H)			
Neil W. Barclay BSc BEd BD	1986	26 Ash Road, Cumbernauld G67 3ED	01236 723833
Marilyn Douglas (Miss) DCS		201 Almond Road, Cumbernauld G67 3LS	01236 732136
Cumbernauld: Condorrat (H)			
H. Taylor Brown BD CertMin	1997	11 Rosehill Drive, Cumbernauld G67 4FD	01236 721464
Janette McNaughton (Miss) DCS		4 Dunellan Avenue, Moodiesburn, Glasgow G69 0GB	01236 870180
Cumbernauld: Kildrum (H)			
James Cochrane LTh	1994	Clouden Road, Cumbernauld G67 2JQ	01236 723204
David Nicholson DCS		2D Doon Side, Kildrum, Cumbernauld G67 2HX	01236 732260

Cumbernauld: Old (H)				
Catriona Ogilvie (Mrs) BD	1999		Baronhill, Cumbernauld, Glasgow G67 2SD	01236 721912
Colin Ogilvie DCS			42 Kirkwall, Cumbernauld G67	01236 734244
Cumbernauld: St Mungo's				
Neil MacKinnon BD	1990	1999	The Manse, Fergusson Road, Cumbernauld G67 1LS	01236 721513
Elsie M. Miller (Miss) DCS			30 Swinton Avenue, Rowanbank, Baillieston, Glasgow G69 6JR	0141 771 0857
Denny: Dunipace (H)				
Jean W. Gallacher (Miss) BD	1989		Dunipace Manse, Denny, Stirlingshire FK6 6QJ	01324 824540
Denny: Old				
Richard Smith BD	1976	1983	31 Duke Street, Denny FK6 6NR	01324 824508
Denny: Westpark (H)				
Andrew Barrie BSc BD	1984	2000	13 Baxter Crescent, Denny FK6 5EZ	01324 876224
Falkirk: Bainsford				
Vacant			1 Valleyview Place, Newcarron Village, Falkirk FK2 7JB	01324 621087
Falkirk: Camelon Irving (H)				
Sally Foster Fulton (Mrs) BA BD	1999		Dorrator Road, Camelon, Falkirk FK1 4BN	01324 623035
Falkirk: Camelon St John's				
Vacant			24 Rennie Street, Falkirk FK1 5QW	01324 623631
Margaret Corrie (Miss) DCS			44 Sunnyside Street, Falkirk FK1 4BH	01324 670656
Falkirk: Erskine (H)				
Glen D. Macaulay BD	1999		Burnbrae Road, Falkirk FK1 5SD	01324 623701
Falkirk: Grahamston United (H)				
Duncan E. McClements MA BD MTh	1967	1976	30 Russel Street, Falkirk FK2 7HS	01324 624461
Falkirk: Laurieston linked with Redding and Westquarter				
Ronald J. McDowall BD		1980	11 Polmont Road, Laurieston FK2 9QQ	01324 621196
Falkirk: Old and St Modan's (H)				
A. Sheila Blount (Mrs) BD BA	1978	1998	9 Major's Loan, Falkirk FK1 5QF	01324 623063 (Tel/Fax)
			[e-mail: gkblount@aol.com]	
Ronald W. Smith BA BEd BD (Assoc)	1978		19 Neilson Street, Falkirk FK1 5AQ	01324 621058
Falkirk: St Andrew's West (H)				
Alastair M. Horne BSc BD	1989	1997	1 Maggiewood's Loan, Falkirk FK1 5SJ	01324 623308
Falkirk: St James'				
Eric McKimmon BA BD MTh	1983	1992	13 Wallace Place, Falkirk FK2 7EN	01324 622757

Grangemouth: Charing Cross and West (H) Daniel L. Mathers BD	1982	36 Thistle Avenue, Grangemouth FK3 8YQ	01324 474511
Grangemouth: Dundas Douglas B. Blair LTh	1969	5 Abbotsgrange Road, Grangemouth FK3 9JD	01324 482467
Grangemouth: Kerse Andrew C. Donald BD DPS	1992	8 Naismith Court, Grangemouth FK3 9BQ	01324 482109
Grangemouth: Kirk of the Holy Rood J.G. Finlay (Mrs) DipMusEd BD	1996	Bowhouse Road, Grangemouth FK3 0EX	01324 471595
Grangemouth: Zetland (H) Ian W. Black MA BD Colin Mailer (Aux)	1976 1991 1996 1999	Ronaldshay Crescent, Grangemouth FK3 9JH Innis Chonain, Back Row, Polmont FK2 0RD	01324 472868 01324 712401
Haggs (H) Helen Christie (Mrs) BD	1998	5 Watson Place, Dennyloanhead FK4 2BG	01324 813786
Larbert: East Melville D. Crosthwaite BD DipEd DipMin	1984 1995	1 Cortachy Avenue, Carron, Falkirk FK2 8DH	01324 562402
Larbert: Old (H) Clifford A.J. Rennie MA BD	1973 1985	38 South Broomage Avenue, Larbert FK2 3ED	01324 562868
Larbert: West (H) Gavin Boswell BTheol	1993 1999	11 Carronvale Road, Larbert FK5 3LZ	01324 562878
Muiravonside Joan Ross (Miss) BSc BD PhD	1999	Maddiston, Falkirk FK2 0LX	01324 712876
Polmont Old William G. McKaig	1976 2000	Polmont, Falkirk FK2 0QY	01324 713081
Redding and Westquarter See Falkirk Laurieston			
Slamannan Raymond Thomson BD DipMin	1992	Slamannan, Falkirk FK1 3EN	01324 851307
Stenhouse and Carron (H) Robert K. Hardie MA BD	1968 1969	Stenhousemuir, Larbert FK5 4BU	01324 562393

Name	Years	Role / (Charge)	Address	Tel
Acklam, Cliff BD	1997	Chaplain: Army	Hyderabad Barracks, Colchester, Essex CO2 7TB	
Allan, Robert S.T. LLB DipLP BD	1991 1999	Education and Development Officer, Department of Ministry	1 Lime Grove, Larbert FK5 3LY	01324 562500
Blount, Graham K. LLB BD PhD	1976 1998	Parliamentary Officer	(Office) 14 Johnston Terrace, Edinburgh EH1 2PW [e-mail: gkblount@dial.pipex.com] (Home) 9 Majors Loan, Falkirk FK1 5QF	(Tel) 0131 622 2278 (Fax) 0131 622 7226 01324 623063 0131 244 8459
Fulton, R. Stuart M. MA BD	1991 1998	Specialist Adviser in Chaplaincy to HM Prison Services	(Office) c/o Scottish Prison Service HQ, Calton House, 5 Redheugh Rig, Edinburgh EH12 9DQ (Home) Irving Manse, Dorrator Road, Falkirk FK1 4BN	01324 683035
Gillon, George MA CF JP	1940 1980	(Airth)	4 Buchan Road, Fraserburgh, Aberdeenshire AB43 9UW	01324 621315
Goodman, Richard A.	1976 1986	(Isle of Mull Associate)	13/2 Glenbrae Court, Falkirk FK1 1YT	01324 711352
Heriot, Charles R. JP BA	1962 1996	(Brightons)	20 Eastcroft Drive, Polmont FK2 0SU	01324 634483
Hill, Stanley LTh	1967 1998	(Muiravonside)	28 Creteil Court, Falkirk FK1 1UL	01324 712716
Holland, John C.	1976 1985	(Strone and Ardentinny)	2 Breadalbane Place, Polmont, Falkirk FK2 0RF	01506 511279
Kellock, Chris BD	1998	Scripture Union Evangelist	10 Hillcrest, Bo'ness EH51 9HT	01324 619766
McCallum, John	1962 1998	(Falkirk: Irving Camelon)	11 Burnbrae Gardens, Falkirk FK1 5SB	01786 834535
McDonald, William G. MA BD	1959 1975	(Falkirk Grahamstown United)	19 Union Street, Bridge of Allan FK9 4NS	01324 551274
Maclaren, William B. MA JP	1944 1983	(Bothkennar and Carronshore)	7 Malcolm Drive, Stenhousemuir FK5 4JP	01324 624938
McMullin, Andrew MA	1960 1996	(Blackbraes and Shieldhill)	33 Eastcroft Drive, Polmont FK2 0SU	01324 551362
Martin, Neil DCS		(Deacon)	3 Strathmiglo Place, Stenhousemuir FK5 4UQ	01324 825441
Maxton, Ronald M. MA	1955 1995	(Dollar: Associate)	5 Rulley View, Denny FK6 6QQ	01324 712446
Munroe, Henry BA LTh LTI	1971 1988	(Denny Dunipace North with Old)	Viewforth, High Road, Maddiston, Falkirk FK2 0BL	01324 563764
Murray, Eric J.	1958 1995	(Larbert: East)	21 Redpath Drive, Greenmount Park, Carron FK5 8QL	01324 562641
Paul, Iain BSc PhD BD PhD	1976 1991	(Wishaw Craigneuk and Belhaven)	116 Tryst Road, Larbert FK5 4QJ	01350 727455
Robertson, Iain M. MA	1967 1992	(Carriden)	St. Colme's, Perth Road, Birnam, Dunkeld PH8 0BH	01324 711240
Talman, Hugh MA	1943 1987	(Polmont Old)	Niagara, 70 Lawers Crescent, Polmont FK2 0RQ	

FALKIRK ADDRESSES

Falkirk

Church	Address
Bainsford	Hendry Street, Bainsford
Camelon	
Irving	Dorrator Road, Camelon
St John's	Glasgow Road x Stirling Road
Erskine	Cockburn Street x Hodge Street
Grahamston	Bute Street
Laurieston	Main Falkirk Road
Old and St Modan's	Kirk Wynd
St Andrew's West	Newmarket Street
St James'	Thornhill Road x Firs Street

Grangemouth

Church	Address
Charing Cross and West	Charing Cross
Dundas	Bo'ness Road
Kerse	Abbot's Road
Kirk of the Holy Rood	Bowhouse Road
Zetland	Ronaldshay Crescent

(23) STIRLING

Meets at Dunblane, in the Cathedral Hall, on the second Thursday of September, and at Bridge of Allan Chalmers, on the second Thursday of every other month except January, July and August when there is no meeting.

Presbytery Office:	St Columba's Church, Park Terrace, Stirling FK8 2NA [e-mail: barrydunsmore@compuserve.com]	01786 449522 (Tel) 01786 473930 (Fax) (Mon-Fri: 9.30 am - 12 noon)
Clerk: REV. BARRY W. DUNSMORE MA BD	St Columba's Manse, 5 Clifford Road, Stirling FK8 2AQ	01786 475802

Aberfoyle (H) linked with Port of Menteith (H)
Vacant — The Manse, Loch Ard Road, Aberfoyle, Stirling FK8 3SZ — 01877 382391

Alloa: North (H)
David S.F. Couper MA BD — 1988 — 30 Claremont, Alloa FK10 2DF — 01259 216845

Alloa: St Mungo's (H)
Alan F.M. Downie MA BD — 1977 1996 — 37a Claremont, Alloa FK10 2DG — 01259 213872

Alloa: West
Vacant — 29 Claremont, Alloa FK10 2DF — 01259 214204

Alva
James N.R. McNeil BSc BD — 1990 1997 — The Manse, 34 Ochil Road, Alva FK12 5JT — 01259 760262

Balfron linked with Fintry (H)
John Turnbull — 1994 — Balfron, Glasgow G63 OSX — 01360 440285

Balquhidder linked with Killin and Ardeonaig (H)
John Lincoln MPhil BD — 1986 1997 — The Manse, Killin FK21 8TN [e-mail: gm0jol@zetnet.co.uk] — 01567 820247

Bannockburn: Allan(H)
Jim Landels BD CertMin — 1990 — Bogend Road, Bannockburn FK7 8NP [e-mail: revjimlandels@ic24.net] — 01786 814692

Bannockburn: Ladywell (H)
Elizabeth M.D. Robertson (Miss) BD CertMin — 1997 — 57 The Firs, Bannockburn FK7 OEG — 01786 812467

Bridge of Allan: Chalmers (H)
Alexander G. Horsburgh MA BD — 1996 — 34 Kenilworth Road, Bridge of Allan, Stirling FK9 4EH
[e-mail: alexanderhorsburgh@compuserve.com] — 01786 832118 (Tel)
01786 831176 (Fax)

Bridge of Allan: Holy Trinity (H) (01786 834155)
John C. Nicol MA BD — 1965 — 29 Keir Street, Bridge of Allan, Stirling FK9 4QJ
[e-mail: johncnicol@aol.com] — 01786 832093

Buchanan linked with Drymen
Alexander J. MacPherson BD — 1986 — Buchanan Manse, Drymen, Glasgow G63 0AQ — 01360 870212

Buchlyvie (H) linked with Gartmore (H)
Moira G. MacCormick BA LTh — 1986 — 8 Culbowie Crescent, Buchlyvie, Stirling FK8 3NH — 01360 850249

Callander (H) (Tel/Fax 01877 331409]
Iain M. Goring BSc BD — 1976 — 3 Aveland Park Road., Callander FK17 8FD
[e-mail: gorings@globalnet.co.uk] — 01877 330097
June Cloggie (Mrs) (Aux) — 1997 — 8 Trossachs Road, Aberfoyle FK8 3SW — 01877 382382

Cambusbarron: The Bruce Memorial (H)
Brian Webster BSc BD — 1998 — 14 Woodside Court, Cambusbarron FK7 9PH
[e-mail: revweb@lineone.net] — 01786 450579

Clackmannan (H)
J. Gordon Mathew MA BD — 1973 — The Manse, Port Street, Clackmannan FK10 4JH — 01259 211255)

Cowie (H) linked with Plean
Vacant — The Manse, Plean, Stirling FK7 8BX — 01786 813287

Dollar (H) linked with Glendevon linked with Muckhart
John P.S. Purves BSc BD — 1978 — 1990 — 2 Manse Road, Dollar FK14 7AJ
[e-mail: dollar.parish@btinternet.com] — 01259 743432
Margaret McArthur BD DipMin (Assoc) — 1995 — The Manse, Muckhart FK14 7JN — 01259 781464
Jean S. Watson (Miss) MA (Aux) — 1993 — 1998 — 29 Strachan Crescent, Dollar FK14 7HL — 01259 742872

Drymen See Buchanan

Dunblane: Cathedral (H)
Colin G. McIntosh BSc BD — 1976 — 1988 — Cathedral Manse, Dunblane FK15 0AQ — 01786 822205

Dunblane: St Blane's (H)
George G. Cringles BD — 1981 — 1988 — 49 Roman Way, Dunblane FK15 9DJ — 01786 822268

Fallin
Eleanor D. Muir (Miss) MTheol DipPTheol — 1986 — 4 King Street, Fallin, Stirling FK7 7JY — 01786 812243

Fintry See Balfron

Gargunnock linked with Kincardine in Menteith
Catherine A. Hepburn (Miss) BA BD   1982   1994   The Manse, Gargunnock, Stirling FK8 3BQ   01786 860678

Gartmore See Buchlyvie
Glendevon See Dollar

Killearn (H)
Philip R.M. Malloch LLB BD   1970   1993   2 The Oaks, Killearn, Glasgow G63 9SF   01360 550045

Killin and Ardeonaig (H) See Balquhidder

Kilmadock
Vacant   Doune, Perthshire FK16 6EL   01786 841437

Kincardine in Menteith See Gargunnock.

Kippen (H) linked with Norrieston
Gordon MacRae BA BD   1985   1998   The Manse, Kippen, Stirling FK8 3DN   01786 870229

Lecropt (H)
William M. Gilmour MA BD   1969   1983   5 Henderson Street, Bridge of Allan, Stirling FK9 4NA   01786 832382

Logie (H)
Regine U. Cheyne (Mrs) MA BSc BD   1988   2000   128 Causewayhead Road, Stirling FK9 5HJ   01786 463060

Menstrie (H)
George T. Sherry LTh   1977   The Manse, Menstrie FK11 7EA   01259 761461

Muckhart See Dollar
Norrieston See Kippen
Plean See Cowie
Port of Menteith See Aberfoyle

Sauchie and Coalsnaughton
Agnes A. Moore (Miss) BD   1987   1995   Parish Church Manse, Main Street, Sauchie FK10 3JX   01259 212037

Stirling: Allan Park South (H) linked with Church of the Holy Rude (H)
Morris C. Coull BD   1974   1996   22 Laurelhill Place, Stirling FK8 2JH   01786 473999

Stirling: Church of the Holy Rude (H) See Allan Park South (H)

Stirling: North (H) Paul M.N. Sewell MA BD	1970 1978	18 Shirra's Brae Road, Stirling FK7 OBA	01786 475378
Stirling: St Columba's (H) (01786 449516) Barry W. Dunsmore MA BD	1982 1988	5 Clifford Road, Stirling FK8 2AQ [e-mail: barrydunsmore@compuserve.com]	01786 475802 (Tel) 01786 473930 (Fax)
Stirling: St Mark's Rodney P.T. Robb	1995	176 Drip Road, Stirling FK8 1RR	01786 473716
Stirling: St Ninian's Old (H) Gary J. McIntyre BD DipMin	1993 1998	7 Randolph Road, Stirling FK8 2AJ	01786 474421
Stirling: Viewfield (T)(H) Ian Taylor BD ThM	1995	7 Windsor Place, Stirling FK8 2HY [e-mail: taylorian@btinternet.com]	01786 474534
Strathblane (H) Alex H. Green MA BD	1986 1995	Strathblane, Glasgow G63 9AQ	01360 770226
Tillicoultry (H) Vacant		The Manse, Dollar Road, Tillicoultry FK13 6PD	01259 750340 01259 752951 (Fax)
Tullibody St Serf's (H) Vacant		Tullibody, Alloa FK10 2RG	01259 213236

Aiken, E. Douglas MA	1961	1998	(Clackmannan)	1 Dolan Grove, Saline KY12 9UP	01383 852730
Anderson, Robert S.	1988	1987	Director: SCWE	St John's, Muir Crescent, Doune FK16 6DA	01786 841386
Benson, James W. BA BD DipEd	1975	1996	(Balquhidder)	1 Sunnyside, Dunblane FK15 9HA	01786 822624
Burnett, John B.	1964	1985	(Dollar: Associate)	30 Manor House Road, Dollar FK14 7HB	01259 742892
Campbell, Patrick D.G. MA	1949	1984	(Geneva)	30 Harviestoun Road, Dollar FK14 7HG	01259 742172
Cheyne, Magnus	1963	1996	(Community Minister: Shetland)	128 Causewayhead Road, Stirling FK9 5HJ	01786 463060
Craig, Maxwell D. BD ThM	1966	2000	(Jerusalem: St. Andrew's: Locum)	9 Kilbryde Crescent, Dunblane FK15 9BA	01786 823147
Cruikshank, Alistair A.B. MA	1991		Auxiliary	2A Chapel Place, Dollar FK14 7DW	01259 742549
Doherty, Arthur James DipTh	1957	1993	(Fintry)	1 Murdiston Avenue, Callander FK17 8AY	
Edie, Charles B. MA	1946	1984	(Stirling, Church of the Holy Rude)	6 Calton, Shirras Brae Road, Stirling FK7 0AX	01786 474271
Fleming, Alexander F.	1966	1995	(Strathblane)	4 Horsburgh Avenue, Kilsyth G65 9BZ	01236 821461
Gallan, Alex MA	1955	1989	(Wishaw Cambusnethan North)	16 Dundas Road, Stirling FK9 5QQ	01786 470796
Irvine, R.W.W.	1965	1993	(Kincardine-in-Menteith with Norrieston)	9 Fraser Place, Causewayhead, Stirling FK9 5RE	01786 448802
Izett, William A.F.	1968	2000	(Law)	1 Duke Street, Clackmannan FK10 4EF	01259 724 203
Jamieson, G.T. BA	1936	1969	(Stirling Viewfield)	10 Grendon Court, Snowdon Place, Stirling FK8 2JX	01786 461646
Jamieson, John LTh	1967	1993	(Balfron)	Ardnablane, Dunblane FK15 OOR	01786 823610

Laing, John M. MA	1948	1985	(Buchlyvie with Gartmore)	58 Carseview, Bannockburn, Stirling FK7 8LH	01786 815448
McCallum, Iain D. MA	1943	1984	(Stirling Allan Park South)	Mount View House, Bracklinn Road, Callander FK18	01877 330760
McCutcheon, George A. MA	1948	1984	(Clackmannan)	13 Harviestoun Road, Dollar FK14 7HG	01259 742609
Macdonald, R.M. OBE MA DD	1929	1968	(Calabar)	Pinewood Nursing Home, Leny Road, Callander FK17 8EG	
McIntosh, Hamish N.M. MA	1949	1987	(Fintry)	1 Forth Crescent, Stirling	01786 470453
Macrae, Elaine H.(Mrs) BD	1985	1998	Prison Chaplain	The Manse, Kippen FK8 3DN	01786 870229
McRae, Malcolm H. MA PhD	1986	1994	(Coalsnaughton)	10B Victoria Place, Stirling FK7	
McWilliam, Stuart W. MA STM	1941	1981	(Killearn)	Terreran, Main Street, Gartmore, Stirling FK8 3RN	01877 382640
Orrock, Archibald. A. MA BD	1938	1982	(Teacher: Religious Instruction)	3 Kilbryde Court, Dunblane FK15 9AX	01786 822821
Ovens, Samuel B. BD	1982	1993	(Slamannan)	Ruellen, 28 Norwood Avanue, Alloa FK10 2BY	01259 216172
Pryce, Stuart F.A.	1963	1997	(Dumfries: St George's)	36 Forth Park, Bridge of Allan, Stirling FK9 5NT	01786 831026
Reid, Alan A.S. MA BD STM	1962	1995	(Bridge of Allan Chalmers)	Wayside Cottage, Bridgend, Ceres, Fife KY15 5LS	
Reid, David T. BA BD	1954	1993	(Cleish linked with Fossoway St Serf's and Devonside)	14 Argyle Park, Dunblane FK15 9DZ	01786 824863
Rennie, Alistair M. MA BD	1939	1986	(Kincardine Croick and Edderton)	13 Tullich Terrace, Tillicoultry FK13 6RD	01259 751563
Robertson, Alex	1974	1993	(Baldernock)	4 Moray Park, Doune	01786 841894
Russell, John MA	1959	2000	(Tillicoultry)	Kilblaan, Gladstone Terrace, Birnam, Dunkeld PH8 OOP	01350 728896
Sangster, Ernest G. BD ThM	1958	1997	(Alva)	6 Law Hill Road, Dollar FK14 7BG	
Scott, James F.	1957	1997	(Dyce)	5 Gullipen View, Callander FK17	
Scoular, J. Marshall	1954	1996	(Kippen)	2H Buccleuch Court, Dunblane FK15 0AH	01786 825976
Silcox, John R. BD	1976	1984	School Chaplain	Queen Victoria School, Dunblane FK15 OJA	01786 824944
Stirling, J BSc BD	1962	1998	(Stirling: St Ninian's Old)	42 Fairies Road, Perth PH1 1LZ	01738 442953
Symington, Robert C BA	1954	1997	(Community Minister: Lorn and Mull)	3 Belmont, The Crescent, Dunblane FK15 0DW	01786 823902
Todd, A. Stewart MA BD DD	1952	1993	(Aberdeen: St Machar's Cathedral)	Culearn, Balquhidder, Lochearnhead, Perthshire FK19 8PB	01877 384662
Turner, William MA BD	1934	1970	(Gargunnock)	Flat 18, Malin Court, Turnberry, Ayrshire KA26 9PB	01655 331283
Watt, Robert MA BD	1943	1982	(Aberdeen Woodside South)	1 Coldstream Avenue, Dunblane FK15 9JN	01786 823632
Wright, John P. BD	1977	2000	(Glasgow: New Govan)	Plane Castle, by Stirling	

STIRLING ADDRESSES

Allan Park South	Dumbarton Road	St Ninians Old	Kirk Wynd
Holy Rude	St John Street	St Ninians; Viewfield	Barnton Street
North	Springfield Road	St Columba's	Park Terrace
		St Mark's	Drip Road

(24) DUNFERMLINE

Meets at Dunfermline, in the Abbey Church Hall, Abbey Park Place on the first Thursday of each month except January, July and August when there is no meeting and June when it meets on the last Thursday.

Clerk:	REV. WILLIAM E. FARQUHAR BA BD		Townhill Manse, Dunfermline KY12 OEZ [e-mail: dunfpres@dial.pipex.com]	01383 723835 (Tel/Fax)
Aberdour St Fillan's (H) Peter B. Park BD MCIBS	1997		36 Bellhouse Road, Aberdour, Fife KY3 OTL	01383 860349
Ballingry and Lochcraig Vacant			Ballingry, Lochgelly KY5 8PA	01592 861663
Beath (H) and Cowdenbeath North Vacant			North Manse, Stuart Place, Cowdenbeath KY4 9BN	01383 511033
Cairneyhill (H) (01383 873337) linked with Limekilns (H) Norman M. Grant BD	1990		Limekilns, Dunfermline KY11 3HT	01383 872341
Carnock and Oakley (H) Elizabeth S.S. Kenny (Miss) BD RGN SCM	1989		Carnock, Dunfermline KY12 9JG	01383 850327
Cowdenbeath: Trinity (H) David G Adams BD	1991	1999	66 Barclay Street, Cowdenbeath KY4 9LD	01383 515089
Culross and Torryburn (H) Thomas Moffat BSc BD	1976	2000	Culross, Dunfermline KY12 8JD	01383 880231
Dalgety (H) Donald G. B. McCorkindale BD DipMin Ian Cunningham DCS	1992	2000	9 St Colme Drive, Dalgety Bay, Dunfermline KY11 5LQ 5 Forth Court, Dalgety Bay, Dunfermline KY11 5SF	01383 822316
Dunfermline: Abbey (H) Alistair L. Jessamine MA BD	1979	1991	12 Garvock Hill, Dunfermline KY12 7UU	01383 721022
Dunfermline: Gillespie Memorial (H) (01383 621253) A. Gordon Reid BSc BD	1982	1988	4 Killin Court, Dunfermline KY12 7XF	01383 723329
Dunfermline: North Gordon F.C. Jenkins MA BD PhD	1968	1998	13 Barbour Grove, Dunfermline KY12	01383 721061

Dunfermline: St Andrew's Erskine Anne Allison (Mrs) BSc PhD BD	2000		71A Townhill Road, Dunfermline KY12 0BN	01383 734657
Dunfermline: St Leonard's (01383 620106)				
Alexander B. Mitchell BD	1981		12 Torvean Place, Dunfermline KY11 4YY	01383 721054
Andrew E. Paterson (Aux)	1994		61 Elmwood Terrace, Kelty KY4	01383 830998
Dunfermline: St Margaret's Fiona Richard (Mrs)	1996		38 Garvock Hill, Dunfermline KY12 7UU	01383 723955
Dunfermline: St Ninian's Elizabeth A. Fisk (Mrs) BD	1996		51 St John's Drive, Dunfermline KY12 7TL	01383 722256
Dunfermline: St Paul's Frank T. Smith MA	1957	1964	6 Park Avenue, Dunfermline KY12 7HX	01383 721124
Dunfermline: Townhill and Kingseat(H) William E. Farquhar BA BD	1987		161 Main Street, Townhill, Dunfermline KY12 OEZ	01383 723835
Inverkeithing St John's linked with North Queensferry (T) Sheila Munro (Ms) BD	1995		34 Hill Street, Inverkeithing KY11 1AB	01383 412422
Inverkeithing: St Peter's (01383 412626) George G. Nicol BD DPhil	1982	1988	20 Struan Drive, Inverkeithing KY11 1AR	01383 410032
Kelty Scott Burton BD DipMin	1999		15 Arlick Road, Kelty KY4 OBH	01383 830291
Limekilns See Cairneyhill				
Lochgelly: Macainsh Mary Ann Rennie (Mrs) BD MTh	1998		82 Main Street, Lochgelly KY5 9AA	01592 780435
Lochgelly: St Andrew's (T)(H) Robert F. Duncan MTheol	1986	1990	Station Road, Lochgelly KY5 9QX	01592 780319
Mossgreen and Crossgates See Cowdenbeath Trinity				
North Queensferry See Inverkeithing St John's				
Rosyth Douglas M. Main BD	1986		42 Woodside Avenue, Rosyth KY11 2LA	01383 412776
Morag Crawford (Miss) DCS	2000		118 Wester Drylaw Place, Edinburgh EH4 2TG	0131 332 2253

Saline and Blairingone
Richard J. Hammond BA BD — 1993 — Main Street, Saline, Dunfermline KY12 9PL — 01383 852240

Tulliallan and Kincardine
James G. Redpath BD DipPTh — 1988 — 62 Toll Road, Kincardine, by Alloa FK10 4QZ — 01259 730538

Name			Position / (Charge)	Address	Tel
Archibald, D.Y. BA BD MPhil	1949	1983	(Cairneyhill with Torryburn and Newmills)	Flat 31, Runnymeade Court, Park Hill Rise, Croydon CR0 5JF	0181 681 8398
Baird, William G.G.	1977	1993	(Inverkeithing: St Johns with North Queensferry)		
Bardgett, Frank D. MA BD PhD	1987	1997	Department of National Mission	51 Charles Street, Pittenweem, Fife KY10 2RA	01333 311397
Britchfield, Alison E. P. (Mrs) MA BD	1986	1992	Chaplain RN	6 Inchcolme Drive, North Queensferry KY11 1LD	01383 416863
Brown, Peter MA BD FRAScot	1953	1987	(Holm)	13 Tregoning Road, Torpoint, Cornwall PH11 2LX	01752 818430
Campbell, John MA	1943	1978	(Urquhart)	24 Inchmickery Drive, Dalgety Bay KY11 5NF	01383 822456
Elston, Peter K.	1963	2000	(Dalgety)	15 Foulden Place, Dunfermline KY12 7TQ	01383 738055
Goring, John M. MA	1955	1988	(Dunfermline Gillespie Memorial)	57 Rose Street, Dunfermline KY12 0QT	01383 723971
Mackenzie, R.P. MA BD	1936	1980	(Dunfermline St Leonard's)	23 Foulis Crescent, Juniper Green, Edinburgh EH14 5BN	0131 453 3599
Macpherson, Stewart M. MA	1953	1990	(Dunfermline Abbey)	176 Halbeath Road, Dunfermline KY11 4LB	01383 722851
Orr, J McMichael MA BD PhD	1949	1986	(Aberfoyle with Port of Menteith)	9 Overhaven, Limekilns, Fife KY11 3JH	01383 872245
Pogue, Victor C. BA BD	1945	1980	(Baird Research Fellow)	120 Buckstone Terrace, Edinburgh EH10 6QR	0131 445 1628
Rae, Peter C. BSc BD	1968	2000	(Beath and Cowdenbeath North)		
Reid, David MSc LTh FSAScot	1961	1992	(St Monans with Largoward)	North Lethans, Saline, Dunfermline KY12 9TE	01383 733144
Ross, Evan J LTh	1986	1998	(Cowdenbeath: West with Mossgreen and Crossgates)		
Scott, John LTh	1969	1996	(Aberdour St Fillan's)	43 Auld Mart Road, Milnathort, Kinross KY13 7FR	01577 861484
Scoular, Stanley	1963	2000	(Rosyth)	32 White's Quay, St David's Harbour, Dalgety Bay KY11 5HT	01383 820896
Smith, T. Forrest	1959	1986	(Arbuthnott with Kinneff)	41 Duns Crescent, Dundee DD4 0RY	01382 501653
Stuart, Anne (Miss) DCS			(Deaconess)	Room 15, Hanover Court, 175 Stenhouse Road, Cowdenbeath KY4	
Whyte, Isabel H. (Mrs) BD		1993	Chaplain: Queen Margaret Hospital, Dunfermline	19 St Colne Crescent, Aberdour, Fife KY3 0ST	01383 860049
				34 Shandon Crescent, Edinburgh EH11 1QF	0131 337 0866

(25) KIRKCALDY

Meets at Kirkcaldy, in St Brycedale Hall, on the first Tuesday of February, March, April, May, November and December, on the second Tuesday of September, and on the fourth Tuesday of June.

Clerk: REV. BRYAN L. TOMLINSON TD — 83 Milton Road, Kirkcaldy KY1 1TP — 01592 204319 (Office) / 01592 260315)
[e-mail: ha49@dial.pipex.com]

Depute Clerk: REV. JOHN C. DUNCAN BD MPhil — 21 Ramsay Crescent, Burntisland KY3 9JL — 01592 874303 (Tel/Fax)
[e-mail: john.duncanc@btinternet.com]

Auchterderran linked with Cardenden St Fothad's linked with Kinglassie
J. Ewen R. Campbell MA BD   1967   1977   7 Woodend Road, Cardenden KY5 0NE   01592 720213

Auchtertool linked with Kirkcaldy Linktown (H) (01592 641080)
Catriona M. Morrison (Mrs) MA BD   1995   2000   16 Raith Crescent, Kirkcaldy KY2 5NN   01592 265536

Buckhaven (01592 715577)
Bryce Calder MA BD   1995   181 Wellesley Road, Buckhaven KY8 1JA   01592 712870

Burntisland (H)
John C. Duncan BD MPhil   1987   21 Ramsay Crescent, Burntisland KY3 9JL   01592 874303   (Tel/Fax)
                                                         [e-mail: john.duncanc@btinternet.com]

Cardenden St Fothad's See Auchterderran

Denbeath linked with Methilhill
Elizabeth F. Cranfield (Miss) MA BD 1988   9 Chemiss Road, Methilhill KY8 2BS   01592 713142

Dysart (H)
Tilly Wilson (Miss) MTh   1990   1998   1 School Brae, Dysart KY1 2XB   01592 655887

Glenrothes: Christ's Kirk
James MacMillan BD   1997   12 The Limekilns, Glenrothes KY6 3QJ   01592 620536

Glenrothes: St Columba's (01592 752539)
Alistair G. McLeod   1988   40 Liberton Drive, Glenrothes KY6 3PB   01592 744558
Muriel Wilson (Miss) DCS   22 Well Gardens, Woodside, Glenrothes KY7 5HW   01592 753885

Glenrothes: St Margaret's (H) (01592 610310)
John P. McLean   1994   8 Alburne Park, Glenrothes KY7 5RB   01592 752241

Glenrothes: St Ninian's
Linda Dunbar (Miss)   2000   1 Cawdor Drive, Glenrothes KY6 2HN   01592 611963
Carol Dickson (Miss) DCS   South Lodge, Walkerton Drive, Leslie KY5 3EY   01592 743272

Innerleven East (H)
James L. Templeton BSc BD   1975   77 McDonald Street, Methil KY8 3AJ   01333 426310

Kennoway and Windygates and Balgonie : St Kenneth's (01333 351372) [e-mail: administration@st-kenneth's.freeserve.co.uk]
Richard Baxter MA BD   1997   2 Fernhill Gardens, Windygates, Leven KY8 5DZ   01333 352329
                                                         [e-mail: richard.baxter@msn.com]

Kinghorn
James Reid BD — 1985 1997 — 17 Myre Crescent, Kinghorn, Fife KY3 9UB — 01592 890269
[e-mail: jim17reid@aol.com]

Kinglassie See Auchterderran

Kirkcaldy: Abbotshall (H)
Bryan L. Tomlinson TD — 1969 1980 — 83 Milton Road, Kirkcaldy KY1 1TP — 01592 260315 (Tel/Fax)
[e-mail: ha49@dial.pipex.com]

Kirkcaldy: Linktown (01592 641080) See Auchtertool

Kirkcaldy: Old (01592 641672)
Vacant — 2 Townsend Place, Kirkcaldy KY1 1HB — 01592 260448

Kirkcaldy: Pathhead (H) (01592 204635 Tel/Fax) [e-mail: pathhead@btinternet.com]
John D. Thomson BD — 1985 1993 — 73 Loughborough Road, Kirkcaldy KY1 3DD — 01592 652215
[e-mail: john.d.thomson@cableinet.co.uk]
Maureen Paterson (Mrs) BSc (Aux) — 1992 1994 — 91 Dalmahoy Crescent, Kirkcaldy KY2 6TA — 01592 262300
[e-mail: m.e.paterson@talk21.com]

Kirkcaldy: St Andrew's (H)
Donald M. Thomson BD — 1975 2000 — 15 Harcourt Road, Kirkcaldy KY2 5HQ — 01592 260816

Kirkcaldy: St Brycedale (H) (01592 640016) [e-mail: office@stbee.freeserve.co.uk]
Ken Froude MA BD — 1979 — 6 East Fergus Place, Kirkcaldy KY1 1XT — 01592 264480
[e-mail: jkfroude@kfroude.freeserve.co.uk]

Kirkcaldy: St John's
Samuel M. McNaught MA BD MTh — 1968 1975 — 25 Bennochy Avenue, Kirkcaldy KY2 5QE — 01592 263821

Kirkcaldy: Templehall (H)
Brock A. White LTh — 1971 — Appin Crescent, Kirkcaldy KY2 6EJ — 01592 260156

Kirkcaldy: Torbain
Ian Elston BD MTh — 1999 — 91 Sauchenbush Road, Kirkcaldy KY2 5RN — 01592 263015

Kirkcaldy: Viewforth (H) linked with Thornton
Vacant — 66 Viewforth Street, Kirkcaldy KY1 3DJ — 01592 652502
[e-mail: dc@thefree.net]

Leslie Trinity
David J. Smith BD DipMin — 1992 1997 — 4 Valley Drive, Leslie KY6 3BQ — 01592 741008

Leven: St Andrew's (H) (01333 428511)
Vacant
5 Forman Road, Leven, Fife KY8 4HH
[e-mail: levenparish@compuserve.com]
01333 423843

Leven: Scoonie Kirk (H)
Edgar J. Ogston BSc BD   1976   1987
Links Road, Leven, Fife KY8 4HR
01333 426518

Markinch
I.D. Gordon LTh   1972
7 Guthrie Crescent, Markinch KY7 6AY
01592 758264

Methil (H)
Allan B. Brown BD MTh   1995   2000
14 Methilbrae, Methil KY8 3LW
01333 426255

Methilhill See Denbeath
Thornton See Kirkcaldy: Viewforth

Wemyss
Kenneth W. Donald BA BD   1982   1999
33 Main Road, East Wemyss, Fife KY1 4RE
[e-mail: kwdonald@4unet.co.uk]
01592 713260

Cooper, M.W. MA	1944	1979	(Kirkcaldy Abbotshall)	Applegarth, Sunny Park, Kinross KY13 7BX	01577 263204
Crawford, S.G. Victor	1980	1991	(Glasgow: Calton Parkhead)	Crofton, 65 Main Road, East Weymss KY1 4RI	01592 712325
Dick, James S. MA BTh	1988	1997	(Glasgow: Ruchazie)	1 Hawkmuir, Kirkcaldy KY1 2AN	01592 260289
Forrester, Ian L. MA	1964	1996	(Friockheim, Kinnell with Inverkeilor and Lunan)	8 Bennochy Avenue, Kirkcaldy KY2 5QE	01592 260251
Gatt, David W.	1981	1995	(Thornton)	15 Beech Avenue, Thornton KY1 4AT	01592 774328
Gibson, Ivor MA	1957	1993	(Abercorn with Dalmeny)	15 McInnes Road, Glenrothes KY7 6BA	01592 759982
Howden, Margaret (Miss) DCS			(Deaconess)	38 Munro Street, Kirkcaldy KY1 1PY	01592 205913
McAlpine, Robin J. BDS BD	1988	1997	Adviser in Mission and Evangelism	10 Seton Place, Kirkcaldy KY2 6UX [e-mail: robin.mcalpine@virgin.net]	01592 643518
McDonald, Iain J.M. MA BD	1984	1996	Chaplain, Kirkcaldy Acute Hospitals	26 Cairngorm Crescent, Kirkcaldy KY2 5RG	
McKenzie, Donald M. TD MA	1947	1986	(Auchtertool with Burntisland)	76 Forth Park Gardens, Kirkcaldy KY2 5TD	01592 263012
MacLeod, Norman	1960	1988	(Orwell with Portmoak)	324 Muirfield Drive, Glenrothes KY6 2PZ	01592 610281
Munro, Andrew, MA BD PhD	1972	2000	(Glencaple with Lowther)	7 Dunvegan Avenue, Kirkcaldy, Fife	
Reid, Martin R.B.C.	1960	1990	(Falkirk West)	13 Rothes Park, Leslie KY6 3LL	01592 620053
Simpson, Gordon M. MA BD	1959	1996	(Leslie Trinity)	37 Spottiswoode Gardens, St Andrews KY16 8SA	01334 473406
Sutherland, William	1964	1993	(Bo'ness Old)	88 Dunrobin Road, Kirkcaldy KY2 5YT	01592 205510
Taylor, John T.H.	1947	1983	(Glenrothes Christ's Kirk on the Green)	9 Douglas Road, Leslie KY6 3JZ	01592 741009
Thomson, Gilbert L. BA	1965	1996	(Glenrothes Christ's Kirk)	3 Fortharfield, Freuchie KY15 7JJ	01387 857431
Webster, Elspeth H. (Miss) DCS			(Deaconess)	82 Broomhill Avenue, Burntisland KY3 0BP	01592 873616
Young, W. Finlayson MA	1943	1979	(Kinglassie)	17 Whitecraig Road, Newburgh, Fife KY14 6BP	01337 840646

KIRKCALDY ADDRESSES

Abbotshall	Abbotshall Road	St Andrew's	Victoria Road x Victoria Gdns	Templehall	Beauly Place
Linktown	Nicol Street x High Street.	St Brycedale	St Brycedale Avenue x Kirk Wynd	Torbain	Lindores Drive
Old	Kirk Wynd	St John's	Elgin Street	Viewforth	Viewforth Street x Viewforth Terrace
Pathhead	Harriet Street x Church Street				

(26) ST ANDREWS

Meets alternately at Cupar, in St John's Church Hall, and at St Andrews, in Martyrs Church Hall, on the second Wednesday of February, March, April, May, September, October, November and December, and on the last Wednesday of June.

Clerk:	REV. PETER MEAGER MA BD CERTMGMT		7 Lorraine Drive, Cupar KY15 5DY [e-mail: st.andrews.clerk@dial.pipex.com]	01334 656991

Abdie and Dunbog (H) linked with Newburgh (H)

Robert J.V. Logan MA BD	1962	1998	2 Guthrie Court, Cupar Road, Newburgh, Fife KY14 6HA [e-mail: rjvlogan@aol.com]	01337 840275 (Tel/Fax)

Anstruther

Ian A. Cathcart BSc BD	1994	The James Melville Manse, Anstruther KY10 3EX	01333 311808

Auchtermuchty (H)

Ann G. Fraser (Mrs) BD CertMin	1990	2 Burnside, Auchtermuchty KY14 7AJ	01337 828519

Balmerino (H) linked with Wormit (H)

Graeme W. Beebee BD	1993	5 Westwater Place, Newport-on-Tay DD6 8NS	01382 542626

Boarhills and Dunino linked with St Andrews Martyrs'

J. Mary Henderson (Miss) MA BD DipEd PhD	1990	2000	49 Irvine Crescent, St Andrews KY16 8LG [e-mail: jmh@smokeypuss.freeserve.co.uk]	01334 472948

Cameron linked with St Andrews: St Leonard's

Alan D. McDonald LLB BD MTh	1979	1998	1 Cairnhill Gardens, St Andrews KY16 8UR [e-mail: alan.d.mcdonald@talk21.com]	01334 472793

Carnbee linked with Pittenweem

Charles G. Thrower BSc	1965	1970	Pittenweem, Fife KY10 2LR [e-mail: C-Thrower@pittenweem2.freeserve.co.uk]	01333 311255

Cellardyke (H) linked with Kilrenny
David J.H. Laing BD DPS — 1976 — 1999 — Toll Road, Cellardyke, Anstruther KY10 3BH
[e-mail: davith@uk.packardbell.org] — 01333 310810

Ceres and Springfield
Matthew Z. Ross LLB BD FSAScot — 1998 — The Manse, St Andrews Road, Ceres, Cupar KY15 5NQ
[e-mail: mzross@aol.com] — 01334 828233 (Tel/Fax)
07050 191367 (Mbl)

Crail linked with Kingsbarns (H)
George Fairlie BD BVMS MRCVS — 1971 — 1989 — Crail, Fife KY10 3UH — 01333 450358

Creich, Flisk and Kilmany linked with Monimail
Mitchell Collins BD CPS — 1996 — Brunton, Cupar, Fife KY15 4PA
Chellc@care4free.net] — 01337 870332

Cupar: Old (H) & St Michael of Tarvit
Derek Browning MA BD DMin — 1987 — Eden Manse, Cupar, Fife KY15 4HQ
[e-mail: Derek.Browning@btinternet.com] — 01334 653196 (Tel/Fax)

Cupar: St John's
John D. Hegarty LTh ABSC — 1988 — 1997 — 23 Hogarth Drive, Cupar, Fife KY15 5YH
[e-mail: J.Hegarty@btinternet.com] — 01334 655851

Dairsie linked with Kemback linked with Strathkinness (H)
Alexander Strickland JP LTh — 1971 — 1981 — Dairsie, Cupar, Fife KY15 4RS — 01334 653283

Edenshead and Strathmiglo
Thomas G.M. Robertson LTh — 1971 — 1984 — Strathmiglo, Fife KY14 7QD — 01337 860256

Elie (H) linked with Kilconquhar and Colinsburgh (H)
Iain F. Paton BD FCIS — 1980 — 1998 — 30 Bank Street, Elie, Leven KY9 1BW
[e-mail: IainPaton@tesco.net] — 01333 330685

Falkland (01337 858442) linked with Freuchie (H)
John W. Jarvie BD CertMin MTh — 1990 — 1 Newton Road, Falkland, Fife KY15 7AQ
[e-mail: jarvie@cwcom.net] — 01337 857696

Freuchie (H) See Falkland

Howe of Fife
Marion J. Paton (Miss) BMus BD — 1991 — 1994 — 83 Church Street, Ladybank, Fife KY15 7ND
[e-mail: marion@marionpaton.f9.co.uk] — 01337 830513

Kemback See Dairsie

Kilconquhar and Colinsburgh See Elie
Kilrenny See Cellardyke
Kingsbarns See Crail

Largo and Newburn(H) linked with Largo St David's
Rosemary Frew (Mrs) MA BD   1988   The Manse, Church Place, Upper Largo Fife KY8 6EH   01333 360286
[e-mail: rosemaryfrew@breathemail.net]

Largo St David's See Largo and Newburn

Largoward linked with St Monans (H)
Gilbert C. Nisbet CA BD   1993   St Monans, Fife KY10 2DD   01333 730258

Leuchars: St Athernase and Guardbridge
A. Ray C. Gaston MA BD   1969 1998   7 David Wilson Park, Balmullo, Fife KY16 0NP   01334 870038 (Tel/Fax)
[e-mail: gkk52@dial.pipex.com]

Monimail See Creich, Flisk and Kilmany
Newburgh See Abdie and Dunbog

Newport-on-Tay (H)
W. Kenneth Pryde DA BD   1994   57 Cupar Road, Newport-on-Tay DD6 8DF   01382 543165 (Tel/Fax)
[e-mail: wkpryde@aol.com]

Pittenweem See Carnbee

St Andrews: Holy Trinity
Charles Armour MA   1939 1949   17 Queen's Gardens, St Andrews KY16 9TA   01334 474494

St Andrews: Hope Park (H)
A. David K. Arnott MA BD   1971 1996   20 Priory Gardens,, St Andrews KY16 8XX   01334 472912 (Tel/Fax)
[e-mail: adka@st-andrews.ac.uk]

St Andrews: Martyrs'(H) See Boarhills and Dunino
St Andrews: St Leonard's (H) See Cameron
St Monans See Largoward
Springfield See Ceres
Strathkinness See Dairsie

Tayport
Colin J. Dempster BD   1990   27 Bell Street, Tayport DD6 9AP   01382 552861

Wormit See Balmerino

Alexander, Jas. S. MA BD BA PhD	1966	1973	University of St Andrews (Strathkinness)	5 Strathkinness High Road, St Andrews KY16 9RP	01334 472680
Bennett, Alestair TD MA	1938	1976		7 Bonfield Park, Strathkinness, St Andrews KY16 9SY	01334 850249
Best, Ernest MA BD PhD DD	1949	1982	(University of Glasgow)	13 Newmill Gardens, St Andrews KY16 8RY	01334 473315
Bews, James MA	1942	1981	(Dundee Craigiebank)	21 Balrymonth Court, St Andrews KY16 8XT	01334 476087
Bogie, A.P. MA FSAScot	1944	1979	(Forgan)	7 Gourlay Wynd, St Andrews KY16 8HP	
Bradley, Ian MA BD DPhil	1990	1990	Lecturer: University of Aberdeen	4 Donaldson Gardens, St Andrews KY16 9DN	01334 475389
Brown, Lawson R MA	1960	1997	(Cameron with St Andrew's St Leonard's)	10 Park Street, St Andrews KY16 8AQ	01334 473413
Buchan, Alexander MA BD	1975	1992	(North Ronaldsay with Sanday)	26 Allan Robertson Drive, St Andrews KY16 8EY	01334 473875
Buchan, Isabel C. (Mrs)	1975			26 Allan Robertson Drive, St Andrews KY16 8EY	01334 473875
Cameron, James K. MA BD PhD FRHistS	1953	1989	(University of St Andrews)	Priorscroft, 71 Hepburn Gardens, St Andrews KY16 9LS	01334 473996
Casebow, Brian C. MA BD	1959	1993	(Edinburgh: Salisbury)	"The Rowans", 67 St Michael's Drive, Cupar KY15 5BP	01334 656385
Douglas, J.D. MA BD PhD	1957			2 Doocot Road, St Andrews KY16 8QP	01334 474876
Douglas, Peter C. JP	1966	1993	(Boarhills linked with Dunino)	The Old Schoolhouse, Flisk, Newburgh, Fife KY14 6HN	01337 870218
Duncan, James SDA NDA	1962	1972	Teacher: Religious Education	14 Largo Road, Lundin Links, Leven KY8 6DG	
Earnshaw, Philip BA BSc BD	1986	1996	(Glasgow: Pollokshields)	22 Castle Street, St Monans KY10 2AP	01333 730640
Edington, George L.	1952	1989	(Tayport)	646 Burghmuir Road, Perth PH1 1LH	
Galloway, Robert W.C. LTh	1970	1998	(Cromarty)	22 Haughgate, Leven KY8 4SG	
Gibson, Henry M. MA BD PhD	1960	1999	(Dundee: The High Kirk)	4 Comerton Place, Drumoig, by Leuchars, St Andrews KY16 0NQ	01382 542199
Gordon, Peter M. MA BD	1958	1995	(Airdrie West)	3 Cupar Road, Cuparmuir, Cupar KY15 5RH	01334 652341
Gordon, Fiona S. (Mrs) DCS			(Deacon)	3 Cupar Road, Cuparmuir, Cupar KY15 5RH	01334 652341
Henney, William MA DD	1957	1996	(Lisbon)	46 Hepburn Gardens, St Andrews KY16 9DF	01334 472560
Hill, Roy MA	1962	1997	(Newport-on-Tay St Thomas's)	Forgan Cottage, Kinnessburn Road, St Andrews KY16 8AO	01334 472121
Howieson R.A. JP MA	1937	1977	(Baillieston Mure Memorial)	3 Baker Lane, St Andrews KY16 9PJ	01334 473711
Kinnis, Robert L. MA BD	1931	1972	(Kincardine in Menteith with Norrieston)	Gibson House, St Andrews KY16 9JE	01334 654213
Law, Arthur ACIB	1968	1988	(Ceres with Springfield)	13 South Road, Cupar KY15 5JF	01334 656290
Learmonth, Walter LTh	1968	1997	(Banchory Devenick with Maryculter)	14 Marionfield Place, Cupar KY15 5JN	01334 655537
Lithgow, Thomas MA	1945	1982	(Caputh and Clunie with Kinclaven)	124 Balgarvie Crescent, Cupar, Fife KY15 4EG	01333 451194
McCartney, Alexander C. BTh	1973	1995	(Whiteinch)	10 The Glebe, Crail KY10 3UT	01333 320434
McFadyen, Gavin J.	1963	1992	(Channelkirk with Lauder Old)	62 Toll Court, Lundin Links, Leven, Fife KY8 6HH	01334 478314
McGregor, Duncan J. FIMA	1982	1996	(Crail with Kingsbarns)	14 Mount Melville, St Andrews KY16 8NG	01333 450327
Macintyre, William J. MA BD DD	1951	1989		Tigh a'Ghobhainn, Lochton, Crail KY10 3XE	01334 473797
McKane, William MA PhD DLitt DD FBA	1949	1990	(University of St Andrews)	51 Irvine Crescent, St Andrews KY16 8LG	
Mackenzie, A.C. MA	1955	1995	(Biggar)	Hedgerow, 5 Sheils Avenue, Freuchie KY7 7JD	
Mackenzie, J.A.R. MA	1947	1987	(Largo St David's)	Moss-side. Croy, Inverness-shire IV2 5PG	
MacNab, Hamish S.D. MA	1948	1987	(Kilrenny)	Fairhill, Northmuir, Kirriemuir DD8	01575 72564
McPhail, Peter MA BD	1940	1982	(Creich, Flisk and Kilmany)	44 Doocot Road, St Andrews KY16 8QP	01334 473093
Marshall, James S. MA PhD	1939	1979	(Edinburgh: South Leith Assoc)	25 St Mary's Street, St Andrews KY16 8AZ	01334 476136
Meager, Peter MA BD CertMgmt(Open)	1971	1998	(Elie with Kilconquhar and Colinsburgh)	7 Lorraine Drive, Cupar KY15 5DY	01334 656991
Murdoch, J.A.H. BA BD DPSS	1979	1998	Chaplain: St. Leonard's School	Priorsgate, South Street, St. Andrews KY16 9QU	01334 470084
Nicol, Robert M.	1984	1996	(Jersey: St Columba's)	35 Upper Greens, Auchtermuchty, Cupar, Fife KY14 7BX	01337 828327

Name	Ord.		Charge / Position	Address	Tel.
Ord, J.K.	1963		(Falkirk Condorrat)	24 Forth Street, St Monance KY10 2AX	01333 730461
Patterson, John W. BA BD	1948	1989	(St Andrews Martyrs)	34 Claybraes, St Andrews KY16 8RS	01333 473606
Portenmouth, Roland John NDD ATD	1980	1989	(Bendochy)	1 West Braes, Pittenweem, Fife KY10 2FS	01333 311448
Porteous, James K. DD	1944	1997	(Cupar St John's)	16 Market Street, St Andrews KY16 9NS	
Robb, Nigel J. FCP MA BD ThM MTh	1981	1998	Director of Educational Services, Board of Ministry	121 George Street, Edinburgh EH2 4YN [e-mail: nrobb@cofscotland.org.uk]	0131 225 5722
Roy, Alan J. BSc BD	1960	1999	(Aberuthven with Dunning)	14 Comerton Place, Drumoig, nr Leuchars KY16 0NQ	01382 542225
Salters, Robert B. MA BD PhD	1966	1971	University of St Andrews	Vine Cottage, 119 South Street, St Andrews KY16 9UH	01334 473198
Scott, J. Miller MA BD FSAScot DD	1949	1988	(Jerusalem)	St Martins, 6 Trinity Place, St Andrews KY16 8SG	01334 479518
Shaw, D.W.D. BA BD LLB WS DD	1960	1990	(University of St Andrews)		
Sinclair, David I BSc BD PhD DipSW	1990	1998	(Boarhills and Dunino with St Andrews Martyrs)	4 Alexandra Court, St Andrews KY16 9XH	(Tel/Fax) 01334 477254
Spowart, Mary G. (Mrs)	1978	1991	(Papa Westray with Westray)	42 South Road, Cupar KY15 5JF	01334 656957
Stevenson A.L. LLB MLitt DPA FPEA	1984	1993	(Balmerino linked with Wormit)	Aldersyde, St Abbs Road, Coldingham, Eyemouth TD14 5NR	01890 771697
Stoddart, David L.	1961	1987	(Laggan with Newtonmore)	41 Main Street, Dairsie, Fife KY15 4SR	01334 870582
Strong, Clifford LTh	1983	1995	(Creich, Flisk and Kilmany with Monimail)	3 Castle Street, Anstruther KY10 3DD	01333 310668
Taylor, Ian BSc MA LTh DipEd	1983	1997	(Abdie and Dunbog with Newburgh)	60 Maryknowe, Gauldry, Newport-on-Tay DD6 8SL	01382 330445
Thomson, P.G. MA BD MTh ThD	1947	1989	(Irvine Fullarton)	Lundie Cottage, Arncroach, Fife KY10 2RN	01333 720222
Torrance, Alan MA BD Dr Theol	1984	1999	University of St Andrews	Fullarton, 2 Beech Walk, Crail KY10 3UN	01333 450423
Turnbull, James J. MA	1940	1981	(Arbirlot with Colliston)	2 Kinburn Terrace, St Andrews KY16 9DU	(Home) 01334 472720 / (Office) 01334 462843
Walker, James B. MA BD DPhil	1975	1993	Chaplain: University of St Andrews	Woodlands, Beech Avenue, Ladybank KY7 7NG	01337 830279
Whyte, James A. MA LLD DD DUniv	1945	1987	(University of St Andrews)	1 Gillespie Terrace, The Scores, St Andrews KY16 9AT [e-mail: jbw1@st-andrews.ac.uk]	(Tel) 01334 477471 / (Fax) 01334 462697
Wilson, Robert McL. MA BD PhD DD FBA	1946	1983	(University of St Andrews)	13 Hope Street, St Andrews KY16 9HJ	01334 472323
				10 Murrayfield Road, St Andrews KY16 9NB	01334 474331
Wright, Lynda (Miss) BEd DCS			Deacon: Retreat Leader, Key House	6 Key Cottage, High Street, Falkland, Fife KY15 7BD	01337 857705

(27) DUNKELD AND MEIGLE

Meets at Pitlochry on the first Tuesday of September and December; on the third Tuesday of February, April and October, and at the Moderator's Church on the third Tuesday of June.

Clerk:	REV. BRUCE DEMPSEY BD	The Manse, Caddam Road, Coupar Angus, Perthshire PH13 9EF [e-mail: dunkeldmeigle@dial.pipex.com]	01828 628871 (Tel/Fax)

Aberfeldy (H) linked with Amulree and Strathbraan linked with Dull and Weem

Alexander M. Gunn MA BD	1967	1986	Taybridge Terrace, Aberfeldy, Perthshire PH15 2BS [e-mail: sandy@aberfeldypc.co.uk]	01887 820656 (Tel/Fax)

Alyth (H) Neil N. Gardner MA BD	1991	1998	Cambridge Street, Alyth, Perthshire PH11 8AW [e-mail: nng@surfaid.org]	01828 632104
Amulree and Strathbraan See Aberfeldy				
Ardler, Kettins and Meigle Albert B. Reid BD BSc	1966	1993	The Manse, Dundee Road, Meigle, Blairgowrie PH12 8SB [e-mail: abreid@nationwideisp.net]	01828 640278 (Tel/Fax)
Bendochy linked with Blairgowrie St Mary's South Michael R. Philip BD	1988		83 Smithfield Crescent, Blairgowrie PH10 6UE [e-mail: mrphilip@onet.co.uk]]	01250 874717
Blair Atholl and Struan Neil Gow BSc MEd BD	1996		Blair Atholl, Perthshire PH18 5SX [e-mail: the-gows@lineone.net]	01796 481213
Blairgowrie: St Andrew's (H) Robert Sloan BD	1997		Upper David Street, Blairgowrie PH10 6HB [e-mail: robertsloan@lineone.net]	01250 872146
Blairgowrie: St Mary's South See Bendochy				
Braes of Rannoch linked with Foss and Rannoch (H) David G. Hamilton MA BD	1971	1998	Kinloch Rannoch, Pitlochry PH16 5QA [e-mail:dghamilton@bigfoot.com]	01882 632381
Caputh and Clunie (H) linked with Kinclaven (H)(T) Linda J. Broadley (Mrs) LTh DipEd	1996		Caputh, Perth PH1 4JH	01738 710520
Coupar Angus Abbey Bruce Dempsey BD	1997		Caddam Road, Coupar Angus, Perthshire PH13 9EF [e-mail: demp01@aol.com]	01828 627331
Dull and Weem See Aberfeldy				
Dunkeld (H) Vacant			Cathedral Manse, Dunkeld PH8 0AW	01350 727249
Fortingall and Glenlyon linked with Kenmore and Lawers Anne J. Brennan BSc BD MTh	1999		The Manse, Balnaskeag, Kenmore, Aberfeldy PH15 2HB [e-mail: annebrennan@yahoo.com]	01887 830218
Foss and Rannoch See Braes of Rannoch				

Grantully Logierait and Strathtay
Christine M. Creegan (Mrs) MTh   1993   2000   Strathtay, Perthshire PH9 OPG   01887 840251
[e-mail: christine@creegans.co.uk]

Kenmore and Lawers (H) See Fortingall and Glenlyon
Kinclaven See Caputh and Clunie

Kirkmichael Straloch and Glenshee linked with Rattray (H)
Hugh C. Ormiston BSc BD MPhil PhD   1969   1998   The Manse, Alyth Road, Rattray PH10 7HF   01250 872462
[e-mail: hugh@ormistonh fsnet co uk]]

Pitlochry (H) (01796 472160)
Malcolm Ramsay BA LLB DipMin   1986   1998   Manse Road, Moulin, Pitlochry PH16 5EP   01796 472774
[e-mail:amramsay@aol.com]

Rattray See Kirkmichael Straloch and Glenshee

Tenandry
Continued Vacancy

Barbour, Robin A.S. KCVO MC BD STM DD	1954	1982	(University of Aberdeen)	Fincastle, Pitlochry PH16 5RJ	01796 473209
Bell, F. Routledge	1944	1983	(Caputh with Murthly)	Hawthornbank House, Wolfhill, Perth PH2 6DA	01821 650421
Cassells, Alexander K. MA BD	1961	1997	(Leuchars St Athernase and Guardbridge)	Tighaness, Keltney Burn, By Aberfeldy PH15 2LS	01887 830758
Dick, Tom MA	1951	1982	(Dunkeld)	Mo Dhachaidh, Callybrae, Dunkeld PH8 OEP	01350 727338
Duncan, James BTh FSAScot	1980	1995	(Blair Atholl and Struan)	25 Knockard Avenue, Pitlochry PH16 5JE	01796 474096
Forsyth, David Stuart MA	1948	1992	(Belhelvie)	Birchlea, 38 Fonab Crescent, Pitlochry PH16 5SR	01796 473708
Fulton, Frederick H. MA	1942	1983	(Clunie, Lethendy and Kinloch)	Grampian Cottage, Chapel Brae, Braemar AB35 5YT	01339 741277
Grieve, David S.A. MA BD	1954	1991	(Arbirlot with Carmyllie with Colliston)	Dundarroch, Meigle Road, Alyth, Blairgowrie PH11 8EU	01828 632318
Henderson, John D. MA BD	1953	1992	(Cluny with Monymusk)	Aldersyde, George Street, Blairgowrie PH10 6HP	01250 875181
Knox, John W. MTheol	1992	1997	(Lochgelly: Macainsh)	Heatherlea, Main Street, Ardler, Blairgowrie PH12 8SR	01828 640731
Low, J.E. Stewart MA	1957	1997	(Tarbat)	Floreal, Perth Road, Blairgowrie PH10 6QB	01250 873108
McAlister, D.J.B. MA BD PhD	1951	1989	(North Berwick Blackadder)	2 Duff Avenue, Moulin, Pitlochry PH16 5EN	01796 473591
Macdonald, James F. TD	1930	1984	(Bendochy with Kinclaven)	6 Cluny Court, Grant Road, Blairgowrie PH10 6PU	01250 875737
Macpherson, Norman J. TD	1954	1980	(Blairgowrie St Mary's South)	31 Glenburn Drive, Inverness IV2 4NE	01463 230536
MacVicar, Kenneth MBE DFC TD MA	1950	1990	(Kenmore with Lawers with Fortingall & Glenlyon)	Illeray, Kenmore, Aberfeldy PH15 2HE	01887 830514
Martin, Francis BL	1956	1991	(Pitlochry East)	58 West Moulin Road, Pitlochry PH16 5EQ	01796 472619
Shannon, W.G.H. MA BD	1955	1998	(Pitlochry)	19 Knockard Road, Pitlochry PH16 5HJ	01796 473533
Stewart, Walter T.A.	1964	1999	(Barry)	7A Tummel Crescent, Pitlochry PH16 5DF	01796 473422
Tait, Thomas W. BD	1972	1997	(Rattray)	20 Cedar Avenue, Blairgowrie PH10 6TT	01250 874833
Young, G. Stuart	1961	1996	(Blairgowrie: St Andrew's)	7 James Place, Stanley PH1 4PD	01738 828473

(28) PERTH

Meets at Scone: Old, at 7.00pm, in the Elizabeth Ashton Hall, on the second Tuesday of every month except January, July and August, when there is no meeting, and on the last Tuesday of June when it meets in the church of the incoming Moderator

Clerk: Rev. ALEX. M. MILLAR MA BD MBA
Presbytery Office   Scone: New Church, Angus Road, Scone, Perth PH2 6QU
[e-mail: perth@dial.pipex.com]

01738 553605 (Tel)
01738 553607 (Fax)

Abernethy and Dron linked with Arngask
Kenneth G. Anderson MA BD   1967   1988   Abernethy, Perth PH2 9JP   01738 850607

Almondbank Tibbermore
Donald Campbell BD   1998   Pitcairngreen, Perth PH1 3LT   01738 583217

Ardoch (H) linked with Blackford (H)
Hazel Wilson (Ms) MA BD DipEd DMS   1991   Braco, Dunblane FK15 9RE   01786 880217

Arngask See Abernethy and Dron

Auchterarder (H)
Michael R.R. Shewan MA BD CPS   1985   1998   24 High Street, Auchterarder, Perth PH3 1DF   01764 662210

Auchtergaven and Moneydie
William McGregor LTh   1987   Bankfoot, Perth PH1 4BS   01738 787235

Blackford See Ardoch

Cargill Burrelton linked with Collace
Robert J. Watt BD   1994   Woodside, Blairgowrie PH13 9NQ
[e-mail: rjw@tesco.net]   01828 670352

Cleish (H) linked with Fossoway St Serf's and Devonside
A. David Macleod MA BD   1993   1994   Cleish, Kinross KY13 7LR   01577 850231 (Tel/Fax)

Collace See Cargill and Burrelton

Comrie (H) linked with Dundurn (H)
P.D. Thomson MA BD   1968   1978   Comrie, Perthshire PH6 2HE
[e-mail: revpdt@the-manse.freeserve.co.uk]   01764 670269

Crieff (H)
Bruce Ritchie BSc BD   1977   1987   8 Strathearn Terrace, Crieff PH7 3AQ   01764 653907

Dunbarney (H) linked with Forgandenny
W. Duncan Stenhouse MA BD   1989   Dunbarney Manse, Bridge of Earn, Perth PH2 9DY   01738 812463
[e-mail: duncan@stenhouse58.freeserve.co.uk]

Dundurn See Comrie and Strowan

Errol (H) linked with Kilspindie and Rait
John M. Pickering BSc BD   1997   Errol, Perth PH2 7PZ   01821 642279
[e-mail: john.m.pickering@talk21.com]

Forgandenny See Dunbarney
Fossoway St Serf's and Devonside See Cleish

Fowlis Wester linked with Madderty linked with Monzie
Alexander F. Bonar LTh LRIC   1988   1996   Beechview, Abercairney, Crieff PH7 3NF   01764 652116

Gask (H) linked with Methven and Logiealmond (H)
Brian Bain LTh   1980   1986   Methven, Perth PH1 3QD   01738 840274 (Tel/Fax)
[e-mail: brian@methvenmanse.freeserve.co.uk]

Kilspindie and Rait See Errol

Kinross (H)
John P. L. Munro MA BD PhD   1977   1998   15 Station Road, Kinross KY13 7TG   01577 862952
[e-mail: john@lochleven.freeserve.co.uk]

Madderty See Fowlis Wester
Methven and Logiealmond See Gask
Monzie See Fowlis Wester

Muthill (H) linked with Trinity Gask and Kinkell
Elinor J. Gordon (Miss) BD   1988   Muthill, Perthshire PH5 2AR   01764 681205

Orwell (H) linked with Portmoak (H)
Una B. Stewart (Miss) BD DipEd   1995   3 Perth Road, Milnathort, Kinross KY13 9XU   01577 863461

Perth: Craigend Moncreiffe linked with Rhynd (T)
Isobel Birrell (Mrs) BD   1994   Wester Tarsappie, Rhynd, Perth PH2 8PT   01738 625694

Perth: Craigie (H)
Vacant   46 Abbot Street, Perth PH2 OEE   01738 623748

Perth: Kinnoull (H)				
John F. Ferguson MA BD	1987	1993	1 Mount Tabor Avenue, Perth PH2 7BT	01738 626046
Perth: Letham St Mark's (H)				
James C. Stewart BD	1997		35 Rose Crescent, Perth PH1 1NT	01738 624167
Kenneth McKay DCS			11F Balgowan Road, Perth PH1 2JG	01738 621169
Perth: North (01738 622298)				
David W. Denniston BD	1981	1996	127 Glasgow Road, Perth PH2 OLU	01738 625728
			[e-mail: david.denniston@virgin.net]	
Brian R. Hendrie BD (Assoc)	1992	2000	98 Duncansby Way, Perth PH1 5XF	01738 441029
Patricia Munro (Miss) BSc DCS			4 Hewat Place, Perth PH1 2UD	01738 627549
			[e-mail: patm@tesco.net]	
Perth: Riverside (New Charge Development)				
Alfred G. Drummond BD	1991		44 Hay Street, Perth PH1 5HS	01738 621305
			[e-mail: fred.drummond@lycosmail.com]	
John Buchanan DCS			22 Brora Court, North Muirton, Perth PH1 3DQ	01738 631697
Perth: St John the Baptist's (H) (01738 626159)				
David D. Ogston MA BD	1970	1980	15 Comely Bank, Perth PH2 7HU	01738 621755
Elizabeth Brown (Mrs) SRN (Aux)	1996		25 Highfield Road, Scone PH2 6RN	01738 552391 (Tel/Fax)
Perth: St Leonard's-in-the-Fields and Trinity (H) (01738 632238)				
Vacant			5 Strathearn Terrace, Perth PH2 OLS	01738 621709
Perth: St Matthew's (01738 627708)				
Ewen J. Gilchrist BD DipMin DipComm	1982	1988	23 Kincarrathie Crescent, Perth PH2 7HH	01738 626828
Portmoak See Orwell				
Redgorton linked with Stanley				
Derek G. Lawson LLB BD	1998		22 King Street, Stanley, Perth PH1 4ND	01738 828247
			[e-mail: lawson@stanley9835.freeserve.co.uk]	
Rhynd See Perth Craigend Moncreiffe				
St Madoes and Kinfauns				
Marc F. Bircham	2000		Glencarse, Perth PH2 7NF	01738 860837)
St Martin's linked with Scone New (H) (01738 553900)				
Alexander M. Millar MA BD MBA	1980	1987	24 Victoria Road, Scone PH2 6JW	01738 551467
			[e-mail: millar@amillar62.freeserve.co.uk]	

Scone: New See St Martin's

Scone: Old (H)

J. Bruce Thomson JP MA BD	1972	1983	Burnside, Scone, Perth PH2 6LP [e-mail: bruce@agape45.freeserve.co.uk]	01738 552030

Stanley See Redgorton

Stewartry of Strathearn

Colin R. Williamson LLB BD	1972	2000	Aberdalgie, Perth PH2 0QD	01738 625854

(Charge created by uniting the charge of Aberdalgie and Dupplin linked with Forteviot and the charge of Aberuthven linked with Dunning)

Trinity Gask and Kinkell See Muthill

Name			(Previous charge / Role)	Address	Phone
Alexander, William M. BD	1971	1998	(Berriedale and Dunbeath with Latheron)	23 Muirend Avenue, Perth PH1 1JL	01764 670454
Barr, George K. ARIBA BD PhD	1967	1993	(Uddingston: Viewpark)	7 Tay Avenue, Comrie PH6 2PE [e-mail: gbarr@compuserve.com]	
Barr, John BSc PhD BD	1958	1979	(Kilmacolm: Old)	5 Abbey Park, Auchterarder PH3 1EN	01764 663056
Barr, T. Leslie LTh	1969	1997	(Kinross)	10 Auld Mart Lane, Milnathort KY13 7FP	01577 861192
Bertram, Thomas A.	1972	1995	(Patna Waterside)	The Hydro, Crieff PH7 3LQ	01764 655555
Birrell, John M. MA LLB BD	1974	1996	Hospital Chaplain, Perth Royal Infirmary	Wester Tarsappie, Rhynd, Perth PH2 8QL	01738 625694
Bonomy, William MA BD	1946	1987	(Inverkip)	16 Juniper Place, Perth PH1 1EZ	01738 623803
Brown, R. Russell MA	1940	1986	(Perth Kinnoull)	Viewlands House, Viewlands Road, Perth PH1 1BU	01738 632469
Carr, W. Stanley MA	1951	1991	(Largs: St Columba's)	16 Gannochy Walk, Perth PH2 7LW	01738 627422
Cowie, J.L. MA	1950	1977	(Edinburgh: Richmond Craigmillar)	16 Curate Wynd, Kinross KY13 7DX	01577 864762
Donaldson, Robert B. BSocSc	1953	1997	(Kilchoman with Portnahaven)	11 Strathearn Court, Crieff PH7 3DS	01764 654976
Galbraith, W. James L. BSc BD MICE	1973	1996	(Kilchrenan and Dalavich with Muckairn)	45 Hawthorn Drive, Craigneuk, Airdrie ML6 8AP	01577 863887
Gilchrist, Kay (Miss) BD	1996	1999	Chaplain, Rachel House	19 Mayfield Gardens, Kinross KY13 7GD	
Gregory, J.C. LTh	1968	1992	(Blantyre St Andrew's)	2 Southlands Road, Auchterarder PH3 1BA	01764 664594
Grimson, John A. MA	1950	1986	(Glasgow Wellington: Associate)	29 Highland Road, Turret Park, Crieff PH7 4LE	01764 653063
Halliday, Archibald R. BD	1964	1999	(Duffus with Forres: St Leonard's with Rafford)	2 Pitenzie Place, Crieff PH7 3JL	01764 681275
Henry, Malcolm N. MA BD	1951	1987	(Perth Craigie)	Kelton, Castle Douglas DG7 1RU	01556 504144
Hill, Robert S. BA	1967	1973	(Glenshee and Glenericht)	16 Highland Crescent, Crieff PH7 4LH	01764 652975
Houston, Alexander M.	1939	1977	(Tibbermore)	120 Glasgow Road, Perth PH2 0LU	01738 628056
Jackson, William BD CertMin	1994	2000	(Perth: Craigie)	7 Bargarry Road, Crookston, Glasgow G53 7JB	01592 840387
Kelly, T. Clifford	1973	1995	(Ferintosh)	7 Bankfoot Park, Scotlandwell, Kinross KY13 7JP	01738 828871
Lawson, Ronald G. MA BD	1964	1999	(Greenock: Wellpark Mid Kirk)	6 East Brougham Street, Stanley PH1 4NJ	01764 652506
Leckie, Joseph L. MA MPhil	1954	1996	(Fowlis Wester with Madderty with Monzie)	"Caddam", Perth Road, Crieff PH7 3EQ	
Longmuir, T. Graeme MA BEd	1976	1984	School Chaplain	The Manse, Strathallan School, Forgandenny, Perth PH2 9HP	01738 812110
McCormick, Alastair F.	1962	1998	(Creich with Rosehall)	14 Balmanno Park, Bridge of Earn PH2 9RJ	01738 813588
McDonald, John A. MA BD	1978	1997	(Cumbernauld: Condorrat)	22 Commissioner Street, Crieff PH7 3AY	01764 653647
Macdonald, W.U. JP MA	1939	1984	(Aberdalgie and Dupplin with Forteviot)	30 Muircroft Terrace West, Perth PH1 1DY	01738 627948

MacKenzie, Donald W. MA	1941	1983	(Auchterarder The Barony)	81 Kingswell Terrace, Perth PH1 2DA	01738 633716
MacLean, Nigel R. MA BD	1940	1986	(Perth St Paul's)	9 Hay Street, Perth PH1 5HS	01738 626728
MacLeish, D. Nairn MA	1938	1977	(Fisherton)	Wardside House, Muthill, Crieff PH5 2AS	01764 681275
MacMillan, Riada M. (Mrs) BD	1991	1998	(Perth: Craigend Moncreiffe with Rhynd)	73 Muirend Gardens, Perth PH1 1JR	01738 628867
McNaughton, David J.H. BA CA	1976	1995	(Killin and Ardeonaig)	30 Hollybush Road, Crieff PH7 3HB	01764 653028
MacPhee, Duncan P.	1951	1980	(Braemar with Crathie: Associate)	Braemar Cottage, Ben Alder Place, Kirkcaldy KY2 5RH	01592 201984
McQuilken, John E. MA BD	1969	1992	(Glenaray and Inveraray)	18 Clark Terrace, Crieff PH7 3QE	01764 655764
Millar, Archibald E. DipTh	1965	1991	(Perth St Stephen's)	7 Maple Place, Perth PH1 1RT	01738 621813
Millar, Jennifer (Mrs) BD DipMin	1986	1995	Teacher, Religious Education	24 Victoria Road, Scone PH2 6JW	01738 551467
Shirra, James MA	1945	1987	(St Martin's with Scone New)	17 Dunbarney Avenue, Bridge of Earn, Perth PH2 9BP	01738 812610
Simpson, James A. BSc BD STM DD	1960	2000	(Brechin Cathedral)	"Dornoch", Perth Road, Bankfoot, Perth PH1 4ED	01738 787710
Stewart, Gordon G. MA	1961	2000	(Perth: St. Leonard's-in-the-Fields and Trinity)	"Balnoe", South Street, Rattray, Blairgowrie PH10 7BZ	01250 870626
Stewart, Anne (Mrs) BD CertMin	1998		Hospital Chaplain	35 Rose Crescent, Perth PH1 1NT	01738 624167
Stewart, Robin J. MA BD STM	1959	1995	(Orwell with Portmoak)	Oakbrae, Perth Road, Murthly PH1 4HF	01738 710220
Tait, H.A.G. MA BD	1966	1997	(Crieff: South and Monzievaird)	14 Sheiling Hill Place, Crieff PH7 4ER	01764 652325
Taylor, A.H.S. MA BA BD	1957	1992	(Hoddam with Brydekirk)	41 Anderson Drive, Perth PH1 1LF	01738 626579
Urquhart, J. MacNeill MA	1942	1980	(Kilspindie and Rait with Kinfauns)	4 Afton Drive, Denny FK6 5PD	01324 815380
Varwell, Adrian P.J. BA BD PhD	1983	1998	Director, St Ninian's Centre, Crieff	St Ninian's Centre, Crieff PH7 4BG	(Tel) 01764 653766
					(Fax) 01764 655824
Whitson, William S. MA	1959	1999	(Cumbernauld: St Mungo's)	6 Latch Burn Wynd, Dunning, Perthshire PH2 0SP	01764 684272

PERTH ADDRESSES

Craigend Moncreiffe	Glenbruar Crescent	North	Mill Street near Kinnoull Street.
Craigie	Abbot Street	Riverside	At North Muirton Primary School, Uist Place
Kinnoull	Dundee Rd near Queen's Bridge	St. John's	St. John's Street
Letham St Mark's	Rannoch Road	St Leonard's-in-the-Fields and Trinity	Marshall Place
		St Matthew's	Tay Street

(29) DUNDEE

Meets at Dundee, Meadowside St Paul's Church Halls, Nethergate, on the second Wednesday of February, March, May, September, October, November and December and on the fourth Wednesday of June.

Clerk:	**REV. JAMES A. ROY MA BD**	**Nicoll's Lane, Dundee DD2 3HG**
		[e-mail: a2103475@infotrade.uk.7]
Presbytery Office:		**01382 611415**

Abernyte linked with Inchture and Kinnaird linked with Longforgan (H)
J.A.P. Jack DMin BSc BArch BD   1989   Longforgan DD2 5EU   01382 360238
[e-mail: jpa@jpaj.demon.co.uk]

Elizabeth Kay (Miss) DipYCS (Aux)   1993   1999   1 Kintail Walk, Inchture PH14 9RY   01828 686029
[e-mail: lizkay@clara.co.uk]

Auchterhouse (H) linked with Murroes and Tealing (T)
Sydney S. Graham DipYL MPhil   1987   1995   The Manse, Balgray, Tealing DD4 OQZ   01382 380224
[e-mail: graythorn@sol.co.uk]

Dundee: Albany-Butterburn linked with St David's North
Gideon G. Scott MA BD ThM   1963   1973   2 Anstruther Road, Dundee DD4 7EA   01382 456579

Dundee: Balgay (H)
George K. Robson LTh DPS   1983   1987   150 City Road, Dundee DD2 2PW   01382 668806

Dundee: Barnhill St Margaret's (H)
Vacant   Invermark Terrace, Barnhill DD5 2QU   01382 779278

Dundee: Broughty Ferry East (H) (01382 738264)
Alan H. MacKay BD   1974   8 West Queen Street, Broughty Ferry DD5 1AR   01382 778972

Dundee: Broughty Ferry St Aidan's (T)(H)
Caroline Jackson (Mrs) MA BD   1995   63 Collingwood Street, Barnhill DD5 2UF   01382 736828

Dundee: Broughty Ferry St James' (H)
Thomas P. Robertson   1963   1970   95 Seafield Road, Broughty Ferry DD5 3AP   01382 779803

Dundee: Broughty Ferry St Luke's and Queen Street
Vacant   22 Albert Road, Broughty Ferry DD5 1AZ   01382 779212

Dundee: Broughty Ferry St Stephen's and West (H)
John U. Cameron BA BSc PhD BD ThD   1974   33 Camperdown Street, Broughty Ferry DD5 3AA   01382 477403

Dundee: Camperdown (H) (01382 623958)
Sheila Craik (Mrs) BD   1989   Camperdown Manse, Myrekirk Road, Dundee DD2 4SF   01382 621383
James H. Simpson BSc (Aux)   1996   1999   11 Claypotts Place, Broughty Ferry DD5 1LG   01382 776520

Dundee: Chalmers Ardler (H)
Kenneth D. Stott MA BD   1989   1997   The Manse, Turnberry Avenue, Dundee DD2 3TP   01382 827439
[e-mail: arkstott@aol.com]

Jane Martin (Miss) DCS   12A Carnoustie Court, Ardler, Dundee DD2 3RB   01382 813786

Dundee: Clepington
Vacant   17A Claypotts Road, Broughty Ferry DD5 1BS   01382 730085

Dundee: Craigiebank (H) (01382 457951) linked with Douglas and Angus (01382 739884)

Michael V.A. Mair MA BD	1967	1998	244 Arbroath Road, Dundee DD4 7SB	01382 452337
Edith F. McMillan (Mrs) MA BD (Assoc)	1981	1999	19 Americanmuir Road, Dundee DD3 9AA	01382 812423

Dundee: Douglas and Angus (01382 739884) See Dundee: Craigiebank

Dundee: Downfield South (H) (01382 810624)
Lezley J. Kennedy (Mrs) BD ThM MTh   2000   15 Elgin Street, Dundee DD3 8NL   01382 889498

Dundee: Dundee (St Mary's) (H) (01382 226271)
Keith F. Hall MA BD   1980   1994   33 Strathern Road, West Ferry, Dundee DD5 1PP   01382 778808

Dundee: Fairmuir (H)
David C. McLeod BSc MEng BD   1969   1978   6 Carseview Gardens, Dundee DD2 1NE   01382 641371

Dundee: Lochee Old and St Luke's (T)
Vacant   16 Coupar Angus Road, Dundee DD2 3HN   01382 611440

Dundee: Lochee West
James A. Roy MA BD   1965   1973   Beechwood, 7 Northwood Terrace, Wormit DD6 8PP   01382 543578
[e-mail: j.roy@btinternet.com]

Dundee: Logie and St John's Cross (H)
David S. Scott MA BD   1987   1999   7 Hyndford Street, Dundee DD2 1HQ   01382 641572

Dundee: Mains (H) (01382 812166)
Michael S. Goss BD DPS   1991   9 Elgin Street, Dundee DD3 8NL   01382 825562
[e-mail:gossdundee@aol.com]
Jean Allan (Mrs) DCS   12C Hindmarsh Avenue, Dundee DD3 7LW   01382 827299

Dundee: Mains of Fintry (01382 508191)
Peter M. Humphris BSc BD   1976   1977   4 Clive Street, Dundee DD4 7AW   01382 458629
[e-mail: humphris@xc.org]

Dundee: Meadowside St Paul's (H) (01382 225420)
Maudeen I. MacDougall (Miss) BA BD   1978   36 Blackness Avenue, Dundee DD2 1HH   01382 668828

Dundee: Menzieshill
Harry J. Brown LTh   1991   1996   The Manse, Charleston Drive, Dundee DD2 4ED   01382 667446
[e-mail: harrybrown@aol.com]
Sarah Hankey (Miss) DCS   9 Earn Crescent, Dundee DD2 4BS   01382 641549

Dundee: Mid Craigie (T) (01382 506147)
Colin A. Strong BSc BD   1989 1992   96 Forfar Road, Dundee DD4 7BG   01382 453926
[e-mail: colinstrong@bigfoot.com]

Dundee: St Andrew's (H) (01382 224860)
Ian D. Petrie MA BD   1970 1986   77 Blackness Avenue, Dundee DD2 1JN   01382 641695

Dundee: St David's North See Dundee: Albany Butterburn

Dundee: Steeple (H) (01382 223880)
Vacant   128 Arbroath Road, Dundee DD4 7HR   01382 455411

Dundee: Stobswell (H)
Jane Barron (Mrs) BA DipEd BD MTh   1999   23 Shamrock Street, Dundee DD4 7AH   01382 459119
[e-mail: jane.ian@virgin.net]

Dundee: Strathmartine (H) (01382 825817)
Stewart McMillan BD   1983 1990   19 Americanmuir Road, Dundee DD3 9AA   01382 812423

Dundee: The High Kirk (H) (01382 224433)
William B. Ross LTh CPS   6 Adelaide Place, Dundee DD3 6LF   01382 322955

Dundee: Trinity (H) (01382 459997)
James L. Wilson BD CPS   1986 1993   75 Clepington Road, Dundee DD4 7BJ   01382 457430

Dundee: West
Andrew T. Greaves BD   1985 2000   22 Hyndford Street, Dundee DD2 1HX   01382 646586
(Charge formed by the union of Dundee: Roseangle Ryehill and Dundee: St. Peter's McCheyne)

Dundee: Whitfield (E) (H) (01382 503012)
Vacant

Fowlis and Liff linked with Lundie and Muirhead of Liff (H) (01382 580550)
Martin R.H. Thomas CEng MIStructE   1987   149 Coupar Angus Road, Muirhead of Liff, Angus DD2 5QN   01382 580210
[e-mail: martynthomas@beeb.net]

Inchture and Kinnaird See Abernyte

Invergowrie (H)
Robert J. Ramsay LLB NP BD   1986 1997   2 Boniface Place, Invergowrie, Dundee DD2 5DW   01382 561118

Longforgan See Abernyte
Lundie and Muirhead of Liff See Fowlis and Liff

Monifieth: Panmure (H)
David B. Jamieson MA BD STM | 1974 | 8A Albert Street, Monifieth DD5 4JS | 01382 532772

Monifieth: St Rule's (H)
R.W. Massie LTh | 1989 1999 | Church Street, Monifieth DD5 4JP | 01382 532607

Monifieth: South
Donald W. Fraser MA | 1958 1959 | Queen Street, Monifieth DD5 4HG | 01382 532646

Monikie and Newbigging
Gordon R. Mackenzie BScAgr BD | 1977 1985 | 59B Broomwell Gardens, Monikie DD5 3QP | 01382 370200

Murroes and Tealing See Auchterhouse

Chisholm, W. Douglas MA	1943	1983	(Monifieth North and Newbigging with Monikie)	8 Musgrave Road, Chinnor, Oxon OX9 4TF	01844 352029
Clarkson, Robert G.	1950	1989	(Dundee Strathmartine)	320 Strathmartine Road, Dundee DD3 8QG	01382 825380
Craig, Iain R. MA	1948	1988	(Invergowrie)	Hope View, Burton Row, Brent Knoll, Highbridge, Somerset TA9 4BX	
Cramb, Erik M. LTh	1973	1989	Industrial Mission Organiser	65 Clepington Road, Dundee DD4 7BQ	01278 760719
Doig, David M. BA BD	1972	1986	(Dundee Mid-Craigie)	13 Balmoral View, Rattray, Blairgowrie PH10 7LJ	01382 458764
Douglas, Fiona C. (Miss) MA BD PhD	1989	1997	Chaplain: University of Dundee	10 Springfield, Dundee DD1 4JE	01250 875592
Gammack, George BD	1985	1999	(Dundee: Whitfield)	13A Hill Street, Broughty Ferry, Dundee DD5 2JP	01382 344157
Hamilton, James BA BD	1939	1982	(Auchterhouse)	Ivydene, Blair Logie FK9 5PX	01382 778636
Hawdon, John E. BA MTh AICS	1961	1995	(Dundee: Clepington)	12 Rosewood Terrace, Dundee DD2 1NS	01259 761633
Hudson, J. Harrison DipTh MA BD	1961	1999	(Dundee: St Peter's McCheyne)	22 Hamilton Avenue, Tayport DD6 9BW	01382 646212
Ingram, J.R.	1954	1978	(Chaplain: RAF)	48 Marlee Road, Broughty Ferry DD5 3EX	01382 736400
Laidlaw, John J. MA	1964	1973	(Adviser in Religious Education)	14 Dalhousie Road, Barnhill DD5 2SQ	01382 477458
Macdonald, John AEA MA	1949	1985	(Lochee Old)	12 Hyndford Street, Dundee DD2 1HQ	01382 668655
Mackenzie, George R.R. MA BD	1942	1987	(Dundee Logie and St John's Cross)	39 Middlebank Crescent, Dundee DD2 1HZ	01382 668491
McMillan, Hector G.	1964		(Hamilton North)	6 Kinghorne Terrace, Dundee DD3 6HX	01382 224803
Macnab, S.G. BD	1938	1994	(Broughty Ferry: St Luke's)	58 Kenilworth Avenue, Dundee DD4 6LG	01382 456196
Malvenan, Dorothy DCS	1964	1990	The Deaf Association, Dundee	Flat 19, 6 Craigie Street, Dundee DD4 6PF	01382 462495
Miller, Charles W. MA	1953	1994	(Fowlis and Liff)	"Palm Springs", Parkside, Auchterhouse DD3 0RS	01382 320407
Milroy, Tom	1960	1992	(Monifieth: St Rule's)	9 Long Row, Westhaven, Carnoustie DD7 6BE	01241 856654
Mitchell, Jack MA BD CTh	1987	1996	(Dundee: Menzieshill)	10 Invergowrie Drive, Dundee DD2 1RF	01382 642301
Mowat, Gilbert M. MA	1948	1986	(Dundee Albany Butterburn)	7 Dunmore Gardens, Dundee DD2 1PP	01382 566013
Powrie, James E. LTh	1969	1995	(Dundee: Chalmers Ardler)	3 Kirktonhill Road, Kirriemuir DD8 4HU	01575 572503
Rae, Robert LTh	1968	1983	Chaplain: Dundee Acute Hospitals	47 Mains Loan, Dundee DD4 7AJ	01382 450158
Rogers, James M. BA DB DCult	1955	1996	(Gibraltar)	24 Mansion Drive, Dunclaverhouse, Dundee DD4 9DD	01382 506162
Scroggie, John C.	1951	1985	(Mains)	4 Bell Tree Gardens, Balmossie DD5 2LJ	01382 739354
Smith, Lilian MA DCS			(Deaconess)	6 Fintry Mains, Dundee DD4 9HF	01382 500052

DUNDEE ADDRESSES

Albany Butterburn	2 Hill Street	
Balgay	200 Lochee Road	
Barnhill St Margaret's	10 Invermark Terrace	
Broughty Ferry		
East	370 Queen Street.	
St Aidan's	408 Brook Street	
St James'	5 Fort Street	
St Luke's and Queen Street	5 West Queen Street	
St Stephen's and West	96 Dundee Road	
Camperdown	Brownhill Road.	
Chalmers Ardler	Turnberry Avenue	
Clepington	Isla Street x Main Street	
Craigiebank	Craigie Avenue at	
	Greendyke Road.	

Douglas and Angus	Balbeggie Place
Downfield South	Haldane Street off
	Strathmartine Road.
Dundee (St Mary's)	Nethergate.
Fairmuir	329 Clepington Road
High Kirk	119A Kinghorne Road
Lochee	
Old and St Luke's	Bright Street, Lochee
West	191 High Street, Lochee
Logie and	
St John's (Cross)	Shaftsbury Rd x Blackness Ave
Mains	Foot of Old Glamis Road
Mains of Fintry	Fintry Road x Fintry Drive.
Meadowside St Paul's	114 Nethergate.

Menzieshill	Charleston Drive, Lochee
Mid Craigie	Longtown Terrace
St Andrew's	2 King Street.
St David's North	273 Strathmore Avenue
Steeple	Nethergate.
Stobswell	Top of Albert Street
Strathmartine	315 Strathmartine Road.
Trinity	73 Crescent Street
West	130 Perth Road.
Whitfield	Haddington Crescent.

(30) ANGUS

Meets at Forfar in St Margaret's Church Hall, on the first Tuesday of each month, except June when it meets on the last Tuesday, and January, July and August when there is no meeting.

Clerk:	REV. MALCOLM I.G. ROONEY DPE BEd BD
DeputeClerk:	MRS HELEN McLEOD MA
Presbytery Office:	St Margaret's Church, West High Street, Forfar DD8 1BJ
	[e-mail: AngusPresbytery@dial.pipex.com]

01307 464224 (Tel)
01307 465589 (Fax)

Aberlemno linked with Guthrie and Rescobie
Brian Ramsay BD DPS   1980 1984   The Manse, Guthrie, Forfar DD8 2TP   01241 828243

Airlie Ruthven Kingoldrum linked with Glenisla (H) Kilry Lintrathen
Leslie Barrett BD FRICS   1991 1999   Balduff House, Kilry, Blairgowrie PH11 8HS   01575 560260

Arbirlot linked with Carmyllie linked with Colliston
Kenneth Brown BD CPS MLitt   1991   The Manse, Arbirlot, Arbroath DD11 2NX   01241 875118 (Tel/Fax)
[e-mail: kennethbrown@aol.com]

Arbroath: Knox's (H) linked with Arbroath: St Vigeans (H)
Ian G. Gough MA BD MTh   1974 1990   The Manse, St Vigeans, Arbroath DD11 4RD   01241 873206

Arbroath: Old and Abbey (H) Valerie L. Allen (Miss) BMus MDiv	1990	1996	51 Cliffburn Road DD11 5BA [e-mail: vl2allen@aol.com]	01241 872196 (Tel/Fax)
Arbroath: St Andrew's (H) Martin Fair BA BD	1992		Albert Street, Arbroath DD11 1RA [e-mail: MartinFair@aol.com]	01241 873238 (Tel/Fax)
Arbroath: St Vigeans See Arbroath: Knox's				
Arbroath: West Kirk (H) Alasdair G. Graham BD DipMin	1981	1986	1 Charles Avenue, Arbroath DD11 2EY [e-mail:alasdair.graham@lineone.net]	01241 872244
Barry Wilma Cairns (Miss) BD	1999		41 Corbie Drive, Carnoustie DD7 7NT	01241 858701
Brechin: Cathedral (H) Scott Rennie MA BD STM	1999		Chanonry Wynd, Brechin DD9 6JS	01356 622783
Brechin: Gardner Memorial (H) Moira Herkes (Mrs) BD	1985	1999	36 Park Road, Brechin DD9 7AP	01356 622789
Carmyllie See Arbirlot				
Carnoustie J. Colin Caskie BA BD	1977	1983	44 Terrace Road, Carnoustie DD7 7AR	01241 852289
Carnoustie Panbride Matthew S. Bicket BD	1989		8 Arbroath Road, Carnoustie DD7 6BL [e-mail: matthew@bicket.freeserve.co.uk]	01241 854478 (Tel) 01241 855088 (Fax)
Colliston See Arbirlot				
Dun linked with Hillside Christine Houghton (Mrs) BD	1997		4 Manse Road, Hillside, Montrose DD10 9FB [e-mail: christinehoughton@hillsidemanse.freeserve.co.uk]	01674 830288
Dunnichen, Letham and Kirkden Allan F. Webster MA BD	1978	1990	7 Braehead Road, Letham, Forfar DD8 2PG [e-mail: allanweb@globalnet.co.uk]	01307 818916
Eassie and Nevay linked with Newtyle Carleen Robertson (Miss) BD	1992		2 Kirkton Road, Newtyle, Blairgowrie PH12 8TS	01828 650461

Edzell Lethnot (H) linked with Fern, Careston and Menmuir linked with Glenesk

Alexander Forsyth TD BA MTh	1973	2000	Glenesk Cottage. Dunlappie Road, Edzell DD9 7UB [e-mail: FORSYTHAR@aol.com]	01356 648455

Farnell linked with Montrose St Andrew's

| Iain M. Douglas MA BD MPhil DipEd | 1960 | 1980 | 49 Northesk Road, Montrose DD10 8TQ | 01674 672060 |

Fern, Careston and Menmuir See Edzell Lethnot

Forfar: East and Old (H)

| Graham Norrie MA BD | 1967 | 1978 | Lour Road, Forfar DD8 2BB | 01307 464303 |

Forfar: Lowson Memorial (H)

| Robert McCrum BD | 1982 | 1992 | 1 Jamieson Street, Forfar DD8 2HY [e-mail: robert.mccrum@virgin.net] | 01307 462248 |

Forfar: St Margaret's (T)(H)

| Jean B. Montgomerie (Miss) MA BD | 1973 | 1998 | 15 Potters Park Crescent, Forfar DD8 1HH [e-mail: revjeanb@dial.pipex.com] | 01307 466390 (Tel/Fax) |

Friockheim Kinnell linked with Inverkeilor and Lunan

| David Taverner MCIBS ACIS BD | 1996 | | 18 Middlegate, Friockheim DD11 4TS | 01241 828781 |

Glamis, Inverarity and Kinnettles (T)

| Vacant | | | The Manse, Glamis, Forfar, Angus DD8 1RT | 01307 840206 (Tel) |
| | | | | 01307 840724 (Fax) |

Glenesk See Edzell Lethnot
Glenisla Kilry Lintrathen: See Airlie Ruthven Kingoldrum

Glens, The and Kirriemuir Old

| Malcolm I.G. Rooney DPE BEd BD | 1993 | 1999 | 20 Strathmore Avenue, Kirriemuir DD8 4DJ [e-mail: malcolmrooney@gkopc.freeserve.co.uk] | 01575 573724 |
| | | | | 0403 196091 (Mbl) |

Guthrie and Rescobie See Aberlemno
Hillside See Dun

Inchbrayock linked with Montrose Melville South

| David S. Dixon MA BD | 1976 | 1994 | The Manse, Ferryden, Montrose DD10 9SD | 01674 672108 |

Inverkeilor and Lunan See Friockheim Kinnell

Kirriemuir: St Andrew's linked with Oathlaw Tannadice

| William McCulloch BD | 1997 | | 26 Quarry Park, Kirriemuir DD8 4DR | 01575 575561 |

Montrose: Melville South See Inchbrayock

Montrose: Old

Laurence A.B. Whitley MA BD PhD	1975	1985	2 Rosehill Road, Montrose DD10 8ST	01674 672447

Montrose: St Andrew's See Farnell
Newtyle See Eassie and Nevay
Oathlaw Tannadice See Kirriemuir St Andrew's

Name			(Charge)	Address	Tel
Anderson, James W. BSc MTh	1986	1997	(Kincardine O'Neil with Lumphanan)	47 Glebe Road, Arbroath DD11 4HJ	01241 873298
Brodie, James BEM MA BD STM	1955	1974	(Hurlford)	25A Keptie Road, Arbroath DD11 3ED	01241 873062
Brownlie, Gavin D. MA	1955	1990	(Arbroath Ladyloan St Columba's)	12 Cliffburn Road, Arbroath DD11 5BB	01241 411078
Bruce, William C. MA BD	1961	1995	(Motherwell: Dalziel)	31 Kirkton Terrace, Carnoustie DD7 7BZ	01241 828030
Butters, David	1964	1998	(Turriff: St Ninian's and Forglen)	68A Millgate, Friockheim, Arbroath DD11 4TN	01356 625201
Drysdale James P.R.	1967	1999	(Brechin Gardner Memorial)	51 Airlie Street, Brechin DD9 6JX	01674 675522
Finlay, Quintin BA BD	1975	1996	(North Bute)	1 Brougham Square, Northesk Road, Montrose DD10 8TD	01575 582256
Henderson, David C. CBE DD	1938	1981	(Glamis)	Isla View, Glenisla, Alyth PH11 8PH	01307 461944
Hodge, William N.T.	1966	1995	(Longside)	"Tullochgorum", 61 South Street, Forfar DD8 2BS	01307 463193
Jones, William	1952	1987	(Kirriemuir St Andrew's)	14 Muir Street, Forfar DD8 3JY	
Keith, Donald MA BD	1971	1998	(Chaplain RN)	Comacchio Group Royal Marines, RM Condor, Arbroath DD11 3JS	
MacKinnon, A.W.	1951	1986	(South Ronaldsay and Burray) (Fern, Careston and Menmuir with Oathlaw Tannadice)	18 Pearse Street, Brechin DD9 6JR	01241 872201
MacLeod, Ian I.S. MA BD	1954	1991	(Arbroath St Andrew's)	19 Gallowhill, Brechin DD9 6BL	01356 623812
Milton, Eric G.	1963	1994	(Blairdaff)	13 Trinity Fields Crescent, Brechin DD9 6YF	01356 625599
Perry, Joseph B.	1955	1989	(Farnell)	16 Bruce Court, Links Parade, Carnoustie DD7 7JE	01241 854928
Russell, A.C. CMG ED MA	1959	1976	(Aberlemno)	19 Guthrie Street, Letham, Forfar DD8 2PS	01307 818741
Shackleton, Scott J.S.	1993	1993	(Chaplain: 45 Commando Unit, RM Condor)	Balgavies Lodge, by Forfar DD8 2TH	01307 818571
Smith, Hamish G.	1965	1993	(Auchterless with Rothienorman)	31 Condor Drive, Arbroath DD11 3ER	01241 879481
Stevens, David MA	1935	1972	(Glenesk)	11A Guthrie Street, Letham, Angus DD8 2PS	01307 818973
Tyre, Robert	1960	1998	(Aberdeen: St Ninian's with Stockethill)	2 Rowan Cottages, Tarfside, Brechin, Angus DD9 7YU	01356 670241
Warnock, Denis MA	1952	1990	(Kirkcaldy Torbain)	8 Borrowfield Crescent, Montrose DD10 9BR	01674 676961
Weatherhead, James L. CBE MA LLB DD	1960	1996	(Principal Clerk)	19 Keptie Road, Arbroath DD11 3ED	01241 872740
Youngson, Peter	1961	1996	(Kirriemuir St Andrew's)	59 Brechin Road, Kirriemuir DD8 4DE; Coreen, Woodside, Northmuir, Kirriemuir DD8 4PG	01575 572237; 01575 572832

ANGUS ADDRESSES

Arbroath
Abbey — West Abbey Street
Knox's — Howard Street
StAndrew's — Hamilton Green
West Kirk — Keptie Street

Brechin
Cathedral — Bishops Close
Gardner Memorial — South Esk Street

Carnoustie
Panbride — Dundee Street / Arbroath Road

Forfar
East: Old — East High Street
Lowson Memorial — Jamieson Street
St Margaret's — West High Street

Kirriemuir
Old —
St Andrew's — High Street / Glamis Road

Montrose
Melville South —
Old — Castle Street / High Street
St Andrew's — George Street

(31) ABERDEEN

Meets at St Mark's Church, Rosemount Viaduct, Aberdeen, on the first Tuesday of February, March April, May, September, October, November and December and on the fourth Tuesday of June.

Clerk:	REV. ANDREW M. DOUGLAS MA		
Presbytery Office:		Mastrick Church, Greenfern Road, Aberdeen AB16 6TR [e-mail: aberdeen@dial.pipex.com]	01224 690494 (Tel/Fax)
Hon. Treasurer:	MR A. SHARP	27 Hutchison Terrace, Aberdeen AB10 7NN	01224 315702

Aberdeen: Beechgrove (H) (01224 632102)
Iain M. Forbes BSc BD   1964   2000   156 Hamilton Place AB15 5BB   01224 642615

Aberdeen: Bridge of Don Oldmachar(E) (01224 709244)
Jim Ritchie BD MTh DipTh   2000   60 Newburgh Circle AB22 8QZ   01224 705060
[e-mail: revjim@tinyworld.co.uk]

Aberdeen: Cove (E)
Fyfe Blair BA BD   1989   1998   4 Charleston Way, Cove, Aberdeen AB12 3FA   01224 898030
[e-mail: ncdcove@dial.pipex.com]]

Aberdeen: Craigiebuckler (H) (01224 311367)
Kenneth L. Petrie MA BD   1984   1999   185 Springfield Road AB15 8AA   01224 315125

Aberdeen: Denburn (H)
Lesley Risby (Mrs) BD   1994   1999   122 Deswood Place AB15 4DQ   01224 642845
[e-mail: andrew@risby.freeserve.co.uk]

Aberdeen: Ferryhill (H) (01224 583070)
John H.A. Dick MA MSc BD   1982   54 Polmuir Road AB11 7RT   01224 586933

Aberdeen: Garthdee (H)
James Weir BD   1991   27 Ramsay Gardens AB10 7AE   01224 317452

Aberdeen: Gilcomston South (H) (01224 616144)
D. Dominic Smart BSc BD MTh   1988   37 Richmondhill Road AB15 5EQ   01224 314326
                                                     [e-mail: smartdd@lineone.net]

Aberdeen: Greyfriars John Knox (T) (01224 644719)
S. Ian Dennis BD   1997   41 Gray Street AB10 6JD   01224 584594

Aberdeen: High Hilton (H) (01224 494717)
A. Peter Dickson BSc BD   1996   24 Rosehill Drive AB24 4JJ   01224 484155
                                                     [e-mail: apdickson@binternet.com]

Aberdeen: Holburn Central (H) (01224 580967)
George S. Cowie BSc BD   1991   6 St Swithin Street AB10 6XE   01224 593302

Aberdeen: Holburn West (H) (01224 571120)
Duncan C. Eddie MA BD   1992   31 Cranford Road AB10 7NJ   01224 325873

Aberdeen: Mannofield (H) (01224 310087)
John F. Anderson MA BD FSAScot   1966   21 Forest Avenue AB15 4TU   01224 315748

Aberdeen: Mastrick (H) (01224 694121)
Brian C. Rutherford BSc BD   1977   13 Beechgrove Avenue AB15 5EZ   01224 638011

Aberdeen: Middlefield (H)
Ernest Chapman   1977   73 Manor Avenue AB16 7UT   01224 685214

Aberdeen: New Stockethill (New Charge Development)
Ian M. Aitken   1999   52 Ashgrove Road West AB16 5EE   01224 682617
                                                     [e-mail: ncdstockethill@dial.pipex.com]

Aberdeen: Nigg (01224 894599)
Vacant   7 Redmoss Avenue AB12 3JR   01224 871168

Aberdeen: North of St Andrew (T) (01224 643567)
Graeme W .M. Muckart MTh MSc FSAScot   1983   51 Osborne Place AB25 2BX   01224 646429
                                                     [e-mail: gwzm@clara.net]

Aberdeen: Northfield			
Scott C. Guy BD	1989	28 Byron Crescent AB17EX	01224 692332
Duncan Ross DCS	1999	64 Stewart Crescent AB16 5SR	01224 692519
Aberdeen: Queen's Cross (H) (01224 644742)			
Robert F. Brown MA BD ThM	1971 1984	1 St Swithin Street AB10 6XH	01224 322549
Aberdeen: Rosemount (H) (01224 620111)			
A. David M. Graham BA BD	1971 1983	22 Osborne Place AB25 2DA	01224 648041
Aberdeen: Rubislaw (H) (01224 645477)			
Andrew G.N. Wilson MA BD	1977 1987	45 Rubislaw Den South AB15 4BD	01224 314878
Aberdeen: Ruthrieston South (H) (01224 211730)			
Hugh F. Kerr MA BD	1968 1985	39 Gray Street AB10 6JD	01224 586762
Aberdeen: Ruthrieston West (H)			
Sean Swindells BD DipMin	1996	451 Great Western Road AB10 6NL	01224 313075
Aberdeen: St Columba's Bridge of Don (H) (01224 825653)			
Louis Kinsey BD	1991	151 Jesmond Avenue AB22 8UG [e-mail: lous.kinsey@tinyworld.co.uk]	01224 705337
Aberdeen: St George's Tillydrone (H) (01224 482204)			
Shirley A. Fraser (Miss) MA BD	1992	127 Clifton Road AB24 3RH [e-mail: safraser@internet.com]	01224 483976
Aberdeen: St John's Church for Deaf People (H) (01224 494566)			
John R. Osbeck BD	1979 1991	15 Deeside Crescent AB15 7PT	(Voice/Text) 01224 315595
Aberdeen: St Machar's Cathedral (H) (01224 485988)			
Richard E. Frazer BA BD	1986 1993	18 The Chanonry, Old Aberdeen AB24 1RQ [e-mail: stmachar@ifb.co.uk]	01224 483688
Aberdeen: St Mark's (H) (01224 640672)			
John M. Watson LTh	1989	65 Mile-end Avenue AB15 5PU [e-mail: jmwat@globalnet.co.uk]	01224 632028
Aberdeen: St Mary's (H) (01224 487227)			
Michael S.M. Crawford LTh	1966 1967	456 King Street AB24 3DE	01224 633778
Aberdeen: St Nicholas, Kirk of (H) (01224 643494)			
Vacant		48 Gray Street AB10 6JE	01224 314056

Charge / Minister	Year	Address	Telephone
Aberdeen: St Nicholas South of Kincorth W. E. Wilkie LTh	1978	Kincorth Circle AB12 5NX	01224 872820
Aberdeen: St Ninian's (T) (01224 319519) Alison Swindells (Mrs) LLB BD	1998 2000	451 Great Western Road, AB10 6NL	01224 317667
Aberdeen: St Stephen's (H) (01224 624443) James M. Davies BSc BD	1982 1989	6 Belvidere Street AB25 2QS	01224 635694
Aberdeen: Summerhill Ian A. McLean BSc BD	1981	36 Stronsay Drive AB15 6JL	01224 324669
Aberdeen: Torry St Fittick's (H) Iain C. Barclay TD MA BD MTh MPhil	1976	11 Devanha Gardens East AB11 7UH [e-mail: i.c.barclay@abdn.ac.uk]	01224 588245
Ann V. Lundie (Miss) DCS		20 Langdykes Drive, Cove, Aberdeen AB12 3HW	01224 898416
Aberdeen: Woodside (H) (01224 277249) Alistair Murray BD	1984	322 Clifton Road AB24 4HQ	01224 484562
Bucksburn Stoneywood (H) (01224 712411) Nigel Parker BD MTh	1994	25 Gilbert Road, Bucksburn, Aberdeen AB21 9AN	01224 712635
Cults: East (T)(H) (01224 869028) Flora J. Munro (Mrs) BD	1993	Cults, Aberdeen AB15 9TD	01224 867587
Cults: West (H) (01224 869566) Thomas C. Richardson LTh ThB	1971 1978	3 Quarry Road, Cults, Aberdeen AB15 9EX [e-mail: richardson-tc@msn.com]	01224 867417
Dyce (H) (01224 771295) Russel Moffat BD MTh	1986 1998	144 Victoria Street, Dyce, Aberdeen AB21 7BE	01224 722380
Kingswells Harvey L. Grainger LTh	1975 1989	Lang Stracht, Aberdeen AB15 8PL [e-mail: revhlg@talk21.com]	01224 740229 (Tel) 0705 0030 649 (Mbl)
Newhills (H) (01224 716161 Tel/Fax) Norman Maciver MA BD	1976	Bucksburn, Aberdeen AB21 9SS [e-mail: newhillsnm@aol.com]	01224 712655
Peterculter (H) (01224 735845) John A. Ferguson BD DipMin	1988 1999	7 Howie Lane, Peterculter, Aberdeen AB14 0LJ	01224 735041

Name	Years	Position	Address	Tel.
Aitchison, James W.	1993	Chaplain: Army	2 Bn ITC Catterick (EP), Helles Barracks, Catterick, N Yorks DL9 4HH	
Allsop, Thom D. A. MA BD	1959 1999	(Aberdeen: Beechgrove)	2 Carnegie Gardens AB15 4AW	01224 318474
Ballantyne, Samuel MA BD	1941 1982	(Rutherford)	26 Cairncry Road, Aberdeen AB16 5DP	01224 483049
Blythe, Scott C. BSc BD	1997 1999	Chaplain: Robert Gordon University	8 Thistle Place, Aberdeen AB10 1UZ	01224 636856
Bryden, Agnes Y. (Mrs) DCS		(Deaconess)	9 Rosewell Place, Aberdeen AB15 6HN	01224 315042
Campbell, W.M.M. BD CPS	1970 1986	Hospital Chaplain	43 Murray Terrace, Aberdeen AB21 7SA	01224 591174
Coutts, Fred MA BD	1973 1989	Hospital Chaplain	9A Millburn Street, Aberdeen, AB11 6SS	01224 583805
Deans, John Bell	1951 1986	(Hospital Chaplain)	14 Balmoral Avenue, Ellon AB41 9EN	01358 721539
Dickson, John C. MA	1950 1987	(Aberdeen St Fittick's)	56 Countesswells Road, Aberdeen AB15 7YE	01224 314488
Douglas, Andrew M. MA	1957 1995	(High Hilton)	49 Hopetoun Avenue AB21 9QU	01224 713882
Falconer, James B.	1982 1992	Hospital Chaplain	3 Brimmond Walk, Westhill, Skene AB32 6HX	01224 744621
Fergusson, David A.S. MA BD DPhil	1984 1990	University of Aberdeen	44 Ashley Road, Aberdeen AB10 6RJ	01224 583817
Finlayson, Ena (Miss) DCS		(Deaconess)	16E Denwood AB15 6JF	01224 321147
Goldie, George D. ALCM	1953 1995	(Greyfriars)	27 Broomhill Avenue, Aberdeen AB10 6JL	01224 322503
Gordon, Laurie Y.	1960 1995	(John Knox)	1 Alder Drive, Portlethen, Aberdeen AB12 4WA	01224 782703
Grant, A. Rae MA BD	1923 1966	(Cults West)	10 Crown Circus, Inverness IV2 3NQ	01463 237764
Haddow, Angus BSc	1963 1999	(Methlick)	25 Lerwick Road, Aberdeen AB16 6RF	01224 696362
Hutchison, A. Scott MA BD DD	1957 1991	(Hospital Chaplain)	Ashfield, Drumoak, Banchory AB31 5AG	01330 811309
Hutchison, Alison (Mrs) M. BD DipMin	1988 1988	Hospital Chaplain	Ashfield, Drumoak, Banchory AB31 5AG	01330 811309
Hutchison, David S BSc BD ThM	1991 1999	(Aberdeen: Torry St Fittick's)	71 University Road, Aberdeen AB24 3DR	
Johnstone, William MA BD	1963 1963	University of Aberdeen	37 Rubislaw Den South, Aberdeen AB15 6BD	01224 316022
McCallum, Moyra (Miss) MA BD DCS		(Deaconess)	176 Hilton Drive, Aberdeen AB24 4LT	01224 486240
Mackay, Murdoch M. MA	1941 1986	(Hospital Chaplain)	17 Hillview Terrace, Cults, Aberdeen AB15 9HJ	01224 868082
Main, Alan TD MA BD STM PhD	1963 1980	University of Aberdeen	Kirkfield, Barthol Chapel, Inverurie AB51 8TD	01651 806773
Mirrilees, J.B. MA BD	1937 1977	(High Hilton)	22 King's Gate, Aberdeen AB15 4EJ	01224 638351
Munro, Gillian (Miss) BSc BD	1989 1995	Chaplain's Assistant: Aberdeen Royal Infirmary	685 George Street, Aberdeen AB25 3XP	
Russell, Andrew M. MA BD	1940 1976	(Woodside North)	3 Hill Place, Alloa FK10 2LP	01259 213115
Sefton, Henry R. MA BD STM PhD	1957 1992	(University of Aberdeen)	25 Albury Place, Aberdeen AB11 6TQ	01224 572305
Skakle, George S. MA	1945 1987	(Aberdeen Powis)	30 Whitehall Terrace, Aberdeen AB25 2RY	01224 646478
Smith, Angus MA LTh	1965 1991	Industrial Chaplain	1 Fa'burn Terace, Lumphanan AB31 4AG	01339 883395
Stewart, James C. MA BD STM	1960 2000	(Aberdeen: Kirk of St. Nicholas)	54 Murray Terrace, Aberdeen AB11 7SB	01224 825637
Swinton, John BD PhD	1999	University of Aberdeen	4 Whitestairs Close. Bridge of Don, Aberdeen AB22 8WE	01224 790902
Torrance, Iain R. TD MA BD DPhil	1982 1993	University of Aberdeen (01224 272274)	Concraig Smiddy, Clinterty, Kingswells, Aberdeen AB15 8RN	01224 318218
Walton, Ainslie MA MEd	1954 1995	(University of Aberdeen)	359 Great Western Road, Aberdeen AB10 6NU	01224 697014
Watt, William G.	1970 1977	(South of St Nicholas Kincorth)	12 Eriskay Drive, Lang Stracht, Aberdeen AB16 6FJ	01224 632323
Welsh, Jessie R. (Miss) DCS		(Deaconess)	40 Thomson Areet, Aberdeen AB25 2QP	01224 722543
Wood, James L.K.	1967 1995	(Ruthrieston West)	1 Glen Dryce, Dyce, Aberdeen AB21 7EN	
Young, Henry J.	1953 1980	(Edinburgh Dean)	Bank House, 1 Stewarton Road, Dunlop KA3 4AA	01560 484669

ABERDEEN ADDRESSES

Beechgrove	Beechgrove Avenue	Mannofield	Great Western Road x Craigton Road	St George's	Hayton Road, Tillydrone
Bridge of Don		Mastrick	Greenfern Road	St John's for the Deaf	Smithfield Road
Old Machar	Ashwood Park	Middlefield	Manor Avenue	St Machar's	The Chanory
Cove	Loirston Primary School, Loirston Avenue	Nigg	Kirk Road, Nigg	St Mark's	Rosemount Viaduct
Craigiebuckler	Springfield Road	North Church of St Andrew	Queen Street	St Mary's	King Street
Denburn	Summer Street	Northfield	Byron Crescent	St Nicholas, Kirk of	Union Street
Ferryhill	Fonthill Road x Polmuir Road	Queen's Cross	Queen's Cross	St Nicholas, South of Kincorth	Kincorth Circle
Garthdee	Ramsay Gardens	Rosemount	Rosemount Place	St Ninian's	Mid-Stocket Road
Gilcomston South	Union Street x Summer Street	Rubislaw	Queen's Cross	St Stephen's	Powis Place
Greyfriars John Knox	Broad Street	Ruthrieston		New Stockethill	Castleton Crescent
High Hilton	Hilton Drive	South	Holburn Street	Summerhill	Stronsay Drive
Holburn		West	Broomhill Road	Torry St Fittick's	Walker Road
Central	Holburn Street	St Columba's	Braehead Way, Bridge of Don	Woodside	Church Street, Woodside
West	Great Western Road				

(32) KINCARDINE AND DEESIDE

Meets at Banchory on the first Tuesday of February, March, November and December, and at Stonehaven, the first Tuesday of May, September and October and the last Tuesday of June.

Clerk:	REV. J.W.S. BROWN BTh			10 Forestside Road, Banchory AB31 5ZH	01330 824353

Aberluthnott linked with Laurencekirk (H)
Vacant   1983 1999   Aberdeen Road, Laurencekirk AB30 1AJ   01561 378838

Aboyne - Dinnet (H)
David Deveney BD   1997   49 Charleton Crescent, Charleton Park, Aboyne AB34 5GN   013398 86447

Arbuthnott linked with Bervie
Alastair McKillop BD DipMin   1995   10 Kirkburn, Inverbervie, Montrose DD10 0RT   01561 362633

Banchory-Devenick linked with Maryculter and Cookney
Vacant   The Manse, Kirkton of Maryculter, Aberdeen AB12 5FS   01224 735776

Banchory Ternan: East (H)
Hamish K. Fleming MA   1966 1986   East Manse, Banchory, Kincardineshire AB31 5YP   01330 822481

Banchory Ternan: West (H) Donald K. Walker BD	1979 1995	2 Wilson Road, Banchory AB31 5UY	01330 822811
Benholm and Johnshaven See Mearns Coastal **Bervie** See Arbuthnott			
Birse and Feughside Jack Holt BSc BD	1985 1994	Finzean, Banchory AB31 6PB	01330 850237
Braemar linked with Crathie Robert P. Sloan MA BD	1968 1996	Crathie, Ballater AB35 5UL	01339 742208
Cromar Vacant		Aberdeen Road, Tarland, Aboyne AB34 4UA	01339 881464
Dinnet See Aboyne - Dinnet			
Drumoak (H) linked with Durris (H) James Scott MA BD	1973 1992	The Manse, Durris, Banchory AB31 6BU [e-mail: jimscott@durrismanse.freeserve.co.uk]	01330 844557
Fettercairn See West Mearns **Finzean** See Birse and Feughside **Fordoun** See West Mearns **Garvock St Cyrus** See Mearns Coastal **Glenbervie** See West Mearns			
Glenmuick (Ballater) (H) Anthony Watts BD	1999	The Manse, Craigendarroch Walk, Ballater AB35 5ZB	013397 54014
Kincardine O'Neil linked with Lumphanan Norma P. Robertson (Miss) BD	1993 1998	Lumphanan, Banchory AB31 4PR	01339 883249
Kinneff linked with Stonehaven South (H) Vacant		Cameron Street, Stonehaven AB39 2HE	01569 762576
Laurencekirk See Aberluthnott **Lumphanan** See Kincardine O'Neil **Maryculter and Cookney** See Banchory-Devenick			
Mearns Coastal George I Hastie MA BD	1971 1998	The Manse, Kirkton, St Cyrus, Montrose DD10 0BW	01674 850880 (Tel/Fax)
Newtonhill Vacant		39 St Ternans Road, Newtonhill, Stonehaven AB39 3PF	01569 730143

Portlethen (H) (01224 782883)
John R. Notman BSc BD — 1990 1997 — 18 Rowanbank Road, Portlethen, Aberdeen AB12 4QY — 01224 780211

Stonehaven: Dunnottar (H)
Gordon Farquharson MA BD DipEd — 1998 — Dunottar Manse, Stonehaven AB39 2XL — 01569 762874

Stonehaven: Fetteresso (H)
Vacant — 1977 1983 — 13 Bath Street, Stonehaven AB39 2DH — 01569 762876

Stonehaven: South See Kinneff
Strachan See Birse and Feughside

Torphins
Peter R. Taylor JP BD — 1977 1987 — Torphins, Banchory AB31 4GQ — 01339 882276

West Mearns
Catherine A. Hepburn (Miss) BA BD — 1982 2000 — Fettercairn, Laurencekirk AB30 1YE — 01561 340203

Name	Dates	Charge	Address	Tel
Angus, J.A. Keith LVO TD MA	1955 1995	(Braemar with Crathie)	Darroch Den, Hawthorn Place, Ballater AB35 5QH	01339 756260
Beattie, Walter G. MA BD	1956 1995	(Arbroath Old and Abbey)	25 St Aidan Crescent, Banchory AB31 5XY	01330 824051
Brown, Alastair BD	1986 1992	(Glenmuick, Ballater)	52 Henderson Drive, Kintore, Inverurie AB51 0FB	01467 632787
Brown, J.W.S. BTh	1960 1995	(Cromar)	10 Forestside Road, Banchory AB31 5ZH	01330 824353
Caie, Albert LTh	1983 1997	(Glenmuick [Ballater])	16 Swann Place, Ballater AB35 5RW	01339 755787
Campbell, Donald MA	1934 1979	(Bervie)	Clashfarquhar House, Robert Street, Stonehaven AB3 2DJ	01569 762438
Christie, Andrew C. LTh	1975 2000	(Banchory-Devenick with Maryculter and Cookney)	17 Strait Place, Elrick, Aberdeen AB32 6JP	
Collie, Joyce P. (Miss) MA PhD	1966 1994	(Corgarff Strathdon and Glenbuchat Towie)	28 Queen Victoria Park, Inchmarlo, Banchory AB31 4AL	01330 824981
Forbes, John W.A. BD	1973 1999	(Edzell Lethnot with Fern, Careston and Menmuir with Glenesk)	Mid Clune, Finzean, nr Banchory AB31 6PL	01330 850283
Gray, Robert MA BD	1942 1982	(Stonehaven Fetteresso)	4 Park Drive, Stonehaven AB39 2NW	01569 767027
Hood, E.C.P. MA	1946 1989	(Methlick)	1 Silver Gardens, Stonehaven AB39 2LH	
Jack, David LTh	1984 1999	(West Mearns)	7 Cromwell Road, Aberdeen AB15 4UH	01224 325355
Kinninburgh, Elizabeth B.F. (Miss) MA BD	1970 1986	(Birse with Finzean with Strachan)	7 Huntly Cottages, Aboyne AB31 5HD	01339 886757
MacLeod, Kenneth	1950 1986	(Bourtreebush with Portlethen)	30 Woodlands Place, Inverbervie, Montrose DD10 OSL	01561 362414
Nicholson, William	1949 1986	(Banchory Ternan East with Durris)	10 Pantoch Gardens, Banchory AB31 5ZD	01330 823875
Rennie, Donald B. MA	1956 1996	(Industrial Chaplain)	Memis Howe, Inverurie Street, Auchenblae, Laurencekirk AB30 1XS	01561 320622
Skinner, Silvester MA	1941 1979	(Lumphanan)	29 Silverbank Gardens, Banchory AB31 3YZ	01330 823032
Smith, J.A. Wemyss MA	1947 1983	(Garvock St Cyrus)	30 Greenbank Drive, Edinburgh EH10 5RE	0131 447 2205
Tierney, John P. MA	1945 1985	(Peterhead West Associate)	3 Queenshill Drive, Aboyne AB34 5DG	01339 886741
Urie, D.M.L. MA BD PhD	1940 1980	(Kincardine O'Neil)	Cochrane Cottage, North Deeside Road, Kincardine O'Neil AB34 5AA	01339 884204
Watt, William D. LTh	1978 1996	(Aboyne - Dinnet)	2 West Toll Crescent, Aboyne AB34 5GB	01339 886943

(33) GORDON

Meets at various locations on the first Tuesday of February, March, April, May, September, October, November and December, and on the fourth Tuesday of June.

Clerk: REV. G. EUAN D. GLEN BSc BD The Manse, 26 St. Ninian's, Monymusk Inverurie AB51 7HF   01467 651470
[e-mail: gordonpresb@dial.pipex.com]

Auchindoir and Kildrummy See Upper Donside

Barthol Chapel linked with Tarves
Alan T. McKean BD 1992 1999 Tarves, Aberdeenshire AB41 7SF 01651 851250

Belhelvie (H)
Daniel Hawthorn MA BD 1965 1998 Balmedie, Aberdeenshire AB23 8YR 01358 742227
[e-mail: DonHawthorne@compuserve.com]

Blairdaff linked with Chapel of Garioch
Kim C ran (Mrs) MDiv BA 1993 2000 Chapel of Garioch, Inverurie AB51 9HE 01467 681619
[e-mail: blairdaff.chapelofgariochparish@btinternet.com]

Chapel of Garioch See Blairdaff

Cluny linked with Monymusk (T)
G. Euan D. Glen BSc BD 1992 26 St. Ninian's, Monymusk, Inverurie AB51 7HF 01467 651470
[e-mail: euang@tesco.net]

Corgarff and Strathdon See Upper Donside

Culsalmond and Rayne linked with Daviot
Mary M. Cranfield (Miss) MA BD 1989 Daviot, Inverurie AB51 0HY 01467 671241
[e-mail: marymc@ukgateway.net]

Cushnie and Tough
Margaret Garden (Miss) BD 1993 2000 The Manse, Muir of Fowlis, Aberdeenshire AB33 8JU 01975 581239
[e-mail: m.garden@virginnet.co.uk]

Daviot See Culsalmond and Rayne

Drumblade linked with Huntly Strathbogie
Neil MacGregor 1995 Deveron Road, Huntly AB54 5DU 01466 792702

Echt linked with Midmar (T)
David I. Souter — 1996 — Echt, Aberdeenshire AB32 7AB [e-mail: d.souter@virgin.net.uk] — 01330 860533

Ellon
Eleanor MacAlister (Mrs) BD — 1994 — 1999 — The Manse, Ellon, Aberdeenshire AB41 9BA [e-mail: macallster@aol.com] — 01358 720476
Pauline Steenbergen (Ms) MA BD (Assoc) — 1996 — 1999 — 1 Landale Road, Peterhead AB42 1QN [e-mail: psteen9689@aol.com] — 01779 472141

Fintray and Kinellar linked with Keithhall
Vacant — Keithhall, Inverurie AB51 OLJ — 01467 620435

Foveran
Vacant — Foveran, Ellon, Aberdeenshire AB41 6AP — 01358 789288

Glenbuchat Towie See Upper Donside

Howe Trinity
John A. Cook MA BD — 1986 — 2000 — The Manse, 110 Main Street, Alford AB33 8AD [e-mail: j-a-cookehowe.trinity.freeserve.co.uk] — 019755 62282
(Charge formed by the union of Alford, Tullynessle and Forbes and Keig)

Huntly Cairnie Glass
Thomas R. Calder LLB BD WS — 1994 — Queen Street, Huntly AB54 8EB — 01466 792630

Huntly Strathbogie See Drumblade

Insch-Leslie-Premnay-Oyne (T)
Robert S. McLeish LTh — 1970 — 1984 — Insch, Aberdeenshire AB52 6JR — 01464 820914

Inverurie: St Andrew's
Iain J.M. Telfer BD DPS — 1978 — 1989 — 1 Ury Dale, Inverurie, Aberdeenshire AB51 3XW [e-mail: standrew@ukonline.co.uk] — 01467 620468

Inverurie: West
Ian B. Groves BD CPS — 1989 — West Manse, Westfield Road,Inverurie, Aberdeenshire AB51 3YS [e-mail: ian@gowest.free-online.co.uk] — 01467 620285

Keithhall See Fintray and Kinellar

Kennay John P. Renton BA LTh	1976	1990	Kemnay, Inverurie AB51 9ND [e-mail: john.renton@tesco.net]	01467 642219
Kintore (H) Alan Greig BSc BD	1977	1992	6 Forest Road, Kintore AB51 0XG [e-mail: greig@kincarr.free-online.co.uk]	01467 632219 (Tel/Fax)
Meldrum and Bourtie A. Grainger Stoddart	1975	1988	Old Meldrum, Aberdeenshire AB51 OEQ	01651 872250
Methlick Albert E. Smith BD FSAScot	1983	1999	Methlick, Aberdeenshire AB41 ODS [e-mail: RESMethlick@aol.com]	01651 806215
Midmar See Echt **Monymusk** See Cluny				
New Machar Ian Dryden MA DipEd	1988		Newmachar, Aberdeenshire AB2 ORD [e-mail: ian@drydenfreeserve.co.uk]	01651 862278
Noth John M'Callum BD DipPTh	1989		Kennethmont AB54 4NP [e-mail: jmccallum@Talk21.com]	01464 831244
Skene (H) Iain U. Thomson MA BD Marion G. Stewart (Miss) DCS	1970	1972	Skene, Westhill, Aberdeenshire AB32 6LX Kirk Cottage, Kirkton of Skene, Westhill, Aberdeenshire AB32 6XX	01224 743277 01224 743407
Tarves See Barthol Chapel **Tough** See Leochel Cushnie and Lynturk				
Udny and Pitmedden George R. Robertson LTh	1985		Udny, Aberdeenshire AB41 ORS	01651 842052
Upper Donside (H) Richard Darroch BD MTh	1993	1999	Lumsden, Huntly AB54 4GQ [e-mail: RichDarr@aol.com]	01464 861757
John C. Mack JP (Aux)	1985	1996	The Willows, Auchleven, Insch AB52 6QD	01464 820387

Andrew, John MA BD DipRE DipEd	1961	1972	Teacher: Religious Education	Carter's Croft, Midmar, Inverurie AB51 7NJ	01330 833208
Bowie, Alfred LTh	1974	1998	(Alford with Keig with Tullynessle Forbes)	17 Stewart Road, Alford AB33 8UD	01975 563824
Collie, Jeannie P. (Miss) DCS			(Deaconess)	3 Formartindale, Udny Station, Ellon AB41 6QJ	01651 842575
Davidson, James M. MA	1947	1989	(Inverurie St Andrew's)	Ardlair, Montgarrie Road, Alford AB33 8LY	01975 563471
Jones, Robert A. LTh CA	1966	1997	(Marnoch)	13 Gordon Terrace, Inverurie AB51 4GT	01467 622691
Ledgard, J. Christopher BA	1969	1998	(Upper Donside)	Streonshalh, South Road, Rhynie, Huntly AB54 4SA	01464 861429
Lister, Douglas	1945	1986	(Largo and Newburn)	Gowanbank, Port Elphinstone, Inverurie AB51 3UN	01467 621262
Macallan, Gerald B.	1954	1992	(Kintore)	82 Angusfield Avenue, Aberdeen AB15 6AT	01224 316125
Mellis, Robert J. BTh CA	1982	1998	(Shapinsay)	81 Western Avenue, Ellon AB41 9EX	01358 721929
Milligan, Rodney	1949	1985	(Culsalmond with Rothienorman)	Cameron House, Culduthel Road, Inverness IV2 4YG	01463 243241
Rennie, James B. MA	1959	1992	(Leochel Cushnie and Lynturk linked with Tough)	11 Westfield Avenue, Inverurie AB51 9RD	01467 622069
Rodger, Matthew A. BD	1978	1999	(Ellon)	57 Eilean Rise, Ellon AB41 9NF	01358 724556
Scott, Allan D. BD	1977	1989	(Culsalmond with Daviot with Rayne)	20 Barclay Road, Inverurie AB51 9QP	01467 625161
Skinner, Alistair BD	1964	1989	(Edinburgh Priestfield)	36 Hillhead Drive, Ellon AB41 9WB	01358 720890
Stewart, George C. MA	1952	1995	(Drumblade with Huntly Strathbogie)	104 Scott Drive, Huntly AB54 5PF	
Wallace, R.J. Stuart MA	1947	1986	(Foveran)	Manse View, Manse Road, Methlick, Ellon AB41 7DW	01651 806843

(34) BUCHAN

Meets at the places listed on the first Tuesday of the following months September and October (Peterhead), November and December (Banff), February and March (Fraserburgh), April and June (Turriff).

Clerk:	REV. R. NEILSON JP BSc BD	Hatton, Peterhead AB42 0QQ [e-mail: Buchan@dial.pipex.com]	01779 841229 (Tel) 01779 841822 (Fax)

Aberdour linked with New Pitsligo

Vacant			137 High Street, New Pitsligo, Fraserburgh AB43 6NH	01771 653256

Auchaber United linked with Auchterless

Alison Jaffrey (Mrs) MA BD	1990	1999	The Manse, Auchterless, Turriff AB53 8BA [e-mail: Alison.Jaffrey@bigfoot.com]	01888 511217
Margaret McKay (Mrs)	1991	1999	The Smithy, Knowes of Elrick, Aberchirder AB54 7PP	01466 780208 (Tel) 01466 780015 (Fax)

Auchterless See Auchaber United

Banff linked with King Edward				
Alan Macgregor BA BD	1992	1998	7 Colleonard Road, Banff AB45 1DZ [e-mail: alan.macgregor@banf98.freeserve.co.uk]	01261 812107 (Tel) 01261 818526 (Fax)
James Cook MA MDiv (Assoc)	1999	1999	3B St Catherine Street, Banff AB45 1HT	01261 815512
Crimond linked with St Fergus				
James E. Lyall BD	1993		Crimond, Fraserburgh AB43 8QJ	01346 532431 (Tel) 01346 532175 (Fax)
Cruden				
Rodger Neilson JP BSc BD	1972	1974	Hatton, Peterhead AB42 0QQ [e-mail: Buchan@dial.pipex.com]	01779 841229 (Tel) 01779 841822 (Fax)
Deer(H)				
James Wishart JP BD	1986		Old Deer, Peterhead AB42 5JB	01771 623582
Fordyce				
Vacant			Portsoy, Banff AB45 2QB	01261 842272
Fraserburgh: Old				
Douglas R. Clyne BD	1973		97 Saltoun Place, Fraserburgh AB43 9RY	01346 518536
Fraserburgh: South (H) linked with Inverallochy and Rathen East				
Ronald F. Yule	1982		15 Victoria Street, Fraserburgh AB43 9PJ	01346 518244 (Tel) 0870 0554665 (Fax)
Fraserburgh: West				
B. Andrew Lyon LTh	1971	1978	23 Strichen Road, Fraserburgh AB43 9SA [e-mail: rex@balyon.demon.co.uk]	01346 513303 (Tel) 01346 512398 (Fax)
Fyvie linked with Rothienorman				
Alexander B. Noble MA BD ThM	1982	1999	Fyvie, Turriff AB53 8RD	01651 891230
Gardenstown				
Donald N. Martin BD	1996		The Manse, Fernie Brae, Gardenstown, Banff AB45 3YL [e-mail: d.n.martin@virgin.net]	01261 851256 (Tel) 01261 851022 (Fax)
Inverallochy and Rathen East See Fraserburgh South				
King Edward See Banff				
Longside				
Norman Smith MA BD	1997		9 Anderson Drive, Longside, Peterhead AB42 4XG [e-mail: normsmith@aol.com]	01779 821224

Lonmay linked with Rathen West
Vacant

Lonmay, Fraserburgh AB43 8UJ

01346 532227 (Tel)
01346 532733 (Fax)

Macduff
David J. Randall MA BD ThM   1971

Macduff, Banff AB45 3QL
[e-mail: djrandall@macduff.force9.co.uk]

01261 832316 (Tel)
01261 832301 (Fax)

Marnoch
Rosemary Legge (Mrs) BSc BD MA   1992   1997

Aberchirder, Huntly AB54 7TS

01466 780276

Maud and Savoch linked with New Deer
Alastair Donald MA PhD BD   1999

Fordyce Terrace, New Deer, Turriff AB52 6TD
[e-mail: alistair@donalds99 freeserve.co.uk]

01771 644216

Monquhitter and New Byth
H. Stewart Congdon DMin   1968   2000

10 Teuchar Road, Cuminestown, Turriff AB53 5YD
[e-mail: stewartandjean@congdons.freeserve.co.uk]

01888 544279

New Deer St Kane's See Maud and Savoch
New Pitsligo See Aberdour

Ordiquhill and Cornhill (H) linked with Whitehills
Gordon Henig BSc BD   1997

6 Craigneen Place, Whitehills, Banff AB45 2NE

01261 861671

Peterhead: Old
David S. Ross MSc PhD BD   1978

1 Hawthorn Road, Peterhead AB42 2DW

01779 472618 (Tel/Fax)

Peterhead: St Andrew's (H)
David G. Pitkeathly LLB BD   1996

1 Landale Road, Peterhead AB42 1QN

01779 472141

Peterhead: Trinity
L. Paul McClenaghan BA   1973   1996

18 Landale Road, Peterhead AB42 1QP
[e-mail: paul.mcclenaghan@virgin.net]

01779 472405

Pitsligo linked with Sandhaven
Vacant

49 Pitsligo Street, Rosehearty, Fraserburgh AB43 7JL

01346 571237

Rathen West See Lonmay
Rothienorman See Fyvie
St Fergus See Crimond
Sandhaven See Pitsligo

Strichen linked with **Tyrie**
Vacant   Kingsville, Strichen, Fraserburgh AB43 6SQ   01771 637365

Turriff: St Andrew's
Vacant   Balmellie Road, Turriff AB53 4DP   01888 563240 (Tel)
                                                                                              01888 569071 (Fax)

Turriff: St Ninian's and Forglen
Vacant   "Balloch", Station Road, Turriff AB53 4ER   01888 563383

Tyrie See Strichen
Whitehills see Ordiquhill and Cornhill

Bell, Douglas W. MA LLB	1975	1993	(Alexandria: North)	76 Burnside Road, Mintlaw AB42 5PE	01771 623299
Birnie, Charles J. MA	1969	1995	(Aberdour and Tyrie)	"The Dookit", 23 Water Street, Strichen AB43 6ST	01771 637775
Blaikie, James BD	1972	1997	(Berwick-on-Tweed: St Andrew's Wallace Green and Lowick)	57 Glenugie View, Peterhead AB42 2BW	01779 490625
Brown, William H.	1953	1990	(Peterhead St Andrew's)	11 Henderson Park, Peterhead AB42 2WR	01779 472592
Douglas, Ian P. LTh	1974	1998	(Aberdeen: Craigiebuckler)	1 Tortorston Drive, Peterhead	
Dunlop, M. William B. LLB BD	1981	1995	(Peterhead St Andrew's)	18 Iona Avenue, Peterhead AB42 1NZ	01779 479189
Fawkes, G. M. Allan JP BA BSc	1979	2000	(Lonmay with Rathen West)	3 Northfield Gardens, Hatton AB42 OSW	01779 841814
Jeffrey, Stewart D. BSc BD	1962	1997	(Banff with King Edward)	8 West End, Whitehills, Banff AB42 2NL	01261 861523
Mackenzie, Seoras L. BD	1996	1998	Chaplain, Army	1 RHF BFPO 38	
Noble, George S. DipTh	1972	2000	(Carfin with Newarthill)	Craigowan, 3 Main Street, Inverallochy, Fraserburgh AB43 8XX	01346 582749
Scott, W.D.	1956	1989	(Maud with Savoch)	2 Thistle Gardens, Mintlaw AB42 5FG	01771 622258
Shaw, Andrew BSc FRIC	1964	1985	(Gardenstown)	39 Bridge Street, Banff AB45 1HD	01261 812949
Strachan, Ian M. MA BD	1959	1994	(Ashkirk with Selkirk)	20 Westfield Road, Turriff AB53 4AF	01888 568403
Taylor, William MA MEd	1984	1996	(Buckie North)	23 York Street, Peterhead AB42 6SN	01779 481798
Walker, Colin D.	1977	1982	(Auchindoir and Kildrummy)	The Old Manse, Alvah, Banff AB54 3US	01261 821656

(35) MORAY

Meets at St Andrew's Lhanbryd and Urquhart on the first Tuesday of February, March, April, May, September, October, November, December and at the Moderator's Church on the fourth Tuesday of June.

Clerk: REV. G. MELVYN WOOD MA BD   3 Seafield Place, Cullen, Buckie, Banffshire AB56 4UU   01542 841851 (Tel)
                                            [e-mail: melvynwood@cullenmanse.freeserve.co.uk]   01542 841991 (Fax)
                                                                                                          0797 409 5840 (Mbl)

Aberlour (H)
Elizabeth M. Curran (Miss) BD 1995 1998
Mary Avenue, Aberlour, Banffshire AB38 9QN
01340 871027

Alves and Burghead linked with Kinloss and Findhorn
John C. Beck BD 1975 1995
Dunbar Street, Burghead, Elgin, Moray IV30 5XB
01343 830365

Bellie linked with Speymouth
David J. Ferguson 1966 1982
11 The Square, Fochabers, Moray IV32 7DG
[e-mail: bellierev@aol.com]
01343 820256 (Tel)
01343 820256 (Fax)

Birnie linked with Pluscarden
Ronald J. Scotland BD 1993
Birnie, Elgin IV30 8SU
01343 542621

Buckie: North (H)
Robert P. Boyle LTh 1990 1996
14 St Peter's Road, Buckie AB56 1DL
01542 831328

Buckie: South and West (H) linked with Enzie
Eric W. Foggitt MA BSc BD 1991
East Church Street, Buckie AB56 1ES
[e-mail: ericleric@compuserve.com]
01542 832103 (Tel/Fax)

Cullen and Deskford
G. Melvyn Wood MA BD 1982 1997
3 Seafield Place, Cullen, Buckie, Banffshire AB56 4UU
[e-mail: melvynwood@cullenmanse.freeserve.co.uk]
01542 841851 (Tel)
01542 841991 (Fax)
0797 409 5840 (Mbl)

Dallas linked with Forres St Leonard's (H) linked with Rafford
Paul Amed LTh DPS 1992 2000
Nelson Road, Forres IV36 1DR
01309 672380

Duffus, Spynie and Hopeman (H)
Vacant
Duffus, Elgin IV30 5QP
01343 830276

Dyke linked with Edinkillie
Ann McColl Poole (Mrs) DipEd ACE LTh 1983
Brodie, Forres IV36 2TD
01309 641239

Edinkillie See Dyke

Elgin: High
Charles D. McMillan LTh 1979 1991
5 Forteath Avenue, Elgin IV30 1TQ
[e-mail: revchaselginhigh@btinternet.com]
01343 542449 (Tel/Fax)

Elgin: St Giles' (H) and St Columba's South (01343 551501) (Office and Church Halls: Greyfriars Street, Elgin IV30 1LF)
George B. Rollo BD   1974   1986   18 Reidhaven Street, Elgin IV30 1QH   01343 547208
[e-mail: gbrstgiles@hotmail.com]

Norman R. Whyte BD DipMin (Assoc)   1982   2000   2 Hay Place, Elgin IV30 1LZ   01343 540 143
(Charge formed by the union of Elgin South and Elgin St. Giles')

Enzie See Buckie South and West

Findochty linked with Portknockie linked with Rathven
Graham Austin BD   1997   20 Netherton Terrace, Findochty, Buckie AB56 4QD   01542 833484
[e-mail: gaustin@cwcom.net]

Forres: St Laurence (H)
Barry J. Boyd LTh DPS   1993   12 Mackenzie Drive, Forres IV36 2JP   01309 672260
07778 731018 (Mbl)

Forres: St Leonard's See Dallas

Grange linked with Rothiemay
Vacant   Rothiemay, Huntly AB54 5NE   01466 711334

Keith: North, Newmill and Boharm (H) (01542 886390)
Michael G. Lyall BD   1993   Keith, Banffshire AB55 5BR   01542 882559
[e-mail: mgl@keithnorthchurch.demon.co.uk]

Keith: St Rufus and Botriphnie (H)
Ranald S.R. Gauld MA LLB BD   1991   The Manse, Keith, Banffshire AB55 5BR   01542 882799
Kay Gauld (Mrs) BD STM PhD (Assoc)   1999   The Manse, Keith, Banffshire AB55 5BR   01542 882799

Kinloss and Findhorn See Alves and Burghead

Knockando, Elchies and Archiestown (H) linked with Rothes
Vacant   Manse Brae, Rothes AB38 7AA   01340 831381

Lossiemouth: St Gerardine's High (H)
Duncan Murray BTh   1986   St Gerardine's Road, Lossiemouth IV31 6RA 01343 813146

Lossiemouth: St James'
George L. Cordiner BD   1973   Prospect Terrace, Lossiemouth IV31 6JS   01343 813135

Mortlach and Cabrach (H)
Hugh M.C. Smith LTh   1973   1982   Church Street, Dufftown, Keith AB55 4AR   01340 820380

Pluscarden See Birnie

Portknockie See Findochty
Rafford See Dallas
Rathven See Findochty linked with Portknockie
Rothes See Knockando, Elchies and Archiestown
Rothiemay See Grange

St Andrew's-Lhanbryd (H) and Urquhart
Vacant   St Andrews Road, Lhanbryde, Elgin IV30 8PU   01343 842208

Speymouth See Bellie

Name			(Role)	Address	Phone
Cowie, Gordon S. MA LLB	1986	1992	(Birnie with Pluscarden)	Strathspey, Lower Inchberry, Orton, Fochabers IV32 7QH	01343 880377
Davidson, A.A.B. MA BD	1960	1997	(Grange with Rothiemay)	9 Woodlands Park, Rosemount, Blairgowrie PH10 6UW	01250 875957
Diack, Peter MA	1951	1994	(Elgin South)	3A Gordon Street, Elgin IV30 1JQ	01343 542545
Douglas, Christina A. (Mrs)	1987	1993	(Inveraven and Glenlivet)	The Shieling, Dyke, Forres IV36 2SP	01309 641221
Evans, John W. MA BD	1945	1984	(Elgin High)	15 Weaver Place, Elgin IV30 1HB	01343 543607
Fraser, Donald R. MA BD	1944	1985	(Kinloss and Findhorn)	Brisbane, Orchard Road, Forres IV36 1LG	01309 672596
Macaulay, Alick Hugh MA	1943	1981	(Bellie with Speymouth)	5 Duke Street, Fochabers IV32 7DN	01343 820726
Miller, W.B.	1950	1987	(Cawdor with Croy and Dalcross)	10 Kirkhill Drive, Lhanbryde, Elgin IV30 8QA	01343 842368
Porter, John C.	1962	1987	(Forres St Leonard's)	17 Coppice Court, Grantown-on-Spey PH26 3LF	01479 873082
Robertson, John T. FPhS	1961	1993	(Keith: North, Newmill and Boharm)	43 Nelson Terrace, Keith AB55 5EF	01542 886339
Shaw, Duncan LTh CPS	1984		Chaplain RAF	37 Hebenton Road, Bishopmill, Elgin IV30 2EP	01343 549384
Spence, Alexander	1944	1989	(Elgin St Giles': Associate)	20 Back Braes, Brechin, Angus DD9 6HP	01356 622867
Stuart, John T. MA	1958	1993	(Duffus, Spynie and Hopeman)	1 Seaview Farm Paddock, Cummingston, Elgin IV30 5XY	01343 830890
Watt, H. Forbes	1950	1976	(Lossiemouth St Gerardine's High)	Buchanan House, 39 Victoria Street, Fraserburgh AB43 9PJ	01346 517068
Whiteford, Robert S. MA	1945	1986	(Shapinsay)	Lochinver Croft, Mosstowie, Elgin IV30 3TT	01343 541438
Wright, David L. MA BD	1957	1998	(Stornoway: St Columba)	84 Wyvis Drive, Nairn IV12 4TP	01667 451613
Thomson, James M. BA	1952	2000	(Elgin: St. Giles' and St. Columba's South: Assoc)	48 Mayne Road, Elgin IV30 1PD	01343 547664

(36) ABERNETHY

Meets at Boat of Garten on the first Tuesday of February, March, April, June, September, October, November and December.

Clerk: REV. JAMES A.I. MACEWAN MA BD   The Manse, Nethy Bridge PH25 3DG   01479 821280
[e-mail: manse@nethybridge.freeserve.co.uk]

Abernethy (H) linked with Cromdale (H) and Advie
James A.I. MacEwan MA BD 1973 1980   Nethy Bridge, Inverness-shire PH25 3DG   01479 821280

Alvie and Insh (T)(H)
Vacant   Kincraig, Kingussie, Inverness-shire PH21 1NA   01540 651221

Boat of Garten (H) and Kincardine linked with Duthil (H)
David W. Whyte LTh 1993 1999   Deshar Road, Boat of Garten, Inverness-shire PH24 3BN   01479 831252

Cromdale and Advie See Abernethy

Dulnain Bridge linked with Grantown-on-Spey (H)
Morris Smith BD 1988   Golf Course Road, Grantown-on-Spey, Moray PH26 3HY
[e-mail: janmo@tinyworld.co.uk]   01479 872084

Duthil See Boat of Garten and Kincardine
Grantown-on-Spey See Dulnain Bridge

Inveraven and Glenlivet
Margaret A. Muir (Miss) MA LLB BD 1989 1993   Ballindalloch, Banffshire AB37 9EB   01807 500311

Kingussie (H)
Vacant   Kingussie, Inverness-shire PH21 1HA   01540 661311

Kirkmichael and Tomintoul (H)
Sven S. Bjarnason Cand.Theol 1975 1992   Tomintoul, Ballindalloch, Banffshire AB37 9HA
[e-mail: sven@bjarnason.org.uk]   01807 580254

Laggan linked with Newtonmore (H)
Irene C. Gillespie (Mrs) BD 1991   Newtonmore, Inverness-shire PH20 1DG
[e-mail: revicg@btclick.com]   01540 673238

Newtonmore See Laggan

Rothiemurchus and Aviemore (H)
Ron C. Whyte BD CPS 1990   Rothiemurchus, Aviemore, Inverness-shire PH22 1QH
[e-mail: ron4xst@aol.com]   01479 810280

Livesley, Anthony LTh 1979 1997 (Kiltearn)   87 Beech Avenue, Nairn IV12 4SJ   01667 455126
Stewart, Matthew S. LTh 1981 1998 (Boat of Garten and Kincardine with Duthil)   2 Ruarden Court, Grantown-on-Spey PH26 3DA   01479 872210
[mattstewart1@tinyworld.co.uk]

(37) INVERNESS

Meets at Inverness, in the Dr Black Memorial Hall, on the first Tuesday of February, March, April, May, September, October, November and December and at the Moderator's Church on the fourth Tuesday of June.

Clerk:	REV. ALASTAIR S. YOUNGER BScEcon ASCC	3 Elm Park, Inverness IV2 4WN [e-mail: gob07@Dial.Pipex.Com]	01463 232462 (Tel/Fax)

Ardclach linked with Auldearn and Dalmore				
John L. Waugh LTh	1973	1993	Auldearn, Nairn IV12 5SX	01667 453180
Ardersier (H) linked with Petty				
Alexander Whiteford LTh	1996		Ardersier, Inverness IV2 7SX	01667 462224
Auldearn and Dalmore See Ardclach				
Cawdor (H) linked with Croy and Dalcross (H)				
Matthew Robertson LTh	1968	1994	Croy, Inverness IV25PH	01667 493217
Croy and Dalcross See Cawdor				
Culloden The Barn (H)				
James H. Robertson BSc BD	1975	1994	45 Oakdene Court, Culloden IV2 7XL	01463 790504
Daviot and Dunlichity linked with Moy, Dalarossie and Tomatin				
Lilian M. Bruce (Miss) BD ThM	1971	1986	Daviot, Inverness IV2 5XL	01463 772242
Dores and Boleskine				
James Christie LTh	1993		The Manse, Foyers, Inverness IV2 6XU	01456 486206
Inverness: Crown (H) (01463 238929)				
Peter H. Donald MA PhD BD	1991	1998	39 Southside Road, Inverness IV2 4XA	01463 231140
Inverness: Dalneigh and Bona (GD)(H)				
Fergus A. Robertson MA BD	1971	1999	9 St Mungo Road, Inverness IV3 5AS	01463 232339
Inverness: East (H)				
Aonghas I. MacDonald MA BD	1967	1981	2 Victoria Drive, Inverness IV2 3QD	01463 231269
Inverness: Hilton				
Duncan MacPherson LLB BD	1994		4 Tomatin Road, Inverness IV2 4UA	01463 231417

Inverness: Kinmylies (E) (H) Fraser M.C. Stewart BSc BD	1980	1992	2 Balnafettack Place, Inverness IV3 8TQ	01463 712479
Inverness: Ness Bank (T) (H) S. John Chambers OBE BSc	1972	1998	15 Ballifeary Road, Inverness IV3 5PJ	01463 234653
Inverness: St Columba High (H) Alastair S. Younger BScEcon ASCC	1969	1976	3 Elm Park, Inverness IV2 4WN [e-mail: gob07@Dial.Pipex.Com]	01463 232462 (Tel/Fax)
Inverness: St Stephen's linked with The Old High (1st Charge) (T) (H) Colin M. Anderson BA BD STM MPhil	1968	1994	24 Damfield Road, Inverness IV2 3HU	01463 237129
Inverness: The Old High See Inverness: St Stephen's				
Inverness: Trinity (H) Norman I. MacRae LTh	1966		60 Kenneth Street, Inverness IV3 5PZ	01463 234756
Inverness: West (2nd Charge) (T)(H) Alistair Malcolm BD DPS	1976	1992	52 Crown Drive, Inverness IV2 3QG	01463 237420
Kilmorack and Erchless George Duthie BSc Msc PhD BD	1998		"Roselynn", Croyard Road, Beauly, Inverness-shire IV4 7DJ	01463 782260
Kiltarlity linked with Kirkhill Campbell Mackinnon BSc BD	1982		Kirkhill, Inverness IV5 7PX	01463 831662
Kirkhill See Kiltarlity				
Moy, Dalarossie and Tomatin See Daviot and Dunlichity				
Nairn: Old (H) Ian W.F. Hamilton BD LTh ALCM AVCM	1978	1986	3 Manse Road, Nairn IV12 4RN	01667 452203
Nairn: St Ninian's (H) William B. Whyte BD	1973	1975	Queen Street, Nairn IV12 4AA	01667 452202
Petty See Ardersier				
Urquhart and Glenmoriston (H) Hugh F. Watt BD DPS	1986	1996	Blairbeg, Drumnadrochit, Inverness-shire IV3 6UG	01456 450231
Black, Archibald T. BSc	1964	1997	(Inverness: Ness Bank)	16 Elm Park, Inverness IV2 4WN 01463 230588
Brown, Derek G. BD DipMin DMin	1989	1994	Chaplain: Raigmore Hospital and Highland Hospice	Cathedral Manse, Croc-an-Lobht, Dornoch IV25 3HN 01862 810296

Buell, F. Bart BA MDiv	1980	1995	(Urquhart and Glenmoriston)	6 Towerhill Place, Cradlehall, Inverness IV1 2FN	01463 794634
Charlton, George W.	1952	1992	(Fort Augustus with Glengarry)	61 Druntfield Road, Inverness IV2 4XL	01463 242802
Chisholm, Archibald F. MA	1957	1997	(Braes of Rannoch with Foss and Rannoch)	32 Seabank Road, Nairn IV12 4EU	01667 452001
Donn, Thomas M. MA	1932	1969	(Duthil)	6 Cawdor Road, Inverness IV2 3NR	01463 236410
Edgar, William M.G. MA	1937	1976	(Auchindoir and Kildrummy)	Whinnieknowe, Mill Road, Nairn IV12 5EN	01667 452387
Frizzell, R. Stewart BD	1961	2000	(Wick Old)	98 Boswell Road, Inverness IV2 3EW	01463 231907
Gibbons, Richard BD	1997		Adviser in Mission and Evangelism	3 Holm Burn Place, Inverness IV2 6WT	01463 226889
Gibson, A. Cameron MRCVS	1962	1990	(Eskdalemuir with Hutton and Corrie with Tundergarth)	Langleigh, 10 Rowan Place, Nairn IV12 4TL	01667 455413
Graham, John	1950	1984	(Edinburgh St Andrew's Clermiston)	1 Edington Road, Milton of Culcaboc, Inverness IV2 3DB	01463 242426
Henderson, Roderick B.	1973	1982	(Kingswells)	5 Holm Park, Inverness IV2 4XT	01463 224022
Macaskill, Duncan	1952	1974	(Lochs-in-Bernera)	71 Smithton Park, Inverness IV2 7PD	01463 791376
Macritchie, Ian M. BSc BD STM PhD	1987	1998	Hospital Chaplain: Inverness Hospitals	7 Merlin Crescent, Inverness IV2 3TE	01463 235204
Morrison, Hector BSc BD MTh	1981	1994	Lecturer: Highland Theological College	24 Oak Avenue, Inverness IV2 4NX	01463 238561
Stirling, G. Alan S. MA	1960	1999	(Leochel Cushnie and Lynturk linked with Tough)	97 Lochlaan Road, Culloden, Inverness IV2 7HS	01463 798313
Wilson, Ian M.	1988	1993	(Cawdor with Croy and Dalcross)	3 Kilravock Crescent, Nairn IV12 4QZ	01667 452977
Wilson, John M. MA	1964	1979	(Adviser: Religious Education)	25 Crown Drive, Inverness IV2 3QF	01463 240855

INVERNESS ADDRESSES

Inverness

Crown	Kingsmills Road x Midmills Road.
Dalneigh and Bona	St Mary's Avenue
East	Academy Street x Margaret Street
Hilton	Druid Road x Tomatin Road
Kinmylies	Kinmylies Way
Ness Bank	Ness Bank x Castle Road
St Columba High	Bank Street x Fraser Street
St Stephen's	Old Edinburgh Road x Southside Road
Old High	Church Street x Church Lane
Trinity	Huntly Place x Upper Kessock Street
West	Huntly Street x Greig Street

Nairn

Old	Academy Street x Seabank Road
St Ninian's	High Street x Queen Street

(38) LOCHABER

Meets at Caol, Fort William, in Kilmallie Church Hall, on the first Tuesday of each month except January, May, July and August when there is no meeting.

Clerk: REV. ALAN RAMSAY MA   MacIntosh Manse, 26 Riverside Park, Lochyside, Fort William PH33 7RB   01397 702054

Acharacle (H) linked with Ardnamurchan

Vacant   Acharacle, Argyll PH36 4JU   01967 431665

Ardgour linked with Strontian James A. Carmichael LTh	1976		Ardgour, Fort William PH33 7AH	01855 841230
Ardnamurchan See Acharacle				
Arisaig and the Small Isles Vacant			Mid Road, Arisaig, Inverness-shire PH39 4NJ	01687 450227
Duror (H) linked with Glencoe St Munda's (H) Anne M. Jones (Mrs) BD	1998		Ballachulish, Argyll PA39 4JG	01855 811998
Fort Augustus linked with Glengarry Vacant Alan H.W. Lamb BA MTh (Assoc)	1959	1992	Fort Augustus, Inverness-shire PH32 4BH Millfield Cottage, Market Hill, Fort Augustus PH32 4DS	01320 366210 01320 366605
Fort William: Duncansburgh (H) linked with Kilmonivaig Donald A. MacQuarrie BSc BD	1979	1990	Fort William, Inverness-shire PH33 6BA	01397 702297
Fort William: MacIntosh Memorial (H) Alan Ramsay MA	1967		26 Riverside Park, Lochyside, Fort William PH33 7RB	01397 702054
Glencoe St Munda's See Duror				
Glengarry See Fort Augustus				
Kilmallie James A. Munro BD DMS	1979	1994	Corpach, Fort William PH33 7JS	01397 772210
Kilmonivaig See Fort William Duncansburgh				
Kinlochleven (H) linked with Nether Lochaber (H) Vacant			Kinlochleven, Argyll PA40 4QW	01855 831227
Mallaig St Columba and Knoydart Ben Johnstone MA BD	1973	1989	Mallaig, Inverness-shire PH41 4RG	01687 462256
Morvern Alicia Ann Winning MA BD	1984		Lochaline, Morvern, by Oban PA34 5UU	01967 421267
Nether Lochaber See Kinlochleven				
Strontian See Ardgour				

Anderson, David M. MSc FBCO	1984 1995	Auxiliary	1 Dumfries Place, Fort William PH33 6UQ	01397 702091
Beaton, Janesina (Miss) DCS		(Deaconess)	"Fairhills", Fort Augustus PH32 4DS	01320 366252

Donaldson, Moses	1972 2000	(Fort Augustus with Glengarry)	"Tabgha", 10 Garden Place, Beauly, IV4 7AN	01463 783701
Gillies, Hugh M. MA JP	1939 1980	(Fort Augustus)	4 Broadstone Park, Inverness IV2 3LA	
MacLean, Hector A.M. MA	1937 1978	(Duror with Glencoe)	Gearra Beag, Duror, Argyll PA38 4BW	01631 74215
Millar, John L. MA BD	1981 1990	(Fort William Duncansburgh with Kilmonivaig)	7 Orchard Gardens, Strathaven ML10 6UN	

LOCHABER Communion Sundays

Acharacle	1 Mr., Je., Sp., Dc.	Fort William		Kilmonivaig	1 My., Nv.
Ardgour	1 Je., Sp., Dc., E.	Duncansburgh	1 Ap., Je., Oc.	Kinlochleven	1 Fb., Ap., Je., Oc., Dc.
Ardnamurchan	1 Ap., Au., Dec.	M'Intosh Memorial	1 Mr., Je., Sp., Dc.	Mallaig	4 My., 3 Nv.
Arisaig and Moidart	1 My., Nv.	Glencoe	1 Ap., Oc.	Morvern	E., 1 Jl., 4 Sp., 1 Dc.
Duror	2 Jn., 3 Nv.	Glengarry	1 Ja., Ap., Jl., Oc.	Nether Lochaber	1 Ap., Oc.
Fort Augustus	2 My., 4 Oc.	Kilmallie	3 Mr., My., Sp., 1 Dc.	Strontian	1 Je., Sp. Dc.

(39) ROSS

Meets in Dingwall on the first Tuesday of each month, except January, May, July and August.

Clerk: REV. THOMAS M. McWILLIAM MA BD   The Manse, Contin, Strathpeffer, Ross-shire IV14 9ES   01997 421380
[e-mail: gmc77@dial.pipex.com]

Alness
Ronald Morrison BD   1996   27 Darroch Brae, Alness, Ross-shire IV17 OSD   01349 882238

Avoch linked with Fortrose and Rosemarkie
Samuel Torrens BD   1995   5 Nessway, Fortrose IV10 8SS   01381 620068

Contin
Thomas M. McWilliam MA BD   1964 1997   Contin, Strathpeffer, Ross-shire IV14 9ES   01997 421380

Cromarty
John Tallach MA MLitt   1970 1999   Cromarty, Ross-shire IV11 8YT   01381 600802

Dingwall: Castle Street (H)
Grahame M. Henderson BD   1974 1987   16 Achany Road, Dingwall, Ross-shire IV15 9JB   01349 863167

Congregation / Minister	Year	Address	Telephone
Dingwall: St Clement's (H) Russel Smith BD	1994	8 Castlehill Road, Dingwall IV15 9PB	01349 861011
Fearn Abbey and Nigg with Tarbat Vacant		Fearn, Ross-shire IV20 1TN	01862 832626
Ferintosh Daniel J.M. Carmichael MA BD	1994	Conon Bridge, Ross-shire IV7 8BE	01349 861275
Fodderty and Strathpeffer Ivan C. Warwick MA BD	1980 1999	Strathpeffer, Ross-shire IV14 9DL	01997 421398
Fortrose and Rosemarkie See Avoch			
Invergordon Kenneth Donald Macleod BD CPS	1989 2000	Cromlet Drive, Invergordon, Ross-shire IV18 OBA	01349 852273
Killearnan linked with Knockbain Ian Ramsden	2000	Killearnan, Muir of Ord, Ross-shire IV6 7SQ	01463 870234
Kilmuir and Logie Easter Kenneth J. Pattison MA BD STM	1967 1996	Delny, Invergordon, Ross-shire IV18 0NW [e-mail: ken@thepattisons.fsnet.co.uk]	01862 842280
Kiltearn (H) Donald A. MacSween BD	1991 1998	Evanton, Ross-shire IV16 9UY	01349 830472
Knockbain See Killearnan			
Lochbroom and Ullapool (GD) James Gemmell BD MTh	1999	Ullapool, Ross-shire IV26 2SX	01854 612050
Resolis and Urquhart (T) Alasdair J. MacLennan BD DCE	1979 1994	The Manse, Culbokie, Conon Bridge IV7 8JN	01349 877452
Rosskeen Robert Jones BSc BD	1990	Alness, Ross-shire IV17 OSX	01349 882265
Tain Douglas A. Horne BD	1977	14 Kingsway Ave, Tain, Ross-shire IV19 1BN	01862 894140
Tarbat (T): See Fearn Abbey and Nigg			
Urray and Kilchrist J. Alastair Gordon BD	2000	Muir of Ord, Ross-shire IV6 7TL	01463 870259

Bolster, Richard F. JP	1956 1984	(Killearnan)	c/o 8 Craigray, Kessock, by Inverness IV1 1XH	01463 731337
Buchan, John BD MTh	1968 1993	(Fodderty and Strathpeffer)	"Faithlie", 45 Swanston Avenue, Inverness IV3 6QW	01463 713114
Dupar, Kenneth W. BA BD PhD	1965 1993	(Christ's College, Aberdeen)	The Old Manse, The Causeway, Cromarty IV11 8XJ	01381 600428
James Forsyth LTh	1970 2000	(Fearn Abbey with Nigg Chapelhill)	Rhivs Lodge, Golspie, Sutherland KW10 6DD	
Harries, David A.	1950 1990	(British Sailors Society)	17 Chanonry Crescent, Fortrose IV10 8RH	
Holroyd, Gordon BTh FPhS FSAScot	1959 1993	(Dingwall: St Clement's)	22 Stuarthill Drive, Maryburgh, Dingwall IV15 9HU	01349 863379
Howe, Andrew Y. BTh	1957 1989	(Rosskeen)	Bredon Cottage, Springfield Road, Alness IV17 0XG	01349 882302
Liddell, Margaret (Miss) BD DipTh	1987 1997	(Contin)	20 Wyvis Crescent, Conon Bridge IV7 8BZ	01349 865997
MacAlpine, A.G. MA BD STM	1935 1975	(Tain)	Maybank, St Catherine's Road, Forres IV36 0LL	01309 672027
Macdonald, Norman MA BD	1937 1970	(Aberdeen Trinity)	44 Alder Drive, Perth PH1 3EU	
McGowan, Andrew T.B. BD STM PhD	1979 1994	Highland Theological College	6 Kintail Place, Dingwall IV15 9RL	01862 89305
Mackenzie, A. Ian	1945 1986	(Glenelg with Glenshiel with Kintail)	4 St Mary's Well, Tain IV19 1LS	
Mackenzie, Iain MA BD	1967 2000	(Tarbat)	3 Southern Beaches, Sandbank, Dunoon	
Mackinnon, R.M. LTh	1968 1995	(Kilmuir and Logie Easter)	27 Riverford Crescent, Conon Bridge, Ross-shire IV7 8HL	01349 866293
Maclennan, William	1952 1981	(Lochbroom and Ullapool)	8 Firthview Road, Inverness IV3 8LZ	01463 225253
Macleod, Donald R. MA	1953 1986	(Ferintosh)	1 Top Street, Conon Bridge IV7 8BH	01349 863160
Macleod, John MA	1959 1993	(Resolis and Urquhart)	"Benview" 19 Balvaird, Muir of Ord IV6 7RG	01463 871286
Niven, William W. BTh	1982 1995	(Alness)	4 Obsdale Park, Alness IV17 0XG	01349 882427
Rutherford, Ellon B. (Miss) MBE DCS		(Deaconess)	41 Duncanston, Conon Bridge IV7 8JB	01349 877439

(40) SUTHERLAND

Meets at Lairg on the first Tuesday of March, May, September, November and December and on the first Tuesday of June at the Moderator's Church.

Clerk: REV.J.L. GOSKIRK LTh		The Manse, Lairg, Sutherland IV27 4EH	01549 402373

Altnaharra and Farr			
John M. Wilson MA BD	1965 1998	Bettyhill Sutherland,by Thurso, Caithness KW14 7SZ	01641 521208
Assynt and Stoer			
Frederick R. Hurst MA	1965 1971	Lochinver, by Lairg, Sutherland IV27 4LH	01571 844342
Clyne (H)			
Ian W. McCree BD	1971 1987	Golf Road, Brora, Sutherland KW9 6QS [e-mail: Ian@McCree1freeserve.co.uk]	01408 621239
Creich linked with Rosehall			
Olsen, Heather C. (Miss) BD	1978 1999	Bonar Bridge, Ardgay, Sutherland IV24 3EB	01863 766256

Dornoch Cathedral (H)
Susan M. Brown (Mrs) BD DipMin   1985   1998   Dornoch, Sutherland IV25 3HN   01862 810296
[e-mail: revsbrown@aol.com]

Durness and Kinlochbervie
John T. Mann BSc BD   1990   1998   Kinlochbervie, by Lairg, Sutherland IV27 4RG   01971 521287
[e-mail: JTMKLB@aol.com]

Eddrachillis
John MacPherson BSc BD   1993   Scourie, by Lairg, Sutherland IV27 4TQ   01971 502431

Golspie
George M. Donaldson MA BD   1984   1989   Fountain Road, Golspie, Sutherland KW10 6TH   01408 633295

Kildonan and Loth Helmsdale (H)
Melvyn James Griffiths BTh.DipTheol   1978   1996   Helmsdale, Sutherland KW8 6HT   01431 821674
[e-mail: thehavyn@tesco.net]

Kincardine Croick and Edderton
Alan Watt MTh   1996   Ardgay, Sutherland IV24 3BG   01863 766285
[e-mail: ALAN@AWATTARDGAY.FREESERVE.CO.UK]

Lairg (H) linked with Rogart (H)
J.L. Goskirk LTh   1968   Lairg, Sutherland IV27 4EH   01549 402373

Melness and Tongue (H)
John F. Mackie BD   1979   2000   Tongue, by Lairg, Sutherland IV27 4XL   01847 611230

Rogart See Lairg
Rosehall See Creich

Rettie, James A. BTh   1981 1999   2 Trentham Drive, Westhill, Inverness IV1 2TQ   01463 798896
Wilson, Mary D. (Mrs) (Aux) RGN SCM DTM   1990 1998   The Manse, Bettyhill Sutherland, by Thurso Caithness KW14 7SZ   01641 521208

(41) CAITHNESS

Meets alternately at Wick and Thurso on the first Tuesday of Feburary, March, May, September, November and December, and the third Tuesday of June.

Clerk: MRS. MYRTLE GILLIES, MBE   Ardachadh, Forsinard, Caithness KW13 6YT   01641 571241

Congregation / Minister	Ord.	Ind.	Address	Telephone
Berriedale and Dunbeath linked with Latheron Vacant			Ross Manse, Dunbeath, Caithness KW6 6EA	01593 731228
Bower linked with Watten C.J. Grant Bell	1983	1999	Watten, Caithness KW1 5YN	01955 621220
Canisbay linked with Keiss Iain Macnee LTh BD MA PhD	1975	1998	Canisbay, Wick, KW1 4YH	01955 611309
Dunnet linked with Olrig James F. Todd BD CPS	1984	1999	Olrig, Castletown, Thurso KW14 8TP	01847 821221
Halkirk and Westerdale Kenneth Warner BD DA DipTD	1981		Abbey Manse, Halkirk, KW12 6UU	01847 831227
Keiss See Canisbay				
Latheron See Berriedale and Dunbeath				
Lybster and Bruan (T) Iain A. Sutherland BSc BD	1996		Central Manse, Lybster, Caithness KW3 6BN	01593 721231
Olrig See Dunnet				
Reay linked with Strathy and Halladale (H) Vacant			Reay, Thurso, KW14 7RE	01847 811272
Strathy and Halladale See Reay				
Thurso: St Peter's and St Andrew's (H) Kenneth S. Borthwick MA BD	1983	1989	46 Rose Street, Thurso KW14 7HN	01847 895186
Thurso: West (H) Ronald Johnstone BD	1977	1984	Thorkel Road, Thurso KW14 7LW	01847 892663
Watten See Bower				
Wick: Bridge Street A.A. Roy MA BD	1955		Mansfield, Miller Avenue, Wick KW1 4DF	01955 602822
Wick: Old (H)(L) Vacant			Miller Avenue, Wick, KW1 4DF	01955 604252

Wick: Pulteneytown (H) and Thrumster
William F. Wallace BDS BD   1961 1998   Coronation Street, Wick KW1 5LS   01955 603166

Mappin, Michael G. BA   Mundays, Banks Road, Watten, by Wick KW1 5YL   01955 621720

CAITHNESS –
Communion Sundays

Berriedale and Dunbeath	2 Mr., Je., Sp., Dc.	
Bower	1 Jl., Dc.	(Bower with Watten) 1968 1974
Canisbay	1 Je., Nv.	
Dunnet	last My., Nv.	
Halkirk	Oct., Ap., Jl.	
Westerdale	Ap., Oc., 4 Dc.	
Keiss	1 My., 3 Nv.	
Latheron	1 Jl., 2 Sp., 1 Dec., 2 Mr.	
Lybster and Bruan	3 Je., Nv., E.	
Olrig	last My., Nv.	
Reay	last Ap., Sp.	
Strathy and Halladale	1 Jn., last Nv.	
Thurso		
St Peter's and St Andrew's	1 Fb., Ap., Je., Sp., Nv.	
West	4 Mr., Je., Nv.	
Watten	1 Jl., Dc.	
Wick		
Bridge Street	1 Ap., Oc.	
Old	4 Ap., Sp.	
Pulteneytown and Thrumster	1 Mr., Je., Sp., Dc.	

(42) LOCHCARRON – SKYE

Meets in Kyle on the first Tuesday of each month except January, May, July and August.

Clerk: REV. ALLAN J. MACARTHUR BD   High Barn, Croft Road, Lochcarron, Ross-shire IV54 8YA   01520 722278 (Tel)
[e-mail: a.macarthur@btinternet.com]   01520 722674 (Fax)

Applecross, Lochcarron and Torridon(GD)
Vacant
David Scott BTh (Assoc)   1994   Lochcarron, Ross-shire IV54 8YD   01520 744263
Applecross, Ross-shire IV54 8LU

Bracadale and Duirinish (GD)
Gary Wilson BD   1996   2000   Dunvegan, Isle of Skye IV55 8WQ   01470 521457

Gairloch and Dundonnell
Derek Morrison   2000   The Manse, Gairloch, Ross-shire IV21 2BT   01445 712053 (Tel/Fax)

Glenelg and Kintail
Donald Beaton MA BD MTh   1961   1988   Inverinate, Kyle, Ross-shire IV40 8HE   01599 511245

Kilmuir and Stenscholl (GD)
Ivor MacDonald BSc MSc BD   1993   2000   Staffin, Isle of Skye IV51 9JX   01470 562759 (Tel/Fax)

Lochalsh
Vacant — Kyle, Ross-shire IV40 8DA — 01599 534294

Lochcarron and Sheildaig See Applecross

Portree (GD)
John Ferguson LTh BD DD — 1973 1980 — Viewfield Road, Portree, Isle of Skye IV51 9ES — 01478 612019 (Tel/Fax)

Snizort (H)(GD)
Donald MacLeod LTh — 1988 — Snizort, Portree, Isle of Skye IV51 9XE — 01470 532260 (Tel/Fax)

Torridon and Kinlochewe See Applecross

Strath and Sleat (GD)
Iain M.A. Reid BD — 1990 — Broadford, Isle of Skye IV49 9AA
John Nicolson BD DipMin (Assoc) — 1997 — The Manse, The Glebe, Kilmore, Sleat, Sleat, Isle of Skye IV44 8RG — 01471 822538 (Tel/Fax) 01471 844469 [e-mail: jnico84967@aol.com]

Macarthur, Allan J. BD	1973 1998	(Applecross, Lochcarron and Torridon)	High Barn, Croft Road, Lochcarron, Ross-shire, IV54 8YA	Tel 01520 722278 Fax 01520 722674
McCulloch, Alan J.R.	1990 1995	Chaplain: Army	IRHF, BFPO 38	
MacDonald, Kenneth	1965 1992	(Associate: Applecross l/w Lochcarron)	Tigharry, Main Street, Lochcarron, Ross-shire IV54	01520 722433
MacDougall, Angus	1940 1982	(Sleat)	Tigh Ard, Earlish, by Portree, Isle of Skye, IV51 9XL	01470 542466
Mackinnon, Duncan	1956 1989	(Plockton and Kyle)	7 Garth Road, Inverness IV2 4DA	01463 230971
MacLeod, R. BA MBA BD	1994 1998	Chaplain: Royal Navy	32 Cross Keys Close, Norton, Fitzwarren, Taunton TA2 6QE	01823 325120
Matheson, James G. MA BD DD	1936 1979	(Portree)	10 Husabost, Dunvegan, Isle of Skye IV49	01470 511335
Ritchie, Walter M.	1973 1999	(Uphall South)	"Strathardle", Fernilea, Carbost, Isle of Skye IV47 8SJ	01478 640458
Williamson, Tom MA BD	1941 1982	(Dyke with Edinkillie)	16 Cove, Inverasdale, Poolewe, Achnasheen IV22 2LT	01445 781423

LOCHCARRON – SKYE
Communion Sundays

Applecross	1 Jl.	Kilmuir	1 Mr., Sp.	Portree	E., P., X., 2 Mr., Au., 1 Nv.
Bracadale	3 Mr., Sp.	Kintail	3 Ap., Jl.	Sleat	2 Je., Dc.
Duirinish	3 Ja., E., 2 Je., 3 Sep.	Lochalsh and Stromeferry	4 Je., Sp., X., E.	Snizort	1 Je., Dc.
Dundonnell	4 Je.	Lochcarron and Shieldaig	E., 3 Je., 1 Oc.	Stenscholl	1 Je., Dec.
Gairloch	3 Je., Nv.	Plockton and Kyle	2 My., 1 Oc.	Strath	1 Mr., Au.
Glenelg	2 Je., Nv.			Torridon and Kinlochewe	2 My.
Glenshiel	1 Jl.				

(43) UIST

Meets on the fourth Wednesday of January, March, September and November in Lochmaddy and the fourth Wednesday of June in Leverburgh.

Clerk:	REV. MURDO SMITH MA BD	Scarista, Isle of Harris HS3 3HX [e-mail: gmw88@dial.pipex.com]		01859 550200
Barra (GD) John D. Urquhart BA BD	1998	2000	Cuithir, Castlebay, Isle of Barra HS9 5XD [e-mail: JUrquh8218@aol.com]	01871 810230
Benbecula (GD)(H) Kenneth J. Macpherson BD	1988	1998	Griminish, Isle of Benbecula HS7 5QA	01870 602180
Bernera (GE) (H) Vacant			Isle of Berneray, Lochmaddy, Isle of North Uist HS6 5BD	01876 540234
Carinish (GD) (H) Thomas J.R. Mackinnon LTh DipMin	1996	1998	Clachan, Isle of North Uist HS6 5HD [e-mail: TMackinnon@aol.com]	01876 580219
Kilmuir and Paible (GE) Fergus J. MacBain BD DipMin	1999		Paible, Isle of North Uist HS6 5ED	01876 510310
Lochmaddy and Trumisgarry (GD) Angus MacDonald BSc BD	1995		Lochmaddy, Isle of North Uist HS6 5AA [e-mail: angus@lochmaddychurch.freeserve.co.uk]	01876 500414
Manish-Scarista (GD) (H) Murdo Smith MA BD	1988		Scarista, Isle of Harris HS3 3HX [e-mail: gmw88@dial.pipex.com]	01859 550200
South Uist (GD) James B. Lawson MA BD	1961	1998	Daliburgh, Isle of South Uist HS8 5SS [e-mail: jlawson18@compuserve.com]	01878 700265
Tarbert (GE) (H) Norman MacIver BD	1976	1988	Tarbert, Isle of Harris HS3 3DF	01859 502231

MacInnes, David MA BD	1966	1999	(Kilmuir and Paible)	9 Golf View Road, Kinmylies, Inverness IV3 8SZ	01859 502310
Macrae, D.A. JP MA	1942	1988	(Tarbert)	5 Leverhulme Road, Tarbert, Isle of Harris HS3 3DD	01859 540288
			(Deacon)	6 Park View Terrace, Isle of Scalpay, Tarbert, Isle of Harris HS4 3XX	
Muir, Alexander MA BD	1982	1996	(Carinish)	14 West Mackenzie Park, Inverness IV2 3ST	01463 712096
Smith, John M.	1956	1992	(Lochmaddy)	Hamersay, Clachan, Isle of North Uist HS6 5HD	01876 580332

UIST
Communion Sundays

Barra	Easter, Pentecost, Christmas	Kilmuir and Paible	1 Jn., 3 Nv.
Benbecula	2 Mr., Sp.	Lochmaddy and Trumisgarry	4 Jn., Oc.
Bernera	2 Jl. Nv.	Manish-Scarista	3 Ap., 1 Oc.
Carinish	4 Mr., Au.		

South Uist – Iochdar		1 Mr.
Howmore		1 Jn.
Daliburgh		1 Sp.
Tarbert		2 Mr., 3 Sp.

(44) LEWIS

Meets at Stornoway, in St Columba's Church Hall, on the first Tuesday of February, March, April, June, September, November and December.

Clerk: REV. THOMAS S. SINCLAIR MA BD — Martin's Memorial Manse, Matheson Road, Stornoway, Isle of Lewis HS1 2LR [e-mail:gof39@dial.pipex.com] — 01851 702206 / 07780 925 080 (Mbl)

Barvas (GD) (H)
Vacant — Barvas, Isle of Lewis HS2 0QY [e-mail: ivormacd@aol.com] — 01851 840218

Carloway (GD) (H)
Murdo M. Campbell BD DipMin — 1997 — Carloway, Isle of Lewis HS2 9AU [e-mail: cam204576@aol.com] — 01851 643255

Cross Ness (GE) (H)
Vacant — Swainbost, Ness, Isle of Lewis HS2 0TB — 01851 810375

Kinloch (GE) (H)
Donald Angus MacLennan — 1975 1989 — Laxay, Lochs, Isle of Lewis HS2 9LA — 01851 830218 / 07799 668 270 (Mbl)

Knock (GE) (H)
James Macdonald LTh CPS 1984 Garrabost Point, Isle of Lewis HS2 0PW 01851 870917

Lochs-in-Bernera (GD) (H)
Vacant Bernera, Isle of Lewis HS2 9LU 01851 612371

Lochs-Crossbost (GD) (H)
Andrew W.F. Coghill BD DPS 1993 Leurbost, Lochs, Isle of Lewis HS2 9NS [e-mail: andcoghill@aol.com] 01851 860243 (Tel/Fax) 07776 480 748 (Mbl)

Stornoway: High (GE) (H)
William B. Black MA BD 1972 1998 Goathill Road, Stornoway HS1 9NJ 01851 703106

Stornoway: Martin's Memorial (H)
Thomas Suter Sinclair MA BD 1966 1976 Matheson Road, Stornoway HS1 2LR [e-mail:gof39@dial.pipex.com] 01851 702206 07780 925 080 (Mbl)

Stornoway: St Columba (GD) (H)
Vacant Lewis Street, Stornoway HS1 2JF 01851 703350

Uig (GE)
William Macleod 1957 1964 Miavaig, Uig, Isle of Lewis HS2 9HW 01851 672216 (Tel/Fax)

Name		Years	Address	Telephone
Macaulay, Donald OBE JP	(Park)	1968 1992	6 Kirkibost, Bernera, Isle of Lewis HS2 9RD	01851 612341
Macdonald, Alexander	(Cross Ness)	1957 1991	5 Urquhart Gardens, Stornoway, Isle of Lewis HS1 2TX	01851 702825
MacRitchie, Murdanie	(Acharacle)	1958 1969	15A New Garrabost, Isle of Lewis HS2 OPR	01851 870763
MacSween, Norman	(Kinloch)	1952 1986	7 Balmerino Drive, Stornoway, Isle of Lewis HS1 2TD	01851 703369
Montgomery, Donald J.	(Deacon)		17 Murray Place, Stornoway, Isle of Lewis HS1 2JB	01851 704346
Morrison, Alexander	(Barvas)	1952 1973	Ceol Mara, Marig, Isle of Harris HS3 3AG	01859 502267

LEWIS
Communion Sundays

Barvas	3 Mr., Sp.	Lochs-Crossbost	4 Mr., Sp.	Stornoway	
Carloway	1 Mr., last Sp.			St Columba	3 Fb., last Au.,
Cross, Ness	2 Mr., Oc.	Stornoway			Thurs before Easter,
Kinloch	3 Mr., 2 Je., 2 Sp.	High	3 Fb., last Au.		and before Remembrance
Knock	1 Ap., Nv.	Martin's Memorial	3 Fb., last Au.	Uig	3 Je., 1 Sp.
Lochs-in-Bernera	1 Ap., 2 Sp.				

(45) ORKNEY

Meets at Kirkwall, in the Town Hall, on the first Tuesday of September, December and February, on the second Tuesday of October, on the fourth Tuesday of April, and on the third Tuesday in June.

Clerk: REV. TREVOR G. HUNT BA BD

The Manse, Finstown, Orkney KW17 2EG
[e-mail: (personal) TghOrkney@aol.com]
[e-mail: (Presbytery) prsb.orkney@dial.pipex.co.uk]
[Internet: http://members.aol.com/OrkneyPrsb/index.htm]

01856 761328   (Tel/Fax)
07799 404227   (Mbl)

Birsay linked with Harray and Sandwick

Deerness linked with Holm linked with St Andrews
Joan H. Craig (Miss) MTheol   1986   1993

Holm, Orkney KW17 2SD
[e-mail: JoanHCraig@compuserve.com]

01856 781422   (Tel/Fax)

Eday linked with Stronsay Moncur Memorial (H)
Joyce Keyes (Mrs)   1996

Stronsay, Orkney KW17 2AF

01857 616311

Evie linked with Firth linked with Rendall
Trevor G. Hunt BA BD   1986

Finstown, Orkney KW17 2EG
[e-mail: TghOrkney@aol.com]
[Internet: http://members.aol.com/OrkneyEFR/index.htm]

01856 761328   (Tel/Fax)
07799 404227   (Mbl)

Firth See Evie

Flotta linked with Hoy and Walls (T)
Vacant

South Isles Manse, Longhope, Stromness, Orkney KW16 3PG

01856 701325

Harray and Sandwick See Birsay
Holm See Deerness
Hoy and Walls See Flotta

Kirkwall: East
Allan McCafferty BSc BD   1993

Thom Street, Kirkwall, Orkney KW15 1PF
[e-mail: 106611.440@compuserve.com]

01856 875469

Kirkwall: St Magnus Cathedral (H)
Ronald Ferguson MA BD ThM — 1972 1990 — Berstane Road, Kirkwall, Orkney KW15 1NA
[e-mail: ronferguson@clara.co.uk] — 01856 873312 (Tel/Fax)

[Eleanor Morson (Mrs) (Assist)
Scottish Episcopal Church — The Rectory, Dundas Crescent, Kirkwall, Orkney KW15 1JQ — 01856 872024]

North Ronaldsay linked with Sanday (H)
Vacant — Sanday, Orkney KW17 2BW — 01857 600429

Orphir (H) linked with Stenness (H)
Thomas L. Clark BD — 1985 — Stenness, Stromness, Orkney KW16 3HH — 01856 761331

Papa Westray linked with Westray
Iain D. MacDonald BD — 1993 — The Manse, Rapness, Westray, Orkney KW17 2DE
[e-mail: macdonald@rapnessmanse.freeserve.co.uk] — 01857 677357 (Tel/Fax) / 07710 443780 (Mbl)

Rendall See Evie

Rousay
Vacant

St Andrew's See Deerness
Sanday See North Ronaldsay

Shapinsay
Joyce Lynn (Mrs) MIPM BD — 1995 1999 — Shapinsay, Balfour, Orkney KW17 2EA — 01856 711332

South Ronaldsay and Burray
Vacant — St Margaret's Hope, Orkney KW17 2RN — 01856 831288

Stromness (H)
Fiona L. Lillie (Mrs) BA BD MLitt — 1995 1999 — 5 Manse Lane, Stromness, Orkney KW16 3AP — 01856 850203

Stronsay See Eday
Westray See Papa Westray

Brown, R. Graeme BA BD — 1961 1998 — (Birsay with Rousay) — Bring Deeps, Orphir, Orkney KW17 2LX
[e-mail: grasibrown@bringdeeps.fsnet.co.uk] — (Tel/Fax) 01856 811707

Cant, H.W.M. MA BD STM — 1951 1990 — (Kirkwall St Magnus Cathedral) — Quoylobs, Holm KW17 2RY — 01856 781300

Ward, Michael J. BSc BD PhD — 1983 1999 — Community Minister — Ploverhall, Deerness, Orkney KW17 2QJ
[e-mail: revmw@aol.com] — 01856 741349 / (Mbl) 07788 817 190

(46) SHETLAND

Meets at Lerwick on the first Tuesday of March, April, June, September, October, November and December.

Clerk: REV. CHARLES H. M. GREIG MA BD   The Manse, Sandwick, Shetland, ZE2 9HW   01950 431244
[e-mail: c.greig@bosinternet.com]

Burra Isle linked with Tingwall
Vacant — Park Neuk, Meadowfield Place, Scalloway ZE1 0UE — 01595 880865

Delting linked with Nesting and Lunnasting
Winnie Munson (Ms) BD   1996 — The Manse, Grindwell, Brae, Shetland ZE2 9QJ — 01806 522219

Dunrossness and St Ninians inc Fair Isle linked with Sandwick Cunningsburgh and Quarff
Charles H.M. Greig MA BD   1976 1997 — The Manse, Sandwick, Shetland ZE2 9HW [e-mail: c.greig@bosinternet.com] — 01950 431244

Fetlar linked with Yell
Vacant — Mid Yell, Shetland ZE2 9BN — 01957 702283

Lerwick and Bressay
James A.M. Dowswell   1991 — The Manse, St Olaf Street, Lerwick, Shetland ZE1 0ES — 01595 692125

Nesting and Lunnasting See Delting

Northmavine
Alice H. Kirkpatrick (Miss) MA BD FSAScot   1987 — Northmavine Manse, Hillswick, Shetland ZE2 9RW — 01806 503223

Sandsting and Aithsting linked with Walls and Sandness
William J. McMillan CA LTh BD   1969 1997 — Westside Manse, Effirth, Bixter, Shetland ZE2 9LY — 01595 810386

Sandwick, Cunningsburgh and Quarff See Dunrossness and St Ninian's

Tingwall See Burra Isle

Unst
John L. McNab MA BD   1997 — The Manse, Baltasound, Unst, Shetland ZE2 9DZ — 01957 711335

Walls See Sandsting and Aithsting

Whalsay and Skerries

Irene A. Charlton (Mrs) BTh   1994 1997   The Manse, Marrister, Symbister, Whalsay, Shetland ZE2 9AE   01806 566767
[e-mail: irene.charlton@virgin.net]

Yell See Fetlar

Blair, James N.	1962	1986	(Sandsting and Aithsting with Walls)		01950 431472
Smith, Catherine (Mrs) DCS	1964	1998	Presbytery Assistant	2 Swinister, Sandwick, Shetland ZE2 9HH	01595 810207
Williamson, Magnus J. C.	1982	1999	(Fetlar with Yell)	21 Lingaro, Bixter, Shetland ZE2 9NN	01595 880023
Wilson, W. Stewart DA	1980	1997	(Kirkcudbright)	Creek Haven, Houll Road, Scalloway, Shetland ZE1 0XA	01595 760273
				Aesterhoull, Fair Isle, Shetland ZE2 9JU	

(47) ENGLAND

Meets at London, in Crown Court Church, on the second Tuesday of March and December and at St Columba's Pont Street on the second Tuesday of June and October.

Clerk: REV. W.A. CAIRNS BD   St Columba's Church, Pont Street, London SW1X OBD   020 7584 2321 (Home)
[e-mail: office@stcolumbas.org.uk]   020 7373 1823
020 7584 5446 (Fax)

Corby: St Andrew's (H)
Vacant   -   6 Honiton Gardens, Corby NN18 8BW   01536 203175

Corby: St Ninian's (H) (01536 265245)
Alan Sharp BSc BD   1980 1989   46 Glyndebourne Gardens, Corby NN18 0PZ   01536 741179
[e-mail: alansharp@compuserve.com]

Guernsey: St Andrew's in the Grange (H)
David Donaldson MA BD   1969 2000   The Manse, Le Villocq, Castel Guernsey   01481 57345

Jersey: St Columba's (H)
James G. Mackenzie BA BD   1980 1997   18 Claremont Avenue, St Saviour, Jersey   01534 30659
[e-mail: jim@jgmackenzie.softnet.co.uk]

Liverpool: St Andrew's
Continued Vacancy
Session Clerk: E. Graham (Mr)   53 Sidmouth Street, London WC1H 8JB   0151 525 4496

London: Crown Court (H) (020 7836 5643)
Vacant   0207 278 5022
Timothy Fletcher BA FCMA (Aux)   1998   37 Hareston Valley Road, Caterham, Surrey CR3 6HN   01883 340826

London: St Columba's (H) linked with Newcastle St Andrew's (H)

Vacant				St Columba's, Pont Street, London SW1X 0BD	020 7584 2321
W.A. Cairns BD (Assoc)	1978	1980		St Columba's, Pont Street, London SW1X 0BD	020 7584 5446 (Fax)
				[e-mail: office@stcolumbas.org.uk]	
Bayes, Muriel (Mrs) DCS	1954	1984	(Deaconess)	6 Blenheim Close, Rushdean, Northants NN10 9JA	01480 381425
Bowie, A. Glen CBE BA BSc	1993		(Principal Chaplain: RAF)	16 Weir Road, Hemingford Grey, Huntingdon PE18 9EH	01489 557735
Brown, Scott J. BD	1975	1981	Chaplain: RN	HMS Sultan, Portsmouth	
Cameron, R.N.			Chaplain: Community	The Church Centre, Rhine Area Support Unit, BFPO 140	0049 2161 472770
Coulter, David G. BA BD	1989	1994	Chaplain: Army	21 Godley Road, Salisbury, Wilts SP2 8EQ	01722 330436
Craig, Gordon W. MBE MA BD	1972	2000	(Chaplain: RN)	The Round House, Venterden, Stoke Climsland, Callington, Cornwall PL17 8PD	01579 370195
Davison, Charles F. MA	1947	1987	(Guernsey St Andrew's in the Grange)	Maryfield, Green Lanes, St Peter Port, Guernsey C1	01481 27446
Drummond, J.S. MA	1946	1978	(Corby St Ninian's)	77 Low Road, Hellesdon, Norwich NR6 5AG	01603 417736
Duncan, Denis M. BD PhD	1944	1986	(Editor: *The British Weekly*)	1 Cranbourne Road, London N10 2BT	020 8883 1831
Fyall, Robert S. MA BD	1986	1989	Tutor: St John's College, Durham	7 Briardene, Durham DH1 4QU	
Hood, Adam I. J. MA BD DPhil	1989		Lecturer	Queen's Foundation, Somerset Road, Birmingham B15 2QH [e-mail: adamhood1@hotmail.com]	0121 452 2619
Hughes, O. Tudor MBE BA	1934	1976	(Guernsey St Andrew's in the Grange)	4 Belcher Court, Dorchester on Thames, Oxon	01865 340779
Jolly, Andrew J. BD	1989	1996	Chaplain: RAF	Chaplaincy Centre, RAF Halton, Aylesbury, Bucks HP22 5PG	01296 623535 (ext 6374)
Lupton, George L. MA BD	1955	1997	(Guernsey St Andrew's in the Grange)	6 Clos de Beauvoir, Rue Cohu, Guernsey GY5 7TE	01481 54285
MacDonald, James W. BD	1976	1990	Principal Chaplain: British Sailors' Society	43 Beattie Rise, Hedge End, Southampton SO3 4OJ	01489 790106
McEnhill, Peter BD PhD	1992	1996	Lecturer	Westminster College, Madingley Road, Cambridge CB3 0AA	01223 353997
Macfarlane, Peter T. BA LTh	1970	1994	(Chaplain: Army)	Caen na Coille, 42 Muirs, Kinross KY13 7AU	
McIndoe, John H. MA BD STM DD	1966	2000	(London: St. Columba's with Newcastle St. Andrew's)	5 Dunlin, Westerlands Park, Glasgow G12 0FE	0141 579 1366
Majcher, Philip L. BD1	1982	1987	Chaplain: Army	HQ 3rd Infantry Brigade BFPO 809	01762 391027
Martin, A.M. BA BD	1989	1989	Chaplain: Army	HQ ARRC, BFPO 40	0049 2161 5655551
Milloy, A. Miller DPE LTh DipTrMan	1979	1998	Regional Secretary: United Bible Societies	United Bible Societies, Allied Dunbar House, East Park, Crawley, West Sussex RH10 6AS	
Mills, Peter W. BD CPS	1984		Chaplain: RAF	Chaplaincy and Welfare Centre, RAF Bruggen, BFPO 25	0049 2163 972517
Morrison, James G. MBE MA	1942	1980	(Rotterdam)	Auchenshiel, Rhonehouse, Castle Douglas DG7 1SA	
Norwood, David W. BA	1948	1980	(Lisbon)	15 Brooklands, Hockley Road, Rayleigh, Essex SS6 8BE	01268 774095
Rae, Scott M. MBE BD CPS	1976	1981	Chaplain: RN	Armed Forces' Chaplaincy Centre, Amport House, Andover, Hants SP11 8BG	01264 773144
Richmond, James MA BD PhD	1956	1994	(Lancaster University)	10 Wallace Lane, Forton, Preston, Lancs PR3 0BA	01524 791705
Stewart, Charles E. BSc BD PhD	1976	2000	(Chaplain of the Fleet)	The Royal Hospital School, Holbrook, Ipswich IP9 2RX	01296 623535 (ext 6374)
Wallace, Donald S.	1950	1980	(Chaplain: RAF)	7 Dellfield Close, Watford, Herts WD1 3BL	01923 223289
White, Earlsley M. BA	1957	1998	(Uddingston: Park)	27 North Lodge, Epsom Cottage, Epsom, Surrey KT17 4JH	01372 821227

ENGLAND – Church Addresses

Corby	Liverpool	London
St Andrew's — Occupation Road	Newcastle	Crown Court — The Western Rooms, Anglican Cathedral — Crown Court WC2
St Ninian's — Beanfield Avenue		St Columba's — Sandyford Road — Pont Street SW1

(48) EUROPE

Clerk: REV. JAMES W. McLEOD MA — 6 Chemin Taverney, 1218 Grand Saconnex, Geneva, Switzerland [e-mail: cofsg@pingnet.ch] — 00 41 22 798 29 09 (Tel/Fax)

Amsterdam John A. Cowie BSc BD	1983	1989	J.W. Brouwersstraat 9, 1071 LH Amsterdam, The Netherlands [e-mail: j.cowie@cable.a2000.nl]	00 31 20 672 2288
Brussels Thomas C. Pitkeathly MA CA BD	1984	1991	23 Square des Nations, 1000 Brussels, Belgium [e-mail:Pitkeathly@compuserve.com]	00 32 2 672 40 56
Budapest Kenneth I MacKenzie BD CPS	1990	1999	St Columba'a Scottish Mission, Vorosmarty utca 51, 1064 Budapest, Hungary Budapest 1112, Olitvany arok 25, Hungary (Manse) [e-mail:mackenzie@mail.datanet.hu]	00 36 1 343 8479 / 00 36 1 246 2258
Costa del Sol linked with Gibraltar John R. Page BD DipMin	1988	1996	11 Calle Margarita Blanca, Fuengirola, Spain	00 34 5 258 8394
Geneva James W. McLeod MA	1965	1994	6 Chemin Taverney, 1218 Grand Saconnex, Geneva, Switzerland [e-mail:cofsg@pingnet.ch]	00 41 22 798 29 09
Gibraltar linked with Costa del Sol John R. Page BD DipMin	1988	1996	29 Scud Hill, Gibraltar	00 350 77040
Lausanne Douglas R. Murray MA BD	1965	1994	26 Avenue de Rumine, 1005 Lausanne, Switzerland [e-mail: scotskirklausanne@bluewin.ch]	00 41 21 323 98 28

Lisbon Gordon Oliver BD	1979	1998	Rua da Arriaga 11, 1200 - 608 Lisbon [e-mail: st.andrewschurch@clix.pt]	00 351 1 3995 7677
Malta Colin A. Westmarland MBE BD	1971	1975	206/3 Old Bakery Street, Valletta, Malta	(Tel/Fax) 00 356 222 643
Paris William M. Reid MA BD	1966	1993	10 Rue Thimmonier, 75009 Paris, France [e-mail: scotskirkparis@free.fr]	00 33 1 48 78 47 94
Rome St Andrew's David F. Huie MA BD	1962	1991	Via XX Settembre 7, 00187 Rome, Italy [e-mail:david.huie@flashnet.it]	(Tel) 00 39 06 482 7627 (Fax) 00 39 06 487 4370
Rotterdam Robert A. Calvert BSc BD	1983	1995	Gelebrem 59, 3068 TJ Rotterdam, The Netherlands [e-mail:Scots-International-Church-@compuserve.com]	00 31 10 220 4199
Joost Pot BSc (Aux)	1992		Rijksstraatweg 12, 2988 BJ Ridderkerk, The Netherlands	00 31 18 042 0894
With Romanian Reformed Church Celia G. Kenny (Mrs) MA MTh	1995	1998	Protestant Theological Institute, RO-3400 Cluj, Piata Avram Iancu 13, Romania [e-mail: celiakenny@aol.com]	
Conference of European Churches Stewart J. Lamont BSc BD	1972	1999	Church and Society Commission, Ecumenical Centre, 174 Rue Joseph II, B-1000 Brussels, Belgium [e-mail: sjl@cec-kek.be] Avenue de Broqueville 140, 1200 Brussels, Belgium (Home)	(Tel) 00 32 2 234 6834 (Fax) 00 32 2 231 14 13 00 32 2 772 71 22
World Alliance of Reformed Churches Paraic Raemonn BA BD	1982	1993	WARC, 150 Route de Ferney, 1211 Geneva 2, Switzerland [e-mail:par@warc.ch]	00 41 22 791 62 43
World Council Secretariat Alan D. Falconer MA BD DLitt	1972	1995	WCC, 150 Route de Ferney, 1211 Geneva 2, Switzerland [e-mail:af@wcc-coe.org]	00 41 22 791 63 37

CORRESPONDING MEMBERS

James M. Brown MA BD	1982		Neustrasse 15, D-4630 Bochum, Germany Institut fur Angelistik,	00 49 234 133 65
R. Graeme Dunphy	1988	1993	Universitatsstrasse 31, D-93053 Regensburg, Germany	

Rhona Dunphy (Mrs)

Professor A.I.C. Heron BD DTheol	1975	1987	University of Erlangen, Kochstrasse 6, D-91054, Erlangen, Germany [e-mail: arheron@theologie.uni-erlangen.de]	00 49 9131 85 2202
Jane Howitt (Miss)			Scripture Union, PO Box 476, LV 1050 Riga, Latvia [e-mail:janesu@com.latnet.lv]	00 371 7 220877
Bertalan Tamas			St. Columba's Scottish Mission, Vorosmarty utca 51, 1064 Budapest, Hungary [e-mail: rch@mail.elender.hu]	00 36 1 343 8479

(Brussels)	A.J. Macleod MA BD	1943	(1974)	27A Cathcart Road, London SW10	
(Brussels)	Charles C. McNeill OBE BD	1962	(1991)	17 All Saints Way, Beachamwell, Swaffham, Norfolk PE37 8BU	
(Gibraltar)	D. Stuart Philip MA	1952	(1990)	6 St Bernard's Crescent, Edinburgh EH4 1NP	0131 332 7499
(Paris)	Bruce Robertson MA BD	1953	(1992)	Old Dairy Cottage, School Lane, Winfrith Newburgh, Dorset DT2 8JX	01305 852050

(49) JERUSALEM

Jerusalem: St Andrew's

| Clarence W. Musgrave BA BD ThM | 1966 | 2000 | PO Box 8619, 91086 Jerusalem, Israel [e-mail: standjer@netvision.net.il] | (Tel) 00 972 2 673 2401 (Fax) 00 972 2 673 1711 |

Tiberias: St Andrew's

| Frederick W. Hibbert BD | 1986 | 1995 | Sea of Galilee Centre, PO Box 104, 14100 Tiberias, Israel [e-mail: scottie@netvision.net.il] | (Tel) 00 972 6 672 1165 (Fax) 00 972 6 679 0145 |

SECTION 6

Additional Lists
of Personnel

LIST A – AUXILIARY MINISTERS

NAME	ORD	ADDRESS	TEL	PR
Anderson, David M. MSc FBCO	1984	1 Dumfries Place, Fort William PH33 6UQ	01397 702091	38
Brown, Elizabeth (Mrs) JP RGN	1996	25 Highfield Road, Scone, Perth PH2 6RN	01738 552391	28
Cloggie, June (Mrs)	1997	8 Trossachs Road, Aberfoyle FK8 3SW	01877 382382	23
Cruikshank, Alistair A.B. MA	1991	2A Chapel Place, Dollar FK14 7DW	01259 742549	23
Davidson, David W.	1987	Grianail, Glenegedale, Port Ellen, Isle of Islay PA42 7AS	01496 302194	19
Durno, Richard C. DSW CQSW	1989	31 Springfield Road, Bishopbriggs G64 1PJ	0141 772 1052	16
Ferguson, Archibald M. MSc PhD CEng FRINA	1989	The Whins, Barrowfield, Cardross G82 5NL	01389 841517	18
Fletcher, Timothy E.G. BA FCMA	1998	37 Hareston Valley Road, Caterham, Surrey CR3 6HN	01883 340826	47
Glass, Alexander OBE MA	1998	Craigton, Tulloch Avenue, Dingwall IV15 9TU	01349 863258	39
Howie, Marion L.K. (Mrs) MA ARCS	1992	51 High Road, Stevenston KA20 3DY	01294 466571	12
Jenkinson, John J. JP LTCL ALCM DipEd DipSen	1991	8 Rosehall Terrace, Falkirk FK1 1PY	01324 625498	22
Kay, Elizabeth (Miss) Dip YCS	1993	1 Kintail Walk, Inchture, Perthshire PH14 9RY	01828 686029	29
McCann, George McD. BSc ATI	1994	Rosbeg, Parsonage Road, Galashiels TD1 3HS	01896 752055	4
MacFadyen, Anne M. (Mrs) BSc BD	1995	295 Mearns Road, Newton Mearns G77 5LT	0141 639 3605	16
Mack, Elizabeth (Miss) Dip PEd	1994	24 Roberts Crescent, Dumfries DG2 7RS	01387 264847	8
Mack, John C. JP	1985	The Willows, Auchleven, Insch AB52 6QD	01464 820387	33
Mailer, Colin	2000	Innis Chonain, Back Row, Polmont FK2 0RD	01324 712401	22
Manson, Eileen (Mrs) DCE	1994	1 Cambridge Avenue, Gourock PA19 1XT	01475 632401	15
Munro, Mary (Mrs) BA	1993	High Barbeth, Leswalt DG9 0QS	01776 870250	9
Paterson, Andrew E. JP	1994	6 The Willows, Kelty KY4 0FQ	01383 830998	24
Paterson, Maureen (Mrs) BSc	1992	91 Dalmahoy Crescent, Kirkcaldy KY2 6TA	01592 262300	25
Pot, Joost BSc	1992	Rijksstraateg 12, 2988 BJ Ridderkerk, The Netherlands	00 31 18 042 0894	48
Ramage, Alistair E. BA	1996	16 Claremont Gardens, Milngavie, Glasgow G62 6PG	0141 956 2897	18
Riddell, Thomas S. BSc CEng FIChemE	1993	4 The Maltings, Linlithgow EH49 6DS	01506 843251	2
Shaw, Catherine A.M. MA	1998	40 Marrygreen Place, Stewarton KA3 5EP	01560 483352	11
Simpson, James H. BSc	1996	11 Claypotts Place, Broughty Ferry DD5 1LG	01382 776520	29
Wandrum, David	1993	42C Clouden Road, Kildrum, Cumbernauld G67 2EW	01236 723288	22
Watson, Jean S. (Miss) MA	1993	29 Strachan Crescent, Dollar FK14 7HL	01259 742872	23
Wilson, Mary D. (Mrs) RGN SCM DTM	1990	The Manse, Bettyhill, Thurso KW14 7SS	01641 521208	40
Wilson, Roy DA ARIBA ARIAS	1986	20 William Ure Place, Bishopbriggs G64 3BH	0141 563 1829	18
Zambonini, James LIA Dip	1997	100 Old Manse Road, Netherton, Wishaw ML2 0EP	01698 350889	17

LIST B – CHAPLAINS TO HM FORCES

NAME	ORD	COM	BCH	ADDRESS
Abeledo, Benjamin J. A BTh DipTh PTh.	1991	1999	A	1 Highlanders, Somme Barracks, Catterick Garrison, N Yorks DL9 3AQ
Aitchison, James W.	1993	1993	A	2 Bn ITC Catterick (EP), Helles Barracks, Catterick, N Yorks DL9 4HH
Britchfield, Alison E. P. (Mrs) MA BD	1987	1992	RN	13 Tregonning Road, Torpoint, Cornwall PH11 2LX
Brown, Scott J. BD	1993	1993	RN	HMS Sultan, Portsmouth
Cameron, R.N.	1975	1981	A	Church Centre, BFPO 40
Connolly, Daniel BD DipTheol DipMin	1983		A	1 A and S H, Redford Barracks, Colinton Road, Edinburgh EH13 0PP
Coulter, David G. BA BD	1989	1994	A	RMCS, Shrivenham, Swindon, Wilts SN6 8LA
Craig, Gordon T. BD DipMin	1988	1988	RAF	Room 34, Whittle Hall, AF Cranwell, NG34 8HB
Craig, Gordon W. MBE MA BD	1972	1972	RN	42 CDO RM, Bickleigh Barracks, Plymouth, Devon PL6 7AJ
Dailly, J.R. BD DipPS	1979	1979	A	DACG, HQ 42(NW) Bde, Fulwood Barracks, Preston PR2 8AA
Jolly, Andrew J. BD CertMin	1983	1996	RAF	Chaplains Centre, RAF Holton, Aylesbury HP22 5PG
Keith, Donald MA BD	1971	1984	RN	Comacchio Gp RM, RM Condor, Arbroath, Angus DD11 3SJ
Kingston, David V.F. BD	1993	1993	A	1 HLDRS, Somme Barracks, Catterick Garrison, N Yorks DL9 34LD
McCulloch, Alen J.R.	1990	1995	A	BRHA, BFPO 30
McFadzean, Iain MA BD	1989	1999	RN	HMS Neptune, Faslane, Helensburgh
Mackenzie, Seoras L. BD	1996	1998	A	1 RHF, BFPO 38
MacLeod, C.A. BD	1996	1996	A	1 Scots Guards, Wellington Barracks, Birdcage Walk, London SW1E 6HQ
MacLeod, Rory A.R. BA BD MBA	1994	1998	RN	Commando Training Establishment, Lympstone, Devon
MacLeod, R.N.	1986	1992	A	Army Training Regiment, Glencorse Barracks, Penicuik EH26 0NP
Majcher, Philip L. BD	1982	1987	A	Senior Chaplain, Sldr Tre, AG Corps Centre, Army Worthy Down, Winchester, Hants SO21 2RG
Martin, A.M. BA BD	1989	1989	A	HQ ARRC, JHQ, BFPO 40
Mills, Peter W. BD CPS	1984	1984	RAF	Chaplaincy Centre, RAF Bruggen, BFPO 25
Murning, John BD	1988	1999	A	38 Regt RE, Claro Bks, Ripon, N Yorks HG4 2DR
Prentice, Donald K. BSc BD	1987	1992	A	IRNF, Fort George, Inverness IV2 7TE
Rae, Scott M. MBE BD CPS	1976	1981	RN	Naval Director, Armer Forces Chaplaincy Navy Centre, Amport House, Andover
Shackleton, Scott J.S. BD	1993	1993	RN	Staff Chaplain Commandant General Royal Navy Marines, RM Stonehouse,Plymouth
Shaw, Duncan LTh CPS	1984	1984	RAF	CSFC Chaplains Office, RAF Lossiemouth, RAF Morayshire IV31 6SD
Whitton, John P. MA BD	1977	1977	A	Assistant Chaplain General, HQ 2nd Division, Craigiehall, South Queensferry EH30 9TN

CHAPLAINS TO HM FORCES (retired)

NAME	ORD	RTD	BCH	ADDRESS
Blakey, Stephen A. BSc BD	1977	1994	(A)	Kingsville, Strichen, Fraserburgh AB43 6SQ
Bowie, A. Glen CBE BA BSc	1954	1984	(RAF)	16 Weir Road, Hemingford Grey, Huntingdon PE18 9EH
Brown, P. MA	1953	1987	(RN)	24 Inchmickery Drive, Dalgety Bay, Fife KY11 5NF
Edwards, Michael S. MA	1982	1996	(A)	Flat 1G, Ascot Court, Dorchester Avenue, Glasgow G12 0BE
Harkness, James CB OBE QHC MA DD	1961	1995	(A)	13 Saxe Coburg Place, Edinburgh EH3 5BR
Huie, David F. MA BD	1962	1991	(RN)	Via XX Settembre 7, 00187 Rome, Italy
Ingram, J.R.	1954	1978	(RAF)	48 Marlee Road, Broughty Ferry DD5 3EX
Macfarlane, Peter T. BA LTh	1970	1994	(A)	42 The Muirs, Kinross KY13 7AU
Neill, Bruce F. MA BD	1966	1996	(RN)	The Manse, Main Street, St Boswells TD6 0BB
Robertson, Matthew LTh	1968	1994	(A)	The Manse, Croy, Inverness IV1 2PH
Shedden, John QHC BD DipPSS	1971	1998	(RAF)	4 Wilton Hill Terrace, Hawick TD9 8BE
Shields, John MBE LTh	1972	1997	(A)	The Manse, Lauder, Berwickshire TD2 6QD
Wallace, Donald S.	1950	1980	(RAF)	7 Dellfield Close, Watford, Herts WD1 3LB

CHAPLAINS TO HM FORCES (Territorial Army)

NAME	ORD	COM	ADDRESS
Barclay, Dr Iain C TD	1976	1982	HQ 2nd Division
Blakey, Stephen A.	1977	1996	32 Sig R (V)
Forsyth, Alex R. TD	1973	1983	71 (AS) Regt RE (V)
Gibson, James M.	1978	1986	205 (S) Fd Hosp (V)
Kinsey, Louis	1991	1992	205 (S) Fd (Hosp) (V)
Thomson, John M.A.	1978	1992	105 Regt RA (V)
Warwick, Ivan C.	1980	1990	51st Highland Regt (V)

CHAPLAINS TO HM FORCES (Army Cadet Force)

Almond, David M.	1996	1998	Glasgow & Lanarkshire Bn.

NAME	ORD	COM	ADDRESS
Andrews, J. Edward	1985	1998	Lothian & Borders Bn
Barclay, Dr Iain C. TD	1976	1996	BW Bn
Campbell, Roderick D.M. TD	1975	1998	Argyll & Sutherland Highlanders Bn
Fisk, E. A.	1996	1999	BW Bn
Goskirk, J. Leslie	1968	1985	1 Hldrs Bn
Homewood, I. Max	1997	1998	Argyll & Sutherland Highlanders Bn.
Sherratt, Arthur	1994	1999	West Lowland Bn
Sutherland, Iain A.	1996	1999	1 Hldrs Bn
Swindells, Sean	1996	1998	2 Hldrs Bn
Whyte, Margaret A.	1988	1997	West Lowland Bn
Wilson, G. N.			Glasgow & Lanarkshire Bn

LIST C – HOSPITAL CHAPLAINS ("Full-Time" Chaplains are listed first in each area)

LOTHIAN

EDINBURGH – LOTHIAN UNIVERSITY HOSPITALS NHS TRUST
ROYAL INFIRMARY [0131 536 3085]
  Rev. Dr Ewan Kelly   29 Buckstone Crescent, Edinburgh EH10 6PJ
  Miss Anne Mulligan   Chaplain's Assistant   1/6 Coxfield, Edinburgh EH11 2SY   0131 536 3086
WESTERN GENERAL HOSPITAL [0131 537 1000]
  Rev. Alexander Young   48 Whiteloch Road, Macmerry EH33 1PG
  Rev. Alistair K. Ridland
LOTHIAN PRIMARY CARE NHS TRUST
ROYAL EDINBURGH HOSPITAL [0131 537 6734]
  Rev. Murray Chalmers   25 Greenbank Road, Edinburgh EH10 5RX
  Mrs Alison Wagstaff   Chaplain's Assistant   27 Cambridge Gardens, Edinburgh EH6 5DH

LIVINGSTON –
WEST LOTHIAN HEALTHCARE N.H.S. TRUST [01506 419666]
  Rev. Thomas Crichton   18 Carlton Terrace, Edinburgh EH7 5DD
  Rev. Dr Georgina Nelson   6 Pentland Park, Craigshill, Livingston EH54 5NR

HOSPICES

			(Tel) / (Fax)
MARIE CURIE CENTRE	Rev. Tom Gordon	Frogston Road West, Edinburgh EH10 7DR	0131 445 2141 / 0131 445 5845

ST COLUMBA'S HOSPICE	Rev. Derek Murray	Challenger Lodge, 15 Boswall Road, Edinburgh EH5 3RW	0131 551 1381
CITY	Rev. Harry Telfer	32 Mayfield Road, Edinburgh EH9 2NJ	0131 667 1629
CORSTORPHINE	Rev. J. William Hill	23 Belgrave Road, Edinburgh EH12 6NG	0131 334 3188
EASTERN GENERAL	Rev. John Tait	52 Pilrig Street, Edinburgh EH6 5AS	0131 554 1842
ROYAL EDINBURGH HOSPITAL	Rev. John Whitley	114 Viewforth, Edinburgh EH10 4LN	0131 229 0133
LIBERTON	Rev. Donald M. Skinner	43 Ravenscroft Street, Edinburgh EH17 8QJ	0131 664 2147
PRINCESS MARGARET ROSE	Rev. Kenneth J. Mackay	122 Sighthill Loan, Edinburgh EH11 4NT	0131 453 6921
ROYAL HOSPITAL FOR SICK CHILDREN	Rev. Andrew Ritchie	202 Colinton Road, Edinburgh EH14 1BP	0131 443 2020
LINLITHGOW ST MICHAEL'S	Rev. D. Graham Leitch	38 Cluny Gardens, Edinburgh EH10 6BN	0131 447 8702
	Rev. John Paterson	St Michael's Manse, Linlithgow EH49 7AL	01506 842195
BELHAVEN	Rev. Laurence H. Twaddle	7 Ashfield Place, Dunbar DH42 1NH	01368 863098
EDENHALL	Rev. Patricia Allen	1 Westgate, Dunbar EH42 1JL	01368 865711
HERDMANFLAT	Rev. William C. Thomas	11 Muirfield Crescent, Gullane EH31 2HN	01620 842415
LOANHEAD	Mrs Susan Duncan	35 Kilmaurs Road, Edinburgh EH16 5DB	0131 667 2995
ROODLANDS	Rev. Kenneth D.F. Walker	The Manse, Athelstaneford, North Berwick EH39 5BE	01620 880378
ROOSLYNLEE	Rev. John W. Fraser	North Manse, Penicuik EH26 8AG	01968 672213
ROSSLYNLEE	Mrs Muriel Willoughby	32 Marchburn Drive, Penicuik EH26 9HE	01968 675249

BORDERS

MELROSE – BORDERS GENERAL HOSPITAL N.H.S. TRUST [01896 754333]	Rev. J. Ronald Dick	Chaplaincy Centre, Borders General Hospital, Melrose TD6 9BS	01835 863223
DINGLETON	Rev. John Riddell	42 High Street, Jedburgh TD8 6NQ	01721 721749
HAY LODGE, PEEBLES	Rev. James H. Wallace	Innerleithen Road, Peebles EH45 8BD	01890 781333
KNOLL	Rev. David Hebenton	Grey Gables, Beanburn, Ayton, Eyemouth TD14 5QY	01573 420308
INCH	Rev. Robin McHaffie	Kirk Yetholm, Kelso TD5 8RD	

DUMFRIES AND GALLOWAY

DUMFRIES HOSPITALS [01387 246246]	Rev. Alexander E. Strachan	2 Leafield Road, Dumfries DG1 2DS	01387 279460

THOMAS HOPE, LANGHOLM	Rev. Robert Milne	The Manse, Langholm DG13 OBL	01896 668577
LOCHMABEN	Rev. W. Logan Kirk	The Manse, Hightae, Lockerbie DG11 1JL	01387 811499
MOFFAT	Rev. John Stewart	The Manse, Beattock, Moffat DG10 9RF	01683 300349
NEW ANNAN	Rev. S.E.P. Beveridge	The Manse, Ecclefechan, Lockerbie DG11 3BU	01576 300357
CASTLE DOUGLAS	Rev. John Young	Craigview, North Street, Moniaive, Thornhill DG3 4HR	01848 200318
CRESSWELL	Rev. Mary Hutchison (Mrs)	25 Twiname Way, Heathhall, Dumfries DG1 3ST	01387 250610
DUMFRIES AND GALLOWAY ROYAL INFIRMARY	Rev. Mary Hutchison (Mrs)	25 Twiname Way, Heathhall, Dumfries DG1 3ST	01387 250610
	Rev. D.K.P. Bennett	Irongray Manse, Dumfries DG2 9TR	01387 720227
KIRKCUDBRIGHT	Rev. Douglas R. Irving	6 Bourtree Avenue, Kirkcudbright DG6 4AU	01557 330489
THORNHILL	Rev. John E. Gisbey	The Manse, Thornhill DG3 5DP	01848 331191
DALRYMPLE			
GARRICK	Rev. Samuel McC. Harris	Linden, Leswalt Road, Stranraer DG9 OAA	01776 706387
NEWTON STEWART	Rev. Neil G. Campbell	The Manse, Newton Stewart DG8 6HH	01671 402259

AYRSHIRE AND ARRAN

AYRSHIRE AND ARRAN PRIMARY CARE N.H.S. TRUST [01292 513023]			
AILSA HOSPITAL, AYR	Rev. John Banks	19 Victoria Drive, Troon KA10 6JF	01292 317758
AYRSHIRE AND ARRAN ACUTE HOSPITALS N.H.S. TRUST [01563 521133]			
CROSSHOUSE HOSPITAL KILMARNOCK	Rev. Judith Huggett	4 Westmoor Crescent, Kilmarnock KA1 1TX	
AYR/BIGGART HOSPITALS [01292 610555]	Rev. Roderick H. McNidder	6 Hollow Park, Alloway KA7 4SR	01292 442554
ARROL PARK	Mrs Norma Livingstone	31 Victoria Drive, Troon KA10 6JF	01292 269161
BALLOCHMYLE	Rev. A.M. McPhail	87 Forehill Road, Ayr KA7 3JR	
DAVIDSON	Rev. Robert Bell	The Manse, Ballantrae, Girvan KA26 0UH	01465 831282
HOLMHEAD	Rev. John Paterson	33 Barrhill Road, Cumnock KA18 1PJ	01290 420769
CROSSHOUSE	Mrs Norma Livingstone	31 Victoria Drive, Troon KA10 6JF	
KIRKLANDSIDE	Mrs Barbara Urquhart	Manse of Kilmaurs, 9 Standalane, Kilmaurs KA3 2NB	01863 538289
STRATHLEA	Mrs Barbara Urquhart	Manse of Kilmaurs, 9 Standalane, Kilmaurs KA3 2NB	01863 538289
AYRSHIRE CENTRAL	Rev. Hugh M. Adamson	Mure Church Manse, West Road, Irvine KA12 8RE	01294 279916
	Rev. Scott Robertson	31 Milgarholm Avenue, Irvine KA12 0EL	
BROOKSBY HOUSE LARGS	Rev. Stephen J. Smith	31 Douglas Street, Largs KA30 8PT	01475 672370
WAR MEMORIAL, ARRAN	Rev. Elizabeth Watson	The Manse, Whiting Bay, Isle of Arran KA27 8RE	01770 700289
LADY MARGARET, MILLPORT	Rev. Marjory MacKay	The Manse, Millport, Isle of Cumbrae KA28 0EE	01475 530460

LANARKSHIRE

Hospital	Chaplain	Address	Tel.
WILLIAM SMELLIE AND LOCKHART	Rev. Catherine Collins	2 Friarsdene, Lanark ML11 9EJ	01555 663363
	Rev. John M.A. Thomson	32 Braxfield Road, Lanark ML11 9BS	01555 662600
	Rev. Bruce Gordon	The Rectory, Cleghorn Road, Lanark ML11 7QT	
CLELAND	Rev. John Jackson	The Manse, Bellside Road, Cleland ML1 5NP	01698 860260
KELLO	Rev. Gavin Elliott	61 High Street, Biggar ML12 6DA	01899 220227
LADY HOME	Rev. Lawrie I. Lennox	The Manse, Douglas, Lanark ML11 0PZ	01555 851213
LAW	Rev. David A. Young	The Manse, Kirkmuirhill, Lanark ML11	01555 892409
	Rev. J. Allardyce (Roadmeetings)	Congregational Manse, Rhyde Road, Wishaw ML2 7DU	01698 372657
	Rev. David Collins	Greyfriars Manse, Friarsdene, Lanark ML11 9EJ	01355 663363
	Rev. Geoff McKee	Kirkstyle Manse, Church Street, Carluke ML8 4BA	
	Rev. Graeme McKay	75 Mossneuk Park, Wishaw ML2 8LX	01698 384905
STRATHCLYDE	Rev. David W. Doyle	19 Orchard Street, Motherwell ML1 3JE	01698 263472
BIRKWOOD	Rev. Sheila Mitchell	Calsay Cottage, New Trows Road, Lesmahagow ML11 0ER	01555 892445
HAIRMYRES	Rev. John Brewster	21 Turnberry Place, East Kilbride G75 8TB	01355 242564
	Rev. Douglas Clark	41 Kirkintilloch Road, Lenzie G66 4LB	0141 776 2184
KIRKLANDS	Rev. Iain Greenshields	2 Orchard Gate, Larkhall ML9 1HA	01698 882457
STONEHOUSE	Rev. Iain Greenshields	2 Orchard Gate, Larkhall ML9 1HA	01698 882457
	Rev. James S.G. Hastie	The Manse, Quarry Road, Larkhall ML9 1HM	01698 882238
UDSTON	Rev. James P. Fraser	26 Hamilton Road, Strathaven ML10 6JA	01357 522758
BELLSHILL	Rev. J. Stanley Cook	43 Bothwell Road, Hamilton ML3 0BB	01698 458770
COATHILL	Rev. Sharon Colvin	48 Dunrobin Road, Airdrie ML6 8LR	01236 763154
MONKLANDS GENERAL	Rev. James Munton	Old Monkland Manse, Coatbridge ML5 5QT	01236 423788
	Rev. James S. Salmond	Manse of Holytown, Motherwell ML1 5RU	01698 832622
	Rev. Scott McKenna	14 Holmbrae Road, Uddingston G71 6NP	01698 813113
	Rev. James Grier	47 Blair Road, Coatbridge ML5 1JQ	01236 432427
	Rev. Thomas Pollock	Clarkston Manse, Forrest Street, Airdrie ML6 7BE	01236 769676
	Rev. Henry J.W. Findlay	St Mark's Manse, Coltness Road, Wishaw ML2 7EX	01698 384596
WESTER MOFFAT	Rev. John Handley	12 Airbles Crescent Motherwell ML1 3AR	01698 262733
HARTWOODHILL	Rev. J. Stanley Cook	43 Bothwell Road, Hamilton ML3 0BB	01698 458770
MOTHERWELL – PSYCHIATRIC	Rev. Sharon Colvin	48 Dunrobin Road, Airdrie ML6 8LR	01236 763154
COMMUNITY MENTAL HEALTH CARE	Rev. Rosemary Smith	Blantyre Old Manse, High Blantyre G72 9UA	01698 823130

GREATER GLASGOW

NORTH GLASGOW UNIVERSITY HOSPITALS NHS TRUST

GLASGOW ROYAL INFIRMARY [0141 211 4000/4661]

Rev. Anne J.M. Harper	122 Greenock Road, Bishopton PA7 5AS	
Rev. Keith Saunders	1 Beckfield Drive, Robroyston, Glasgow G33 1SR	0141 211 2000/2812
Rev. Keith Saunders	1 Beckfield Drive, Robroyston, Glasgow G33 1SR	0141 211 3000/3026
Rev. Keith Saunders	1 Beckfield Drive, Robroyston, Glasgow G33 1SR	0141 211 1600

WESTERN INFIRMARY [0141 211 2000]
GARTNAVEL GENERAL [0141 211 3000]
GLASGOW HOMEOPATHIC [0141 211 1600]

GREATER GLASGOW PRIMARY CARE N.H.S. TRUST

GARTNAVEL ROYAL HOSPITAL [0141 211 3600]

Rev. Cameron H. Langlands	Flat G/1, 28 Plantation Park Gardens, Glasgow G51 1NW

SOUTH GLASGOW UNIVERSITY HOSPITALS NHS TRUST

SOUTHERN GENERAL HOSPITAL [0141 201 2156]

Rev. Janet P.H. Macmahon	6 Jubilee Gardens, Bearsden, Glasgow G61 2RT	
Rev. Blair Robertson	14 Crosbie Street, Glasgow G20 0BD	
Rev. Christopher L. Levison	5 Deaconsbank Avenue, Stewarton Road, Glasgow G46 7UN	0141 201 5164

Facility	Name	Address	Telephone
VICTORIA INFIRMARY	Rev. Patricia McDonald	4 Whithope Terrace, Glasgow G53 7LT	0141 876 1408
LIGHTBURN GERIATRIC	Rev. H. Marshall Gibson	29 Broompark Drive, Glasgow G31 2JB	0141 554 0997
ROYAL MATERNITY	Mrs Sandra Bell	62 Loganswell Road, Thornliebank, Glasgow G46 8AX	
ROYAL INFIRMARY	Rev. Patricia McDonald	4 Whithope Terrace, Glasgow G53 7LT	0141 876 1408
STOBHILL	Rev. E. Gwynfai Jones	42 Melville Gardens, Bishopbriggs, Glasgow G64 3DE	0141 772 2848
	Rev. Elizabeth W. Sutherland	54 Etive Crescent, Bishopbriggs, Glasgow G54 1ES	0141 772 1453
	Rev. John Beaton	33 North Birbiston Road, Lennoxtown, Glasgow G65 7LZ	
	Rev. Kenneth Coulter	8 Abbotsford Avenue, Rutherglen G73 3NX	0141 647 6250
	Miss Anne MacDonald	62 Berwick Drive, Glasgow G52 3JA	0141 883 5618
WYNDFORD LOCKS	Rev. Robert Owen	5 Firdon Crescent, Glasgow G15 6QQ	0141 944 8797
CANNIESBURN	Rev. Margaret Yule	Radnor Park Manse, Spencer Street, Clydebank G81 3AS	0141 951 1007
PARKHEAD	Rev. Ronald Anderson	97 Drumover Drive, Glasgow G31 5RP	0141 556 2520
	Rev. John Graham	87 Drumover Drive, Glasgow G31 5RR	0141 554 3640
LENNOX CASTLE	Rev. D.J. Torrance	19 Redhills View, Lennoxtown G65 7BL	01360 312527
LEVERNDALE	Rev. Alexander Macdonald	The Manse, Neilston, Glasgow G78 3NP	0141 881 1958
	Miss Anne MacDonald	62 Berwick Drive, Glasgow G52 3JA	0141 883 5618
DARNLEY COURT	Rev. Gordon Armstrong	22 Colquhoun Street, Dumbarton G82 2HL	01389 764376
WOODILEE	Rev. Colin Brown	2 Waukglen Drive, Southpark Village, Glasgow G43 7UG	0141 954 4744
	Rev. Alastair MacDonald	65 Woodend Drive, Glasgow G13 1QF	0141 883 5618
	Miss Anne MacDonald	62 Berwick Drive, Glasgow G52 3JA	
VICTORIA INFIRMARY/MEARNSKIRK	Rev. Alan Raeburn	110 Mount Annan Drive, Glasgow G44 4RZ	0141 632 1514
GARTNAVEL GENERAL/WESTERN	Rev. Stuart Macdonald	28 Kessington Road, Bearsden G61 2HL	0141 942 1313

Hospital	Chaplain	Address	Telephone
BLAWARTHILL	Rev. Neil Galbraith	21 Cartwell Avenue, Cathcart, Glasgow G44 5AA	0141 633 5248
COWGLEN	Rev. Michael Gibson	41 Rouken Glen Road, Thornliebank G46 7JD	0141 638 3023
GREENFIELD PARK	Rev. Patricia McDonald	4 Whithope Terrace, Glasgow G53 7LT	0141 876 1408
KNIGHTSWOOD/DRUMCHAPEL	Rev. Andrew McMillan	1 Swallow Gardens, Glasgow G13 4QD	0141 959 7158
LENZIE	Rev. James Ferguson	The Manse, Larch Avenue, Lenzie G66 4HX	0141 776 3831
RUTHERGLEN TAKARE	Rev. J.W. Drummond	21 Albert Drive, Rutherglen G73 3RT	0141 643 0234
	Rev. A.M. Morrice	80 Blairbeth Road, Rutherglen G73 4JA	0141 634 4366
YORKHILL QUEEN MOTHER'S	Rev. Alexander Thomson	31 Highburgh Drive, Rutherglen G73 3RR	0141 647 6178
YORKHILL SICK CHILDREN	Rev. Sandra Black	36 Glencairn Drive, Glasgow G41 4PN	0141 423 4000
PRINCE AND PRINCESS OF WALES HOSPICE	Rev. Patricia McDonald	4 Whithope Terrace, Glasgow G53 7LT	0141 876 1408
FOURHILLS NURSING HOME	Rev. Alan Donald	71 Carlton Place, Glasgow G5 9TD	0141 429 5599
	Rev. W.G. Ramsay	3 Tofthill Avenue, Bishopbriggs G64 3PN	0141 762 1844

ARGYLL AND CLYDE

Hospital	Chaplain	Address	Telephone
INVERCLYDE ROYAL HOSPITAL GREENOCK [01475 633777]	Rev. Elizabeth Crumlish	146 South Street, Greenock PA16 8TD,	01475 721048
	Rev. William Hewitt	50 Ardgowan Street, Greenock PA16 5RP	
DYKEBAR	Rev. Alistair Morrison	36 Newtyle Road, Paisley PA1 3JX	0141 889 4279
	Rev. J.C. MacColl	The Grange, Park Road, Johnstone PA5 8LS	01505 320142
	Rev. Brian L. Farmer	27 Oakwood Avenue, Paisley PA2 9NG	0141 884 4502
	Miss Margaret McBain	33 Quarry Road, Paisley PA2 7RD	0141 854 2920
HAWKHEAD	Rev. David Palmer	19 Corsebar Drive, Paisley PA2 9QD	0141 882 2277
MERCHISTON HOUSE	Rev. Thomas Cant	18 Oldhall Road, Paisley PA1 3HL	0141 886 2896
JOHNSTONE	Rev. James Rule	6 St Andrews Road, Renfrew PA4 0SN	01805 702669
ROYAL ALEXANDRA	Rev. Arthur Sherratt	West Manse, Kilbarchan PA10 2JR	01505 320060
	Rev. James Boag	61 Auchenlodement Road, Elderslie PA5 9PN	01805 702621
	Rev. Alister W. Bull	East Manse, Church Street, Kilbarchan PA10 2JQ	0141 883 3505
	Rev. Douglas Ralph	24 Kinpurnie Road, Paisley PA1 3HM	0141 887 0884
	Rev. Ian S. Currie	9 Hawkhead Road, Paisley PA1 3ND	0141 886 2074
	Rev. E. Lorna Hood (Mrs)	North Manse, 1 Alexandra Drive, Renfrew PA4 0SN	01505 325131
	Rev. Edward Marshall	The Manse, Linwood PA3 3DL	01475 722338
RAVENSCRAIG	Rev. James H. Simpson	76 Finnart Street, Greenock PA16 8HJ	01505 873271
	Rev. Douglas Cranston	6 Churchill Road, Kilmacolm PA13 4LH	01389 873130
DUMBARTON JOINT	Rev. Alistair MacKichan	Old Kilpatrick Manse, Glasgow G60 5JQ	01389 753039
VALE OF LEVEN GENERAL	Rev. Ian Miller	1 Glebe Gardens, Bonhill, Alexandria G83 9HB	01389 752734
VALE OF LEVEN GERIATRIC	Rev. Kenneth Russell	Appin House, Drymen Road, Balloch G83 8MT	01586 830667
CAMPBELTOWN	Rev. W. Bristow	Laill, Lepenstrath, Southend, Argyll PA28 6RU	01546 870611
LOCHGILPHEAD	Rev. Robert Malloch	Church of Scotland Manse, Tayvallich, Lochgilphead PA31 8PG	01496 810271
ISLAY	Rev. Anne McIvor	The Manse, Bowmore, Isle of Islay PA43 7LH	

Location	Chaplain	Address	Telephone
DUNOON	Rev. Patricia Lang	1 Royal Crescent, Dunoon PA23 7AH	01369 701291
DUNOON ARGYLL UNIT	Rev. J.A. Gray	Holyns, Ardentinny, Dunoon PA23 8TR	01369 810243
ROTHESAY	Rev. Ronald Samuel	9 Bishop Terrace, Rothesay PA20 9HF	01700 504378
LORN AND THE ISLANDS DISTRICT GENERAL	Rev. William Gray	Lochnagar, Longsdale Road, Oban PA34 5DZ	01561 567471

FORTH VALLEY

BELLSDYKE	Rev. Ann Smith	16 Mannerston Holdings, Linlithgow, EH49 7ND	01506 834350
BO'NESS	Rev. Henry Munroe	Viewforth, High Road, Maddiston, Falkirk FK2 OBL	01324 712446
BONNYBRIDGE	Rev. Robert MacLeod	13 CannonsWay, Falkirk FK2 7QG	01324 631008
FALKIRK ROYAL INFIRMARY	Rev. James Marshall	Craigmailen Manse, Braehead, Bo'ness EH51 0BZ	01506 823784
R.S.N.H. LARBERT	Rev. Joanne Finlay	The Manse, Bowhouse Road, Grangemouth FK3 0EX	01324 471595
BANNOCKBURN	Rev. John McCallum	11 Burnbrae Gardens, Falkirk FK1 5SB	01324 619766
CLACKMANNAN COUNTY	Rev. Robert Philip	Congregational Church Manse, Avonbridge FK1 2LU	01324 861252
KILDEAN	Rev. James Landels	Allan Manse, Bogend Road, Bannockburn FK7 8NP	01786 814692
SAUCHIE	Rev. R.W.W. Irvine	9 Fraser Place, Causewayhead, Stirling FK9 5RE	01786 448802
STIRLING ROYAL INFIRMARY	Rev. Malcolm MacRae	10b Victoria Place, Stirling FK8 2QU	01786 465547
	Rev. James W. Benson	1 Sunnyside, Dunblane FK15 9HA	01786 822624
	Rev. Stuart Pryce	36 Forth Park, Bridge of Allan FK9 5NT	01786 831026
	Rev. Gary McIntyre	7 Randolph Road, Stirling FK8 2AJ	01786 474421

FIFE

FIFE ACUTE HOSPITALS NHS TRUST	Rev. Isabel Whyte	34 Shandon Crescent, Edinburgh EH11 1QF	0131 337 3559
QUEEN MARGARET HOSPITAL DUNFERMLINE [01383 674136]	Rev. Iain J.M. McDonald	11 James Grove, Kirkcaldy KY1 1TN	01592 253775
VICTORIA HOSPITAL, KIRKCALDY [01592 643355]	Rev. Sally Foster Fulton	Irving Manse, Dorrator Road, Camelon, Falkirk FK1 4BN	01324 623035
RSNH LARBERT	Rev. Elizabeth Fisk	51 St John's Drive, Dunfermline FK12 7TL	01383 720256
LYNEBANK	Rev. Isabel Whyte	34 Shandon Crescent, Edinburgh EH11 1QF	0131 337 3559
MILESMARK	Rev. James L. Templeton	Innerleven Manse, McDonald Street, Methil KY8 3AJ	01333 426310
CAMERON	Rev. Ian D. Gordon	7 Guthrie Crescent, Markinch KY7 6AY	01592 758264
GLENROTHES	Rev. Elizabeth Cranfield	9 Chemiss Road, Methilhill KY8 2BS	01592 713142
RANDOLPH WEMYSS	Rev. James O. Hegarty	23 Hogarth Drive, Cupar KY15 5YH	01334 655851
ADAMSON, CUPAR	Rev. Kenneth Donald	33 Main Road, East Wemyss KY1 4RE	01592 713260
CAMERON	Rev. Colin Dempster	27 Bell Street, Tayport DD6 9AP	01382 552861
NETHERLEA, NEWPORT	Rev. Peter Meager	7 Lorraine Drive, Cupar KY15 5DY	01334 656991
STRATHEDEN, CUPAR	Miss Margaret Browning	4 Wellpark Terrace, Newport-on-Tay DD6 8HT	01382 542140
ST ANDREWS MEMORIAL	Rev. David Arnott	20 Priory Gardens, St Andrews KY16 8XX	01334 472912

TAYSIDE

TAYSIDE UNIVERSITY HOSPITALS N.H.S. TRUST
DUNDEE NINEWELLS HOSPITAL
[01382 660111]

PERTH ROYAL INFIRMARY [01738 473896]

	Rev. John M. Birrell	5 Hewat Place, Perth PH1 2UD	
ABERFELDY	Rev. Alexander M. Gunn	The Manse, Taybridge Terrace, Aberfeldy PH15 2BS	01887 820656
BLAIRGOWRIE RATTRAY	Rev. Ian Kn ox	Heatherlea, Main Street, Ardler, Blairgowrie PH12 8SR	01828 640731
IRVINE MEMORIAL	Rev. Christopher Brown	8 Tom Na Moan Road, Pitlochry PH16 5HN	01796 472719
CRIEFF COTTAGE	Rev. Henry A.G. Tait	14 Sheiling Hill Place, Crieff PH7 4ER	01764 652325
MACMILLAN HOSPICE	Rev. Anne Stewart	35 Rose Crescent, Perth PH1 1NT	01738 624167
MURRAY ROYAL	Rev. Peter Meager	7 Lorraine Drive, Cupar KY15 5DY	01334 656991
ST MARGARET'S COTTAGE	Rev. Randal MacAlister	St Kessog's Rectory, High Street, Auchterarder PH3 1AD	01764 662525
ASHLUDIE	Mr Iain Law	Royal Victoria Hospital, Dundee DD2 1SP	01382 423000
TAYSIDE ORTHOPAEDIC AND REHAB. CENTRE	Rev. Thomas P. Robertson	95 Seafield Road, Broughty Ferry, Dundee DD5 3AP	01382 779803
DUNDEE, ROYAL LIFF	Mr Iain Law	Royal Victoria Hospital, Dundee DD2 1SP	01382 423000
ROYAL VICTORIA	Mr Iain Law	Royal Victoria Hospital, Dundee DD2 1SP	01382 423000
NINEWELLS	Rev. Tom Milroy	9 Long Row, Westhaven, Carnoustie DD7 6BE	01241 856654
STRATHMARTINE	Mr Iain Law	Royal Victoria Hospital, Dundee DD2 1SP	01382 423000
ARBROATH INFIRMARY	Rev. Alasdair G. Graham	1 Charles Avenue, Arbroath DD11 2EZ	01241 872244
BRECHIN INFIRMARY	Rev. James P.R. Drysdale	36 Park Road, Brechin DD9 7AP	01356 622789
FORFAR INFIRMARY	Rev. Graham Norrie	East Manse, Lour Road, Forfar DD8 2BB	01307 464303
WHITEHILLS	Rev. Brian Ramsay	The Manse, Guthrie, Forfar DD8 2TP	01241 828243
LITTLE CAIRNIE	Rev. Ian G. Gough	St Vigeans Manse, Arbroath DD11 4RD	01241 873206
MONTROSE ROYAL	Rev. Iain M. Douglas	49 North Esk Road, Montrose DD10 8TQ	01674 672060
STRACATHRO	Rev. James Drysdale	51 Airlie Street, Brechin DD9 6JX	01356 625201
SUNNYSIDE ROYAL	Mr Gordon Anderson	33 Grampian View, Montrose DD10 9SU	01674 674915

GRAMPIAN

GRAMPIAN UNIVERSITY HOSPITALS N.H.S. TRUST
ABERDEEN ROYAL INFIRMARY
[01224 681818 and 01224 840747]

Rev. Fred Coutts	9a Millburn Street, Aberdeen AB11 6SS	
Rev. James Falconer	3 Brimmond Walk, Westhill, Skene, Aberdeenshire AB32 6XH	
Rev. Gillian Munro	685 George Street, Aberdeen AB25 3XP	01224 208341
Mrs Muriel Knox (Chaplain's Assistant)	35 Valentine Drive, Aberdeen AB22 8YF	
Miss Monica Stewart (Chaplain's Assistant)	9 Craigton Avenue, Aberdeen AB15 7RD	
Rev. Alison Hutchison (part-time)	"Ashfield", Drumoak, Banchory AB31 3AA	

ABERDEEN GENERAL HOSPITALS [01224 556788]	Rev. Alan Stoddart	21 Creel Road, Bayside, Cove AB1 4BX	
GRAMPIAN PRIMARY CARE N.H.S. TRUST ROYAL CORNHILL and WOODLANDS HOSPITAL [01224 663123]	Rev. William Campbell	43 Murray Terrace, Aberdeen AB1 2SA	
	Mr Donald Meston (Chaplain's Assistant)	20 Rosehill Place, Aberdeen AB2 2LE	
	Miss Pamela Adam (Chaplain's Assistant)	409 Holburn Street, Aberdeen AB10 7GS	
ABOYNE	Rev. David Devenney	The Manse, St Eunan's Road, Aboyne AB34 5HH	01339 886447
KINCARDINE COMMUNITY	Rev. Gordon Farquharson	Dunnottar Manse, Stonehaven AB39 3XL	01569 762874
	Rev. Ian Pittendreich	3 Coastguard Houses, Cowie, Stonehaven AB39 2RT	
	Rev. Leonard Bridgeman	53 Carron Gardens, Stonehaven AB39 3FE	
GLEN O' DEE	Rev. Donald Walker	2 Wilson Road, Banchory AB31 3UY	01330 822811
KINCARDINE O'NEIL	Rev. Peter R. Taylor	The Manse, Torphins AB31 4JS	01339 882276
KINCARDINE COMMUNITY	Rev. Kenneth L. Petrie	South Manse, Cameron Street, Stonehaven AB3 2HE	01569 762576
INVERURIE	Rev. Ian B. Groves	West Manse, Inverurie AB51 9YS	01467 620285
	Rev. Iain J.M. Telfer	St Andrew's Manse, Inverurie AB5 9XT	01467 620468
INSCH	Rev. Robert S. McLeish	The Manse, Insch AB52 6JR	01464 820914
JUBILEE	Rev. Thomas Calder	The Manse, Queen Street, Huntly AB54 5EB	01466 792630
CAMPBELL	Rev. David Anderson	The Manse, Portsoy, Banff AB45 2QB	01261 842272
CHALMERS	Rev. Alan Macgregor	7 Colleonard Road, Banff AB45 1DZ	01261 812107
FRASERBURGH	Rev. Douglas R.Clyne	97 Saltoun Place, Fraserburgh AB43 5RY	01346 518536
LADYSBRIDGE	Rev. Gordon Henig	6 Craigneen Place, Whitehills, Banff AB45 2NE	01261 861671
MAUD	Rev. Alastair Donald	New Deer Manse, Turriff AB53 6TG	01771 644216
PETERHEAD COTTAGE	Rev. David S. Ross	1 Hawthorn Road, Peterhead AB42 6DW	01779 472618
TURRIFF	Rev. Sylvia Dyer	The Sheiling, Westfield Road, Turriff AB53 4AF	01888 562530
UGIE	Rev. David Pirkeathly	1 Landale Road, Peterhead AB42 1QN	01779 472141
BILBOHALL	Rev. George B. Rollo	18 Reidhaven Street, Elgin IV30 1QH	01343 547208
DR GRAY'S	Rev. George B. Rollo	18 Reidhaven Street, Elgin IV30 1QH	01343 547208
FLEMING COTTAGE	Rev. Margaret Muir	The Manse, Ballindalloch Banffshire AB37 9EB	01807 500311
LEANCHOIL	Rev. John Beck	The Manse, Dunbar Street, Burghead, Elgin IV30 2XB	01343 830365
SPYNIE	Rev. Ray Hall	21 St Peter's Road, Duffus, Elgin IV30 5QL	01343 830985
SEAFIELD	Rev. Eric Foggit	The Manse, East Church Street, Buckie AB56 1ES	01542 832103
STEPHEN AND COUNTY HOSPITALS	Rev. Hugh M.C. Smith	The Manse, Dufftown AB55 4AR	01340 820380
TURNER MEMORIAL	Rev. Michael Lyall	North Church Manse, Keith AB55 3BR	01542 882559

HIGHLAND

HIGHLAND ACUTE HOSPITALS NHS TRUST
THE RAIGMORE HOSPITAL [01463 704000]

	Rev. Iain MacRitchie	7 Merlin Crescent, Inverness IV2 3TE	
	Rev. Derek Brown	Cathedral Manse, Dornoch IV25 3HV	
IAN CHARLES	Rev. Morris Smith	Golfcourse Road, Grantown on Spey PH26 3HY	01479 872084
ST VINCENT	Dr John Berkeley	Drumbeg, Coylumbridge, Aviemore PH22 1QY	01479 811055
CRAIG DUNAIN	Rev. William J. Campbell	20 Birchview Court, Inverness IV22.5WA	01463 791690
NAIRN TOWN AND COUNTY	Rev. William B. Whyte	St Ninian's Manse, Queen Street, Nairn IV12 4AA	01667 452202
BELFORD AND BELHAVEN	Rev. Donald A. MacQuarrie	Manse of Duncansburgh, Fort William PH33 6BA	01397 702297
GLENCOE	Rev. Anne Jones	The Manse, Ballachulish PA39 4JG	01855 811998
INVERGORDON COUNTY	Rev. Kenneth D. Macleod	The Manse, Cromlet Drive, Invergordon IV18 0BA	01349 852273
LAWSON MEMORIAL			
MIGDALE			
CAITHNESS GENERAL	Rev. A.A. Roy	Mansefield, Miller Avenue, Wick KW1 4DF	01955 602822
	Rev. William Wallace	The Manse, Coronation Street, Wick KW1 5LS	01955 603166
DUNBAR	Rev. Kenneth Borthwick	46 Rose Street, Thurso KW14 7RE	01847 895186
BROADFORD MACKINNON MEMORIAL	Rev. Iain M.A. Reid	The Manse, Broadford, Isle of Skye IV49 9AA	01471 822538
GESTO	Rev. Donald MacLeod	Snizort, Portree, Isle of Skye IV51 9XE	01470 532260

WESTERN ISLES HEALTH BOARD

LOCHMADDY	Rev. Angus MacDonald	The Manse, Lochmaddy, North Uist H56 5AA	01876 500414

ORKNEY HEALTH BOARD

BALFOUR AND EASTBANK	Rev. Michael J. Ward	Ploverhall, Deerness, Orkney KW17 2QJ	01856 741349
			(Mbl) 0370 895543

LIST D – FULL-TIME INDUSTRIAL CHAPLAINS

EDINBURGH (Edinburgh City Mission Appointment)	Mr John Hopper	26 Mulberry Drive, Dunfermline KY11 5BZ	01383 737189
EDINBURGH (Methodist Appointment)	Rev. Bill Rayne	5 Dudley Terrace, Edinburgh EH6 6QQ	0131 554 1636
EDINBURGH (part-time)	Mrs Dorothy Robertson	12 Clerwood Park, Edinburgh EH12 8PW	0131 334 5440
GLASGOW (part-time)	Rev. Elisabeth Spence Mr William Shirlaw	45 Selvieland Road, Glasgow G52 4ES 77 Southpark Avenue, Glasgow G12 8LE	0141 883 8973 0141 339 0456 0141 332 4458 (Office)
WEST OF SCOTLAND	Rev. Alister Goss	79 Weymouth Crescent, Gourock PA19 1HR	01475 638944 01475 629383 (Office)
NORTH EAST	Rev. Angus Smith	1 Fa'burn Terrace, Lumphanan AB31 4AG	01339 883395 01224 233532/3 (Office)
NORTH OF SCOTLAND	Mr Lewis Rose DCS	16 Gean Drive, Blackburn AB21 0YN	01224 790145
TAYSIDE & NATIONAL CO-ORDINATOR	Rev. Erik Cramb	65 Clepington Road, Dundee DD4 7BQ	01382 458764

LIST E – PRISON CHAPLAINS

ABERDEEN CRAIGINCHES	Rev. David Souter Rev. Harvey Grainger	The Manse, Echt AB32 7AB Kingswells Manse, Lang Stracht, Aberdeen AB15 8PL	01330 860533 01224 740229
CASTLE HUNTLY	Rev. James Jack Rev. David MacLeod	The Manse, Longforgan DD2 5EU 6 Carseview Gardens, Dundee DD2 1NE	01382 360238 01382 641371
CORNTON VALE	Rev. Elaine MacRae	The Manse, Kippen, Stirling FK8 3DN	01786 870229
DUMFRIES	Rev. William Kelly Rev. Dennis S. Rose	The Manse, Troqueer Road, Dumfries DG2 7DF The Manse, Kirkmahoe, Dumfries DG1 1ST	01387 253043 01387 710572

EDINBURGH: SAUGHTON	Rev. Jennifer Booth	39 Lilyhill Terrace, Edinburgh EH8 7OR	0131 661 3813
	Rev. I. David Miller	146 Craigleith Road, Edinburgh EH4 2EQ	0131 332 6378
	Miss Max. Homewood	5 Essex Brae, Edinburgh EH4 6LN	0131 339 3884
	Miss Norma Ronald	43/26 Gillespie Crescent, Edinburgh EH10 4HY	0131 228 1008
AND SPS ADVISER IN CHAPLAINCY	Rev. R. Stuart M. Fulton	c/o Scottish Prison Service HQ, 5 Redheugh Rig, Edinburgh EH12 9DQ	0131 244 8459
GLASGOW: BARLINNIE	Rev. Edward V. Simpson	5 Langtree Avenue, Glasgow G46 7LN	0141 638 8767
	Rev. Robert J.M. Anderson	The Manse, Carmunnock, Glasgow G76 9AJ	0141 644 1578
	Rev. C. Blair Gillon	3 Dargarvel Avenue, Glasgow G41 5LD	0141 427 1282
	Rev. Russell McLarty	38 Lochview Drive, Glasgow G33 1QF	0141 770 9611
	Rev. Ian McInnes	46 Earlbank Avenue, Glasgow G14 9HL	0141 954 0328
LOW MOSS	Rev. George Cranston	26 Parkhill Drive, Glasgow G73 2PW	0141 647 6688
	Rev. David Cameron	122 Broomfield Avenue, Newton Mearns G77 5JR	0141 616 0642
GLENOCHIL	Rev. George Sherry	The Manse, Menstrie FK11 7EA	01259 761461
	Rev. Malcolm MacRae	10b Victoria Place, Stirling FK8 2QU	01786 465547
	Rev. Alan F.M. Downie	37A Claremont, Alloa FK10 2DG	01259 213872
GREENOCK	Rev. Kenneth Fisher	33 Halfway Street, West Kilbride KA23 9EQ	01294 829973
	Rev. Peter Webster	84 Forsyth Street PA16 8QY	01475 721439
INVERNESS	Rev. Colin Anderson	24 Damfield Road, Inverness IV2 4HU	01463 237129
	Rev. George Charlton	61 Drumfield Road, Inverness IV2 4LX	01463 242802
KILMARNOCK	Rev. Andrew Downie	HMP Bowhouse, Mauchline Road, Kilmarnock KA1	
NORANSIDE	Rev. William McCulloch	26 Quarry Park, Kirriemuir DD8 4DR	01575 575561
PERTH	Rev. John McQuilken	18 Clark Terrace, Crieff PH7 3QE	01764 655764
	Rev. J. Bruce Thomson	The Manse, Burnside, Scone, Perth PH2 6LP	01738 552030
	Rev. Colin Williamson	The Manse, Aberdalgie, Perth PH2 0QD	01738 625854
	Mrs Deirdre Yellowlees	Ringmill House, Gannochy Farm, Perth PH2 7JH	01738 633773
	Rev. Isobel Birrell	Wester Tarsappie, Rhynd, Perth PH2 8QL	01738 625694
PERTH: FRIARTON			
PETERHEAD	Rev. G.M. Allan Fawkes	The Manse, Lonmay, Fraserburgh AB43 4UJ	01346 532227
	Rev. James Lyall	The Manse, Crimond, Fraserburgh AB43 8QJ	01346 532431

POLMONT			
	Rev. Daniel L. Mathers	36 Thistle Avenue, Grangemouth FK3 8YQ	01324 474511
	Rev. John Fairful	The Manse, Airth, Falkirk FK2 8JQ	01324 831474
	Rev. James Drysdale	The Manse, Shieldhill, Falkirk FK1 2EG	01324 621938
	Rev. Ian Watson	The Manse, Main Street, Caldercruix ML6 7KF	01236 842279
SHOTTS			
	Rev. Andrew Campbell	70 Baron's Road, Motherwell ML1 2NB	01698 263803
	Rev. James Seath	1 Allan Avenue, Carluke ML8 5UA	01555 771644
	Rev. Derek Pope	3 Kirkland Street, Motherwell ML1 3JW	01698 266716
SHOTTS: N.I.C.			
	Rev. Iain Greenshields	2 Orchard Gate, Larkhall ML9 1HA	01698 882457

LIST F – UNIVERSITY CHAPLAINS

ABERDEEN	Easter Smart MDiv	01224 484271
ABERTAY, DUNDEE		
CALEDONIAN	Fiona C. Douglas BD PhD	0141 331 3823
DUNDEE	Diane Williams	01382 623181 (ext 4156)
EDINBURGH	Fiona Mathieson BD	0131 650 2596
GLASGOW	Howard G. Taylor BSc BD	0141 330 5419
HERIOT WATT	Deryck Collingwood	0131 449 5111 (ext 4508)
NAPIER	Alister W. Bull BD DipMin	0131 444 2266
PAISLEY	Scott Blythe BSc BD	01505 702621
ROBERT GORDON	James B. Walker MA BD DPhil	01224 262000 (ext 3506)
ST ANDREWS	Alexander Horsburgh MA BD	01334 462866
STIRLING	Marjory Macaskill LLB BD	01786 832118
STRATHCLYDE		0141 553 4144

LIST G – THE DIACONATE

NAME	COM	APP	ADDRESS	TEL	PRES
Allan, Jean (Mrs)	1989	1988	12C Hindmarsh Avenue, Dundee DD3 7LW	01382 827299	29
Anderson, Janet (Miss)	1979	1982	322 Gartcraig Road, Glasgow G33 2TB	0141 774 5329	16
Beaton, Margaret (Miss)	1989	1988	64 Gardenside Grove, Fernlee Meadows, Carmyle, Glasgow G32 8DS	0141 646 2297	16
Black, Linda (Miss) BSc	1993	1992	127B Spateston Road, Johnstone PA5 0SY	01505 345735	14
Buchanan, John (Mr)	1988	1994	22 Brora Court, North Munton, Perth PH1 3DQ	01738 631697	28
Buchanan, Marion (Mrs)	1983	1997	6 Hamilton Terrace, Edinburgh EH15 1NB	0131 669 5312	1
Burns, Marjorie (Mrs)	1997	1998	16A Park Lodge, Elizabeth Street, Corby, Northants NN17 1FP	01536 264819	47
Carson, Christine (Miss) MA	1992	1998	7 Kirkwood Street, Cessnock, Glasgow G51 1QQ	0141 427 2349	16
Cathcart, John (Mr)	1989	1993	Flat 2/1, 39 Broomlands Street, Paisley PA1 2NQ	0141 848 5163	14
Corrie, Margaret (Miss)	1989	1988	44 Sunnyside Street, Camelon, Falkirk FK1 4BH	01324 670656	22
Crawford, Morag (Miss)	1977	1998	118 Wester DrylawPlace, Edinburgh EH4 2TG	(Tel/Fax) 0131 332 2253	24
			[e-mail:morag.crawford@virgin.net]		
Crocker, Elizabeth (Mrs)	1985	1992	2 Gardiner Grove, Edinburgh EH4 3RT	0131 332 0227	1
Cunningham, Ian (Mr)	1994	1997	5 Forth Court, Dalgety Bay, Fife KY11 5SF	01383 823339	24
Deans, Raymond (Mr)	1994	1998	22 Garrowhill Drive, Garrowhill, Glasgow G69 6HL	0141 771 6847	17
Dickson, Carol (Miss)	1991	1996	South Lodge, Walkerton Drive, Leslie KY5 3EY	01592 743272	25
Douglas, Marilyn (Miss)	1988	1987	201 Almond Road, Abronhill, Cumbernauld G67 3LS	01236 732136	22
Dunnett, Linda (Mrs)	1976	1999	17 Munro Road, Glasgow G13 1SQ	0141 959 3732	[16]
				(Office) 0141 204 4800	
Erskine, Morag (Miss)	1979	1986	111 Main Drive, Erskine PA8 7JJ	0141 812 6096	14
Evans, Mark (Mr)	1988	2000	13 Easter Drylaw Drive, Edinburgh EH4 2QA,	0131 343 3089	1
			[e-mail: mevansdcs@aol.com]	(mbl) 07808 444609	
Gargrave, Mary (Mrs)	1989	1998	229/2 Calder Road, Edinburgh EH11 4RG	0131 476 3493	1
				(office) 0131 663 9603	
Gordon, Margaret (Mrs)	1998	1997	92 Lanark Road West, Currie, Midlothian EH14 5LA	0131 449 2554	1
Gray, Greta (Miss)	1992	1991	67 Crags Avenue, Paisley PA2 6SG	0141 884 6178	14
Hamilton, James (Mr)	1997	1995	6 Beckfield Gate, Glasgow G33 1SW	0141 558 3195	16
			[e-mail: kgrimes999@aol.com]	(mbl) 0970 872859	
Hamilton, Karen (Mrs)	1995	1998	6 Beckfield Gate, Glasgow G33 1SW	0141 558 3195	16
Hankey, Sarah (Miss)	1991	1990	9 Earn Crescent, Menzieshill, Dundee DD2 4BS	01382 641549	29
Hughes, Helen (Miss)	1977	1980	Flat 2/2, 43 Burnbank Terrace, Glasgow G20 6UQ	0141 333 9459	16
Johnston, Mary (Miss)	1988	1987	19 Lounsdale Drive, Paisley PA2 9ED	0141 849 1615	14
Lamont, Fay (Miss) BA	1978	1988	St Ninian's Church House, Kingsway East, Dundee DD4 7RN	01382 453818	29
			[e-mail: faylamont@hotmail.com]	(mbl) 07931 22209	
Love, Joanna (Ms) BSc	1992	2000	Flat 2R, 11 Grantley Gardens, Glasgow G41 3PY	0141 401 8066	16

Name	Year 1	Year 2	Address	Telephone	No.
Lundie, Anne V. (Miss)	1972	1992	20 Langdykes Drive, Cove, Aberdeen AB12 3HW	01224 898416	31
Lyall, Ann (Miss)	1980	1979	117 Balia Drive, Glasgow G45 0AY	0141 631 3643	16
McBain, Margaret (Miss)	1974	1989	33 Quarry Road, Paisley PA8 7RD	0141 884 2920	14
MacDonald, Anne (Miss) BA	1980	1998	62 Berwick Drive, Glasgow G52 3JA	0141 883 5618 / (mbl) 0976 786174	16
MacKay, Kenneth (Mr)	1996	1995	11F Balgowan Road, Letham, Perth PH1 2JG	01738 621169	28
MacKinnon, Ronald (Mr)	1996	1995	70 Eildon Road, Hawick TD9 8ES	01450 374816	6
McLellan, Margaret (Mrs)	1986	1997	5 Kinloch Road, Crookfur, Newton Mearns, Glasgow G77 6LY	0141 639 6853	16
McNaughton, Janette (Miss)	1982	1997	4 Dunellan Avenue, Moodiesburn, Glasgow G69 0GB	01236 870180	22
McPheat, Elspeth (Miss)	1985	1997	11/5 New Orchardfield, Edinburgh EH6 5ET	0131 554 4143/01224 486240	1
MacPherson, James B. (Mr)	1988	1998	13 Leslie Street, Glasgow G41 2LQ	0141 423 6868	16
McVean, M. Christine (Miss)	1969	1987	38 Cruachan Street, Glasgow G46 8LY	0141 638 9035	16
Mair, Alex (Mr)	1988	1984	53 Gardenside Grove, Carmyle, Glasgow G32 8DS	0141 646 2165	16
Martin, Jane (Miss)	1979	1979	12A Carnoustie Court, Ardler, Dundee DD2 3RB [e-mail: janemar@aol.com]	01382 813786	29
Merrilees, Ann (Miss)	1994	2000	15 Crookston Grove, Glasgow G52 3PN [e-mail: ann@ merrilees.freeserve.co.uk]	0141 883 2488	16
Miller, Elsie M. (Miss)	1974	1998	30 Swinton Avenue, Rowanbank, Baillieston, Glasgow G69 6JR	0141 771 0857	22
Mitchell, Joyce (Mrs)	1994	1993	16/4 Murrayburn Place, Edinburgh EH14 2RR	0131 453 6548	1
Morrison, Jean (Mrs)	1964	1994	45 Corslet Road, Currie, Midlothian EH14 5LZ	0131 449 6859	
Mulligan, Anne (Miss)	1974	1986	1/6 Coxfield, Edinburgh EH11 2SY	0131 346 7092	1
Munro, Patricia (Miss) BSc	1986	1985	4 Hewat Place, Perth PH1 2UD [e-mail: patm@esco.net]	(Office) 0131 536 3086 / 01738 627549	28
Nicholson, David (Mr)	1994	1993	2D Doon Side, Kildrum, Cumbernauld G67 2HX	01236 732260	22
Nicol, Joyce (Mrs)	1974	1998	93 Brisbane Street, Greenock PA16 8NY	01475 723235	15
Nicol, Senga (Miss)	1993	1998	Flat 2/1, 160 Tollcross Road, Glasgow G31 4UX	0141 554 3028	16
Ogilvie, Colin (Mr)	1998	1998	42 Kirkwall, Cumbernauld G67	01236 734244	22
Rennie, Agnes M. (Miss)	1974	1979	3/1 Craigmillar Court, Edinburgh EH16 4AD	0131 661 8475	1
Rose, Lewis (Mr)	1993	1998	16 Gean Drive, Blackburn, Aberdeenshire AB21 0YN [e-mail: scimnorth@dial.pipex.com]	01224 790145 / (Mbl) 07901 607331	31
Ross, Duncan (Mr)	1996	1996	64 Stewart Crescent, Aberdeen AB16 5SR	01224 692519	31
Smith, Catherine (Mrs)	1964	1998	21 Lingaro, Bixter, Shetland ZE2 9WN	01595 810207	46
Steele, Marilynn J. (Mrs) BD	1991	1994	2 Northfield Gardens, Prestonpans EH32 9LQ	01875 811497	1
Stewart, Marion (Miss)	1995	1994	Kirk Cottage, Kirkton of Skene, Aberdeenshire AB32 6XX	01224 743407	33
Tait, Agnes (Mrs)	1965	1998	2 Lennox Drive, Faifley, Clydebank G81 5JU	01389 873196	18
Teague, Yvonne (Mrs)			46 Craigcrook Avenue, Edinburgh EH4 3PX [e-mail: yteague@cofscotland.org.uk]	0131 336 3113 / (Office) 0131 225 5722 Ext 304	1
Urquhart, Barbara (Mrs)	1986	1994	9 Standalane, Kilmaurs, Kilmarnock KA3 2NB	01563 538289	11
Wilson, Glenda (Mrs)	1990	1994	41 Colintraive Crescent, Hogganfield, Glasgow G33 1BJ	0141 770 8490	14
Wilson, Muriel (Miss)	1997	1997	22 Well Gardens, Woodside, Glenrothes KY7 5HW	01592 753885	25
Wishart, William (Mr)	1994	1993	17 Swiftbank, Earrock, Hamilton ML3 8PX	01698 429371	17
Wright, Lynda (Miss) BEd	1979	1992	6 Key Cottage, High Street, Falkland KY15 7BD	01337 857705	26

THE DIACONATE (Retired List)

NAME	COM	ADDRESS	TEL	PRES
Anderson, Catherine B. (Mrs)	1975	13 Mosshill Road, Bellshill, Motherwell ML4 1NQ	01698 745907	17
Anderson, Mary (Miss)	1955	33 Ryehill Terrace, Edinburgh EH6 8EN	0131 553 2818	
Bayes, Muriel C. (Mrs)	1963	6 Blenheim Close, Rushden, Northants		47
Beaton, Jamesina (Miss)	1953	Fairhills, Fort Augustus PH32 4DS	01320 366252	38
Bryden, Agnes Y. (Mrs)	1963	9 Rosewell Place, Aberdeen AB15 6HN	01224 315042	31
Cameron, Margaret (Miss)	1961	2 Rowans Gate, Paisley PA2 6RD	0141 840 2479	14
Campbell, Margaret M.M. (Miss)	1958	Tigh-na-Rudha, Port Ellen, Isle of Islay PA42 7DJ	01496 302006	19
Collie, Jeannie P. (Miss)	1950	3 Fortmartindale, Udny Station, Ellon AB41 6QJ	01651 842515	33
Copland, Agnes M. (Mrs) MBE	1950	3 Craigmuschat Road, Gourock PA19 1SE	01475 631870	15
Cunningham, Alison G. (Miss)	1961	23 Strathblane Road, Milngavie G62 8DL	0141 563 9232	18
Drummond, Rhoda (Miss)	1960	23 Grange Loan, Edinburgh EH9 2ER	0131 668 3631	1
Finlayson, Ellena B. (Miss)	1963	16E Denwood, Summerhill, Aberdeen AB15 6JF	01224 321147	31
Flockhart, Andrew (Mr)	1988	31 Castle Street, Rutherglen, Glasgow G73 1DY	0141 569 0716	16
Gillespie, Ann M. (Miss)	1969	Barlochan House, Palnackie, Castle Douglas DG7 1PF	01556 600378	8
Gillon, Phyllis (Miss)	1957	The Elms, 148 Whitehouse Loan, Edinburgh EH9 2EZ	0131 447 4924	
Glass, Irene (Miss)	1976	3E Falcon Road West, Edinburgh EH10 4AA	0131 447 6554	1
Gordon, Fiona S. (Mrs) MA	1958	Machrie, 3 Cupar Road, Cuparmuir, Cupar KY15 5RH	01334 652341	26
Gray, Catherine (Miss)	1969	10C Eastern View, Gourock PA19 1RJ	01475 637479	
Gray, Effie R. (Miss)	1950	8 Station Road, Edinburgh EH12 7AB	0131 334 2083	
Howden, Margaret (Miss)	1954	38 Munro Street, Kirkcaldy KY1 1PY	01592 205913	25
Hutchison, Alan E.W. (Mr)	1988	132 Lochbridge Road, North Berwick EH39 4DR	01620 894077	3
Hutchison, Maureen (Mrs)	1961	23 Drylaw Crescent, Edinburgh EH4 2AU	0131 332 8020	1
McCallum, Moyra (Miss) MA BD	1965	176 Hilton Drive, Aberdeen AB24 4LT [e-mail: moymac@aol.com]	01224 486240	31
McCully, M. Isobel (Miss)	1974	10 Broadstone Avenue, Port Glasgow PA14 5BB	01475 742240	15
McGarva, Sadie (Miss)	1954	87 Hunter Drive, Irvine KA12 9BS	01294 271257	11
Macrae, William (Mr)	1988	6 Park View Terrace, Isle of Scalpay, Isle of Harris HS4 3XX	01859 541288	43
MacLean, Donald A. (Mr)	1988	8 Upper Barvas, Isle of Lewis PA86 0QX	01851 840454	
MacQuien, Duncan (Mr)	1988	2 Manor Crescent, Gourock PA19 1VY	01475 633407	15
MacSween, Helen (Miss)	1960	4 Craig Aonaich, Isle of Scalpay, Isle of Harris PA85 3DH		
Malvenan, Dorothy (Miss)	1955	Flat 19, 6 Craigie Street, Dundee DD4 6PF	01382 462495	29
Martin, Neil (Mr)	1988	3 Strathmiglo Place, Stenhousemuir FK5 4UQ	01324 551362	22
Mickelson, May B. (Miss)	1959	81 Milton Road East, Edinburgh EH15 2NL	0131 669 0482	1

Name	Year	Address	Telephone	No.
Montgomery, Donald (Mr)	1992	17 Murray Place, Stornoway, Isle of Lewis HS1 2JB	01851 704346	44
Mortimer, Aileen (Miss)	1976	38 Sinclair Way, Knightsridge, Livingston EH54 8HW	01506 430504	2
Moyes, Sheila (Miss)	1957	158 Pilton Avenue, Edinburgh EH5 2IZ	0131 551 1731	1
Nicoll, Janet M. (Miss)	1968	74 Brucefield Avenue, Dunfermline KY11 4SY	01383 725734	24
Potts, Jean M. (Miss)	1973	28B East Claremont Street, Edinburgh EH7 4JP	0131 557 2144	1
Ramsay, Katherine (Miss) MA	1958	147 Dalkeith Road, Edinburgh EH16 5HQ	0131 667 4791	1
Ronald, Norma A. (Miss) MBE	1961	43/26 Gillespie Crescent, Edinburgh EH10 4HY	0131 228 1008	1
Rutherford, Ellen B. (Miss) MBE	1962	41 Duncanston, Conon Bridge, Dingwall IV7 8JB	01349 877439	39
Scrimgeour, Alice M. (Miss)	1950	265 Golfhill Drive, Glasgow G31 2PB	0141 564 9602	16
Sloan, Elma C. (Miss)	1957	7 Dunedin Street, Edinburgh EH7 4JB	0131 556 3496	1
Smith, Lillian (Miss)	1977	6 Fintry Mains, Dundee DD4 9HF	01382 500052	29
Steele, Jean (Miss)	1952	93 George Street, Paisley PA1 2JX	0141 889 9512	14
Stuart, Anne (Miss)	1966	19 St Colme Crescent, Aberdour KY3 0ST	01383 860049	24
Thom, Helen (Miss) BA DipEd	1959	84 Great King Street, Edinburgh EH3 6QU	0131 556 5687	1
Trimble, Robert	1988	5 Templar Rise, Livingston EH54 6PJ	01506 412504	2
Webster, Elspeth H. (Miss)	1950	82 Broomhill Avenue, Burntisland KY3 0BP	01592 873616	25
Weir, Minnie Mullo (Miss) MA	1934	37 Strathearn Court, Strathearn Terrace, Crieff PH7 3DS	01764 654189	31
Welsh, Jessie R. (Miss)	1950	40 Thomson Street, Aberdeen AB2 4QP	01224 632323	16
White, Elizabeth (Miss)	1950	Rodger Park Nursing Home, Rutherglen, Glasgow G73		

SUPPLEMENTARY LIST

Name	Year	Address
Forrest, Janice (Mrs)	1990	11E Westercommon Road, Possilpark, Glasgow G22 5ND
Gilroy, Lorraine (Mrs)	1988	29A Church Street, Bulkington, Nuneaton, Warks CV12 9NL
Harris, Judith (Mrs)	1993	46 Afondale, Seaway Parade, Port Talbot, West Glamorgan SA12 7BP
Hood, Katrina (Mrs)	1988	16 Hart Synnot House, Leckford Road, Oxford
Hudson, Sandra (Mrs)	1982	10 Albany Drive, Rutherglen G73 3QN
McIntosh, Kay (Mrs)	1990	4 Jacklin Green, Livingston EH54 8PZ
McLaughlin, Catherine (Mrs)	1966	8 Lamlash Place, Cranhill, Glasgow G33 3XH
Muir, Alison M. (Mrs)	1969	77 Arthur Street, Dunfermline KY12 0JJ
Ramsden, Christine (Miss)	1978	52 Noel Street, Nottingham NG7 6AW
Walker, Wikje (Mrs)	1970	24 Brodie's Yard, Queen Street, Coupar Angus PH13 9RA

LIST H – MINISTERS HAVING RESIGNED MEMBERSHIP OF PRESBYTERY
(in Terms of Act III 1992)

NAME	ORD	ADDRESS	TEL	PRES
Bailey, W. Grahame MA BD	1939	148 Craiglea Drive, Edinburgh EH10 5PU	0131 447 1663	1
Balfour, Thomas MA BD	1945	1 Dean Court, Longniddry EH32 0QT	01875 852694	3
Bogle, Michael M. MA	1936	30 Woodburn Terrace, Edinburgh EH10 4SS	0131 447 3231	1
Chirnside, Charles	1950	11 Stevenson Grove, Edinburgh EH11 2SE	0131 337 2957	23
Cooper, George MA BD	1943	69 Montpelier Park, Edinburgh EH10 4ND	0131 228 2435	1
Craig, Eric MA BD	1959	5 West Relugas Road, Edinburgh EH9 2PW	0131 667 8210	1
Craig, John W. MA BD	1951	83 Milton Road East, Edinburgh EH15 2NL	0131 657 2309	1
Finlayson, D.	1943	3 Nicholson Court, Kinnettas Road, Strathpeffer IV14 9BG	02997 420014	39
Forrester-Paton, Colin MA BD	1944	Acharn, Glen Road, Peebles EH45 9AY	01721 720136	4
Gordon, Alasdair B. BD LLB	1970	2C Ashvale Court, Aberdeen AB10 6FA	01224 571633	31
Greig, James C.G. MA BD STM	1955	St John's Croft, Sorbie, Newton Stewart DG8 8EQ	01988 850270	9
Howie, William MA BD STM	1964	26 Morgan Road, Aberdeen AB2 5JY	01224 483669	31
Inglis, C.G. MA	1944	416 Crow Road, Glasgow G11 7EA	0141 339 3078	16
Lacey, Eric R. BD	1971	1 Ross Court, 96/98 Old Edinburgh Road, Inverness IV2 3HT		37
Lambie, Andrew BD	1957	1 Mercat Loan, Biggar ML12 6DG	01899 221352	13
Levison, L. David MA BD	1943	47 Dunbar Road, Haddington EH41 3PJ	01620 823291	3
Levison, Mary I (Mrs) BA BD DD	1978	2 Gillsland Road, Edinburgh EH10 5BW	0131 228 3118	1
McCaskill, George I.L. MA BD	1953	3/5 Dun-ard Garden, Edinburgh EH9 2HZ	0131 668 2721	1
Macfarlane, Alwyn J.C. MA	1957	4/9 Belhaven Place, Edinburgh EH10 5JN	0131 447 9564	1
Macfarlane, Donald MA	1940	8 Muirfield Gardens, Inverness IV2 4HF	01463 231977	37
Macfarlane, Kenneth	1963	9 Bonnington Road, Peebles EH45 9HF	01721 723609	4
MacLean, Ewen A. MA BD HCF	1945	27/109 West Savile Terrace, Edinburgh EH9 3DR	0131 667 0720	1
McLuskey, J. Fraser MC DD	1938	2 Richmond Court, Park Lane, Milford-on-Sea, Hants SO41 0PT	01590 645405	47
Malcolm, John W. MA BD PhD	1939	16 Abbotsford Court, Edinburgh EH10 5EH	0131 447 0326	1
Masterton, John W.G.	1941	19 Braid Avenue, Edinburgh EH10 4SR	0131 447 4157	1
Monro, George D. TD MA	1935	Flat 79, 303 Colinton Road, Edinburgh EH13 0HS	0131 441 7303	1
Morris, Gordon C. MA BD	1941	42 Regent Street, Edinburgh EH15 2AX	0131 669 4570	1
Murdoch, William M. BSc PhD BD STM	1980	Newton of Middlemuir, Whitecairns AB23 8XP		31
Neill, William G. MA BD BA DipMus	1971	223 Cumbernauld Road, Glasgow G31 2UF	0141 556 7018	10
Nelson, John. MA BD	1941	7 Manse Road, Roslin EH25 9LF	0131 440 3321	3
Ogilvie, Kenneth G. MA	1953	124 Comiston Drive, Edinburgh EH10 5QU	0131 447 8909	1
Petty, P.W.P.	1962	7 Marchbank Place, Balerno, Midlothian EH14 7EU	0131 449 2123	26

Name	Year	Address	Phone	No.
Robertson, Crichton MA	1938	Robin Hill, Ludlow Road, Church Stretton, Salop SY6 6AD	01694 722046	3
Ross, John H.G. OBE MA BD	1940	43 Arden Street, Edinburgh EH9 1BS	0131 447 2027	1
Scott, J. Leonard MA BD	1957	13 Cornwall Street (1 Flat L), Edinburgh EH1 2EQ	0131 229 0395	1
Shaw, Duncan JP PhD ThD Drhc	1951	4 Sydney Terrace, Edinburgh EH7 6SL	0131 669 1089	1
Stewart, Finlay J. BA BD	1936	2/32 Hawthorn Gardens, Loanhead EH20 9EE	0131 440 4117	3
Stobie, Charles I.G.	1942	18 Market Street, St Andrews KY16 9NS	01334 476806	26
Sutherland, Douglas G.	1946	4 Mount Melville Crescent, Strathkinness KY16 9XS	01334 850338	26
Taylor, Alexander T.H. MA BD	1938	4 The Pleasance, Strathkinness KY16 9SD	01334 850585	26
Warnock, John MA BD	1934	Flat 23, Riverside House, Peebles EH45	01721 720095	4
Wilkie, George D. OBE BL	1948	2/37 Barnton Avenue West, Edinburgh EH4 6EB	0131 339 3973	1
Wylie, W. Andrew	1953	Well Rose Cottage, Peat Inn, by Cupar KY15 5LH	01334 840600	26

LIST I – MINISTERS HOLDING MINISTERIAL CERTIFICATES (UNDER ACT II 1987)

Name	Year	Address	Phone	No.
Alexander, Helen (Miss) BD	1981	7 Polwarth Place, Edinburgh EH11 1LG	0131 346 0685	1
Anderson, David MA BD	1975	1a Sanquhar Road, Forres IV36 1DG	0309 672426	35
Arbuthnott, Joan (Mrs) MA BD	1993	23 Ladysmith Road, Edinburgh EH9 3EU	0131 667 8449	1
Archer, Nicholas D.C. BA BD	1971	Myrtlefield, Whitebridge, Inverness IV1 2UR	01456 486456	47
Beattie, Warren	1991	33A Chancery Lane, Singapore 908554	00 1 65 256 3208	1
Black, James S. BD DPS	1976	7 Breck Terrace, Penicuik EH26 0RJ	01968 677559	3
Black, Janette M.K. (Mrs) BD	1993	5 Craigiehall Avenue, Erskine PA8 7DB	0141 812 0794	16
Black, W. Graham MA BD	1983	19 Laurel Braes, Bridge of Don, Aberdeen AB22 8XY	01224 820333	31
Blakey, Stephen A. BSc BD	1977	17A Blacket Place, Edinburgh EH9 1RJ	0131 662 4088	1
Bowman, Norman M. MA BD	1940	18 Eglinton Court, Eglinton Street, Saltcoats KA21 5DN	01294 463453	12
Boyd, Kenneth M. MA BD PhD	1970	1 Doune Terrace, Edinburgh EH3 6DY	0131 225 6485	1
Burnside, Alison H. (Mrs) MA BD	1991	14 Roxburgh Place, Fort William PH33 6UJ	01397 701465	38
Burnside, William A.M.	1991	14 Roxburgh Place, Fort William PH33 6UJ	01397 701465	38
Campbell, Roderick D.M. TD BD FSAScot	1975	22 Greenlaw Road, Newton Mearns G77 6ND	0141 639 7328	16
Campbell, Thomas R. MA BD	1986	14 Falside Avenue, Paisley PA2 6JY	ex directory	14
Chilton, R.M.L. BD BA DipEurHum MA	1972	69 Hill Rise, Market Weighton, York YO4 3JX	01430 871147	33
Cowal, Susan G. (Miss) BA BD	1986	39 Main Street, Symington, Biggar ML12 6LL	01899 308257	13
Cowie, Marion (Mrs) MA BD	1990	6 St Swithin Street, Aberdeen AB10 6XE	01224 593302	31
Currie, Gordon C.M.	1975	43 Deanburn Park, Linlithgow EH49 6HA	01506 842722	2
Davidson, John F. BSc	1970	49 Craigmill Gardens, Carnoustie DD7 6HX [e-mail: jfdavid@bcs.org.uk] [e-mail: jfdavid@breathemail.net]	01241 855412	30
Davies, Gareth W.	1979	8 Inchcolme Drive, North Queensferry KY11 1LD	01383 418863	24
Drummond, Norman W. MA BD	1976	Ellishadder, Staffin, Isle of Skye IV51 9JE	01470 562201	42
Dutch, Morris .M. BD	1998	41 Baronald Drive, Kelvindale, Glasgow G12 0HN	0141 357 2286	16
Ellis, David W. GIMechE GIProdE	1962	Belmont, The Vine, Sevenoaks, Kent TN13 3TZ		16
Fields, James T. MA BD STM	1988	The Bungalow, The Ridgway, Mill Hill, London NW7 1QX	020 8201 1397	47
Fleming, Thomas G.	1961	5 Glenbervie Drive, Larbert FK5 4NP	01324 552004	22

NAME	ORD	ADDRESS	TEL	PRES
Flockhart, D. Ross OBE MA BD	1955	Longwood, Humbie EH36 5PN	01875 833208	3
Fowler, Richard C.A. BSc MSc BD	1978	4 Gardentown, Whalsay, Symbister, Shetland ZE2 9AB	01806 566538	46
Fraser, Ian M. MA BD PhD	1946	Ferndale, Gargunnock FK8 3BW	01786 860612	23
Frew, John M. MA BD	1946	17 The Furrows, Walton-on-Thames KT12 3JQ		16
Galloway, Kathy (Mrs) BD	1977	20 Hamilton Park Avenue, Glasgow G12 8UU	0141 357 4079	16
Gardner, John V.	1997	9 Blackford Glen Road, Edinburgh EH9 3DS	0131 664 3544	1
Gilmour, Robert M. MA BD	1942	"Bellevue", Station Road, Watten, Caithness KY1 5YN	01955 621317	37
Gunn, F. Derek BD	1986	6 Yardley Place, Falkirk FK2 7FH	01324 624938	22
Hendrie, Yvonne (Mrs)	1995	98 Duncansby Way, Perth PH1 5XF	01738 441029	
Higgins, G.K.	1957	150 Broughty Ferry Road, Dundee DD4 6JJ	01382 461288	29
Howitt, Jane (Miss)	1996	PO Box 476, LV 1050, Riga 50, Latvia		16
Ireland, Andrew BA BTh DipRD	1963	19 Glamis Gardens, Dalgety Bay, Dunfermline KY11 5TD	01383 822687	24
Johnstone, Robert MTheol	1973	59 Cliffburn Road, Arbroath, Angus DD11 5BA	01241 439292	32
Kirby, Paul S. BD	1976	Flat 2, 1 Trafalgar Terrace, New St John's Road, St Helier, Jersey JE2 3LE	01534 378889	47
Lawrie, Robert M... BD MSc DipMin LLCM(TD)	1994	West Benview, Main Road, Langbank PA14 6XP	01475 540240	15
Liddiard, F.G.B. MA	1957	34 Trinity Fields Crescent, Brechin DD9 6YF	01356 622966	30
MacArthur, Alexander MA	1946	Luath, St Barchan's Road, Kilbarchan PA10 2AR	01505 702598	14
McKean, Martin J. BD DipMin	1984	14 Morriston Drive, Murieston, Livingston EH54 9HT		1
McKinnon Lily F. (Mrs) MA BD	1993	14B Herries Road, Glasgow G41 4DF	0141 422 1741	
MacPherson, Gordon C.	1963	203 Capalrig Road, Patterton, Newton Mearns, Glasgow G77 6ND		
MacQuarrie, Stuart BD BSc JP	1984	7 Stuart Avenue, Rutherglen, Glasgow G73 4JH	0141 634 4518	11
Main, Arthur W.A. BD	1954	7 Lithgow Avenue, Kirkintilloch G66	0131 556 1344	16
Mair, John BSc	1965	21 Kenilworth Avenue, Helensburgh G84 7JR	01436 671744	16
Marr, Ian	1984	116 Jeanfield Road, Perth PH1 1LP	01738 629883	18
Masson, John D.	1984	5 Wheatlands, Wigton Road, Carlisle CA2 7ER	ex-directory	28
Matheson, Iain G. BD BMus	1985	16 New Street, Musselburgh EH21 6JP	0131 665 2128	7
Merchant, Manson C.	1992	32 Rutherford Folds, Inverurie AB51 4JH	01467 624071	3
Mill, John Stuart MA BD	1974	11 Somerford Place, Beaconsfield, Bucks HP9 1AZ	01494 681906	33
Miller, Irene B. (Mrs) MA PhD	1984	5 Braeside Park, Aberfeldy PH15 2DT	01887 829396	47
Mills, Archibald MA PhD	1953	32 High Street, South Queensferry EH30 9PP	0131 331 3906	27
Munro, Alexander W. MA BD	1978	Clevedon House, Ben Rhydding Drive, Ilkley, West Yorks LS29 8BJ	01943 608515	1
Newell, J. Philip BD PhD	1982	102 Copnor Road, Portsmouth PO3 5AL	01705 666535	47
Ostler, John H. MA LTh	1975	52E Middleshot Square, Prestonpans EH32 9RJ	01875 814358	1
Owen, Catherine MTheol (Mrs)	1984	The Vicarage, St Mary's Road, Worcester Park, Surrey KT4 7JL	020 8337 5025	3
Parker, Andrew H. BSc BD	1967	25 Canton Street, London E14 8JG	020 7538 8505	47
Peat, S. William BSc BD PhD	1977	27/320 West Savile Terrace, Edinburgh EH9 3DS	0131 662 9319	47
Price, Andrea (Mrs)	1997	Mayfield House, St Ola, Kirkwall, Orkney KW15 1SU	01856 875171	1
Provan, Iain W. MA BA PhD	1991	Regent College, 5800 University Boulevard, Vancouver BC V6T 2E4, Canada	001 604 224 3245	45
Quigley, Barbara D (Mrs) MTheol ThM DPS	1979	7 Albany Terrace, Dundee DD3 6HQ	01382 223059	29

Name	Year	Address	Telephone	
Ross, Robin A. MA BD	1977	Yarrow Feus, Selkirk TD7 5BL	01750 82236	4
Sawers, Hugh BA	1968	2 Rosemount Meadows, Castlepark, Bothwell G71 8EL	01698 853960	17
Scott, Donald H.	1987	11 Colebrooke Terrace, Abington ML12 6SB	01864 502732	13
Scouller, Hugh BSc BD	1985	39 Melbourne Place, North Berwick EH39 4JS	01620 893021	3
Selfridge, John BTh BREd	1969	Strathclyde House, Apt 1, Shore Road, Skelmorlie PA17 5AN	01475 529514	37
Squires, J. Finlay R. MA BD	1964	16 Bath Street, Stonehaven AB39 2DH	01569 762458	32
Stein, Jock MA BD	1973	Millfield, Street of Kincardine, Boat of Garten PH24 3BY	01479 831287	36
Stein, Margaret E. DA BD DipRE	1984	Millfield, Street of Kincardine, Boat of Garten PH24 3BY	01479 831287	36
Stewart, M.L. (Mrs) BSc MB ChB BD	1985	28 Inch Crescent, Bathgate EH48 1EU	01506 653428	2
Strachan, David G. BD DPS	1978	1 Deeside Park, Aberdeen AB15 7PQ	01224 324101	31
Strachan, Gordon MA BD PhD	1963	59 Merchiston Crescent, Edinburgh EH10 5AH	0131 229 3654	1
Taylor, Philip	1977	91 Marischal Court, Aberdeen AB11 5DW	01224 587147	31
Thomas, W. Colville BTh BPhil DPS DSc	1964	11 Muirfield Crescent, Gullane EH31 2HN	01620 842415	3
Tollick, Frank BSc	1958	3 Bellhouse Road, Aberdour KY3 0TL	01383 860559	24
Turnbull, Julian S. BSc BD MSc CEng MBCS	1980	25 Hamilton Road, Gullane EH31 2HP [e-mail: jules-turnbull@zetnet.co.uk]	01620 842958	3
Watt, John H.I. MA BD	1960	55 Union Street, Lochgilphead, Argyll PA31 8JS	01546 602143	20
Weir, Mary K. (Mrs) BD PhD	1968	RR*1, V-61 Bowen Island, BC, Vonigo, Canada	604 947 0636	1
Welsh, Alex M. BD	1979	134 Onslow Drive, Glasgow G31	0141 550 0229	16
Wilson, Thomas F. BD	1984	55 Allison Close, Cove AB12 3WG	01224 873501	31
Winn, Fiona M.M. MA BD RGN	1994	35 Ashwood Avenue, Melbourne 3190, Australia	00 61 3 9555 2038	1
Wiseman, Ian	1993	8/4 Lochview Court, Edinburgh EH8 8AR	0131 558 9820	1
Wood, Peter MA BD	1993	c/o 3 Garronhall, Stonehaven AB39 2HF	01569 762591	32

LIST J – ADVISERS IN MISSION AND EVANGELISM

SENIOR ADVISER with South Region	Rev. David Currie BSc BD	5 Eriskay Avenue, Hamilton ML3 8QB [e-mail: nmadvisersouth@dial.pipex.com] Office: contact via the Church of Scotland Offices	01698 428345
CONGREGATIONAL DEVELOPMENT ADVISER	Mr Brian Burden	"Edinbane", Mid Road, Northmuir, Kirriemuir DD8 4QX [e-mail: brian.burden@iname.com]	01575 575280 (Tel/Fax)
MISSIONS CO-ORDINATOR	Rev. Paul Beautyman MA BD	59 Elmbank Street, Glasgow G2 4PQ (Office) [e-mail: gny53@dial.pipex.com]	0141 352 6946 (Tel/Fax) 0468 023385 (Mbl)
PRESBYTERY OF DUNOON (part-time)	Mr John Anderson	9 Berryburn, Kaimes, Tighnabruaich PA21 2BQ [e-mail: jwarmission@aol.com]	01700 811496 (Tel/Fax)

REGIONAL ADVISER (EAST)	Rev. Robin J. McAlpine BDS BD	10 Seton Place, Kirkcaldy KY2 6UX [e-mail:NMadvisereast@dial.pipex.com]	01592 643518 (Tel)
		St Brycedale Church Centre, St Brycedale Avenue, Kirkcaldy KY1 1ET (Office) [e-mail: NatMisskdy@dial.pipex.com]	01592 646406 (Tel/Fax)
REGIONAL ADVISER (NORTH)	Rev. Richard J. Gibbons BD	3 Holm Burn Place, Inverness IV2.6WT [e-mail: rgibbonsIV@aol.com]	01463 223995 (Tel/Fax)
		Inverness West Church, 38 Huntly Street, Inverness IV3 5HR (Office)	01463 223995 (Tel/Fax)
REGIONAL ADVISER (WEST)	Rev. John Campbell MA BD BSc	3 Herries Road, Glasgow G41 4DE [e-mail: campbelljohn@iname.com]	0141 423 3760 (Tel/Fax)
		59 Elmbank Street, Glasgow G2 4PQ (Office) [e-mail: natmisnglasoffice@dial.pipex.com]	0141 333 1948 (Tel/Fax)
URBAN PRIORITY AREAS ADVISER	Rev. Martin Johnstone MA BD	33 Herries Road, Glasgow G41 4DE [e-mail: upaadviser@dial.pipex.com]	0141 423 3760 (Tel/Fax)
		59 Elmbank Street, Glasgow G2 4PQ (Office) [e-mail: natmisnglasoffice@dial.pipex.com]	0141 333 1948 (Tel/Fax)

LIST K – OVERSEAS APPOINTMENTS

['Not a Minister of the Church of Scotland]

NAME	ORD	APP	LOCATION
'Berger, James R.	1968	1993	Bahamas
Burgess, Paul	1983	1994	Pakistan
Calvert, Robert	1983	1995	Rotterdam
Cowie, John A.	1987	1990	Amsterdam
*Dodman, Roy A.		1983	Jamaica
*Duncan, Graham	1978	1998	South Africa
Forbes, Iain	1964	1994	Mozambique
Foreman, Anthony McLean	1988	1995	Sri Lanka
'Fowler, Margaret		1994	Jamaica
Garrity, T. Alan W.	1969	1999	Bermuda
Hibbert, Frederick W.	1986	1995	Tiberias
Huie, David	1962	1991	Rome
*Jenkins, Douglas & Janet		1997	Bahamas
Johnston, Colin D.	1986	1994	Zambia

NAME	ORD	APP	LOCATION
Lamont, Stewart J.	1972	1999	Brussels
Mackenzie, Kenneth	1990	1999	Budapest
McKinnon, Elaine	1988	1992	Kikuyu, Kenya
McLeod, James	1965	1994	Geneva
Milton, A. Leslie		1996	Mozambique
Murray, Douglas	1979	1994	Lausanne
Musgrave, Clarence W.	1966	2000	Jerusalem
Oliver, Gordon	1979	1997	Lisbon
Page, John	1988	1996	Gibraltar
Pikeathly, Tom	1984	1991	Brussels
Reid, William	1966	1993	Paris
'Tamas, Bertalan	1978	1978	Budapest
Westmarland, Colin A.	1971	1975	Malta

LIST L – OVERSEAS LOCATIONS

EUROPE

AMSTERDAM

Rev. John A. Cowie and Mrs Gillian Cowie
Jan Willem Brouwersstraat 9 1071 LH, Amsterdam, The Netherlands
[e-mail: j.cowie@cable.a2000.nl]
The English Reformed Church, The Beginhof (off the Spui).   Service each Sunday at 10.30 am.

(Tel) 00 31 20 672 2288
(Fax) 00 31 20 676 4895

BRUSSELS

Rev. Thomas C. Pitkeathly
23 Square des Nations, 1000, Brussels, Belgium
[e-mail:pitkeathly@compuserve.com]
St Andrew's Church, Chaussee de Vleurgat 181 (off Ave Louise).   Service each Sunday at 11.00 am.

(Tel/Fax) 00 32 2 672 40 56

Rev. Stewart Lamont and Mrs Lara Lamont, Avenue de Broqueville 140, 1200 Brussels, Belgium
Office: CEC/CSC, Rue Joseph II 174, B-1000 Brussels, Belgium
[e-mail: sjl@cec-kek.be]
[private e-mail: sjlamont@wanadoo.be]

(Tel) 00 32 2 772 7122
(Tel) 00 32 2 234 6834
(Fax) 00 32 2 231 1413

BUDAPEST

Rev. Kenneth Mackenzie and Mrs Jayne Mackenzie, 25 Oltvany Ardk, Budapest XI
Scottish Mission, Vorosmarty utca 51, 1064 Budapest, Hungary
[e-mail: mackenzie@mail.datanet.hu]
Service in English and Sunday School each Sunday at 11 am.
(Rev. Bertalan Tamas (1976, held previous appointment) and Mrs Elizabeth Tamas)
[e-mail: rch@mail.elender.hu]

(Tel) 1 00 36 1 246 2258

COSTA DEL SOL

Rev. John Page and Mrs Janet Page,
11 Calle Margarita Blanca,
29640 Fuengirola,
Malaga, Spain.
[e-mail:rico@maptel.es]
Services at Lux Mundi Ecumenical Centre, Fuengirola.   Service each Sunday at 10.30 am.

(Tel) 00 34 95 258 8394

GENEVA

Rev. James Macleod and Mrs Marjorie Macleod
[e-mail:cofsg@pingnet.ch]
6 Chemin Tavernay, 1218 Grand Saconnex, Geneva, Switzerland
The Calvin Auditoire, Place de la Taconnerie (beside Cathedral of St Pierre).   Service each Sunday 11.00 am.

(Tel/Fax) 00 41 22 798 29 09

GIBRALTAR

Rev. John Page and Mrs Janet Page
29 Scud Hill, Gibraltar
[e-mail:billsmith@gibngt.gi]
St Andrew's Church, Governor's Parade.   Service each Sunday 6.00 pm.

(Tel)   00 350 77040
(Fax)   00 350 40852

LAUSANNE

Rev. Douglas R. Murray and Mrs Sheila Murray
26 Avenue de Rumine, 1005 Lausanne, Switzerland
[e-mail: scotskirklausanne@bluewin.ch]
Service each Sunday 10.30 am; Fribourg 1st Sunday of month: 6 p.m. (September - June)

(Tel/Fax)   00 41 21 323 98 28

LISBON

Rev. Gordon Oliver and Mrs Jenny Oliver
The Manse, Rua Arriaga 11, 1200-608, Lisbon, Portugal
[e-mail: st.andrewschurch@clix.pt]
St Andrew's Church, Rua de Arriaga 13-15, Lisbon.   Service each Sunday 11.00 am.

(Tel/Fax)   00 351 21 395 7677

MALTA

Rev. Colin A. Westmarland
206/3 Old Bakery Street, Valletta, Malta
St Andrew's Church, 210 Old Bakery Street, Valletta.   Service each Sunday 10.30 am.

(Tel/Fax)   00 356 222 643

PARIS

Rev. William Reid and Mrs Esther Reid
10 Rue Thimmonier, 75009 Paris, France
[scotskirkparis@free.fr]
The Scots Kirk.
c/o The Eglise Reformee du Sant Esprit
5 Rue De Roquephine (nearest Metros Madeline and St Augustin)
Service each Sunday 11.30 am.

(Tel/Fax)   00 33 1 48 78 47 94

ROME

Rev. David Huie and Mrs Margaret Huie
Via XX Settembre 7, 00187 Rome, Italy   Service each Sunday 11.00 am.
[e-mail:david.huie@flashnet.it]

(Tel)   00 39 06 482 7627
(Fax)   00 39 06 487 4370

ROMANIA

Rev. Celia Kenny
Protestant Theological Institute
Piata Avram Iancli NR13
3400 clu
Romania
[e-mail: celiakenny@aol.com]

(Tel/Fax)   00 4064 191368

ROTTERDAM

Rev. Robert Calvert and Mrs Lesley-Ann Calvert
Gelebrem 59, 3068 TJ Rotterdam
[e-mail scots_international_church@compuserve.com]
The Scots Kirk, Schiedamsevest 121, Rotterdam.   Service each Sunday 10.30 am.

(Tel/Fax)   00 31 10 220 4199

AFRICA

KENYA

Presbyterian Church of East Africa
Dr Elizabeth Borlase, PCEA (1992)
Rev. Elaine McKinnon (1992)
Dr Alison Wilkinson (1992)
Dr Bryson Arthur (1995) and Mrs May Arthur
Dr Angus and Mrs Elizabeth Grant (1997)

PCEA Kikuyu Hospital, PO Box 45, Kikuyu, Kenya
Pastoral Institute, PO Box 387, Kikuyu, Kenya
PCEA Chogoria Hospital Hospital, PO Box 35, Chogoria, Kenya
PO Box 874, Village Market, Nairobi, Kenya
PCEA Chogoria Hospital, PO Box 35, Chogoria, Kenya

Missionary Associates
Miss Elizabeth M. Mudie
Miss Isobel Dick

PO Box 46464, Nairobi, Kenya
PO Box 46464, Nairobi, Kenya

MALAWI

Church of Central Africa Presbyterian
Synod of Blantyre

Synod of Livingstonia
Miss Carol Finlay (1991)
Dr Andrew and Mrs Felicity Gaston (1997)
Mrs Lesley Balaj (1997) and Mr Nglu Balaj
Miss Pat Duncan (1999)
Miss Helen Scott (2000 held previous appointment)

CCAP Hospital, PO Box 19, Ekwendeni, Malawi
CCAP Hospital, PO Box 19, Ekwendeni, Malawi
CCAP Hospital, PO Box 19, Ekwendeni, Malawi
CCAP Hospital, PO Box 19, Ekwendeni, Malawi
Ekwendeni CCAP Girls' Secondary School, PO Box 2, Ekwendeni, Malawi

MOZAMBIQUE

Evangelical Church of Christ in Mozambique
Rev. Dr A. Leslie Milton (1996)

Ricatla Theological Seminary, CX Postal 1057, Maputo, Mozambique

SOUTH AFRICA

Rev. Graham Duncan (1998, held previous appointment)

PO Box 238, Fort Beaufort, Alice 5700,
Eastern Cape, South Africa

Mrs Sandra Duncan (1998)

PO Box 238, Fort Beaufort, Alice 5700,
Eastern Cape, South Africa

ZAMBIA

United Church of Zambia
Rev. Colin D. Johnston (1994)
Mr Martin Harrison (2000)
and Mrs Bridget Kellett

Trinity UCZ, PO Box 30079, Lusaka, Zambia
4CZ Synod Office, PO Box 50122, 15101 Ridgeway, Lusaka, Zambia

THE CARIBBEAN, CENTRAL AND SOUTH AMERICA

BAHAMAS

Rev. Dr James R. Berger (1993)

Rev. Douglas and Rev. Janet Jenkins (1997)

St Andrew's Manse, PO Box N1099, Nassau
[e-mail: jberger@bahamas.net.85]
Lucaya Presbyterian Kirk, PO Box F-40777, Freeport

(Tel) 00 1 242 322 5475
(Fax) 00 1 242 323 1960

BERMUDA

Rev. T. Alan W. Garrity and Mrs Elizabeth Garrity (1999)

The Manse, PO Box PG88, Paget PGBX, Bermuda

(Tel) 00 1 441 236 0400

JAMAICA

United Church of Jamaica and Grand Cayman
Rev. Roy A. Dodman and Mrs Jane Dodman (1983)
8 Wishaw Drive, Kingston 8, Jamaica
[e-mail: rdodman@cwjamaica.com]
(Fax) 00 1 441 232 0552

Rev. Margaret Fowler
PO Box 3097, Negril,
Westmoreland, Jamaica
[e-mail: revm@cwjamaica.com]
(Tel) 00 1 876 925 8491
(Fax) 00 1 876 931 5004

Ms Maureen Burke (1998)
1B Woodley Drive, Kingston 19, Jamaica
(Tel) 00 1 876 905 3106

TRINIDAD

Rev. Harold Sitahal (2000)
Church of Scotland Greyfriars St Ann's,
50 Frederick Street, Port of Spain, Trinidad
(Tel/Fax) 00 1 868 622 1757

ASIA

Ecumenical Appointments

BANGLADESH

Church of Bangladesh
Ms Gillian Rose (1996) — Bollobhpur Hospital, PC Kedargonj, DT Meherpur, Bangladesh
Mr Andrew and Mrs Rosemary Symonds (1999) — St Andrew's College, Dhaka, Bangladesh
Rev. John and Mrs Rita Bennett (2000) — St. Andrew's College, Dkaka, Bangladesh
Ms Ann Thesley (2000) — Rajshani Hospital, Kushtia, Bangladesh

CHINA

Together with Scottish Churches China Group
Mr Ian Groves (1996)
Ms Julie Chrystal (1997)
Mr Mick and Mrs Anne Kavanagh (1997)
Ms Jane Thompson (1997)
Mr Richard Brunt (1998)
Mr David Conkey (1998)
Mrs Valerie King (1999)
Mr Jason Waller (1999)
Sara Ker (2000)
Mark McLeister (2000)

Amity Foundation, Overseas Office, 4 Jordan Road, Kowloon, Hong Kong
Ganzholl Teachers' College, Ganzholl, Jiang-xi Province, China
Nanping Teachers' College, 45 Guanshatian, Nanping, Fujian 353000, China
Changshu Teachers' College, 98 Yuanhe Road, Changshu, Jiangsu 2185009, China
Tai'an Teachers' College, 56 Wenhua Road, Tai'an, Shandong 271000, China
Tai'an Teachers' College, 56 Wenhua Road, Tai'an, Shandong 271000, China
Jiujiang Teachers' College, Jiujiang 332000, Jiangxi Province, China
Fuzhou Teachers' College, Fuzhou, Fujian 350011, China
Jiujiang Teachers' College, Jiiljiang 332000, Jiangxi Province, China
Changwie Teachers' College, 65 Shanglie East Road, Weifang, Shangdong, 261043, China

NEPAL

United Mission to Nepal
Miss Christine Stone (1982) — PO Box 126, Kathmandu, Nepal
Mr John Ross (1995) — PO Box 126, Kathmandu, Nepal

PAKISTAN

Church of Pakistan

Mrs Elizabeth M. McKee — Murree Christian School, Jhika Gali, Murree Hills, Pakistan

Mr William Seaman and Mrs Catherine Seaman (1997) — Murree Christian School, Jhika Gali, Murree Hills, Pakistan

Miss Helen F. McMillan (1981) — United Bible Training Centre, PO Box 14, Gujranwala, Pakistan

Mr Alexander M. Sneddon (1986) and Mrs S. Marie Sneddon — Diocesan Office, Peshawar, Church of Pakistan, 1 Sir Syed Road, Peshawar 25000, Pakistan

Rev. Paul Burgess (1994) and Mrs Cathie Burgess — Gujranwala Theological Seminary, PO Box 13, Gujranwala, Pakistan

SRI LANKA

Presbytery of Lanka

Rev. Anthony McLean Foreman (1995) — Theological College of Lanka, Pilimatalawa, Sri Lanka

THAILAND

Church of Christ in Thailand

Mr Michael D. Fucella and Mrs E. Jane Fucella (1990) — Fellowship of Sivilai, Mu 3 Ampur Sivilai, Nong Khai 43210, Thailand

MIDDLE EAST AND NORTH AFRICA

EGYPT

Dr. Keith Russell (2000) Medical Co-ordinator and Mrs Lai Fun Russell — The Joint Relief Ministry of All Saints' Cathedral, (Tel) 00 202 341 8391 PO Box 87, Zamalek 11211, (Fax) 00 202 340 8941 Cairo, Egypt
[e-mail: rumark@rusys.eg.net] [private e-mail: russell@link.com.eg]

ISRAEL

[Note: Church Services are held in St Andrew's Scots Memorial Church, Jerusalem each Sunday at 10 am; and at Sea of Galilee Church each Sunday at 6 pm.]

Jerusalem

Rev. Clarence W. Musgrave (2000) Minister and Mrs Joan Musgrave — St Andrew's Scots Memorial Church, PO Box 8619, Jerusalem 91086, Israel (Tel: 00 972 2 6732401/Fax: 00 972 2 673 1711) [e-mail: standjer@netvision.net.il]
(Tel: 00 972 2 6732401/Fax: 00 972 2 673 1711)

Mr James Aitken (1998), Pilgrim Co-ordinator — St Andrew's Scots Memorial Church, PO Box 8619, Jerusalem 91086, Israel (Tel: 00 972 2 6732401/Fax: 00 972 2 673 1711) [e-mail: jaitken@ngtvision.net.il]

Ms Emma Given (1997) Manager — St Andrew's Hospice, PO Box 8619, Jerusalem 91086, Israel

Tiberias

Rev. Fred Hibbert (1996), Director and Mrs Diane Hibbert — Sea of Galilee Centre, PO Box 104, Tiberias, Israel [e-mail: scottie@netvision.net.il] (Tel: 00.972.6 6721165/Fax: 00 972 6 6790145)

Jaffa

Mr Christopher Mottershead (2000) Head Teacher and Mrs Sue Mottershead — Tabeetha School, PO Box 8170, 21 Yeffet Street, Jaffa, Israel (Tel: 00 972 3 6821581/Fax: 00 972 3 6819357) [private e-mail: csmott@netvision.net.il]

Mrs Karen Anderson (1992), Teacher — Tabeetha School

Mr Michael Nolan (1996) Teacher and Mrs Margaret Nolan — Tabeetha School

Ms Irene Wilson (1993) Teacher — Tabeetha School

LEBANON	Mr David Kerry (1999)	Near East School of Theology, Sourati Street, PO Box 13-5780, Chouran, Beirut, Lebanon [e-mail: nest.lib@inco.lb]	(Tel) 00 961 1346 708) (Fax) 00 961 1347 129)

LIST M – OVERSEAS RETIRED MISSION PARTNERS (10 or more years' service)

NAME	APP	RET	AREA	ADDRESS
Alexander, Elizabeth (Miss)	1960	1988	Kenya	Flat 22, The Dell, 6 Maryville Avenue, Giffnock, Glasgow G46 7AE
Archibald, Mary L. (Miss)	1964	1982	Nigeria/Ghana	490 Low Main Street, Wishaw ML2 7PL
Bailey, Winifred (Miss)	1949	1979	Kolhapur	22 Mardale Crescent, Edinburgh EH10 5AG
Barbour, Edith R. (Miss)	1952	1983	North India	13/11 Pratik Nagar, Yerwada, Pune 411006, Maharashta, India
Bogle, Rev. Michael M.	1936	1961	Lovedale	30 Woodburn Terrace, Edinburgh EH10 4SS
Boyle, Lexa (Miss)	1959	1992	Aden/Yemen/Sudan	7 Maxwell Grove, Glasgow G41 5JP
Burnett, Dr Fiona	1988	1998	Zambia	Cardon Farm, Broughton, by Biggar ML12 6JF
Burt, M.R.C. (Miss)	1940	1975	Kenya	22 The Loaning, Chirnside, Duns TD11
Campbell, George H.	1957	1971	Livingstonia	27 Avenue Street, Stewarton, Kilmarnock KA3 5AP
Coltart, Rev. Ian O.	1967	1985	North India	161 Kirk Road, Wishaw ML2 7BZ
Conacher, Marion (Miss)	1963	1993	India	41 Magdalene Drive, Edinburgh EH15 3BG
Conn, A. (Mr)	1937	1960	Blantyre	90 Endbutt Lane, Great Crosby, Liverpool 23
Cooper, Rev. George	1966	1986	Kenya	69 Montpelier Park, Edinburgh EH10 4WD
Cowan, Dr Betty	1969	1988	North India	2 Sunningdale Square, Kilwinning KA13 6PH
Dabb, Dr R. Gwen	1943	1971	Blantyre	14/44 Ethel Terrace, Edinburgh EH10 5NA
Dawson, Miss Anne	1976	2000	Malawi	5 Cattle Market, Clackmannan FK10 4EH
Dougall, Ian C.	1960	1990	Kenya	60B Craigmillar Park, Edinburgh EH16 5PU
Drever, Dr Bryan	1962	1982	Aden/Yemen/Pakistan	188 Addison Road, King's Head, Birmingham
Dunlop, Walter T. (Mr)	1979	1994	Malawi/Israel	50 Oxgangs Road, Edinburgh EH13 4DR
Fauchelle, Rev. Don and Mrs Margaret	1971 and 1991	1979 1999	Zambia, Malawi, Zimbabwe	Flat 3, 22 North Avenue, Devonport, Auckland 1309, New Zealand
Ferguson, John K.P. (Mr) and Mrs Margaret	1977	1989	Pakistan	12 Bencleuch Place, Bourtreehill South, Irvine KA11 1EL
Fischbacher, Dr Colin M and Mrs Sally	1984	1998	Malawi	11 Barclay Square, Gosforth, Newcastle-upon-Tyne NE3 2JB
Forbes, Rev. Iain and Mrs Ruth	1993	2000	Mozambique	156 Hamilton Place, Aberdeen AB15 5BB

Forrester-Paton, Rev. Colin	1946	1972	Ghana	Acharn, Glen Road, Peebles EH45 9AY
Gall, E.G. (Miss)	1940	1962	Blantyre	151 Raeburn Heights, Glenrothes KY16 1BW
Glass, Irene (Miss)	1945	1976	Delhi	3E Falcon Road West, Edinburgh EH10 4AA
Hutchison, C.M. (Mr)	1951	1972	Calabar	75 Grampian Road, Torry, Aberdeen AB1 3ED
Irvine, Dr Geoffrey C. and Mrs Dorothy	1952	1989	Kenya	Lakeside, PO Box 1356 Naivasha, Kenya
Kreuger, Dr Hendrikje	1957	1982	Western India	Rm 418, Nellestein Lopikhof 1, 1108, Amsterdam
Lamont, Rev. A. Donald	1941	1975	Kenya	36 St Clair Terrace, Edinburgh EH10 5PS
Liddell, Margaret (Miss)	1964	1980	Zambia	20 Wyvis Crescent, Conon Bridge IV7 8BZ
Lyon, Rev. D.H.S.	1952	1972	Nagpur	30 Mansfield Road, Balerno EH14 7JZ
McArthur, Mr G.	1956	1972	South Africa	3 Craigcrook Road, Edinburgh EH4 3NQ
McCulloch, Lesley (Mrs)	1982	1992	Malawi/Pakistan	c/o 19 North Approach Road, Kincardine FK10 4NW
McCutcheon, Agnes W.F. (Miss)	1957	1989	India	10A Hugh Murray Grove, Cambuslang, Glasgow G72 7NG
Macdonald, Rev. R.M.	1929	1968	Calabar	Pinewood Nursing Home, Leny Road, Callander FK17 8AP
McDougall, Rev. John N.	1935	1960	West Pakistan	2/58 Allendale Road, Mount Albert, Auckland 3, New Zealand
McFarlane, Dr Gordon and Mrs Mary	1990	1999	Kenya	18 Glenburn Drive, Inverness IV2 4ND
McGoff, A.W. (Miss)	1954	1974	Kolhapur	6 Mossvale Walk, Craigend, Glasgow G33 5PF
MacGregor, Rev. Margaret	1959	1994	India	Gordon Flat, 16 Learmonth Court, Edinburgh EH4 1PB
McKenzie, Rev. Robert	1938	1951	India	23 Foulis Crescent, Edinburgh EH14 5BN
McKenzie, Rev. W.M.	1958	1974	Zambia	Troqueer Road, Dumfries DG2 7DF
MacKinnon, E.L. (Miss)	1952	1972	Nigeria	142 Glencairn Street, Stevenston KA20 3BU
McNeel, M.S.H. (Miss)	1938	1975	Seoni	47/5 Gillespie Crescent, Edinburgh EH10 4JB
Malley, Beryl Stevenson (Miss)	1982	1992	Malawi	272/2 Craigcrook Road, Edinburgh EH4 7TF
Marshall, Rev. Fred J.	1946	1992	Bermuda	Flat 3, 31 Oswald Road, Edinburgh EH9 2HT
Millar, Rev. Margaret R.M.	1967	1996	Malawi/Zambia	The Manse, Taynuilt, Argyll PA35 1HW
Millar, Rev. Peter and Mrs Dorothy	1976	1989	South India	104 Baron's Hill Avenue, Linlithgow EH49 7JG
Morrice, Rev Dr Charles and Mrs Margaret	1971	1998	Buenos Aires/Kenya	42 Regent Street, Edinburgh EH5 2AY
Morris, Rev. Gordon C.	1948	1983	Zambia, Argentina	313 Lanark Road West, Currie, Midlothian EH14 5RS
Morton, Rev. Colin	1988	1998	Israel	21 Hailes Gardens, Edinburgh EH13 OIL
Murison, Rev. W.G.	1951	1971	Santalia	Todholes, Greenlaw, Berwickshire TD11 3DS
Nicholson, Rev. Thomas S.	1981	1995	Taiwan	74 Brucefield Avenue, Dunfermline KY11 4SY
Nicoll, J.M. (Miss)	1950	1967	Rajasthan	157 Nithsdale Road, Pollokshields, Glasgow G41 5RD
Pacitti, Rev. Stephen A.	1977	1996	Taiwan	Glasford, Marchmont Road, Greenlaw TD10 6YQ
Paterson, Rev. K.N.	1929	1959	Western Pakistan	

Philip, Rev. David Stuart	1978	1991	Gibralter	6 St Bernard's Crescent, Edinburgh EH4 1NP
Philpot, Rev. David	1981	1995	W.C.C. Geneva	2/27 Pentland Drive, Edinburgh EH10 6PX
Rae, Rev. David and Mrs Margaret	1953	1989	India	29 Falcon Avenue, Edinburgh EH10 4AL
Reid, Margaret I. (Miss)	1964	1982	Malawi	26A Angle Park Terrace, Edinburgh EH11 2T
Rennie, Rev. Alistair M.	1939	1976	Malawi	13 Tullich Terrace, Tillicoultry FK13 6RD
Rhodes, Rev. William S.	1954	1981	North India	22 Hamilton Place, Edinburgh EH3 5AU
Ritchie, Ishbel M. (Miss)	1955	1996	Eastern Himalaya	8 Ross Street, Dunfermline KY12 0AN
Ritchie, Rev. J.M.	1974	1977	Yemen	46 St James' Gardens, Penicuik EH26 9DU
Ritchie, Mary Scott (Miss)	1968	1991	Malawi/Israel	Afton Villa, 1 Afton Bridgend, New Cumnock KA18 4AX
Ross, Rev. Prof. Kenneth and Mrs Hester	1988	1998	Malawi	35 Madeira Street, Edinburgh EH6 4AJ
Rough, Mary E. (Miss)	1966	1987	Blantyre	6 Glebe Street, Dumfries DG1 2LF
Russell, M.M. (Miss)	1946	1969	Nigeria	14 Hozier Street, Carluke ML8 5DW
Samuel, Lynda (Mrs)	1974	1990	Madras	c/o Balgownie, 1 Argyll Street, Brechin, Angus DD9 6JL
Scott, M.A.B. (Miss)	1932	1966	Bengal	27 Woodburn Terrace, Edinburgh EH10 4SS
Scrimgeour, Elizabeth (Miss)	1946	1976	Darjeeling	73 Novar Drive, Glasgow G12 9SS
Smith, Rev. W. Ewing	1962	1978	Delhi	8 Hardy Gardens, Bathgate EH48 1NH
Smith, M.L. (Miss)	1956	1973	Madras	6 Fintry Mains, Dundee DD4 9HF
Smith, Dr R.B.	1939	1958	Yemen	Flat G4, 21 Queen's Bay Crescent, Edinburgh EH15 2NA
Stewart, Marion (Miss)	1976	1989	Malawi/Israel	Kirk Cottage, Kirkton of Skene AB32 6XX
Stone, W. Vernon, MA BD	1949	1966	Zambia	"Santis", Finlaystone Road, Kilmacolm PA13 4RE
Taylor, Rev. A.T.H.	1938	1972	Nigeria/Jamaica	4 The Pleasance, Strathkinnes KY16 9SD
Wallace, A. Dorothy (Miss)	1953	1991	North India	7 Bynack Place, Nethy Bridge PH25 3DU
Wilkie, Rev. James L.	1959	1976	Zambia	7 Comely Bank Avenue, Edinburgh EH4 1EW
Wilkinson, Rev. John	1946	1975	Kenya	70 Craigleith Hill Gardens, Edinburgh EH4 2JH
Wilson, Rev. Mark	1953	1978	Nagpur	37 Kings Avenue, Longniddry EH32 0QN
Wilson, M.H. (Miss)	1946	1977	Nasik	7 Lady's Well, Moat Road, Annan, Dumfriesshire DG12 5AD

LIST N – PARISH ASSISTANTS and PROJECT WORKERS

NAME	APP	ADDRESS		TEL	PRES
Black, Colm	1996	27C Market Street, Musselburgh EH21 6PS	(Kaimes Lockhart Mememorial)	0131 665 3276	1
Carmichael, Colin	1999	60 Glenview Road, Gorebridge EH23 4BW	(Newbattle)	01875 820229	3
Cathcart, Paul	1998	5A Atholl Gardens, Springhall, Rutherglen Glasgow G73 5HF			
Craw, John	1998	21 Redburn Avenue, Culloden, Inverness IV2 7AZ	(East Kilbride: Claremont)	0141 630 0603	17
			(Inverness: Culloden The Barn)	01463 798753	37
Douglas, Jessie (Mrs)	1999	24 Niddrie Marischal Crescent, Edinburgh EH16 4LA	(Edinburgh: Richmond Craigmillar)		1
Edminston, Pauline (Mrs)	1996	24 Miller Court, Dumbarton G82 2JX	(Dumbarton St Andrew's)	01389 732382	18
Falconer, A.J.	1996	59 Waldegrave Road, Carlisle CA2 6EW	(Carlisle Chapel Street with Longtown) St. Andrew's	01228 544757	7
Govan, Alec	1999	1 School Road, Sandford, Strathaven ML10 6BF	(Hamilton: Trinity)	01357 523815	17
How, Margaret Helen (Mrs)	2000	Flat 3/1, 16 Burnmouth Road, Glasgow G33 4SB	(Glasgow: St. Thomas' Gallowgate)		16
McBean, Archie	1999	28 Taransay Crescent, Aberdeen AB15 6UG	(Aberdeen: Mastrick)	01224 789784	31
McCorkindale, Yvonne (Mrs)	1997	118 Ardfin Road, Prestwick KA9 2LE	(Kilmarnock: Shortlees)	01292 678874	11
MacDonald, Ian	1998	St Ninian's Centre, Crieff PH7 4BG	(Crieff and St Ninian's Centre)	01764 653766	28
McIntyre, Lissa (Miss)	1999	8 Wester Drylaw Road, Edinburgh EH4 2SF	(Edinburgh: Muirhouse St. Andrew's)		1
Pearson, Lesley (Mrs)	1997	40 Muir Wood Road, Currie, Midlothian EH14 5JN	(Edinburgh: Leith North)	0131 451 5628	1
Scrimgeour, Anne-Marie (Miss)	2000	16C Abbotsford Street, Dundee DD2 1DD	(Dundee: Craigiebank with Douglas & Angus)		29
Steven, Gordon R. BD	1997	51 Nantwich Drive, Edinburgh EH7 6RB	(Musselburgh: St Clement's & St Ninian's)	0131 669 2054	3
White, Ken	1999	32 Myres Drive, Glenrothes, Fife KY7 4RS	(Glenrothes: St. Margaret's)	01592 631998	25

LIST O – READERS

1. EDINBURGH

Beasley, Ronald E.	37 Warrender Park Terrace, Edinburgh EH9 1EB	0131 229 8383
Campbell Marilyn (Mrs)	9 Sloan Street, Edinburgh EH6 8PL	0131 554 0530
Davies, Ruth (Mrs) (attached to Liberton)	4 Hawkshead Drive EH16 6LS	
Farrant, Yvonne (Mrs) (attached to Kirk o' Field)	Flat 7, 14 Duddingston Mills EH8 7NF	
Farrell, William J.	50 Ulster Crescent, Edinburgh EH8 7JS	0131 661 1026
Kerrigan, Herbert A. MA LLB QC	Airdene, 20 Edinburgh Road, Dalkeith EH22 1JY	0131 660 3007
Kinnear, M.A.	25 Thorburn Road, Edinburgh EH13 OBH	0131 441 3150
Morrison, Peter K.	65 Balgreen Road, Edinburgh EH12 5UA	0131 337 7711
Scott, May (Miss)	34/2 Station Road, Kirkliston EH29 9BE	0131 335 3427
Templeton, Elizabeth (Mrs)	22 Royal Circus EH3 6SS	0131 225 3084
Wyllie, Anne (Mrs) (attached to Carrick Knowe)	46 Jordan Lane EH10 4QX	

2. WEST LOTHIAN

Coyle, Charlotte (Mrs)	28 The Avenue, Whitburn EH47 0DA	01501 740687
Davidson, Sheila (Mrs)	12 Slamannan Road, Avonbridge, Falkirk FK1 2LW	01324 861554
Elliott, Sarah (Miss)	105 Seafield, Bathgate EH47 7AW	01506 654950
Howarth, Jean (Mrs)	25 The Loan, Torphichen, Bathgate EH48 4NF	01506 630449
Notman, Jean G.S. (Miss)	31 South Loch Park, Bathgate EH48 2QZ	01506 633820
Smith, George	15 Manse Avenue, Armadale EH48 3HS	01501 732025

3. LOTHIAN

Booth, Sidney J. IEng CCME	6 Winton Court, Cockenzie, Prestonpans EH32 0JW	01875 813978
Cannon, S. Christopher MA	Briarwood, Winterfield Place, Belhaven, Dunbar EH42 1QQ	01368 864991
Gibson, C.B. Stewart	27 King's Avenue, Longniddry EH32 OQN	01875 853464
Hogg, David MA	82 Eskhill, Penicuik EH26 8DQ	01968 676350
Trevor, A. Hugh	29A Fidra Road, North Berwick EH39 4NE [e-mail: hughtrevor@compuserve.com]	01620 894924

4. MELROSE AND PEEBLES

Butcher, John W.	"Sandal", 11 Ormiston Grove, Melrose TD6 9SR	01896 822339
Cozens, Averil (Mrs)	The Byre, Catrail Road, Galashiels TD1 1NW	01896 755498

5. DUNS

Deans, M. (Mrs) BA	The Lodge, Edrington House, Mordington, Berwick-on-Tweed TD15 1UF	01289 386222
Elphinston, Enid (Mrs)	Edrington House, Berwick-on-Tweed TD15 1UF	01289 386359
Landale, Wm.	Cranshaws House, Cranshaws, Duns TD11 3SJ	01361 890242

6. JEDBURGH

Finlay, Elizabeth (Mrs)	10 Inch Park, Kelso TD5 7EQ	01573 226641
Forbes, William S.	Old Schoolhouse, Burnfoot, Hawick TD9 8EL	01450 372357
Hatton, Audrey (Mrs)	15 Ruberslaw Road, Denholm, Hawick TD9 8PD	01450 870561
Knox, Dagmar (Mrs)	3 Stichill Road, Ednam, Kelso TD5 7QQ	01573 224883
Thomson, Robert R.	34/36 Fisher Avenue, Hawick TD9 9NB	01450 373851

7. ANNANDALE AND ESKDALE

Boncey, David	Redbrae, Beattock, Moffat DG10 9RF	01683 300243
Brown, S. Jeffrey BA	8 Ballplay Rd, Moffat DG10 9AR	01683 220475
Chisholm. Dennis A.G. MA BSc	Moss-side, Hightae, Lockerbie DG11 1JR	01387 811803
Dodds, Alan	Trinco, Battlehill, Annan DG12 6SN	01461 201235
Morton, Andrew A. BSc	19 Sherwood Park, Lockerbie DG11 2DX [e-mail: thccroft@enterprise.net]	01576 203164

8. DUMFRIES AND KIRKCUDBRIGHT

Allison, Douglas BD MEd	2 The Buchan, Castle Douglas DG7 1TH	01556 504279
Archer, Morven (Mrs)	1 Grilloch Drive, Dumfries DG1 4DP	01387 263946
Greer, Kathleen (Mrs)	10 Watling Street, Dumfries DG1 1HF	01387 256113
Ogilvie, D.W. MA FSAScot	Lingerwood, 2 Nelson Street, Dumfries DG2 9AY	01387 264267
Paterson, Dr Ronald M.	Mirkwood, Ringford, Castle Douglas DG7 2AL	01557 820202
Piggins, Janette (Mrs)	Cleugh Wood, Dalbeattie DG5 4PT	01387 780655

9. WIGTOWN AND STRANRAER

Rankin, Stuart	Villa Cree, Cree Bridge, Minigaff, Newton Stewart DG8 6NR	01671 403914
Robinson, J.J.	Kirwaugh, Wigtown, Newton Stewart DG8 9AY	01988 403244
Simpson, George W.	107 George Street, Whithorn, Newton Stewart DG8 8PT	01988 500242

10. AYR

Coghlan, Tony	"Hawthorns", Auchendoon, Hollybush, Ayr KA6 6HA	01242 560307
Fleming, William H.	35 Briar Grove, Ayr KA7 3PD	01292 268599
Jamieson, J.	2 Whinfield Avenue, Prestwick KA9 2BH	01242 476898
Johnstone, B.	15 Northpark Avenue, Girvan KA26 9DH	01465 712006
McNally, David BEd MEd ThDip ACP	50 Kenmore, Troon KA10 6PT	01292 312015
Murphy, I.	56 Lamont Crescent, Cumnock KA18 3DU	01290 423675
Riome, Elizabeth (Mrs)	Monkwood Mains, Minishant, Maybole KA19 8EY	01292 443440
Todd, Joy M. (Mrs) BD	15 Firth Road, Troon KA10 6TF	01292 312995
Todd, S.J.	15 Firth Road, Troon KA10 6TF	01292 312995
Wallace, D.	4 Holmston Crescent, Ayr KA7 3JJ	01292 261620

11. IRVINE AND KILMARNOCK

Bircham, James	8 Holmlea Place, Kilmarnock KA1 1UU	01563 532287
Clark, J. Michael	Brookfield, 81 Loudoun Road, Newmilns KA16 9HQ	01560 320033
Crosbie, Shona (Mrs)	4 Campbell Place, Darvel KA17 0PA	01560 322229
Findlay, Elizabeth (Mrs)	19 Keith Place, Kilmarnock KA3 7NS	01563 528084
Jamieson, John BSc(Hons) DEP AFBPSS	22 Moorfield Avenue, Kilmarnock KA1 1TS	01563 534065
McLean, Donald	1 Four Acres Drive, Kilmaurs, Kilmarnock KA3 2ND	01563 381475
MacTaggart, Elspeth (Miss)	21 Scargie Road, Kilmarnock KA3 1QR	01563 527713
Scott, William BA DipEd	6 Elgin Avenue, Stewarton KA3 3HJ	01560 484273
Storm, Iain	17 Kilwinning Road, Irvine KA12 8RR	01294 277647
Wilson, Robert L.S. MA BD	57 Woodstock Street, Kilmarnock KA1 2JH	01563 526658

12. ARDROSSAN

Allan, J.H.	Creaih Dhubh, Golf Course Road, Whiting Bay, Arran KA27 8RE	01770 700462
Barclay, Elizabeth (Mrs)	2 Jacks Road, Saltcoats KA21 5NT	01294 471855
Mackay, Brenda H. (Mrs)	19 Eglinton Square, Ardrossan KA22 8LN	01294 464491
Mills, Colin J.	Roadend Christian Guesthouse, Shiskine, Brodick, Arran KA27 8EW	01770 860448
Price, James	Dunjara, The Orchard, West Kilbride KA23 9AE	01294 822247

13. LANARK

Allan, Robert — 59 Jenny Lee Drive, Overton ML2 0EE — 01698 376738
Brown, Kay (Mrs) — 16 Abington Road, Symington ML12 6JX — 01899 308838
Grant, Alan — 25 Moss-side Avenue, Carluke ML8 5UG — 01555 771419
Kerr, Sheilagh I. (Mrs) — Dunvegan, 29 Wilsontown Road, Forth, Lanark ML11 8ER — 01555 812214

14. PAISLEY

Campbell, Tom BA FRICS — 100 Craigielea Road, Renfrew PA4 8NJ — 0141 886 2503
McHugh, Jack — "Earlshaugh", Earl Place, Bridge of Weir PA11 3HA — 01505 612789
Ross, Magnus M.B. BA MEd FRSA — "Craigalvie", Kilbarchan Road, Bridge of Weir, PA11 3EZ — 01505 613835

15. GREENOCK

Geddes, Douglas S. — 167 South Street, Greenock PA16 8TE — 01475 723601
Hart, J. — 41 Prospecthill Street, Greenock PA15 4DN — 01475 726687
Jamieson, J.A. — 148 Finnart Street, Greenock PA16 8HY — 01475 729531
Marshall, Leon M. — Glenisla, Gryffe Road, Kilmacolm PA13 4BA — 01505 872417

16. GLASGOW

Birchall, Edwin R. — 11 Sunnybank Grove, Clarkston, Glasgow G76 7SU — 0141 638 4332
Calder, William — 111 Muirside Avenue, Kirkintilloch G66 3PP — 0141 776 5495
Callander, Thomas M.S. — 31 Dalkeith Avenue, Bishopbriggs G64 2HQ — 0141 772 6955
Campbell, Jack T. BD BEd — 27 Springfield Road, Bishopbriggs G64 1PJ — 0141 563 5837
Clarke, Samuel — "Gola", 142 Shelley Road, Glasgow G12 0XN — 0141 337 2238
Findlay, William — 36 Firpark Road, Bishopbriggs G64 1SP — 0141 772 7253
Gibson, James N. — 153 Peveril Avenue, Glasgow G41 3SF — 0141 632 4162
Horner, David J. — 32 Burnside Road, Rutherglen G73 4RS — 0141 634 2178
Lennie, Henry — 14 Clyde Place, Cambuslang G72 7QT — 0141 641 1410
Lockhart, James C. — 56 Springfield Road, Bishopbriggs G64 1PN — 0141 772 7852
MacColl, Duncan N. — 14 Mosspark Avenue, Glasgow G52 1JX — 0141 427 2395
McFarlane, Robert — 25 Avenel Road, Glasgow G13 2PB — 0141 954 5540
McLean, Robert — 50 Pendicle Road, Bearsden G61 1EE — 0141 942 1489
McLellan, Duncan — 138 King's Park Avenue, Glasgow G44 4HS — 0141 632 8433
Middleton, W.G. — 20 Rannoch Avenue, Bishopbriggs G64 1BU — 0141 772 6240
Montgomery, Hamish — 13 Avon Avenue, Kessington, Bearsden G61 2PS — 0141 942 3640
Nairne, Elizabeth (Mrs) — 229 Southbrae Drive, Glasgow G13 1TT — 0141 959 5066
Robertson, Adam — 423 Amulree Street, Glasgow G32 7SS — 0141 778 1563
Sands, Richard — 1 Redwood Place, Lenzie, Kirkintilloch, Glasgow G66 4JQ — 0141 776 4428
Shirlaw, William — 77 Southpark Avenue G12 8LF — 0141 339 0454
Tindall, Margaret (Mrs) — 23 Ashcroft Avenue, Lennoxtown, Glasgow G65 7EN — 01360 310911
Williamson, John G. — 34 King Edward Road, Glasgow G13 1QW — 0141 959 1300
Wilson, George A. — 46 Maxwell Drive, Garrowhill, Baillieston, Glasgow G69 6LS — 0141 771 3862

17. HAMILTON
Chirnside, Peter	141 Kylepark Drive, Uddingston G71 7DB	01698 813769
Clemenson, Anne	25 Dempsey Road, Lochview, Bellshill ML4 2UF	01698 747032
Cruickshanks, William	63 Progress Drive, Caldercruix ML6 7PU	01236 843352
Falconer, Leslie D.	48 Fraser River Tower, East Kilbride G75 8AD	01355 230133
Haggarty, Frank	46 Glen Road, Caldercuix ML6 7PZ	01236 842182
Hawthorne, William	172 Main Street, Plains, Airdrie ML6 7JH	01236 842230
Hewitt, Samuel	3 Corrie Court, Earnock, Hamilton ML3 9XE	01698 457403
Hislop, Eric	3 Kellie Grove, East Kilbride G74 4DN	01355 231600
Leckie, Elizabeth	41 Church Street, Larkhall ML9 1EZ	01698 308933
McCart, Frances BD	26 St Andrew's Court, Sycamore Crescent, East Kilbride G75 9LN	01355 246939
McCleary, Isaac	16 Dalreoch Avenue, Baillieston, Glasgow G69 6EQ	0141 236 0158
McRae, James	36 Crosshill Road, Strathaven ML10 6DS	01357 520053
Queen, Leslie	60 Loch Assynt, East Kilbride G74 2OW	01355 233932
Robertson, Rowan	68 Townhead Road, Coatbridge ML5 2HU	01236 425703
Smith, Alexander	6 Coronation Street, Wishaw ML2 8LF	01698 385797
White, Ian	21 Muirhead, Stonehouse ML9 3HG	01698 792772
Wilson, William	115 Chatelherault Crescent, Low Waters Estate, Hamilton ML3 9PL	01698 421856

18. DUMBARTON
Galbraith, Iain B.	Beechwood, Overton Road, Alexandria G83 0LJ	01389 753563
Hart, R.J.M. BSc	7 Kidston Drive, Helensburgh G84 8QA	01436 672039
McFarlane, Andrew L.	9 Smugglers Way, Rhu, Helensburgh G84 8HX	01436 820058
Neville, Robert	4 Glen Drive, Helensburgh G84 9BJ	01436 671481

19. SOUTH ARGYLL
Holden, Robert	Orsay, West Bank Road, Ardrishaig PA30	01546 603327
Mathisen, Ian M.	Sanaigmore, Campbeltown PA28 6EP	01586 552645
Mitchell, James S.	4 Main Street, Port Charlotte, Islay PA48 7TX	01496 850650
Ramsay, Matthew M.	Portnastorm, Carradale, Campbeltown PA28 6SB	01583 431381
Stewart, Agnes	Creagdhu Mansions, New Quay Street, Campbeltown PA28 6BB	01586 552805
Stewart, John Y.S.	9 Foulis Road, Inveraray PA32 8UW	01499 302077
Wright, D. Gordon B.	Bealach Dearg, Craighouse, Jura PA60 7XS	01496 820212

20. DUNOON
Cameron, Mary (Miss) BD	Ardencraig, Kames, Tighnabruaich PA21 2AG	01700 811376
Challis, John O.	Bay Villa, Strachur PA27 8DE	01369 860436

21. LORN AND MULL
Binner, Aileen	"Ailand", Connel, Argyll PA37	01631 710264
Elwis, Michael,	Erray Farm Cottage, Tobermory, Mull PA75 6PS	01688 302331
Simpson, J.	Ardmhullean, Longsdale Road, Oban PA34 5JW	01631 562022
Taylor, Mary W. (Mrs)	Bunessan Manse, Isle of Mull, Argyll PA67 6DW	01681 700227

22. FALKIRK

Duncan, Lorna (Mrs) BA	Richmond, 28 Solway Drive, Head of Muir, Denny FK5 5NS	01324 813020
Stewart, Arthur MA	29 Ben Nevis Way, Eastfield, Cumbernauld G68 9JG	01236 732532
Struthers, I.	169 The Auld Road, Cumbernauld G67 2RO	01236 733879

23. STIRLING

Durie, Alastair	25 Forth Place, Stirling FK8 1UD	01786 451029
Kimmitt, Alan	111 Glasgow Road, Bannockburn, Stirling FK7 0PF	
Lamont, John	"Serendipity", Wardpark, Gartmore FK8 3RN	01360 850313
Millar, Charles	11 Catherine Road, Bannockburn, Stirling FK7 0XH	01786 811258
Tilly, Patricia	4 Innerdownie Place, Dollar FK14 7BY	01259 742094

24. DUNFERMLINE

Arnott, Robert G.K.	25 Sealstrand, Dalgety Bay, Dunfermline KY11 5GH	01383 822293
Conway, Bernard	4 Centre Street, Kelty KY4 0DU	01383 830442
McCaffery, Joyce (Mrs)	79 Union Street, Cowdenbeath KY4 9SA	ex directory

25. KIRKCALDY

Biernat, Ian	13 Westpark Avenue, Leslie, Glenrothes, Fife KY6 3BX	01592 741487
Biernat, Margaret (Mrs)	13 Westpark Avenue, Leslie, Glenrothes, Fife KY6 3BX	01592 741487

26. ST ANDREWS

Allan, Angus J.	Craigmore, The Barony, Cupar KY15 5ER	01334 653369
Browning, Margaret (Miss)	4 Wellpark Terrace, Newport-on-Tay DD6 8HT	01382 542140
Elder, Morag (Mrs)	5 Provost Road, Tayport DD6 9JE	01382 552218
Hector, Gordon M. CMG CBE MA	3 Montgomery Court, 110 Hepburn Gardens, St Andrews KY16 9LT	01334 473784
Kettle, B.E. (Miss) MTheol	3 Alison Place, Greenside Place, St Andrews KY16 9TJ	01334 474967
Kinnis, Dr W.K.B.	4 Dempster Court, St Andrews KY16 9EU	01334 476959
Smith, Elspeth (Mrs)	Whinstead, Dalgairn, Cupar KY15 4PH	01334 653269

27. DUNKELD AND MEIGLE

Davidson, Margaret (Mrs)	9 Woodlands Park, Blairgowrie PH10 6UW	01250 875957
Macmartin, Duncan M.	Teallach, Old Crieff Road, Aberfeldy PH15 2DG	01887 820693
Wilson, Michael	Moulin Gates Cottage, Atholl Road, Pitlochry PH16 5RQ	01796 473199

28. PERTH

Begg, J.	Craiglea, Addison Terrace, Crieff PH7 3AT	01764 655907
Brown, Stanley	14 Buchan Drive, Perth PH1 1NQ	01738 628818
Buchan, J.S.	47 Dunkeld Road, Perth PH1 5RP	01738 621814
Coulter, Hamish	95 Cedar Drive, Perth PH1 1RW	01738 636761
Hastings, W.P.	5 Craigroyston Road, Scone PH2 6NB	01738 560498
Johnstone, David	92 Duncansby Way, Perth PH1 5XF	01738 442051
Laing, John	14 Cairns Court, Crieff PH7 3SP	01764 654959

Michie, M (Mrs) — 3 Loch Leven Court, Wester Balgedie, Kinross KY13 7NE — 01592 840602
Packer, Joan (Miss) — 11 Moredun Terrace, Perth PH2 0DA — 01738 623873
Thomson, Enid (Mrs) — 12 Strathtay Road, Perth PH1 2LX — 01738 628506
Thorburn, Susan (Mrs) — 3 Daleally Cottages, St Madoes Road, Errol PH2 7QX — 01821 642681
Wilkie R. — 24 Huntingtower Road, Perth PH1 2JS — 01738 628301
Yellowlees, Deirdre (Mrs) — Ringmill House, Gannochy Farm, Perth PH2 7JH — 01738 633773

29. DUNDEE

Baxter, John T.G. — 2 Garten Street, Broughty Ferry, Dundee DD5 3HH — 01382 739997
Bell, R S. — 10 Victoria Street, Newport-on-Tay DD6 8DJ — 01382 542315
Bowser, Charles N. MA — 6 Wellpark Terrace, Newport-on-Tay DD6 8HT — 01382 542157
Doig, Andrew — 6 Lyndhurst Terrace, Dundee DD2 3HP — 01382 610596
Johnston, Wm. — 62 Forthill Road, Broughty Ferry, Dundee DD5 3TJ — 01382 739704
Owler, Harry G. — 43 Brownhill Road, Dundee DD2 4LH — 01382 622902
Ramsay, Thomas A. — Inchcape Place, Broughty Ferry, Dundee DD5 2LP — 01382 778915
Rodgers, Mary (Mrs) — 12 Balmerino Road, Dundee DD4 8RN — 01382 500291
Shepherd, E. — 34 Dalmahoy Drive, Dundee DD2 3UT — 01382 815825
Simpson, Webster — 51 Wemyss Crescent, Monifieth DD5 4RA — 01382 535218
Webster, Charles A. — 16 Bath Street, Broughty Ferry, Dundee DD5 2BY — 01382 739520
Woodley, Dr A.G. — 67 Marlee Road, Broughty Ferry, Dundee DD5 3EU — 01382 739820

30. ANGUS

Anderson, Gordon — 33 Grampian View, Ferryden, Montrose DD10 9SU — 01674 674915
Beedie, A.W. — 62 Newton Crescent, Arbroath DD11 3JZ — 01241 875001
Davidson, P.I. — 27 Dorward Road, Montrose DD10 8SB — 01674 674098
Edwards, Dougal — 25 Mackenzie Street, Carnoustie DD7 6HD — 01241 852666
Gray, Ian — 15 Rossie Island Road, Montrose DD10 9NH — 01674 677126
Ironside, C.T. PhD — 21 Tailyour Crescent, Montrose DD10 9BL — 01674 673959
Leslie Melville, (Hon Mrs) Ruth — Little Deuchar, Fern, Forfar DD8 3RA — 01356 650279
Nicol, Douglas C. — Edenbank, 16 New Road, Forfar DD8 2AE — 01307 463264
Stevens, P.J. — 7 Union Street, Montrose DD10 8PZ — 01674 673710
Thompson, Anne — 22 Braehead Drive, Carnoustie DD7 7SX — 01241 852084
Wade, Nan (Mrs) — Lea-Rig, Charleston, Forfar DD8 1UF — 01307 840204
Wheat, M. — 16A South Esk Street, Montrose DD10 8BJ — 01674 676083

31. ABERDEEN

Dickie, John — 44 Kingsway, Bucksburn AB21 9BP — 01224 714354
Gray, Peter PhD — 165 Countesswells Road, Aberdeen AB15 7RA — 01224 318172
Sinton, George P. FIMLS — 12 North Donside Road, Bridge of Don, Aberdeen AB23 8PA — 01224 702273

32. KINCARDINE AND DEESIDE

Bell, Peter D. BA — 63 St Nicholas Drive, Banchory AB31 5YE — 01330 823661
Cameron, Ann (Mrs) — 30 Wilson Road, Banchory AB31 5UY — 01330 825953
Grant, (Prof) Raymond MA PhD — Ballochbrock, Braemar, Ballater AB35 5YQ — 01339 741340
Haddow, Steven — 18 St Nicholas Drive, Banchory AB31 3YG — 01330 822057

McCafferty, W. John — East Crossley, Netherley, Stonehaven AB39 3QY — 01569 730281
Middleton, Capt. Robbie — 7 St Ternan's Road, Newtonhill, Kincardineshire AB39 2PF — 01569 730852
Mitchell, D. Ronald BDS — Brae House, Raemoir, Banchory AB31 4EB — 01330 823242
Sedgwick, Dr Sheila BA BD MEd PhD — Girnock Shiel, Glengirnock, Ballater AB35 5SS — 01339 755292
Wood, Eric R. MPS — 3 Carronhall, Stonehaven AB39 2HF — 01569 762591

33. GORDON
Hart, Elsie (Mrs) — The Knoll, Craigearn, Kemnay AB51 9LN — 01467 642105
Rennie, Lyall — 5 Urydale, Inverurie AB51 3XW — 01467 624636
Robb, Margaret (Mrs) — Chrislouan, Keithhall AB51 0LN — 01651 882310
Robertson, James Y. — 1 Nicol Road, Kintore AB51 0QA — 01467 633001

34. BUCHAN
Davidson, James — 19 Great Stuart Street, Peterhead AB42 1JX — 01779 470234
Lumsden, Vera (Mrs) — 8 Queen's Crescent, Portsoy, Banff AB45 2PX — 01261 842712
McColl, John — 6 Bracoden Terrace, Gardenstown, Banff AB45 3ZF — 01261 851390
Mair, Dorothy (Miss) — 53 Dennyduff Road, Fraserburgh AB43 9LY — 01346 513879
Michie, William — Rosebank, 9 Seafield Street, Whitehills, Banff AB45 2NA — 01261 861439
Noble, John — 44 Henderson Park, Peterhead AB42 2WR — 01779 472522
Ogston, Norman — Sunnybrae Christian Centre, Woodhead, Fyvie AB53 8LS — 01651 891734
Simpson, Andrew C. — 10 Wood Street, Banff AB45 1JX — 01261 812538
Smith, Ian M.G. MA — Chomriach, 2 Hill Street, Cruden Bay, Peterhead AB42 0HF — 01779 812698
Smith, Jenny (Mrs) — 5 Seatown Place, Cairnbulg, Fraserburgh AB43 5YN — 01346 582980
Sneddon, Richard — 8 School Road, Peterhead AB42 2BE — 01779 474492

35. MORAY
Benson, F. Stuart — 8 Springfield Court, Forres IV36 3WY — 01309 671525
Carson, John — 2 Woodside Drive, Forres IV36 2UF — 01309 674541
MacKenzie, Stuart G. — Woodend Cottage, Blackburn, Fochabers IV32 7LN — 01343 843248
Middleton, Alex — Coral Cottage, Pilmuir Road, Forres IV36 2HU — 01309 676912

36. ABERNETHY
Berkeley, Dr John S. — Drumbeg, Coylumbridge, Aviemore PH22 1QU — 01479 811055

37. INVERNESS
Chalmers, Malcolm — 2 Strath Avenue, Inverness IV2 4LR — 01463 232356
Cook, Arnett D. — 128 Laurel Avenue, Inverness IV3 5RS — 01463 242586
Maclean, Hamish — 63 Ashton Road, Inverness IV2 3UY — 01463 239030
Robertson, Hendry — "Park House", 51 Glenurquhart Road, Inverness IV3 5PB — 01463 231858

38. LOCHABER
Fraser, John A. — 26 Clunes Avenue, Caol, Fort William PH33 7BJ — 01397 703467
Maitland, John — St Monance, Ardgour, Fort William PH33 7AA — 01855 841267
Thomas, Geoff — Achnaholly, Station Road, Arisaig PH39 4NJ — 01687 450230

39. ROSS

Finlayson, Mark	Amberlea, Evanton IV16 9UY	01349 830598
Gilbertson, Ian	Firth View, Crailrory, North Kessock IV1 1XH	01463 73538
McCredie, Frederick	Highfield, Highfield Park, Conon Bridge IV7 8AP	01349 862171
Robertson, Dr John	East Wing, Kincurdie House, Rosemarkie IV10 8SJ	01381 621388
Woodham, Maisey F. (Mrs)	Scardroy, Greenhill, Dingwall IV15 9JQ	01349 862116

40. SUTHERLAND

Betts-Brown, Andrew	54 Muirfield Road, Brora KW9 6QY	01408 621610
Burnett, Michael	16 The Meadows, Dornoch IV25 3SF	01862 810972
Garvie, John	Auchlea, Balnapolaig, Dornoch IV25 3HY	01862 811524
Gazey, Neville	5 Academy Street, Brora KW9 9QP	01408 621607
Mackay, Donald F.	The Retreat, Lillieshall Street, Helmsdale KW8 6JF	01431 821469
Stobo, May (Mrs)	Druim-an-Sgairnich, Lower Gledfield, Ardgay IV24 3BG	01863 766529

41. CAITHNESS

Name	Address	Telephone
Duncan, Esme (Miss)	Avalon, Upper Warse, Canisbay, Wick KW1 4YD	01955 611309
Macnee, Anthea (Mrs)	The Manse, Canisbay, Wick KW1 4YH	

42. LOCHCARRON – SKYE

Mackenzie, Hector	53 Strath, Gairloch IV21 2DB	01445 712433
Macrae, D.E.	Nethania, 52 Strath, Gairloch IV21 2DB	01445 712235
Murray, John W.	Totescore, Kilmuir, Portree, Skye IV51	01470 522297
Ross, R. Ian	St Conal's, Inverinate, by Kyle of Lochalsh IV40 8HB	01599 511371

43. UIST

Name	Address	Telephone
MacAuley, John	Fernhaven, Flodabay, Isle of Harris HS3 3HA	01859 530340
MacNab, Ann (Mrs)	Druim Skillivat, Scolpaig, Lochmaddy, Isle of North Uist HS6 5DH	01876 510701
MacSween, John	5 Scott Road, Tarbert, Isle of Harris HS3 3DL	01859 502338
Morrison, Donald John	Lagnam, Brisgean 22, Kyles, Isle of Harris HS3 3BS	01859 502341
Taylor, Hamish	Tigh na Tobair, Flodabay, Isle of Harris HS3 3HA	01859 530310

44. LEWIS

Name	Address	Telephone
Forsyth, William	1 Berisay Place, Stornoway, Isle of Lewis HS1 2TF	01851 702332
McAlpin, Robert J.G. MA FEIS	24 Upper Coll, Back, Isle of Lewis HS2 0LS	01851 820288
Murray, Angus	4 Cearn Chilleagraidh, Stornoway, Isle of Lewis HS1 2UJ	01851 703550

45. ORKNEY

Name	Address	Telephone
Alexander, Malcolm	Copwillo', Button Road, Stenness, Orkney KW16 3HA	01856 850444
Kent, Reginald F.	Greenfield, Stronsay KW17 2AG	01857 616351

46. SHETLAND

Christie, William C.	11 Fullaburn, Bressay, Shetland ZE2 9ET	01595 820244
Greig, Diane (Mrs)	The Manse, Sandwick, Shetland ZE2 9HW	01950 431244
Jamieson, Ian	Links View, Ringesta, Quendale, Shetland ZE2 9JD	01950 460477
Laidlay, Una (Mrs)	5 Bells Road, Lerwick, Shetland ZE1 0QB	01595 695147
Macdonald, Michael	8 Roebrek, Brae, Shetland ZE2 9QY	01806 522318
MacGregor, Robert	Vistavird, Brae, Shetland ZE2 9SL	01806 522773

47. ENGLAND

Brockett, Alastair BSc	48 Holmeswood Park, Rawenstall, Rossendale, Lancs BB4 6HZ	01706 221363
Green, Dr Peter	Samburu Cottage, Russells Green Road, Ninfield, East Sussex	01424 892033
Lunn, Dorothy (Miss) SRCN	14 Bellerby Drive, Ouston, Durham DH2 1TW	0191 492 0647
Mackay, Donald	90 Hallgarth Street, Elvet, Durham DH1 3AS	0191 383 2110
Twomey, Douglas G.	14 Southsea Avenue, Goring-by-Sea, Worthing BN12 4BN	01903 242019
(Goodbourne, Dr David	145 Westcombe Hill, Blackheath, London SE3 7DP	020 8305 0126)

48. EUROPE

Sharp, James	102 Rue des Eaux-Vives, 1207 Geneva, Switzerland [e-mail:jsharp@world.scout.org]	00 41 22 786 48 47

LIST P – CHURCH REPRESENTATIVES ON COUNCIL EDUCATION COMMITTEES

COUNCIL	NAME	ADDRESS
ABERDEEN CITY	Mr Ronald Riddell	66 Hammersmith Road, Aberdeen AB10 6ND
ABERDEENSHIRE	Mr William Michie	Rosebank, 9 Seafield Street, Whitehills, Banff AB45 2NA
ANGUS	Rev. Carleen Robertson	The Manse, 2 Kirkton Road, Newtyle PH12 8TS
ARGYLL and BUTE	Miss Alexandra Montgomery	Fairfield, 47 Crichton Road, Craigmore, Rothesay PA20 9JT
AYRSHIRE EAST	Rev. John W. Paterson	The Manse, 33 Barrhill Road, Cumnock KA18 1PJ
AYRSHIRE NORTH	Mrs Christine Welch	6 Brodick Close, Kilwinning KA13 6KN
AYRSHIRE SOUTH	Rev. Roger M. Hollins	Smithy Cottage, Dunure, Ayr KA7 4LH
CLACKMANNAN	Rev. George T. Sherry	The Manse, Menstrie FK11 7EA
DUMFRIES and GALLOWAY	Mrs Elizabeth J.Smith	Keltern, Rhonehouse, Castle Douglas DG7 1SL
DUNBARTONSHIRE EAST	Mrs Barbara Jarvie	18 Cannerton Crescent, Glasgow G66 8DR
DUNBARTONSHIRE WEST	Miss Sheila Rennie	128 Dumbuie Avenue, Dumbarton G82 2JW
DUNDEE	Mr K.D. Anderson	10 Douglas Terrace, Broughty Ferry DD5 1EA
EDINBURGH CITY	Mr Henry L. Philip	Lauder Grange, 69/2 Grange Loan, Edinburgh EH9 2EG
FALKIRK	Rev. Duncan E. McClements	30 Russel Street, Falkirk FK2 7HS
FIFE	Rev. John C. Duncan	The Manse, 21 Ramsay Crescent, Burntisland KY3 9JL

GLASGOW CITY	Rev. Andrew J. Philip	The Manse, 43 Smithycroft Road, Riddrie, Glasgow G33 2RH
HIGHLAND	Rev. Alexander Glass	Craigton, Tulloch Avenue, Dingwall IV15 9LH
INVERCLYDE	Rev. David J. MacAdam	80 Bardrainney Avenue, Port Glasgow PA14 6HP
LANARKSHIRE NORTH	Rev. James Munton	Old Monkland Manse, Coatbridge ML5 5QT
LANARKSHIRE SOUTH	Rev. D. Cameron McPherson	Dalserf, by Larkhall ML9 3BN
LOTHIAN EAST	Rev. Cameron Mackenzie	15 West Road, Haddington EH41 3RD
LOTHIAN WEST	Rev. Gordon McCracken	5 Mansewood Crescent, Whitburn, West Lothian EH47 8HA
MIDLOTHIAN	Rev. Alistair K. Ridland	13 Weir Crescent, Dalkeith Midlothian, EH22 3JN
MORAY	Mrs Mhairi Dick	22 West High Street, Portgordon, Buckie AB56 2QS
ORKNEY	Mrs Jenny Deans	Kenmore, Tankerness Orkney KW17 2QT
PERTH and KINROSS	Mrs Mary Reid	The Manse, Dundee Road, Meigle PH12 8SB
RENFREWSHIRE	Mr Allan Millar	24 Duart Drive, Elderslie PA5 9NP
RENFREWSHIRE EAST	Rev. Angus Kerr	28 Waterside Road, Newton Mearns, Glasgow G77 6TJ
SCOTTISH BORDERS	Rev. Alan C.D. Cartwright	The Manse, Swinton, Duns TD11 3JJ
SHETLAND	Rev. James A.M. Dowswell	82 St Olafs Street, Lerwick, Shetland ZE1 0ES
STIRLING	Rev. Moira MacCormick	8 Culbowie Crescent, Buchlyvie, Stirling FK8 3NH
WESTERN ISLES	Rev. Andrew W.F. Coghill	Leurbost, Lochs, Lewis HS2 9NS

LIST Q – RETIRED LAY AGENTS

Elliot, Alexander	24 Broompark View, East Calder EH53 0AD
Lamont, Donald	Old Mission House, Cul-nan-Cnoc, Portree, Isle of Skye IV51 9JD
MacNaughton, Winifred H. (Mrs)	22 Newtown, Cupar KY15 4DD
Macrae, Kenneth	16 Ladysmith Street, Ullapool IV26 2UW
Scott, John W.	15 Manor Court, Forfar DD8 1BR
Shepherd, Denis	Mission House, Norby, Sandness, Shetland ZE2 9PL

LIST R – DECEASED MINISTERS

The Editor has been made aware of the following ministers who have died since the publication of the previous volume of the Year Book.

Adamson, James Telfer Harrison	(Glasgow: Scotstoun East)
Alexander, Dugald Campbell	(Dunscore)
Andrews, John Inglis	(Kirkmaiden)

Auld, Ian Appleby	(Banchory-Devenick)
Barr, David	(Glasgow: Hospital Chaplain)
Beattie, William David	Shotts: Calderhead Erskine
Becke, John Campbell	(Genoa)
Buchanan, George OBE DD	(Bermuda Christ Church, Warwick)
Burnside, William	(West Kilbride: Overton)
Carmichael, William	(Edinburgh: Restalrig)
Colvin, Thomas Stevenson	(Missionary in Malawi)
Couper, James McGregor	(Dunoon: Kilmodan and Colintraive)
Duncan, John Henry	(Earlston)
Dungavel, William	(Olrig and Dunnet)
Dunlop, Alexander Ian	(Edinburgh: St. Stephen's)
Ferguson, Gordon	(Grangemouth: Kirk of the Holy Rood)
Fletcher, John Arnold Horatio	(Blackburn)
Fox, Edward Philips Grieve	(Eday with Stronsay Moncur Memorial)
Fraser, John Hamilton	Castle Douglas
Gray, Ian Alister	(Buchanan with Drymen)
Gray, John DD	(Professor of Hebrew and Semitic Languages: Aberdeen University)
Gunneberg, Herbert Hermann Friedrich	(Gigha and Cara)
Hall, Robert Kellas	(Carnock)
Hislop, David Thomson	(Glasgow: Maryhill High)
Johnstone, Helen Gibson (Mrs)	(Missionary in Zambia)
Kirk, John Fraser	(Edinburgh: Morningside)
Leitch, James Waterston	(Bathgate High)
Lennie, Robert Cranston	(Aberlady)
Levack, John Grant	(Prestonkirk)
Lyall, James Farquhar	(Arnsheen Barrhill with Colmonell)
Macartney, William Macleod	(Vienna)
Macaskill, Norman Roy	(Kingussie)
Macdonald, William	(Knock)
McHardy, William Duff DD	(Regius Professor of Hebrew: Oxford University)
McHutchison, David Wedderburn	(Glasgow: Hospital Chaplain)
McLauchlan, Laurence Smith	(Haywood, Wilsontown and Braehead)
Mackinnon, John Macdougall	(Dollar West)
Maclean, William Duncan	(Dailly)
Macleod, Donald Angus	(Inveraven and Glenlivet)
Macleod, John Angus	(Keith: St. Rufus and Botriphnie)

MacRury, Ian Archibald Macdonald	(Glasgow: Partick East)
Mactaggart, Ian	(Edinburgh: Craigmillar Park)
Malcolm, Kenneth	(Auxiliary Minister: Fowlis and Liff with Lundie and Muirhead of Liff)
Matthews, Laurence John	(Aberdeen: Nigg)
Morton, John	(Dalmellington: Kirk of the Covenant)
Murray, John	(Slains and Forvie)
Napier, James Knox	(Balmaghie)
Neil, Herbert Kitchener	(Portmoak)
Orr, William	(Tarbat)
Poustie, George Todd	(Boyndie, Whitehill and Cornhill)
Riach, William Alexander Drage	(Missionary in Kenya)
Robertson, Alan Ogilvie	(Scone New)
Robinson, Keith Simpson Paton	(Edinburgh: North Merchiston)
Robson, James	(Falkirk: Camelon St. John's)
Rogerson, Alexander Eddington	(Galashiels Ladhope St. Cuthbert's)
Ross, Hector Gilbert	(Gillingham St. Margaret's)
Rutherford, David Wedderburn	(Aberdour)
Shepherd, Henry Arthur	(Bermuda Christ Church, Warwick)
Somerville, Alexander George	(Glenaray and Inveraray)
Thomson, Henry Christie	(Glasgow: Anniesland Cross)
Walker, Grahame Russell	(Torphins)
Watson, David Henry Alexander	(Anstruther)
Wightman, James Petrie Edgar	(Girvan St. Andrew's)
Wills, William Fraser	(Kilsyth Burns)

SECTION 7

Congregational
Statistics
1999

CHURCH OF SCOTLAND STATISTICS
FOR 1999

Congregations 1,568
Communicants 626,665
Elders 44,131
Charges 1,280
Ministers serving charges 1,143
Chaplains to HM Forces 28
Students completing their courses 23

NOTES ON CONGREGATIONAL STATISTICS

Com   Number of communicants at 31/12/99.

Eld   Number of elders at 31/12/99.

G   Membership of The Guild including Young Woman's Group. The letter "j" beside a figure indicates that the figure is a joint figure for all the congregations making up the charge.

In99   Ordinary General Income for 1999. Ordinary General Income consists of members' offerings, contributions from congregational organisations, regular fund-raising events, income from investments, deposits, *etc*. This figure does not include extraordinary or special income, or income from special collections and fundraising for other charities.

Ass   Amount allocated to congregations for Mission and Aid Fund in 1999.

Gvn   Amount contributed by congregations to Mission and Aid Fund in 1999.
The amount shown includes contributions to allocation and voluntary extra contributions. The figures do not take into account late payments made in 2000 for 1999 but may contain late payments made in 1999 for 1998 and prior years.

[N.B. Figures may not be available for new charges created or for congregations which have entered into readjustment late in 1999 or during 2000.]

3-11 and -17   Figures in these columns have customarily shown the number of young people in these age groups receiving Christian Education. The Board of Parish Education, which gathers these figures, is currently undertaking a statistical survey of young people in the Church which may alter the basis and range of the statistical information that will be available. New figures are not available for this year. The figures shown are those for 1996.

Congregation	Com	Eld	G	In98	Ass	Gvn	3-11	-17
1. EDINBURGH								
Abercorn	93	9	12	10421	500	500	–	–
Dalmeny	174	10	12	8231	450	450	–	–
Albany Deaf Church of Edinburgh	152	12	–	n/a	0	0	–	–
Balerno	977	63	75	109707	27812	31697	102	15
Barclay	408	50	29	73455	20100	20100	61	16
Blackhall St Columba	1177	92	63	146390	39470	39470	117	34
Bristo Memorial Craigmillar	191	5	23	17990	0	0	10	–
Broughton St Mary's	362	39	37	46324	7660	7660	12	1
Canongate	467	47	–	60872	11550	11550	–	–
Carrick Knowe	792	58	113	63249	11920	11920	75	24
Cluny	712	59	26	94742	21400	21400	36	23
Colinton	1283	95	–	120552	33400	37567	143	82
Colinton Mains	293	18	23	36542	3380	3498	50	12
Corstorphine Craigsbank	990	62	–	103549	21220	24220	83	45
Corstorphine Old	754	60	82	75416	19670	19920	59	13
Corstorphine St Anne's	562	58	53	72644	19440	24603	41	10
Corstorphine St Ninian's	1215	96	59	125213	33370	34686	130	22
Craigentinny St Christopher's	193	16	–	25854	0	0	–	–
Craiglockhart	619	57	47	103662	23920	23920	90	28
Craigmillar Park	365	29	39	75995	17470	18335	26	7
Cramond	1390	108	32	164842	48460	59000	76	24
Currie	1490	78	73	146862	36880	36880	81	40
Davidson's Mains	903	82	50	124654	31550	31610	83	32
Dean	266	30	30	55201	9480	9480	13	15
Drylaw	259	16	11	21364	0	0	125	—
Duddingston	895	68	62	68817	14950	15260	37	34
Fairmilehead	1121	78	32	112397	21740	40240	205	36
Gilmerton	278	12	–	14406	0	0	12	26
Gorgie	413	31	25	64485	11340	11740	25	9
Granton	455	40	–	35766	4390	4390	30	–
Greenbank	1042	94	97	166085	46210	47710	152	68
Greenside	301	27	-	48131	8070	8720	39	3
Greyfriars Tolbooth and Highland	474	44	20	82670	15570	15570	9	–
High (St Giles')	728	49	–	189598	33960	34770	–	–
Holyrood Abbey	274	38	20	121813	29220	29220	20	20
Holy Trinity	235	28	–	55054	3687	3687	31	19
Inverleith	476	45	–	70847	15460	15888	23	6
Juniper Green	477	36	–	79048	21710	23000	81	14
Kaimes Lockhart Memorial	190	12	14	17002	0	0	28	–
Kirkliston	448	40	46	43065	6560	6560	45	21
Kirk o' Field	270	37	–	40686	6770	6070	17	3
Leith North	554	56	38	65510	13260	13260	53	29
Leith St Andrew's	368	36	–	45873	8130	8130	64	8
Leith St Serf's	341	28	28	41094	4730	4730	21	4
Leith St Thomas' Junction Road	368	27	29	44788	5850	6307	–	—
Leith South	751	87	-	102818	23270	24765	41	–
Leith Wardie	682	85	80	100259	25660	28702	111	24
Liberton	1070	70	83	94218	24020	24320	57	16
Liberton Northfield	350	13	34	26017	0	0	31	4
London Road	451	36	30	48636	8110	8110	24	6

Congregation	Com	Eld	G	In98	Ass	Gvn	3-11	-17
Marchmont St Giles'	388	46	42	69105	15590	19590	47	–
Mayfield Salisbury	901	78	55	171869	46030	47860	77	30
Morningside Braid	409	57	33	47679	6840	7040	–	–
Morningside United	224	26	–	55868	9120	9120	19	–
Muirhouse St Andrew's	162	8	12	8018	0	0	44	17
Murrayfield	663	69	23	117638	35570	35570	56	33
Newhaven	304	15	56	60520	10420	10420	16	26
New Restalrig	511	21	28	69934	13520	13520	54	18
Old Kirk	216	15	–	13952	0	305	–	–
Palmerston Place	566	80	.	135930	34920	36420	36	19
Pilrig St. Paul's	454	29	47	49086	11510	11510	33	48
Polwarth	389	37	27	60821	9490	9762	5	–
Portobello Old	469	46	40	40745	7880	7880	31	4
Portobello St James'	451	39	20	48229	7830	8867	27	–
Portobello St Philip's Joppa	793	71	106	126786	29930	29930	121	16
Priestfield	269	24	35	47566	8410	8410	–	–
Queensferry	883	46	91	61544	9090	9090	111	25
Ratho	274	20	25	33570	0	212	85	12
Reid Memorial	485	24	–	83922	19290	22631	29	7
Richmond Craigmillar	136	8	12	10798	0	0	18	2
St Andrew's and St George's	419	46	27	145809	28630	28630	22	10
St Andrew's Clermiston	383	23	–	38292	0	191	26	–
St Catherine's Argyle	355	28	30	104784	23580	23580	38	37
St Colm's	224	23	31	34750	3460	3460	58	2
St Cuthbert's	740	70	–	158533	37530	37530	15	4
St David's Broomhouse	214	16	–	42670	5760	5858	54	11
St George's West	238	46	–	97048	27480	27624	6	3
St John's Oxgangs	387	29	40	24111	0	803	18	–
St Margaret's	492	39	32	45408	5640	5640	60	12
St Martin's	318	14	25	17824	0	0	50	17
St Michael's	591	41	.	63047	8190	8743	33	16
St Nicholas' Sighthill	657	38	28	45234	7050	7366	40	15
St Stephen's Comely Bank	583	29	46	91658	18910	18910	82	16
Slateford Longstone	374	29	51	45661	5750	5750	24	6
Stenhouse St Aidan's	317	23	–	24566	0	260	10	11
Stockbridge	455	37	43	42130	8610	8610	12	4
Tron Moredun	188	13	–	n/a	0	0	32	–
Viewforth	284	34	19	n/a	12730	14875	49	–

2. WEST LOTHIAN

Congregation	Com	Eld	G	In98	Ass	Gvn	3-11	-17
Addiewell	106	4	23	10360	0	0	10	1
Longridge and Breich	90	5	–	7550	0	0	–	–
Stoneyburn	66	3	–	6352	0	0	–	–
Armadale	738	47	35	54828	9230	9230	60	8
Avonbridge	81	8	12	9284	968	968	8	2
Torphichen	293	22	–	27237	2140	2140	32	9
Bathgate Boghall	492	35	23	52501	9560	9560	65	21
Bathgate High	709	39	63	58648	12400	12400	34	10
Bathgate St David's	357	17	14	44687	6990	4260	9	9
Bathgate St John's	431	27	40	46121	6010	6010	48	–
Blackburn	620	33	–	44404	3700	3700	20	1

Congregation	Com	Eld	G	In98	Ass	Gvn	3-11	-17
Blackridge	148	8	16	12213	1500	1500	13	1
Harthill – St Andrew's	286	23	36	37143	6500	6500	34	6
Broxburn	570	29	51	41064	8050	8050	45	15
Fauldhouse St Andrew's	434	20	21	33985	4230	4230	18	–
Kirknewton and East Calder	582	38	26	54838	10160	10160	90	26
Kirk of Calder	914	46	35	57614	11680	11680	100	6
Linlithgow St Michael's	1676	108	75	206856	34400	38261	234	73
Linlithgow St Ninian's Craigmailen	662	60	89	56451	10880	11892	62	11
Livingston Ecumenical	846	46	35	91479	0	100	107	38
Livingston Old	548	29	–	50930	10120	10120	64	7
Pardovan, Kingscavil and Winchburgh	307	18	42	31804	0	220	12	–
Polbeth Harwood	334	36	–	30509	1700	1700	19	–
Strathbrock	449	43	25	70059	21140	21140	74	28
Uphall South	234	20	–	27756	0	0	68	–
West Kirk of Calder	346	26	43	34358	5030	5030	–	–
Whitburn – Brucefield	483	29	36	47167	10460	10460	36	32
Whitburn – South	451	35	38	56841	8870	8870	49	5

3. LOTHIAN

Congregation	Com	Eld	G	In98	Ass	Gvn	3-11	-17
Aberlady	349	36	–	30694	4690	4690	34	–
Gullane	522	38	46	41360	8240	8240	18	5
Athelstaneford	222	17	12	18868	1610	1610	–	–
Whitekirk and Tyninghame	184	19	–	27015	3825	3825	4	–
Belhaven	822	33	73	51583	7840	7840	51	8
Spott	101	8	–	7788	937	937	–	–
Bolton and Saltoun	252	17	19	16979	2720	2796	32	2
Humbie	120	8	12	12395	3060	3060	17	–
Yester	354	28	35	19819	3880	3880	–	–
Bonnyrigg	946	69	77	70628	15060	15556	84	7
Borthwick	92	5	21	10830	0	1600	10	3
Newtongrange	284	9	28	18057	0	0	37	–
Cockenzie and Port Seton Chalmers Memorial	348	28	60	48381	7660	7660	–	–
Cockenzie and Port Seton Old	465	14	22	28940	0	0	43	5
Cockpen and Carrington	359	27	41	15698	3100	3100	18	–
Lasswade	385	26	16	22150	4480	4480	20	–
Rosewell	225	16	–	10464	1546	1546	16	–
Cranstoun, Crichton and Ford	324	17	27	33859	3940	3940	45	–
Fala and Soutra	87	5	10	6770	880	2821	10	4
Dalkeith St John's and King's Park	642	49	31	62889	10800	10800	59	6
Dalkeith St Nicholas Buccleuch	681	24	30	33557	7080	7080	21	4
Dirleton	292	19	19	22839	5400	5518	6	–
North Berwick Abbey	445	26	42	47031	7390	7390	28	8
Dunbar	886	46	74	45723	8320	8675	–	–
Dunglass	383	24	25	25128	0	300	18	–
Garvald and Morham	48	7	–	10074	1000	1000	–	–
Haddington West	460	36	62	48692	5140	5140	–	–
Gladsmuir	273	15	15	15716	3180	3180	7	–
Longniddry	474	40	50	61376	13000	13000	74	62
Glencorse	377	11	-	21284	4680	4680	26	–

Congregation	Com	Eld	G	In98	Ass	Gvn	3-11	-17
Roslin	417	9	–	24449	2460	2460	68	17
Gorebridge	484	28	47	30918	3540	3540	37	5
Haddington St Mary's	868	57	–	87195	17780	18180	37	–
Howgate	42	5	7	10161	1740	1740	2	5
Penicuik South	346	21	31	74133	14330	17392	43	47
Loanhead	640	33	47	32265	4460	3352	27	–
Musselburgh Northesk	475	37	18	52164	8030	8030	–	–
Musselburgh St Andrew's High	512	46	39	31777	7020	7020	–	–
Musselburgh St Clement's and St Ninian's	412	42	8	28199	0	155	–	–
Musselburgh St Michael's Inveresk	599	41	45	52387	8540	8540	–	5
Newbattle	585	37	31	36464	6251	6251	40	8
Newton	393	13	18	18733	0	0	39	–
North Berwick St Andrew Blackadder	826	53	39	64275	17780	17780	85	14
Ormiston	193	19	29	21109	2475	2475	13	3
Pencaitland	285	24	15	32507	5608	5608	39	10
Penicuik North	707	42	–	61016	10990	10990	81	27
Penicuik St Mungo's	581	37	34	49823	8220	13581	71	7
Prestonpans – Prestongrange	468	59	34	32265	4620	4620	–	–
Tranent	445	21	45	38510	5110	5110	22	4
Traprain	693	31	41	39755	985	985	36	22

4. MELROSE AND PEEBLES

Congregation	Com	Eld	G	In98	Ass	Gvn	3-11	-17
Ashkirk	82	7	13	6599	970	970	–	–
Selkirk	702	27	53	50984	10410	10410	22	3
Bowden	114	11	12	15983	1630	1630	2	2
Newtown	235	12	–	17502	2125	2125	16	8
Broughton Glenholm and Kilbucho	188	17	26j	11099	0	800	12	–
Skirling	94	6	j	4310	0	300	–	–
Stobo and Drumelzier	116	8	j	9061	0	600	8	–
Tweedsmuir	47	5	j	10590	0	300	6	–
Caddonfoot	208	12	–	8867	2040	2040	9	–
Galashiels St Ninian's	629	30	47	46982	12990	12990	18	20
Carlops	75	12	–	8502	1400	1400	4	1
Kirkurd and Newlands	121	10	11	12579	1100	1100	30	7
West Linton – St Andrew's	282	19	40	28266	2570	2570	39	39
Channelkirk	91	7	8	6808	468	468	–	–
Lauder – Old	366	16	38	24543	2590	2590	30	–
Earlston	628	15	44	33183	3520	3520	42	6
Eddleston	143	7	17	7457	1120	1120	19	–
Peebles Old	785	56	33	60302	14340	14340	33	10
Ettrick	131	7	4	6912	0	0	19	–
Yarrow	112	12	11	8816	0	149	11	–
Galashiels Old and St Paul's	453	25	38	44909	7000	7000	33	8
Galashiels St Aidan's	565	25	26	37510	4630	4687	19	34
Galashiels St John's	291	19	–	27400	0	75	17	22
Innerleithen	508	29	45	33230	5850	5850	29	24
Traquair	92	7	–	7554	950	950	7	2
Walkerburn	118	8	22	12411	2670	2670	8	5
Lyne and Manor	113	9	–	18359	160	420	23	3
Maxton and Mertoun	162	12	14	14179	1580	1785	9	–

Congregation	Com	Eld	G	In98	Ass	Gvn	3-11	-17
St Boswells	364	25	30	29597	4590	4590	26	25
Melrose	936	58	47	71934	16750	17199	49	–
Peebles St Andrew's Leckie	757	40	55	63241	11150	12264	45	20
Stow St Mary of Wedale and Heriot	230	17	–	29500	0	1000	41	9

5. DUNS

Congregation	Com	Eld	G	In98	Ass	Gvn	3-11	-17
Ayton and Burnmouth	259	16		12362	0	0	6	-
Grantshouse, Houndswood and Reston	163	6	10	8680	0	0	20	6
Berwick on Tweed St Andrew's Wallace Green and Lowick	476	23	32	35485	3070	3200	9	–
Bonkyl and Preston	91	7	–	7012	875	788	–	–
Chirnside	462	20	27	22117	1900	2087	–	–
Edrom Allanton	93	9	–	4900	525	525	–	–
Coldingham and St. Abb's	120	8	20	12238	810	810	-	-
Eyemouth	309	25	73	31495	4840	4840	43	14
Coldstream	471	23	26	31354	4520	4520	31	11
Eccles	112	10	18	7066	720	720	7	–
Duns	482	22	54	31249	1940	1940	16	–
Fogo and Swinton	195	8	–	8233	1670	1670	11	–
Ladykirk	42	3	10	5038	950	950	–	–
Leitholm	125	8	–	7957	875	875	–	–
Whitsome	61	5	10	4760	600	600	–	–
Foulden and Mordington	99	9	10	6182	0	0	–	–
Hutton and Fishwick and Paxton	110	10	14	8746	0	0	4	–
Gordon St Michael's	103	6	18j	8500	1090	1090	–	–
Greenlaw	160	13	20	15455	3750	3750	12	–
Legerwood	78	6	–	4347	340	340	–	–
Westruther	62	7	j	5715	920	920	16	–
Kirk of Lammermuir	63	7	-	11920	0	61	–	–
Langton and Polwarth	120	10	26	13654	0	0	–	–

6. JEDBURGH

Congregation	Com	Eld	G	In98	Ass	Gvn	3-11	-17
Ancrum	218	11	12	18011	160	160	27	5
Crailing and Eckford	54	9	10	5504	160	160	-	-
Lilliesleaf	154	11	13	11052	160	160	13	5
Bedrule	55	5	-	7166	160	160	10	2
Denholm	213	15	22	18249	160	160	21	–
Minto	90	7	8	8096	160	160	7	–
Cavers and Kirkton	159	10	–	6797	500	500	–	–
Hawick St Mary's and Old	686	33	43	35502	4900	4900	–	–
Oxnam	105	5	17	6727	730	730	–	–
Roxburgh	74	4	–	3700	350	350	12	–
Hawick Burnfoot	246	15	15	19324	0	0	36	8
Hawick Teviot and Roberton	465	16	14	36884	6010	2864	12	7
Hawick Trinity	972	40	50	46352	5620	4982	51	16
Hawick Wilton	470	24	40	24065	4160	7920	23	–
Teviothead	74	4	12	5148	680	680	9	–
Hobkirk and Southdean	177	14	11	8809	0	200	14	–
Jedburgh Old and Edgerston	871	28	31	43220	7030	7030	27	2
Jedburgh Trinity	279	12	35	36645	3660	4415	7	–
Kelso North and Ednam	1577	79	80	84963	16160	16160	35	–

Congregation	Com	Eld	G	In98	Ass	Gvn	3-11	-17
Kelso Old and Sprouston	711	42	47	43420	5860	5976	27	4
Liddesdale	197	8	41	30721	160	521	16	3
Linton	106	6	–	6758	580	580	–	–
Morebattle and Hownam	210	16	29	16410	2200	2200	23	–
Yetholm	201	14	20	18372	2270	2270	26	–
Makerstoun and Smailholm	76	5	–	2090	0	0	–	–
Stichill, Hume and Nenthorn	78	4	13	2645	0	0	–	–

7. ANNANDALE AND ESKDALE

Congregation	Com	Eld	G	In98	Ass	Gvn	3-11	-17
Annan Old	480	42	50	53853	7960	7960	30	5
Annan St Andrew's Greenknowe Erskine	858	41	101	46743	8380	4190	32	4
Applegarth and Sibbaldie	197	8	22	8958	1060	1060	20	12
Lochmaben	605	26	49	33730	6330	7080	27	21
Brydekirk	81	7	–	7240	0	0	–	–
Hoddam	184	9	11	7430	0	0	–	–
Canonbie	191	17	–	16085	1537	1537	25	3
Carlisle	458	33	45	58159	7480	8480	43	14
Longtown	56	8	20	5347	830	830	15	–
Dalton	127	9	8	11349	1237	1387	16	–
Hightae	104	6	17	7855	930	984	8	–
St Mungo	142	10	15	10119	850	850	14	–
Dornock	273	10	14	13550	0	0	–	–
Eskdalemuir	41	3	-	2504	0	0	–	–
Hutton and Corrie	121	10	-	7682	0	0	7	–
Tundergarth	78	9	9	5461	0	0	5	–
Gretna Old, St Andrew's and Half Morton and Kirkpatrick Fleming	475	34	36	31350	1650	3380	65	11
Johnstone	140	10	–	7303	0	0	6	–
Kirkpatrick Juxta	197	9	-	11415	0	0	8	3
Kirtle – Eaglesfield	148	10	20	14265	1570	1570	10	–
Middlebie	114	8	13	6156	293		7	–
Waterbeck	76	6	–	5354	312	312	7	–
Langholm, Ewes and Westerkirk	605	31	71	33690	7560	8030	35	6
Lockerbie Dryfesdale	1056	48	53	41353	7050	7050	34	–
Moffat	516	36	45	41913	7560	9233	25	4
Wamphray	63	7	–	7503	620	620	–	–

8. DUMFRIES AND KIRKCUDBRIGHT

Congregation	Com	Eld	G	In98	Ass	Gvn	3-11	-17
Anwoth and Girthon	459	25	31	46621	6870	7159	6	–
Borgue	62	6	10	3108	220	0	17	–
Auchencairn and Rerrick	156	10	20	13479	890	989	11	–
Buittle and Kelton	277	24	25	19356	2930	2930	16	–
Balmaclellan and Kells	166	13	15	11515	0	0	17	5
Carsphairn	118	10	12	6582	0	600	8	4
Dalry	209	12	35	10981	0	0	13	–
Balmaghie	162	6	19	10887	1800	1800	17	2
Tarff and Twynholm	220	18	32	29870	2800	2800	36	5
Caerlaverock	182	6	–	7000	0	150	24	–
Castle Douglas	624	32	59	37847	4260	4260	45	45
Closeburn	278	13	–	18210	850	850	25	–

Congregation	Com	Eld	G	In98	Ass	Gvn	3-11	-17
Durisdeer 194	8	33	11942	1425	1283	17	–
Colvend, Southwick and Kirkbean 402	29	44	42497	6750	6750	47	21
Corsock and Kirkpatrick Durham. 220	15	15	14283	1840	1840	–	–
Crossmichael and Parton 209	16	16	20914	2130	2130	12	–
Cummertrees 100	5	12	5872	267	267		–
Mouswald 95	7	14	6606	730	654	7	–
Ruthwell. 150	9	20	10015	1550	1550	18	–
Dalbeattie. 754	45	57j	40398	9710	10372	26	10
Urr. 262	14	j	12150	2350	2501	25	–
Dumfries Greyfriars 490	27	29	60522	8780	9180	29	–
Dumfries Lincluden 172	12	–	14265	1220	0	19	3
Holywood 198	13	-	13382	512	512	25	–
Dumfries Lochside. 414	12	30	19701	0	0	15	–
Dumfries Maxwelltown West 801	52	56	57300	11100	11100	47	14
Dumfries St George's. 533	40	51	58288	8280	8280	66	7
Dumfries St Mary's 896	51	53	50924	10020	10674	29	21
Dumfries St Michael's and South 950	45	40	45991	11080	11265	52	–
Dumfries Troqueer. 554	31	29	50854	11000	11000	60	26
Dunscore 301	18	11	21361	2960	2960	14	–
Glencairn and Moniaive 238	13	11	19980	2812	2912	18	–
Kirkconnel 419	11	22	40828	4730	4930	26	4
Kirkcudbright. 1201	53	51	59520	13380	13530	45	–
Kirkgunzeon. 66	9	–	5180	0	0	–	–
Kirkmahoe. 454	16	38	28536	698	698	30	–
Kirkmichael & Tinwald & Torthorwald . . 606	35	46	43243	9660	9660	52	-
Kirkpatrick – Irongray 285	17	9	19346	1670	1670	15	–
Lochrutton 122	9	14	9980	450	450	19	2
Terregles 135	10	9	4089	160	320	–	–
Lochend. 65	4	10	2516	0	0	6	–
New Abbey 247	134	10	16758	0	0	16	–
Penpont Keir and Tynron 228	11	16	20055	0	0	11	–
Sanquhar St Bride's 594	26	45	35879	5340	8210	57	10
Thornhill 349	16	25	21736	850	1100	11	–

9. WIGTOWN AND STRANRAER

Congregation	Com	Eld	G	In98	Ass	Gvn	3-11	-17
Bargrennan. 49	5	–	5341	1600	1636	–	–
Newton Stewart							
Penninghame St John's 648	52	39	52647	14000	14000	43	–
Ervie Kirkcolm. 276	22	–	15840	2000	2000	26	6
Leswalt. 311	15	34	23436	1640	1640	24	–
Glasserton and Isle of Whithorn 153	10	–	11215	1600	1600	7	–
Whithorn St Ninian's Priory 355	12	44	21509	2580	2580	16	–
Inch 283	24	10	11612	1960	1960	11	2
Stranraer St Andrew's. 521	31	–	32760	7180	7180	31	1
Kirkcowan 226	10	16	17203	2180	2180	13	1
Wigtown 299	14	18	27569	4330	4330	15	6
Kirkinner 181	6	14	11803	1000	1000	10	–
Sorbie. 188	9	14	13728	1000	1000	14	–
Kirkmabreck 218	12	24	14905	1100	1150	6	–
Monigaff 480	28	22	30525	5650	5650	27	14
Kirkmaiden 259	22	25	19443	3280	3357	24	–

Congregation	Com	Eld	G	In98	Ass	Gvn	3-11	-17
Stoneykirk	413	26	19	21850	2670	2670	29	–
Mochrum	323	21	59	22486	0	0	54	13
New Luce	122	9	42j	9469	1570	1570	24	–
Old Luce	370	23	j	29855	4760	4760	34	–
Portpatrick	270	12	30	15696	2670	2670	20	3
Stranraer St Ninian's	548	27	34	38902	8400	8400	52	–
Stranraer High Kirk	680	33	40	48773	9500	9500	48	–
Stranraer Old	450	25	47	40205	7330	7330	10	–

10. AYR

Congregation	Com	Eld	G	In98	Ass	Gvn	3-11	-17
Alloway	1424	79	49	146003	37980	42000	99	19
Annbank	359	18	25	34027	0	680	–	–
Arnsheen Barrhill	124	5	12	8834	0	0	8	–
Colmonell	221	15	11	16390	0	200	18	–
Auchinleck	458	26	46	45069	5880	5880	50	26
Ayr Auld Kirk of Ayr								
(St John the Baptist)	922	86	71	92004	16420	17132	19	20
Ayr Castlehill	916	71	89	72349	15020	15020	62	7
Ayr Newton-on-Ayr	573	52	52	75637	15700	16198	55	31
Ayr St Andrew's	744	71	41	72882	16620	16620	32	11
Ayr St Columba	1905	124	76	138165	37620	37620	147	17
Ayr St James'	571	36	49	46263	5660	5660	53	10
Ayr St Leonard's	723	60	49	68333	15100	15100	41	7
Ayr St Quivox	447	38	20	42460	5600	5600	45	–
Ayr Wallacetown	534	29	56	50428	6520	6852	14	17
Ballantrae	309	20	37	30051	2312	2312	22	3
Barr	86	6	14	7993	0	0	–	8
Dailly	170	17	24	13374	0	0	17	5
Girvan South	374	20	26	27326	1760	1173	18	4
Catrine	190	21	42	26644	1250	1250	29	–
Sorn	189	16	20	24585	1300	1300	21	5
Coylton	377	31	–	19620	0	0	46	19
Drongan The Schaw Kirk	314	26	22	14051	0	300	33	–
Craigie	120	6	–	15435	800	800	22	–
Symington	427	24	35	54733	5500	5548	35	5
Crosshill	208	11	28	13536	460	460	20	–
Dalrymple	375	15	–	20275	2437	2193	8	–
Dalmellington	387	27	91	32431	3090	3220	45	7
Dundonald	656	47	62	50033	8570	8844	64	55
Fisherton	173	13	14	11724	893	893	–	–
Maybole West	312	16	29	21548	2810	3171	33	3
Girvan North (Old and St Andrew's)	1262	72	64	63697	16080	16080	83	40
Kirkmichael	263	16	25	21512	0	150	29	–
Straiton St Cuthbert's	177	13	15	11180	0	0	18	–
Kirkoswald	337	18	16	35522	2470	2470	43	14
Lugar	189	10	19	11602	1300	1300	18	12
Old Cumnock Old	443	21	57	44815	5500	5500	46	9
Mauchline	688	32	87	58349	11890	12348	93	11
Maybole Old	474	27	33	42498	5960	6080	34	2
Monkton and Prestwick North	666	54	70	55969	11570	11820	82	23
Muirkirk	288	18	27	27997	0	600	36	50

Congregation	Com	Eld	G	In98	Ass	Gvn	3-11	-17
New Cumnock	717	35	57	41299	5500	5684	42	20
Ochiltree	284	22	22	20411	3250	3250	41	–
Stair	212	14	27	18135	3010	3210	29	–
Old Cumnock Crichton West	378	21	36	33018	4490	4540	20	3
Old Cumnock St Ninian's	106	16	24	7745	937	937	19	23
Patna Waterside	167	15	–	10665	0	0	25	9
Prestwick Kingcase	1264	105	74	82390	12930	13418	136	32
Prestwick St Nicholas'	894	69	85	79605	16240	16640	49	19
Prestwick South	454	42	85	68417	8370	8370	27	12
Tarbolton	630	35	44	36539	5000	5151	55	8
Troon Old	1297	72	–	101955	24310	24310	91	20
Troon Portland	821	61	58	85956	20060	20060	74	13
Troon St Meddan's	1263	127	107	141335	26630	26850	163	68

11. IRVINE AND KILMARNOCK

Congregation	Com	Eld	G	In98	Ass	Gvn	3-11	-17
Crosshouse	397	32	35	31643	700	1055	56	16
Darvel	677	38	42	37405	6080	6080	41	17
Dreghorn and Springside	737	72	40	73039	11370	11370	74	6
Dunlop	452	37	38	51363	6140	6390	57	–
Fenwick	481	30	54	52723	9890	9890	32	–
Galston	909	61	85	91512	10710	10710	54	55
Hurlford	801	30	36	41831	7530	7530	30	18
Irvine Fullarton	594	38	41	79896	14240	14640	164	19
Irvine Girdle Toll	265	18	21	24078	0	0	81	9
Irvine Mure	493	33	39	60543	9950	9950	50	4
Irvine Old	680	50	31	84894	14970	14970	43	11
Irvine Relief Bourtreehill	438	36	41	45656	1000	1000	36	14
Irvine St Andrew's	538	25	59	39278	7160	7160	82	34
Kilmarnock Grange	527	35	56	48800	8960	8960	29	9
Kilmarnock Henderson	865	77	70	86318	22060	22060	68	25
Kilmarnock Howard St Andrew's	517	45	50	62949	8687	8783	18	54
Kilmarnock Laigh	673	49	41	72432	18610	18610	60	8
Kilmarnock Old High Kirk	343	17	30	39830	3720	3820	17	9
Kilmarnock Riccarton	433	32	38	62988	8110	8110	32	17
Kilmarnock St Andrew's Glencairn	205	21	20	24197	1000	1000	9	–
Kilmarnock St John's Onthank	324	26	30	40952	2740	3730	72	13
Kilmarnock St Kentigern's	299	30	–	40145	4880	4880	56	17
Kilmarnock St Marnock's	778	73	27	88832	16340	16340	157	50
Kilmarnock St Ninian's Bellfield	265	21	20	28043	3080	0	18	–
Kilmarnock Shortlees	179	16	21	30157	0	1192	26	6
Kilmarnock West High	438	48	34	50833	8890	5890	46	13
Kilmaurs St Maur's Glencairn	390	18	25	42898	5500	5500	37	16
Newmilns Loudoun	470	14	–	47747	11930	11930	59	20
Stewarton John Knox	439	38	33	57431	10550	10802	43	9
Stewarton St Columba's	686	44	65	43491	9030	9837	65	30

12. ARDROSSAN

Congregation	Com	Eld	G	In98	Ass	Gvn	3-11	-17
Ardrossan Barony St John's	388	18	42	42013	6690	6690	38	10
Ardrossan Park	577	38	45	42660	5770	5805	88	25
Beith High	1039	95	42	61392	15590	16089	72	28
Beith Trinity	269	40	27	40831	6170	6170	30	26

Congregation	Com	Eld	G	In98	Ass	Gvn	3-11	-17
Brodick	216	19	–	30332	0	1017	20	–
Corrie	60	5	–	9800	0	197	8	5
Cumbrae	363	24	52	25689	0	200	24	14
Dalry St Margaret's	1153	60	30	76885	19370	19370	73	11
Dalry Trinity	370	23	35	68424	14170	14330	34	8
Fairlie	325	27	51	42792	5740	6085	32	3
Fergushill	57	5	–	6296	0		3	–
Kilwinning Erskine	139	11	16	26602	0	500	36	5
Kilbirnie Auld Kirk	575	39	36	35948	5320	5320	26	4
Kilbirnie St Columba's	661	51	39	43714	6970	7573	57	24
Kilmory	42	5	-	7350	0	0	7	–
Lamlash	164	15	44	26848	0	0	13	–
Kilwinning Abbey	960	64	50	76605	18125	18125	64	29
Kilwinning Mansefield Trinity	222	19	25	23177	0	0	34	12
Largs Clark Memorial	1029	93	83	87365	20610	20610	130	104
Largs St Columba's	769	68	79	62063	15270	15270	50	1
Largs St John's	854	53	79	91415	19740	20010	64	49
Lochranza and Pirnmill	81	7	33	11670	0	0	8	–
Shiskine	66	7	–	15903	0	0	1	17
Saltcoats New Trinity	421	36	40	47240	6010	6010	40	18
Saltcoats North	478	28	26	40112	4612	4612	30	6
Saltcoats St Cuthbert's	579	57	58	72328	14500	14500	51	8
Stevenston Ardeer	408	27	50	39162	5230	5230	62	19
Stevenston High	298	33	64	52724	10320	7308	43	10
Stevenston Livingstone	407	38	43	43785	8510	10997	30	9
West Kilbride Overton	381	32	49	47708	5610	5610	26	10
West Kilbride St Andrew's	785	56	54	73120	16590	16738	56	25
Whiting Bay and Kildonan	132	13	–	33904	0	2851	24	3

13. LANARK

Biggar	821	51	63	63778	11580	11780	43	30
Black Mount	115	7	19	14013	0	32	19	14
Culter	106	7	-	9531	633	633	4	-
Libberton and Quothquan	94	10	-	9205	650	952	-	-
Cairngryffe	311	22	15	21451	3046	3163	14	1
Symington	264	16	27	22381	4070	4070	24	15
Carluke Kirkton	844	38	27	76706	15330	15330	104	56
Carluke St Andrew's	446	21	28	34878	6270	6270	30	20
Carluke St John's	943	57	67	75679	15680	15680	85	32
Carnwath	451	34	30	32957	1200	1200	42	5
Carstairs	258	13	34	20347	2080	2153	32	–
Carstairs Junction	152	6	29	17610	1400	1400	19	–
Coalburn	200	6	18	11265	160	230	12	–
Lesmahagow Old	801	38	31	40152	4050	4350	33	5
Crossford	216	7	10	24432	3620	3620	14	2
Kirkfieldbank	150	6	20	14394	1100	1100	15	–
Douglas St Bride's	378	26	29	26233	2940	2940	39	8
Douglas Water and Rigside	100	10	17	9248	970	1027	7	–
Forth St Paul's	519	36	53	32972	3520	4520	55	26
Glencaple	299	23	15	23913	500	500	16	–
Lowther	51	6	–	5764	250	250	5	–

Congregation	Com	Eld	G	In98	Ass	Gvn	3-11	-17
Kirkmuirhill	335	20	60	75028	13210	14210	71	59
Lanark Greyfriars	977	63	45	62145	11150	11350	51	24
Lanark St Nicholas'	823	42	35	58799	11670	12170	52	16
Law	173	12	33	26299	0	430	41	7
Lesmahagow Abbeygreen	261	18	27	56476	8380	8380	29	27

14. PAISLEY

Congregation	Com	Eld	G	In98	Ass	Gvn	3-11	-17
Barrhead Arthurlie	466	30	34	68554	12100	12100	38	10
Barrhead Bourock	601	45	84	61788	11750	11750	85	45
Barrhead South and Levern	540	36	39	57996	11670	12070	28	16
Bishopton	877	58	-	62280	12790	12790	98	19
Bridge of Weir Freeland	482	49	35	82027	18840	18840	81	24
Bridge of Weir St Machar's Ranfurly	573	48	84	71238	16670	17170	63	40
Caldwell	282	16	-	47846	6510	7177	45	10
Elderslie Kirk	715	60	88	86326	24200	24580	–	–
Houston and Killellan	773	53	58	90185	17530	17530	327	111
Howwood	277	22	33	46376	5700	5700	36	14
Inchinnan	481	42	25	44244	7010	10363	61	–
Johnstone High	501	44	70	57297	11860	11860	37	63
Johnstone St Andrew's Trinity	295	33	51	43141	5530	5530	63	22
Johnstone St Paul's	797	77	36	67877	12840	12841	80	5
Kilbarchan East	437	39	45	51812	7210	7210	60	55
Kilbarchan West	533	45	45	71330	13859	13859	78	14
Linwood	565	35	36	50443	7400	7400	59	2
Lochwinnoch	173	11	–	26255	0	0	10	2
Neilston	799	48	44	70824	19780	0	108	42
New Erskine	520	32	50	82989	8300	8300	62	36
Paisley Abbey	856	60	14	80417	23500	23500	43	18
Paisley Castlehead	426	37	24	45415	6770	6770	26	–
Paisley Glenburn	542	27	25	37391	5440	5440	33	–
Paisley Laigh High	849	94	68	62356	12670	12670	73	19
Paisley Lylesland	538	52	78	68085	15550	15550	32	4
Paisley Martyrs'	660	68	30	65494	15470	15713	74	27
Paisley Oakshaw Trinity	1017	115	69	126280	20600	20600	105	10
Paisley St Columba Foxbar	349	35	31	40675	3100	3225	16	50
Paisley St James'	416	37	25	49921	8040	15910	25	8
Paisley St Luke's	326	31	34	48680	6460	6460	19	4
Paisley St Mark's Oldhall	823	61	137	85120	20190	20190	51	24
Paisley St Ninian's Ferguslie	81	9	15	12128	0	0	25	10
Paisley Sandyford (Thread Street)	481	36	31	52631	9930	9930	37	10
Paisley Sherwood Greenlaw	846	95	65	107375	25270	25270	86	46
Paisley Wallneuk North	633	59	46	73243	14900	0	39	14
Renfrew North	739	66	51	71350	15080	16584	103	45
Renfrew Old	799	44	87	74353	14410	14410	190	16
Renfrew Trinity	477	42	88	53948	10390	10714	45	11

15. GREENOCK

Congregation	Com	Eld	G	In98	Ass	Gvn	3-11	-17
Gourock Old Gourock and Ashton	1134	79	114	115951	22990	22990	96	87
Gourock St John's	743	67	38	83325	17160	17160	78	27
Greenock Ardgowan	675	60	38	44969	14440	14440	63	54
Greenock Cartsdyke	388	45	-	35820	600	600	20	–

Congregation	Com	Eld	G	In98	Ass	Gvn	3-11	-17
Greenock Finnart St Paul's............ 393	37	27	65085	12700	12700	40	–
Greenock Mount Kirk 440	51	35	55528	8550	8550	28	37
Greenock Old West Kirk 390	38	45	69218	13950	13950	25	12
Greenock St George's North......... 529	41	–	63849	10000	10000	23	46
Greenock St Luke's 865	80	58	105028	25000	25000	65	14
Greenock St Margaret's 361	34	52	38779	3500	1760	44	–
Greenock St Ninian's............... 288	23	22	21779	0	0	29	–
Greenock Wellpark Mid Kirk......... 743	54	30	58190	14380	14380	47	7
Inverkip........................ 440	26	67	44597	8500	8500	67	19
Kilmacolm Old................... 884	75	66	120801	31000	34646	89	22
Kilmacolm St Columba 621	50	30	69095	21000	21000	85	17
Langbank....................... 170	13	–	24196	1000	1000	35	–
Port Glasgow Hamilton Bardrainney 584	27	19	38653	4000	4000	46	40
Port Glasgow St Andrew's 840	66	76	69910	14112	13441	47	86
Port Glasgow St Martin's............ 205	16	–	18064	0	0	21	–
Skelmorlie and Wemyss Bay 428	26	–	50653	9380	9809	25	16

16. GLASGOW

Congregation	Com	Eld	G	In98	Ass	Gvn	3-11	-17
Banton 84	11	–	12378	0	0	14	1
Twechar........................ 116	12	–	8975	0	0	8	–
Bishopbriggs Kenmure 402	24	57	58109	7200	7600	62	51
Bishopbriggs Springfield 1061	59	63	83935	16800	16800	121	53
Blairbeth Rodger Memorial 134	10	30	12170	0	0	8	5
Broom 1119	78	75	163263	38180	39206	152	52
Burnside....................... 810	51	89	145806	44000	44000	110	33
Busby.......................... 464	50	46	59996	11300	11300	69	7
Cadder........................ 1040	93	76	126344	31000	32423	124	40
Cambuslang Flemington Hallside....... 308	18	21	28292	0	0	55	6
Cambuslang Old.................. 526	69	49				62	15
Cambuslang St. Andrew's............ 550	46	26	69329	121000	15412	63	24
Cambuslang Trinity St. Paul's 424	28		66328	13500	13936	34	25
Campsie 371	25	26	44795	1500	1500	39	31
Chryston 872	37	35	135179	21450	23217	96	82
Eaglesham Old................... 798	60	85	103411	24770	24770	114	56
Fernhill and Cathkin.............. 374	24	54	36839	3000	2387	51	5
Gartcosh....................... 178	10	19	19054	0	0	22	19
Glenboig 185	8	14	9887	0	0	48	3
Giffnock Orchardhill 616	57	52	141523	37000	41500	149	29
Giffnock South................... 1020	94	53	152710	39200	41200	107	18
Giffnock The Park 410	34	–	42230	6100	6100	50	11
Greenbank 1273	113	84	221994	52000	52000	217	83
Kilsyth Anderson 488	25	50	51568	9500	9500	80	12
Kilsyth Burns and Old 713	38	45	42725	7600	7600	37	60
Kirkintilloch Hillhead 174	14	22	17499	0	0	9	–
Kirkintilloch St Columba's........... 724	55	49	75091	16700	16700	99	44
Kirkintilloch St David's Memorial Park.................. 920	66	66	93058	23010	23210	85	32
Kirkintilloch St Mary's 806	57	82	83475	20580	20580	89	24
Lenzie Old...................... 497	42	–	65073	14000	14000	76	–
Lenzie Union 1021	85	115	127408	25000	25000	87	25
Maxwell Mearns Castle 342	37	–	91918	18500	18500	49	23

Congregation	Com	Eld	G	In98	Ass	Gvn	3-11	-17
Mearns	805	43	–	105021	36000	36000	38	15
Milton of Campsie	405	39	40	35070	2800	2800	86	–
Netherlee	987	89	70	175608	40000	40845	128	22
Newton Mearns	1123	80	45	112511	33000	33000	120	37
Rutherglen Old	495	36		46255	10500	10589	6	0
Rutherglen Stonelaw	534	47	47	101491	24560	24686	50	75
Rutherglen Wardlawhill	460	47	74	48155	10200	10200	56	32
Rutherglen West	592	29	26	54097	9060	9060	46	12
Stamperland	500	48	36	78276	11160	11160	107	68
Stepps	427	30	17	42653	4250	4250	53	18
Thornliebank	322	16	69	37974	1500	1500	34	6
Torrance	269	20	20	37627	2000	1833	42	36
Williamwood	599	67	44	107323	24700	25300	139	51
Glasgow Anderston Kelvingrove	202	27	19	21070	0	0	13	10
Glasgow Baillieston Mure Memorial	673	41	135	70155	15940	15940	109	53
Glasgow Baillieston St Andrew's	483	38	43	57840	9200	9200	95	18
Glasgow Balshagray Victoria Park	365	40	51	73942	16550	18145	4	294
Glasgow Barlanark Greyfriars	158	14	46	29773	0	50	21	11
Glasgow Battlefield East	233	15	42	37946	2500	8600	–	13
Glasgow Blawarthill	265	31	56	29072	0	0	36	18
Glasgow Bridgeton								
St Francis in the East	130	20	16	25301	0	0	37	3
Glasgow Broomhill	721	69	89	113799	28830	28830	73	40
Glasgow Calton Parkhead	204	16	16	16625	0	219	6	–
Glasgow Cardonald	622	61	109	106943	24100	27501	61	83
Glasgow Carmunnock	400	28	47	57147	9000	9000	75	–
Glasgow Carmyle	132	8	39	16671	1800	1800	13	–
Glasgow Kenmuir Mount Vernon	168	9	40	24034	4110	4110	31	19
Glasgow Carntyne Old	187	21	22	28215	5000	5050	25	8
Glasgow Eastbank	182	19	30	25997	3950	3950	14	8
Glasgow Carnwadric	177	21	38	22663	0	100	29	10
Glasgow Castlemilk East	186	13	16	21453	0	0	21	6
Glasgow Castlemilk West	172	29	45	23761	0	0	38	12
Glasgow Cathcart Old	431	47	40	69660	13000	13000	19	12
Glasgow Cathcart South	497	53	62	100647	24300	25624	48	32
Glasgow Cathedral								
(St Mungo's or High)	500	57	–	71827	13000	13000	11	–
Glasgow Colston Milton	198	19	–	26776	0	0	29	22
Glasgow Colston Wellpark	228	17	–	24731	0	0	28	–
Glasgow Cranhill	76	16	–	12813	0	0	30	10
Glasgow Croftfoot	448	53	38	67377	12270	12334	69	15
Glasgow Crosshill Queen's Park	157	18	–	18771	2260	2260	13	–
Glasgow Dennistoun Blackfriars	191	27	24	32549	2500	2500	22	5
Glasgow Dennistoun Central	283	31	30	43249	2900	2900	22	2
Glasgow Drumchapel								
Drumry St Mary's	163	15	–	11841	0	0	51	19
Glasgow Drumchapel St Andrew's	590	53	-	46732	8000	10710	51	26
Glasgow Drumchapel St Mark's	98	12	15	10438	0	100	11	8
Glasgow Easterhouse St George's								
and St Peter's	52	9	–	4535	0	0	22	9
Glasgow Eastwood	537	56	95	60557	11400	11400	80	26

Congregation	Com	Eld	G	In98	Ass	Gvn	3-11	-17
Glasgow Gairbraid	268	19	33	33651	0	165	14	2
Glasgow Gardner Street	55	8	–	41623	3875	4187	13	9
Glasgow Garthamlock and Craigend East	93	10	-	11120	0	0	25	6
Glasgow Gorbals	140	18	24	25098	0	0	12	10
Glasgow Govan Old	251	26	19	38020	3500	3500	13	23
Glasgow Govanhill Trinity	182	27	48	35013	2750	2773	5	–
Glasgow High Carntyne	772	34	95	64475	15880	16835	44	24
Glasgow Hillington Park	496	36	74	75468	13500	14500	57	23
Glasgow Househillwood St Christopher's	120	14	29	15489	0	39	16	17
Glasgow Hyndland	338	42	47	75040	15190	15500	22	6
Glasgow Ibrox	434	25	40	45456	7090	7090	36	33
Glasgow John Ross Memorial Church for Deaf People	79	7	–	8075	200	200	11	–
Glasgow Jordanhill	726	86	33	134035	34070	35170	103	39
Glasgow Kelvin Stevenson Memorial	228	41	29	38552	4610	4610	11	37
Glasgow Kelvinside Hillhead	307	27	–	62944	11625	11670	12	12
Glasgow King's Park	966	84	102	121421	33000	35705	199	63
Glasgow Kinning Park	217	21	26	40655	4450	4450	41	5
Glasgow Knightswood St Margaret's	743	43	54	56912	11700	11700	17	2
Glasgow Langside	313	49	52	49703	1200	1200	41	10
Glasgow Lansdowne	169	20	–	24060	0	0	23	4
Glasgow Linthouse St Kenneth's	188	18	29	26497	0	0	21	–
Glasgow Lochwood	83	7	18	10232	0	0	12	6
Glasgow Martyrs', The	137	7	–	24203	0	0	12	–
Glasgow Maryhill	259	24	12	32598	3130	3130	36	7
Glasgow Merrylea	594	71	83	81174	18900	18900	54	21
Glasgow Mosspark	347	39	72	57888	10000	10100	18	6
Glasgow Mount Florida	405	40	69	78138	16500	4125	–	–
Glasgow New Cathcart	294	31	45	45798	5000	5000	32	20
Glasgow New Govan	169	23	32	42929	5400	5400	25	17
Glasgow Newlands South	835	87	55	153423	44000	44000	115	34
Glasgow North Kelvinside	95	4	33	37053	4820	4820	7	2
Glasgow Partick South	314	40	36	46650	2100	2100	34	14
Glasgow Partick Trinity	252	33	–	46532	7970	8586	37	16
Glasgow Penilee St Andrew's	206	29	–	37823	1800	1800	27	5
Glasgow Pollokshaws	222	24	34	26435	1900	2035	26	16
Glasgow Pollokshields	406	39	74	97282	27000	10100	18	14
Glasgow Possilpark	249	22	33	32278	750	1082	107	35
Glasgow Priesthill and Nitshill	203	20	23	27372	0	25	84	10
Glasgow Renfield St Stephen's	238	31	40	71696	11020	11820	8	3
Glasgow Ruchazie	89	8	–	12916	0	0	57	24
Glasgow Ruchill	159	24	23	34159	2520	2520	20	12
Glasgow St Andrew's East	192	24	35	27170	0	400	26	2
Glasgow St Columba	144	19	25	30271	2100	2100	29	12
Glasgow St David's Knightswood	799	46	59	71546	13990	14090	49	26
Glasgow St Enoch's Hogganfield	299	16	67	39719	3500	3554	36	2
Glasgow St George's Tron	527	53	–	164217	52890	52890	88	61
Glasgow St James' (Pollok)	318	33	35	40365	1250	900	56	15
Glasgow St John's Renfield	511	63	-	94797	24370	24370	102	27

Congregation	Com	Eld	G	In98	Ass	Gvn	3-11	-17
Glasgow St Luke's and St Andrew's	99	8	17	20045	0	0	16	–
Glasgow St Margaret's Tollcross	173	8	21	29851	0	200	36	16
Glasgow St Nicholas' Cardonald	490	45	39	46587	7210	7612	41	49
Glasgow St Paul's Provanmill	79	7	–	10811	0	0	23	17
Glasgow St Rollox	147	13	16	23657	0	154	18	3
Glasgow St Thomas' Gallowgate	85	9	9	10136	0	0	11	–
Glasgow Sandyford Henderson Memorial	200	24	13	71631	15320	15320	10	3
Glasgow Sandyhills	426	36	66	58820	10250	10250	64	37
Glasgow Scotstoun	360	44	7	59955	9120	9517	67	43
Glasgow Shawlands	646	48	97	117543	0	0	95	13
Glasgow Sherbrooke St Gilbert's	594	47	42	105925	19000	19000	46	41
Glasgow Shettleston Old	353	28	33	42249	6000	6000	31	17
Glasgow South Carntyne	168	13	11	27829	0	635	16	4
Glasgow South Shawlands	255	24	27	57298	9910	9910	45	14
Glasgow Springburn	406	39	34	38676	11660	11660	28	19
Glasgow Strathbungo Queen's Park	316	31	42	50925	1000	1000	29	38
Glasgow Temple Anniesland	590	48	50	78273	17310	18185	46	9
Glasgow Toryglen	151	13	41	23074	0	0	26	–
Glasgow Townhead Blochairn	35	4	–	5710	0	0	34	–
Glasgow Trinity Possil and Henry Drummond	147	9	-	33528	750	750	20	–
Glasgow Tron St Mary's	158	16	13	26774	0	0	18	4
Glasgow Victoria Tollcross	184	15	40	28383	0	1000	36	3
Glasgow Wallacewell	232	14	28	25819	0	858	26	81
Glasgow Wellington	347	41	–	80113	17610	18580	15	22
Glasgow Yoker Old	99	8	15	13378	0	0	32	13
Glasgow Yoker St Matthew's	115	5	24	12577	0	0	–	–

17. HAMILTON

Congregation	Com	Eld	G	In98	Ass	Gvn	3-11	-17
Airdrie Broomknoll	451	48	55	47804	10020	10020	36	12
Calderbank	186	15	27	13068	2430	2430	20	–
Airdrie Clarkston	550	43	31	56027	10210	10210	95	7
Airdrie Flowerhill	852	66	52	82560	18280	18668	65	82
Airdrie High	473	32	20	39608	5130	5130	42	17
Airdrie Jackson	450	50	40	54418	10470	10470	75	7
Airdrie New Monkland	496	41	36	36838	6520	1165	56	11
Airdrie Greengairs	225	8	15	13565	2137	0	23	6
Airdrie St Columba's	270	16	14	16148	0	0	17	–
Airdrie The New Wellwynd	804	88	62	76466	19430	19430	69	17
Bargeddie	232	14	–	49508	9040	9040	38	15
Bellshill Macdonald Memorial	348	35	30	42175	5790	10510	19	–
Bellshill Orbiston	326	27	21	14421	2480	2471	18	–
Bellshill St Andrew's	199	18	17	21999	3470	3470	20	5
Bellshill West	894	62	46	62284	13260	13799	50	11
Blantyre Livingstone Memorial	322	20	27	35184	3075	3075	62	8
Blantyre Old	431	30	50	55596	11000	11000	38	23
Blantyre St Andrew's	328	25	24	52801	5312	5322	56	10
Bothwell	701	56	53	93472	22080	22080	81	53
Caldercruix Longriggend and Meadowfield	253	13	24	42343	5380	5530	39	3

Congregation	Com	Eld	G	In98	Ass	Gvn	3-11	-17
Carfin.	70	6	–	6327	1120	1120	2	–
Newarthill	651	21	30	47200	8230	8230	62	27
Chapelhall	330	26	39	33426	4740	3740	27	10
Chapelton.	216	14	33	18344	3330	3330	31	16
Strathaven Rankin	642	59	30	67456	15470	15744	63	19
Cleland	344	14	19	28482	0	0	22	15
Coatbridge Blairhill–Dundyvan	506	40	39	41477	6470	3470	31	13
Coatbridge Calder	560	40	59	51127	10620	11520	38	35
Coatbridge Clifton	332	29	27	39722	4410	4187	14	26
Coatbridge Middle	455	37	54	43001	4530	5000	54	33
Coatbridge Old Monkland	417	26	56	27731	2450	2450	41	35
Coatbridge St Andrew's	882	81	56	76585	16500	16500	62	10
Coatbridge Townhead	416	35	32	40175	3650	3650	45	48
Dalserf.	298	21	26	40313	7500	7500	49	11
East Kilbride Claremont	931	88	55	96341	15670	16000	114	32
East Kilbride Greenhills	284	21	32	23365	0	0	22	12
East Kilbride Moncreiff	1238	83	53	100482	16290	41500	104	26
East Kilbride Mossneuk	271	17	–	24134	0	0	93	42
East Kilbride Old	811	75	107	69218	11770	12150	–	–
East Kilbride South	450	40	50	75115	16770	16770	65	26
East Kilbride West	777	40	93	56130	11680	11680	128	16
East Kilbride Westwood	849	52	160	61604	12440	12440	68	41
Glasford.	196	12	28	13395	2650	2650	19	2
Strathaven East	343	33	45	45744	6290	6290	13	3
Hamilton Burnbank	178	19	18j	22529	3390	3390	10	2
Hamilton North	200	32	34	28468	5930	5942	18	10
Hamilton Cadzow	838	68	76	79768	18280	18280	97	30
Hamilton Gilmour and Whitehill	244	27	j	33494	4750	5190	41	19
Hamilton Hillhouse	520	52	22	76029	12280	12280	118	44
Hamilton Old	915	71	43	105794	28410	28410	50	17
Hamilton St Andrew's	394	36	59	54266	10930	11030	38	16
Hamilton St John's	695	60	83	87427	19520	20967	84	25
Hamilton South	366	31	40	38491	7180	7385	39	9
Quarter.	122	11	23	12754	3150	3150	13	–
Hamilton Trinity	342	28	–	34771	4110	4110	42	22
Hamilton West	437	32	-	59080	10030	10030	38	19
Holytown	402	25	30	38387	4100	4100	29	–
Kirk o' Shotts	244	11	13	17020	0	0	14	–
Larkhall Chalmers	283	20	31	31510	4100	4100	39	5
Larkhall St Machan's	771	68	64	80508	17500	17500	–	–
Larkhall Trinity	360	26	47	40576	4170	4170	121	47
Motherwell Crosshill	600	65	75	67709	14240	14240	56	47
Motherwell Dalziel St Andrew's	711	87	62	92817	19810	23810	44	7
Motherwell Manse Road	306	28	33	50370	10300	9442	53	10
Motherwell North	327	30	40	39645	4410	4410	42	22
Motherwell St Margaret's	410	21	30	35066	4300	4300	25	35
Motherwell St Mary's	1100	103	97	85404	18730	18818	134	79
Motherwell South Dalziel	533	64	80	70298	14520	14520	41	46
Newmains Bonkle	220	17	29	30491	6040	6040	124	59
Newmains Coltness Memorial	264	27	28	38952	6430	6430	113	30
New Stevenston – Wrangholm Kirk	223	13	27	39467	4810	5470	59	20

Congregation	Com	Eld	G	In98	Ass	Gvn	3-11	-17
Overtown	299	28	49	30419	4920	4920	39	24
Shotts Calderhead Erskine	667	38	38	44467	7030	6211	77	9
Stonehouse St Ninian's	548	36	61	50288	9890	9890	65	78
Strathaven Avendale Old and Drumclog	832	75	60	102650	25365	25365	173	77
Strathaven West	300	21	42	38375	3800	3800	33	4
Uddingston Burnhead	300	28	17	30768	3230	2630	36	14
Uddingston Old	782	61	83	77639	15360	16560	59	15
Uddingston Park	292	20	33	46750	9910	9950	64	18
Uddingston Viewpark	503	34	35	63418	11520	12165	86	35
Wishaw Cambusnethan North	597	46	37	65163	10990	10990	39	30
Wishaw Cambusnethan Old and Morningside	607	61	16	59996	15860	16151	58	49
Wishaw Chalmers	565	32	41	50269	9470	9313	–	–
Wishaw Craigneuk and Belhaven	285	33	36	41472	9070	9070	21	8
Wishaw Old	435	48	-	39832	4510	4510	–	–
Wishaw St Mark's	564	36	57	54857	9070	9363	41	9
Wishaw Thornlie	286	31	40	33402	6700	6760	26	13

18. DUMBARTON

Congregation	Com	Eld	G	In98	Ass	Gvn	3-11	-17
Alexandria	556	38	30	62373	13000	13000	–	–
Arrochar	63	6	10	7797	0	0	19	–
Luss	86	9	22	19664	0	250	5	–
Baldernock	258	15	19	44571	5930	6210	15	–
Bearsden Killermont	814	63	86	114891	24630	24630	94	18
Bearsden New Kilpatrick	1960	135	57	264619	78430	78680	138	51
Bearsden North	714	68	85	101109	22690	22940	125	56
Bearsden South	1046	81	48	133244	32260	40074	129	49
Bearsden Westerton Fairlie Memorial	545	46	48	80870	20250	20250	66	30
Bonhill	934	67	–	61266	14950	14950	83	27
Cardross	543	40	35	88326	20100	20100	57	37
Clydebank Abbotsford	405	31	42	43269	7590	7590	26	7
Clydebank Faifley	266	25	53	32213	0	262	38	8
Clydebank Kilbowie St Andrew's	384	26	49	39571	5500	5500	66	35
Clydebank Radnor Park	307	44	44	42512	6010	6010	12	4
Clydebank St Cuthbert's	159	20	35	19634	0	400	18	2
Craigrownie	252	24	17	31130	5740	6240	35	10
Rosneath St Modan's	244	16	21	20589	3430	3776	30	2
Dalmuir Barclay	396	20	80	43465	6490	6490	43	6
Dumbarton Riverside	999	95	100	89452	15140	15140	92	22
Dumbarton St Andrew's	317	30	19	34375	3830	3830	31	6
Dumbarton West Kirk	411	41	30	47388	10270	10270	41	13
Duntocher	391	30	27	35706	500	805	76	–
Garelochhead	182	11	–	37996	3980	3980	102	18
Helensburgh Park	539	50	44	81903	17410	17677	71	12
Helensburgh St Columba	645	57	48	77833	17220	18979	78	34
Helensburgh West Kirk	732	59	78	112599	23132	23132	38	11
Jamestown	525	25	31	53380	8990	8990	23	2
Kilmaronock Gartocharn	294	12	–	28514	1610	1610	26	–
Milngavie Cairns	836	61	–	98223	26680	26680	95	47
Milngavie St Luke's	476	39	49	67276	14370	14370	68	7

Congregation	Com	Eld	G	In98	Ass	Gvn	3-11	-17
Milngavie St Paul's	1239	98	114	170885	42250	40905	141	37
Old Kilpatrick Bowling	369	23	35	36313	8360	5180	49	45
Renton Trinity	359	32	–	32406	2510	2815	30	30
Rhu and Shandon.................	356	35	41	65152	14012	15105	47	5

19. SOUTH ARGYLL

Congregation	Com	Eld	G	In98	Ass	Gvn	3-11	-17
Ardrishaig	200	29	48	32962	3490	3490	44	11
South Knapdale	39	6	–	5169	325	425	7	–
Campbeltown Highland	513	36	30	46962	3620	3620	33	2
Campbeltown Lorne and Lowland	1027	50	72	72377	13050	13050	77	25
Craignish	45	6	–	8530	0	0	–	–
Kilninver and Kilmelford.............	61	5	–	11579	0	0	–	–
Cumlodden Lochfyneside and Lochgair	110	14	18	17813	0	50	22	–
Gigha and Cara	43	4	–	8023	0	500	6	–
Glassary, Kilmartin and Ford	136	9	16	19719	0	0	13	–
Glenaray and Inveraray	143	12	15	17590	0	55	15	2
Jura	46	6	–	7995	0	300	10	6
Kilarrow.........................	119	13	18	21575	0	0	17	–
Kilmeny.........................	61	8	7	11171	0	0	21	–
Kilberry.........................	18	4	–	1220	0	0	–	–
Tarbert..........................	185	19	45	27411	0	0	31	–
Kilcalmonell	81	10	21	9240	0	0	8	–
Skipness.........................	30	4	–	6821	0	0	2	–
Kilchoman.......................	85	3	–	7109	713	713	13	3
Portnahaven......................	21	3	12	4990	380	380	–	–
Kildalton and Oa	130	13	19	17992	0	450	65	3
Killean and Kilchenzie.............	209	12	24	23394	0	0	24	12
Lochgilphead	246	21	14	30019	0	157	59	14
North Knapdale	84	7	–	16720	0	0	12	13
Saddell and Carradale	257	16	41	30586	0	200	15	–
Southend	256	15	23	22167	0	70	56	–

20. DUNOON

Congregation	Com	Eld	G	In98	Ass	Gvn	3-11	-17
Ascog	68	6	5	6929	535	785	–	–
Rothesay Craigmore St Brendan's	154	15	7	17359	1900	1900	11	–
Kingarth and Kilchattan Bay	101	9	16	13375	3600	3600	6	–
North Bute.......................	173	18	17	16505	0	0	15	–
Rothesay The High Kirk	351	24	41	28326	5000	5275	34	5
Dunoon Old and St Cuthbert's	450	41	30	42111	4180	4380	36	9
Dunoon St John's	293	21	28	33763	6410	6410	–	–
Sandbank.........................	162	12	–	11129	1650	1750	18	–
Innellan	149	8	22	16272	0	0	22	–
Inverchaolain and Toward	117	9	–	14338	0	1000	5	4
Kilfinan	29	5	9	2970	550	550	12	–
Kyles............................	206	14	39	26401	550	550	14	–
Kilmodan and Colintraive	137	12	13	20610	0	0	10	–
Kilmun: (St Munn's)	127	11	19	13529	0	350	15	–
Strone and Ardentinny	147	16	15	14778	0	180	35	–
Kirn............................	421	25	30	46675	8630	10356	32	8
Lochgoilhead and Kilmorich	140	12	23	18420	0	100	14	–

Congregation	Com	Eld	G	In98	Ass	Gvn	3-11	-17
Rothesay Trinity	545	43	61	48340	7580	7780	52	12
Strachur and Strachlachlan	179	11	22	18577	0	589	19	7

21. LORN AND MULL

Congregation	Com	Eld	G	In98	Ass	Gvn	3-11	-17
Appin	95	12	22	13334	0	0	16	–
Lismore	56	6	13	4865	0	0	11	–
Ardchattan	182	14	44	24185	0	397	26	5
Coll	13	3	–	2161	0	0	7	–
Colonsay and Oronsay	15	2	–	3114	0	0	8	–
Kilbrandon and Kilchattan	117	12	14	20110	0	271	13	2
Connel	172	17	27	25801	0	0	52	–
Glenorchy and Innishael	95	9	–	8794	0	0	12	8
Strathfillan	57	8	–	6005	0	0	–	–
Iona	16	2	–	4673	0	0	–	–
Kilfinichen and Kilvickeon and The Ross Of Mull	38	7	–	8140	0	0	–	–
Kilchrenan and Dalavich	38	4	10	6495	0	0	2	–
Muckairn	154	16	20	19222	0	300	17	7
Kilmore and Oban	865	79	77	78827	15625	15685	71	10
Kilninian and Kilmore	43	5	8	6905	0	0	–	–
Salen and Ulva	40	6	–	7944	0	0	14	–
Tobermory	104	17	15	12682	0	100	16	–
Torosay and Kinlochspelvie	31	6	–	6370	0	1000	4	4
Tiree	122	10	24	25584	0	2000	24	3

22. FALKIRK

Congregation	Com	Eld	G	In98	Ass	Gvn	3-11	-17
Airth	221	15	25	35758	2590	2590	16	7
Blackbraes and Shieldhill	289	17	19	24218	0	0	19	24
Bo'ness Old	804	55	44	53267	10840	10840	50	44
Bo'ness St Andrew's	613	33	–	49106	10520	10520	50	45
Bonnybridge St Helen's	735	35	37	38760	5160	5160	29	7
Bothkennar and Carronshore	349	29	15	27719	0	0	36	–
Brightons	777	45	79	79195	12090	13857	92	45
Carriden	749	51	22	45837	6400	6400	37	11
Cumbernauld Abronhill	338	29	36	37963	0	229	92	17
Cumbernauld Condorrat	560	42	35	46133	8370	8370	64	22
Cumbernauld Kildrum	507	44	–	39625	5660	5660	38	10
Cumbernauld Old	472	35	–	45255	7000	7000	67	6
Cumbernauld St Mungo's	379	31	–	35906	5240	5240	34	8
Denny Dunipace	489	35	28	45327	6850	6850	32	10
Denny Old	528	47	24	57868	8500	8500	43	12
Denny Westpark	814	68	52	62809	14860	14860	44	38
Falkirk Bainsford	429	24	23	41515	5410	5740	26	10
Falkirk Camelon: Irving	370	19	18	27130	0	0	31	14
Falkirk Camelon St John's	405	28	35	45260	7330	7330	61	11
Falkirk Erskine	656	62	55	67310	14680	15089	69	14
Falkirk Grahamston United	629	47	44	71728	15930	15930	51	30
Falkirk Laurieston	299	21	38	33201	6610	6610	27	5
Redding and Westquarter	154	13	32	18336	2550	2550	18	10
Falkirk Old and St Modan's	1148	76	39	103377	17210	17585	82	24
Falkirk St Andrew's West	708	36	33	98585	19800	19800	40	10

Congregation	Com	Eld	G	In98	Ass	Gvn	3-11	-17
Falkirk St James'	420	30	16	41952	3375	4123	50	19
Grangemouth Charing Cross and West	289	16	–	28380	1960	784	16	2
Grangemouth Dundas	380	28	–	36229	3150	3150	19	5
Grangemouth Kerse	635	59	30	43337	6050	6200	46	45
Grangemouth Kirk of the Holy Rood	803	46	–	51842	8310	8310	62	8
Grangemouth Zetland	988	67	73	77988	13750	13750	33	6
Haggs	346	29	15	37004	2820	2585	25	16
Larbert East	665	42	59	59558	8460	8648	44	65
Larbert Old	836	51	25	74802	17180	17180	74	74
Larbert West	621	47	41	60602	12030	12030	43	29
Muiravonside	292	26	26	28633	1700	2080	19	10
Polmont Old	592	24	36	57565	12570	12570	62	39
Slamannan	287	17	15	23113	0	0	37	–
Stenhouse and Carron	691	42	34	52710	9870	9870	56	9

23. STIRLING

Congregation	Com	Eld	G	In98	Ass	Gvn	3-11	-17
Aberfoyle	155	10	18	17858	0	0	11	4
Port of Menteith	66	6	11	9698	0	0	2	–
Alloa North	326	18	24	36621	4860	2059	41	–
Alloa St Mungo's	835	59	58	60014	11130	11130	19	6
Alloa West	296	25	53	40158	6480	1080	25	4
Alva	684	50	51	52297	7800	8252	72	10
Balfron	261	21	25	46488	9470	9470	27	12
Fintry	188	14	23	17898	2000	2000	12	3
Balquhidder	105	6	–	13714	1000	1000	–	–
Killin and Ardeonaig	187	12	21	21114	1140	1240	–	16
Bannockburn Allan	567	40	26	43959	6550	6550	31	6
Bannockburn Ladywell	738	44	50	36697	3590	3590	25	1
Bridge of Allan Chalmers	312	30	25	40497	6840	7840	25	13
Bridge of Allan Holy Trinity	651	43	45	80122	14100	14100	60	59
Buchanan	111	10	30j	12739	2500	2500	–	–
Drymen	299	20	j	32627	3500	4309	51	10
Buchlyvie	249	19	19	22656	2680	2680	28	–
Gartmore	87	14	–	15083	2030	2030	9	–
Callander	730	40	58	79986	17940	18232	69	27
Cambusbarron The Bruce Memorial	424	22	27	33677	1980	2690	18	26
Clackmannan	682	40	36	66411	11190	11190	–	–
Cowie	176	13	10	12237	1190	1408	20	–
Plean	306	10	–	13944	1080	780	25	–
Dollar	727	50	45	89771	17020	17020	77	43
Glendevon	55	4	–	4375	790	790	–	–
Muckhart	161	14	17	21282	3960	3960	18	5
Dunblane Cathedral	1174	82	83	158017	43920	44141	107	35
Dunblane St Blane's	461	41	43	72431	16230	20421	41	13
Fallin	268	6	–	34587	0	0	71	9
Gargunnock	273	17	–	16246	2750	2750	28	–
Kincardine-in-Menteith	133	8	–	10078	570	570	23	–
Killearn	661	49	108	68174	12500	12500	54	53
Kilmadock	265	12	23	14057	0	0	–	–
Kippen	375	26	29	27823	3650	3650	–	–
Norrieston	171	8	18	14757	710	710	22	5

Congregation	Com	Eld	G	In98	Ass	Gvn	3-11	-17
Lecropt	277	19	34	36185	4520	4520	15	–
Logie	724	56	85	74914	20630	20760	62	27
Menstrie	467	34	32	54509	8450	8450	42	8
Sauchie and Coalsnaughton	1041	43	18	56071	8820	8820	62	16
Stirling Allan Park South	302	45	51	34595	4930	4930	13	12
Stirling Church of The Holy Rude	271	36	–	26562	7425	4950	4	4
Stirling North	598	40	28	51507	9960	9960	41	13
Stirling St Columba's	720	72	–	79318	14350	14350	74	30
Stirling St Mark's	385	17	13	30178	2450	3010	–	–
Stirling St Ninian's Old	845	37	–	63657	11500	11500	15	41
Stirling Viewfield	641	31	42	59133	9450	9745	38	25
Strathblane	407	28	49	46052	6560	6600	38	22
Tillicoultry	1022	66	66	76859	17640	18042	84	9
Tullibody: St Serf's	645	32	18	49502	7570	14445	–	–

24. DUNFERMLINE

Congregation	Com	Eld	G	In98	Ass	Gvn	3-11	-17
Aberdour St Fillan's	447	40	–	53479	11750	12377	34	–
Ballingry and Lochcraig	119	14	–	18600	0	0	23	4
Beath and Cowdenbeath North	225	15	16	37724	2640	3200	18	6
Cairneyhill	221	24	–	22145	3610	3610	41	11
Limekilns	385	55	–	58069	10980	10980	46	13
Carnock and Oakley	255	23	36	43812	2000	2900	35	11
Cowdenbeath Trinity	451	27	35	33158	160	160	55	24
Culross and Torryburn	328	23	33	30780	2928	3258	38	24
Dalgety	676	41	38	78154	13600	13600	151	67
Dunfermline Abbey	779	61	–	92731	14690	14690	70	18
Dunfermline Gillespie Memorial	627	76	30	85467	16200	16200	68	64
Dunfermline North	240	14	–	26971	0	0	18	2
Dunfermline St Andrew's Erskine	364	24	18	22184	3110	3110	18	–
Dunfermline St Leonard's	736	43	51	56581	11900	11900	105	27
Dunfermline St Margaret's	494	55	45	45341	6920	6420	34	13
Dunfermline St Ninian's	414	33	65	29127	0	0	19	–
Dunfermline St Paul's	184	31	–	28420	2500	2500	7	8
Dunfermline Townhill	492	31	53	45567	8360	8360	43	21
Inverkeithing St John's	250	25	19	27684	2812	3142	22	14
North Queensferry	100	7	–	13904	1325	1619	21	–
Inverkeithing St Peter's	366	16	–	28718	3100	3100	30	8
Kelty	398	29	48	39235	3790	3790	25	10
Lochgelly Macainsh	435	37	–	29650	2500	2500	16	–
Lochgelly St Andrew's	395	29	32	36445	4370	4521	21	10
Rosyth	381	21	–	29778	0	0	19	3
Saline and Blairingone	291	16	23	37334	5710	5710	43	14
Tulliallan and Kincardine	704	51	80	39004	7060	7060	55	20

25. KIRKCALDY

Congregation	Com	Eld	G	In98	Ass	Gvn	3-11	-17
Auchterderran	266	18	14	17012	2500	2500	18	–
Cardenden St Fothad's	208	15	10	16925	3130	3130	16	4
Kinglassie	223	12	15	13687	2370	2370	11	–
Auchtertool	88	7	16	6787	860	860	2	–
Kirkcaldy Linktown	492	39	34	41565	8240	8240	20	2
Buckhaven	261	24	24	34985	3112	2358	29	7

Congregation	Com	Eld	G	In98	Ass	Gvn	3-11	-17
Burntisland	748	51	72	45236	8830	8972	68	41
Denbeath	137	7	24	9441	0	0	4	–
Methilhill	198	19	40	20208	0	200	16	–
Dysart	430	37	19	42478	8030	8030	11	–
Glenrothes Christ's Kirk	327	26	29	21437	0	0	63	23
Glenrothes St Columba's	733	29	26	53678	9012	7467	68	2
Glenrothes St Margaret's	521	38	48	54125	7460	7460	27	17
Glenrothes St Ninian's	333	34	17	43304	4000	4000	19	6
Innerleven East	317	9	25	22847	0	254	8	45
Kennoway, Windygates and Balgonie St Kenneth's	878	52	84	64233	10390	10390	50	10
Kinghorn	502	29	54	43633	7280	7280	26	8
Kirkcaldy Abbotshall	856	70	33	65022	15020	15120	34	8
Kirkcaldy Old	424	40	29	42476	8820	8820	27	16
Kirkcaldy Pathhead	656	52	62	62012	10500	10500	38	9
Kirkcaldy St Andrew's	351	26	38	42041	7180	7180	43	16
Kirkcaldy St Brycedale	558	33	52	60579	8890	8890	44	32
Kirkcaldy St John's	480	56	71	57226	9390	9390	43	8
Kirkcaldy Templehall	446	24	25	44215	5260	2155	35	76
Kirkcaldy Torbain	298	31	24	25697	0	0	–	19
Kirkcaldy Viewforth	439	20	–	28577	4280	4280	7	–
Thornton	280	10	–	16142	600	600	9	–
Leslie Trinity	452	32	56	27327	1812	1812	30	4
Leven: St Andrew's	647	41	51	48430	9410	2053	36	2
Leven Scoonie Kirk	404	27	32	41416	5910	2710	20	8
Markinch	726	36	52	46312	7150	7150	48	4
Methil	442	23	41	27900	4110	12960	17	9
Wemyss	365	18	50	23840	950	1022	20	3

26. ST ANDREWS

Congregation	Com	Eld	G	In98	Ass	Gvn	3-11	-17
Abdie and Dunbog	184	16	15	10778	1380	1380	11	–
Newburgh	374	20	–	14511	2516	2516	13	2
Anstruther	509	37	–	34499	5140	6325	35	15
Auchtermuchty	382	26	17	25454	2560	2560	10	11
Balmerino	210	21	20	20487	3650	3650	24	–
Wormit	314	21	65	27873	7290	7290	43	25
Boarhills and Dunino	197	8	46	11042	2300	2300	–	j
St Andrews Martyrs'	436	37	j	33370	6810	6810	23	10j
Cameron	98	5	12	10390	2350	2350	11	12
St Andrews St Leonard's	724	50	41	76127	18760	18760	34	6
Carnbee	111	10	21	12773	1650	1650	–	–
Pittenweem	336	18	43	22825	4025	4025	48	–
Cellardyke	422	23	45	29281	5130	5130	21	12j
Kilrenny	134	9	24	15497	2470	2470	22	j
Ceres and Springfield	569	30	50	33510	6440	6440	75	31
Crail	493	33	46	33812	7250	7250	31	–
Kingsbarns	114	11	–	11413	2330	2330	–	–
Creich, Flisk and Kilmany	148	11	19	18284	1660	1660	20	–
Monimail	192	14	–	15219	2490	2490	9	–
Cupar Old and St Michael of Tarvit	720	56	28	72103	14570	14770	53	25
Cupar St John's	859	44	76	59224	11290	11290	71	16

Congregation	Com	Eld	G	In98	Ass	Gvn	3-11	-17
Dairsie	143	9	20	10310	1712	1712	14	–
Kemback	123	8	24	8963	2460	2460	5	–
Strathkinness	163	14	21	15987	2320	2320	16	–
Edenshead and Strathmiglo	264	15	29	22058	2200	2200	12	–
Elie	350	26	66	50416	11430	11430	22	10
Kilconquhar and Colinsburgh	200	18	13	20370	2990	2990	14	7
Falkland	379	23	23	26793	5860	6324	48	3
Freuchie	279	17	23	29520	4730	4730	12	–
Howe of Fife	903	46	–	48324	9580	9580	83	–
Largo and Newburn	311	18	–	28780	6970	7134	35	–
Largo: St David's	219	16	55	18385	4010	4410	26	–
Largoward	85	6	13	5715	680	680	–	–
St Monans	282	16	65	32862	5090	4581	30	–
Leuchars: St Athernase and Guardbridge	567	30	34	39918	3860	3860	35	6
Newport-on-Tay	473	36	–	55274	12650	12650	37	32
St Andrews Holy Trinity	774	27	63	38754	12360	12360	33	1
St Andrews Hope Park	975	103	71	115029	23150	23150	56	44
Tayport	500	23	37	37341	4080	4080	44	33

27. DUNKELD AND MEIGLE

Congregation	Com	Eld	G	In98	Ass	Gvn	3-11	-17
Aberfeldy	384	21	26	46923	6580	6697	52	20
Amulree and Strathbraan	23	4	–	2458	550	550	4	–
Dull and Weem	98	7	15	8639	1448	1448	9	–
Alyth	860	37	40	50624	8890	10390	58	–
Ardler Kettins and Meigle	531	23	54	37765	5750	5750	25	–
Bendochy	108	9	17	9472	1350	1350	10	5
Blairgowrie St Mary's South	355	15	28	29042	2020	2020	29	5
Blair Atholl and Struan	190	15	27	15729	0	500	14	–
Blairgowrie St Andrew's	689	32	44	55080	11270	11270	24	13
Braes of Rannoch	32	5	8	10876	0	400	–	–
Foss and Rannoch	146	14	15	18650	0	430	–	–
Caputh and Clunie	217	27	20	18429	1247	1247	5	–
Kinclaven	187	22	14	17157	1270	1770	7	–
Coupar Angus: Abbey	519	34	37	29666	3260	2934	25	–
Dunkeld	486	34	47	53019	12410	12410	32	6
Fortingall and Glenlyon	59	4	–	6718	878	878	–	–
Kenmore and Lawers	120	5	20	16920	1930	1930	–	–
Grantully Logierait and Strathtay	171	12	20	19427	830	1100	–	–
Kirkmichael Straloch and Glenshee	167	13	17	14406	160	160	14	–
Rattray	565	24	38	38269	4090	4090	32	–
Pitlochry	565	56	41	59909	7870	7870	33	–
Tenandry	76	10	10	8647	1740	3740	5	–

28. PERTH

Congregation	Com	Eld	G	In98	Ass	Gvn	3-11	-17
Aberdalgie and Dupplin	116	6	17j	16336	0	247	8	6
Forteviot	120	6	j	9670	0	0	10	5
Abernethy and Dron	293	17	21	21034	2000	2116	16	–
Arngask	168	14	24	15645	2410	2410	30	10
Aberuthven	88	9	–	6246	0	0	3	2
Dunning	254	19	17	14464	0	0	21	–
Almondbank Tibbermore	345	23	33	24030	0	550	–	–

Congregation	Com	Eld	G	In98	Ass	Gvn	3-11	-17
Ardoch	177	11	28	18241	0	1750	20	11
Blackford	100	11	–	10277	0	0	28	8
Auchterarder	895	50	69	63449	12100	12100	44	10
Auchtergaven and Moneydie	563	28	44	32383	2820	2820	35	11
Cargill Burrelton	397	19	64	31502	1390	1390	23	8
Collace	152	10	15	17068	1980	1980	12	–
Cleish	266	17	22	42210	7190	7190	26	–
Fossoway: St Serf's and Devonside	239	21	–	29267	4950	4950	37	10
Comrie	547	31	52j	51505	8870	9990	27	2
Dundurn	62	7	j	9785	1720	1720	5	1
Crieff	1341	58	63	74216	16840	16840	52	16
Dunbarney	592	34	55	43380	9080	9080	57	13
Forgandenny	87	7	12	9149	1550	1550	7	–
Errol	444	23	20	36459	5730	1140	41	5
Kilspindie and Rait	79	5	–	6306	1010	1053	9	–
Fowlis Wester	123	11	8	13746	550	550	9	–
Madderty	113	9	15	11199	450	450	17	–
Monzie	118	12	11	11770	450	450	–	–
Gask	124	9	15	9301	0	500	10	–
Methven and Logiealmond	405	32	32	26671	0	600	39	–
Kinross	737	36	19	57904	10960	10960	97	20
Muthill	379	25	9j	22955	3250	3250	48	14
Trinity Gask and Kinkell	61	5	j	5261	530	530	–	–
Orwell	379	32	29	28583	4880	5711	41	4
Portmoak	171	13	–	16849	3250	3250	30	–
Perth Craigend Moncreiffe	267	15	–	11828	0	200	13	–
Rhynd	76	6	–	2958	0	0	3	–
Perth Craigie	793	41	48	55603	10940	11070	47	–
Perth Kinnoull	443	35	41	57819	11480	11480	30	12
Perth Letham St Mark's	856	45	39	60437	10320	10320	52	–
Perth North	1566	117	41	183958	42870	42870	143	62
Perth St Andrew's and St Stephen's	708	43	32	48150	8240	8240	–	–
Perth St John the Baptist's	952	55	–	58569	14250	12552	13	9
Perth St Leonard's-in-the-Fields and Trinity	640	73	46	80370	19670	19670	25	10
Perth St Matthew's	1050	87	49	72770	17090	17090	51	18
Redgorton	166	11	17	12407	780	780	50	–
Stanley	329	22	30	27711	4590	4590	40	–
St Madoes and Kinfauns	298	21	29	16293	0	0	11	–
St Martin's	221	12	20	10712	1490	2323	15	–
Scone New	654	50	61	52792	8937	8937	53	12
Scone Old	801	54	40	51051	9830	10955	40	24

29. DUNDEE

Abernyte	110	9	–	8822	900	900	15	–
Inchture and Kinnaird	263	22	17	19793	2640	2640	13	–
Longforgan	304	24	25	25011	4500	4500	21	–
Auchterhouse	156	14	20	21612	2575	2575	13	–
Murroes and Tealing	341	18	37	22501	1112	1112	8	12
Dundee Albany – Butterburn	230	9	7	5921	0	0	16	5
Dundee St David's North	144	10	32	11955	0	0	–	–

Congregation	Com	Eld	G	In98	Ass	Gvn	3-11	-17
Dundee Balgay	596	46	30	55350	9770	9770	30	23
Dundee Barnhill St Margaret's	927	69	54	93145	22635	22635	63	8
Dundee Broughty Ferry East	633	45	39	71197	12010	12010	64	14
Dundee Broughty Ferry St Aidan's	708	54	90	58512	11280	11280	40	19
Dundee Broughty Ferry St James'	285	16	38	40186	5630	5630	31	4
Dundee Broughty Ferry St Luke's and Queen Street	582	54	66	64123	11100	11756	24	–
Dundee Broughty Ferry St Stephen's and West	416	25	–	42701	6600	6600	19	9
Dundee Camperdown	266	25	20	30350	0	250	33	4
Dundee Chalmers Ardler	298	19	24	58306	10610	10838	32	24
Dundee Clepington	550	31	-	41825	5210	5210	29	52
Dundee Craigiebank	471	14	32	37635	6600	6600	31	28
Dundee Douglas and Angus	392	19	30	20077	1000	1000	17	6
Dundee Downfield South	515	32	35	55416	5900	5900	46	58
Dundee – Dundee (St Mary's)	743	78	33	91027	22635	23135	15	–
Dundee Fairmuir	332	18	21	33705	1800	1900	22	27
Dundee Lochee Old and St Luke's	390	26	38	33372	2500	3000	24	12
Dundee Lochee: West	693	38	25	34044	4250	4250	41	5
Dundee Logie St John's (Cross)	435	23	25	74087	17770	17770	84	16
Dundee Mains	287	11	-	21881	0	0	44	6
Dundee Mains of Fintry	170	11	–	43536	6070	4914	17	24
Dundee Meadowside St Paul's	616	65	36	66014	14070	14070	17	15
Dundee Menzieshill	531	27	–	41812	1000	1000	76	24
Dundee Mid Craigie	59	4	–	11215	0	0	11	8
Dundee St Andrew's	951	64	55	63890	10660	10760	89	13
Dundee Steeple	376	38	15	62127	14070	14075	34	17
Dundee Stobswell	695	47	-	59526	10360	13723	32	–
Dundee Strathmartine	633	47	46	48901	6380	6880	27	24
Dundee The High Kirk	575	56	63	47160	8230	8230	57	20
Dundee Trinity	849	47	55	38056	5890	5890	43	17
Dundee West	707	62	25	67356	15250	15950	37	13
Dundee Whitfield	218	22	–	13144	0	0	24	–
Fowlis and Liff	176	12	7	11619	2570	2570	13	–
Lundie and Muirhead of Liff	419	27	32	29717	4510	4784	33	10
Invergowrie	546	40	52	41635	5240	5340	22	7
Monifieth Panmure	509	39	38	46952	7410	7760	39	16
Monifieth St Rule's	835	34	68	48620	7470	7693	72	15
Monifieth South	453	22	35	37547	3640	3020	62	46
Monikie and Newbigging	313	18	11	27317	1500	1500	16	9

30. ANGUS

Aberlemno	210	11	–	15884	1250	1250	10	–
Guthrie and Rescobie	230	8	22	17416	1090	1090	14	5
Airlie, Ruthven and Kingoldrum	183	13	–	9657	700	408	16	–
Glenisla	51	6	11j	10117	720	720	5	5
Kilry	56	7	j	8346	600	600	10	–
Lintrathen	92	5	j	6498	630	630	–	–
Arbirlot	305	17	–	16331	3350	3350	25	59
Carmyllie	138	8	5	14683	3500	3500	14	–
Colliston	218	11	12	13814	2790	2790	12	–

Congregation	Com	Eld	G	In98	Ass	Gvn	3-11	-17
Arbroath Knox's	478	29	49	24526	5790	5840	11	–
Arbroath St Vigeans	687	44	29	46025	10140	10140	39	–
Arbroath Old and Abbey	1095	43	55	54327	10040	10040	–	–
Arbroath St Andrew's	995	59	27	62404	10340	10375	73	15
Arbroath West Kirk	1243	98	65	69150	12390	12390	57	6
Barry	421	19	19	23534	2570	2570	12	–
Brechin Cathedral	1301	32	25	31536	7090	10651	8	–
Brechin Gardner Memorial	1054	37	21	45035	6220	6289	43	2
Carnoustie	746	52	39	52429	11690	12012	33	28
Carnoustie: Panbride	864	41	–	49922	7230	7970	113	19
Dun	91	10	j	6619	1218	1218	–	–
Hillside	433	28	58j	33163	1590	1590	18	–
Dunnichen, Letham and Kirkden	521	25	34	37389	5020	6482	36	15
Eassie and Nevay	66	7	12	6399	620	120	–	–
Newtyle	320	15	28	45101	2546	0	14	–
Edzell Lethnot	478	28	59j	33161	8060	8560	16	9
Fern, Careston and Menmuir	146	10	7	11836	900	900	11	–
Glenesk	61	7	j	5316	900	955	11	–
Farnell	111	10	–	7011	780	780	14	–
Montrose St Andrew's	609	25	35	31028	4700	4700	18	–
Forfar East and Old	1660	55	61	72982	15860	15860	68	27
Forfar Lowson Memorial	1188	48	41	54238	9470	9470	35	6
Forfar St Margaret's	1160	45	34	68247	13160	13160	33	2
Friockheim and Kinnell	254	15	22	17130	630	630	27	–
Inverkeillor and Lunan	217	10	12	17154	2080	3305	6	–
Glamis, Inverarity and Kinettles	545	31	34	36134	3925	3925	35	10
Glens, The and Kirriemuir Old	1312	100	49	95780	18800	18800	65	52
Inchbrayock	246	10	–	27419	4570	5670	36	19
Montrose Melville South	432	20	–	32738	7300	7300	12	4
Kirriemuir St Andrew's	607	31	56	37789	5830	6180	24	–
Oathlaw Tannadice	195	7	j	11563	740	1065	–	–
Montrose Old	847	44	54	64803	15920	16420	83	10

31. ABERDEEN

Congregation	Com	Eld	G	In98	Ass	Gvn	3-11	-17
Aberdeen Beechgrove	718	86	66	107619	28086	28586	68	30
Aberdeen Bridge of Don Oldmachar	169	7	–	28261	0	0	41	5
Aberdeen Cove	71	3	–	5486	0	0	–	–
Aberdeen Craigiebuckler	932	64	73	69034	14860	14860	56	40
Aberdeen Denburn	478	42	24	38769	5580	5580	23	20
Aberdeen Ferryhill	608	65	38	60241	11400	11400	56	30
Aberdeen Garthdee	338	21	20	30484	0	1000	55	5
Aberdeen Gilcomston South	258	27	–	84042	17806	17806	16	–
Aberdeen Greyfriars John Knox	896	42	40	49043	9280	9828	25	4
Aberdeen High Hilton	673	56	65	65785	9210	9210	30	32
Aberdeen Holburn Central	671	54	23	49539	12650	12650	18	14
Aberdeen Holburn West	699	52	28	102944	29186	33542	57	8
Aberdeen Mannofield	1882	118	98	146787	39096	46025	135	44
Aberdeen Mastrick	699	27	34	51144	4990	4990	16	10
Aberdeen Middlefield	224	12	–	10414	0	0	51	5
Aberdeen Nigg	179	8	–	14186	0	50	21	15
Aberdeen North of St Andrew	878	72	37	70523	13580	13580	33	3

Congregation	Com	Eld	G	In98	Ass	Gvn	3-11	-17
Aberdeen Northfield	436	22	36	34935	5910	4910	16	10
Aberdeen Queen's Cross	714	65	49	110814	27906	30906	38	8
Aberdeen Rosemount	201	21	17	20649	2050	2050	2	–
Aberdeen Rubislaw	733	81	46	122169	31566	33030	68	27
Aberdeen Ruthrieston South	749	50	68	53384	9920	9920	51	29
Aberdeen Ruthrieston West	478	52	30	45214	5780	6196	16	–
Aberdeen St Columba's Bridge of Don	484	31	–	62203	7500	7500	84	49
Aberdeen St George's Tillydrone	228	14	16	24893	0	0	19	7
Aberdeen St John's for Deaf People	117	8	–	2009	0	50	–	–
Aberdeen St Machar's Cathedral	662	46	10	84037	17046	17046	27	5
Aberdeen St Mark's	608	52	22	64646	10070	10872	22	6
Aberdeen St Mary's	584	51	17	57063	9120	9120	17	4
Aberdeen St Nicholas, Kirk of	622	51	–	59892	10610	10610	11	–
Aberdeen St Nicholas South of Kincorth	581	42	47	44525	7360	7360	34	25
Aberdeen St Ninian's	364	23	30	33872	7600	7600	31	12
Aberdeen Stockethill	183	5	–	7938	300	300	–	–
Aberdeen St Stephen's	339	29	21	47360	6790	7276	18	–
Aberdeen Summerhill	235	20	–	25895	0	0	28	22
Aberdeen Torry St Fittick's	507	29	31	34452	3733	3733	44	19
Aberdeen Woodside	494	39	46	37590	5150	5250	3	14
Bucksburn Stoneywood	698	29	40	34803	7650	7650	14	14
Cults East	346	34	27	42124	6740	14470	20	–
Cults West	679	43	43	93657	19936	19936	62	9
Dyce	1498	74	52	61496	13070	13470	49	43
Kingswells	491	33	16	38945	3970	3970	36	5
Newhills	1034	48	86	76968	18316	18316	57	47
Peterculter	1078	50	28	55795	10640	10640	85	21

32. KINCARDINE AND DEESIDE

Congregation	Com	Eld	G	In98	Ass	Gvn	3-11	-17
Aberluthnott	257	9	16	12922	3696	3768	20	5
Laurencekirk	459	13	56	20075	4090	4090	28	2
Aboyne and Dinnet	585	23	49	36968	8890	8890	24	5
Arbuthnott	129	8	12	9154	1516	1516	7	–
Bervie	586	22	32	32514	4050	4050	28	4
Banchory Devenick	162	11	9	10707	1460	1460	–	–
Maryculter and Cookney	311	21	18	20728	3328	3328	8	–
Banchory Ternan East	1300	66	52	80307	16790	18542	66	42
Banchory Ternan West	713	46	45	65750	12060	12560	78	45
Birse and Feughside	335	28	–	31096	3812	2693	24	10
Braemar	117	11	10	16426	2545	2545	14	–
Crathie	198	16	17	29595	6870	6870	6	–
Cromar	265	14	·	11773	0	0	12	–
Drumoak	268	11	31	25278	0	200	30	3
Durris	212	12	17	15842	0	0	29	5
Glenmuick	404	24	24	34152	4900	4900	–	–
Kincardine O'Neil	238	12	12	7629	0	0	8	–
Lumphanan	300	13	16	14364	0	450	20	–
Kinneff	190	9	11	7092	1140	2065	9	–
Stonehaven South	359	26	19	28856	5895	5895	25	5
Mearns Coastal	416	18	·	28793	5605	4203	28	–

Congregation	Com	Eld	G	In98	Ass	Gvn	3-11	-17
Newtonhill	425	22	23	32153	1257	1257	33	17
Portlethen	561	20	-	46575	11680	11680	83	5
Stonehaven Dunnottar	1059	38	57	58558	10760	10760	43	18
Stonehaven Fetteresso	948	53	33	78352	18250	18250	100	34
Torphins	473	32	26	39886	3910	3910	44	7
West Mearns	652	31	76	43215	6950	7036	25	-

33. GORDON

Congregation	Com	Eld	G	In98	Ass	Gvn	3-11	-17
Barthol Chapel	112	11	12	8876	780	780	17	2
Tarves	557	36	42	36213	5910	6301	70	33
Belhelvie	640	29	31	38200	4580	5135	53	-
Blairdaff	107	13	-	9579	1156	1156	8	-
Chapel of Garioch	302	19	16	21049	2325	2325	21	-
Cluny	236	13	13	15874	2170	2170	16	4
Monymusk	174	7	10	14956	1130	1130	29	-
Culsalmond and Rayne	267	9	8	9409	1770	928	-	-
Cushnie and Tough	297	17	10	20336	0	400	30	3
Daviot	209	12	12	15076	1625	1625	20	2
Drumblade	141	11	11	8167	1800	1800	12	-
Huntly Strathbogie	920	46	43	50669	11580	11580	50	26
Echt	347	19	14	20578	1400	1400	18	8
Midmar	184	12	-	13379	1220	1220	11	6
Ellon	2169	109	59	91580	17410	17410	115	60
Fintray and Kinellar	214	13	19j	14005	860	962	26	-
Keithhall	82	8	j	8162	850	850	7	-
Foveran	429	21	-	31270	3010	3010	33	4
Howe Trinity	742	37	50	19991	4237	4237	39	-
Huntly Cairnie Glass	929	38	41	34003	5340	5340	20	-
Insch – Leslie – Premnay – Oyne	693	40	40	41085	8450	9340	50	12
Inverurie St Andrew's	2000	64	76	79155	25690	25690	67	29
Inverurie West	782	48	46	42592	5630	5660	60	19
Kemnay	669	32	-	36925	7060	7302	64	30
Kintore	893	54	46	50994	16780	22280	56	22
Meldrum and Bourtie	608	33	46	39157	6240	6240	39	8
Methlick	397	26	30	30402	3712	3712	-	-
New Machar	593	37	29	36454	5350	5850	58	8
Noth	400	16	-	15118	0	0	14	-
Skene	1689	101	75	101315	15020	15677	77	42
Udny and Pitmedden	554	29	12	45468	5675	5675	50	15
Upper Donside	527	25	-	35174	0	1844	15	-

34. BUCHAN

Congregation	Com	Eld	G	In98	Ass	Gvn	3-11	-17
Aberdour	180	10	28	10061	400	400	-	-
New Pitsligo	390	16	-	19415	500	583	11	-
Auchaber United	208	14	14	8763	419	419	13	-
Auchterless	255	18	17	16311	2430	2892	21	-
Banff	1000	57	50	70077	17800	18472	52	23
King Edward	187	15	14	13544	2125	1330	11	-
Crimond	325	10	14	16522	0	0	25	16
St Fergus	206	10	17	12942	0	103	21	15
Cruden	530	34	26	40655	5720	5794	24	4

Congregation	Com	Eld	G	In98	Ass	Gvn	3-11	-17
Deer	993	32	36	35954	4050	4194	43	5
Fordyce	570	37	40	40447	7130	7832	44	8
Fraserburgh Old	1011	58	94	103940	26930	22162	204	86
Fraserburgh South	386	26	26	38266	4130	4285	59	–
Inverallochy and Rathen: East	98	10	-	13201	2670	2410	22	–
Fraserburgh West	748	53	100	53892	8830	8830	75	10
Fyvie	458	29	41	32295	8550	8550	32	3
Rothienorman	197	10	11	10575	1220	1220	10	–
Gardenstown	68	9	32	33665	3010	4049	25	–
Longside	632	35	14	37218	4610	5147	100	16
Lonmay	203	15	12	19144	1270	1270	10	30
Rathen: West	131	9	–	11530	1050	895	10	–
Macduff	969	43	48	71594	11450	16923	106	53
Marnoch	448	23	18	29868	4825	5075	54	41
Maud and Savoch	337	18	16	20735	600	600	31	2
New Deer St. Kane's	551	23	24	34937	4910	4910	62	-
Monquhitter and New Byth	463	24	28	27915	0	0	12	–
Ordiquihill and Cornhill	194	13	16	9360	186	186	16	–
Whitehills	388	22	36	23319	3300	3458	32	–
Peterhead Old	600	42	40	49999	9080	9080	82	22
Peterhead St Andrew's	648	42	35	45829	7160	7160	95	8
Peterhead Trinity	440	25	22	82105	12790	12790	28	5
Pitsligo	235	14	16	22975	2420	2420	70	2
Sandhaven	108	8	20	13535	910	910	21	–
Strichen	521	17	39	26892	3788	3788	18	10
Tyrie	192	8	15	10509	500	500	8	3
Turriff St Andrew's	612	27	20	37873	3640	3640	47	13
Turriff St Ninian's and Forglen	1136	53	71	56143	12320	12320	78	6

35. MORAY

Congregation	Com	Eld	G	In98	Ass	Gvn	3-11	-17
Aberlour	502	26	28	32612	3720	3720	–	–
Alves and Burghead	174	17	14	21669	0	0	53	–
Kinloss and Findhorn	108	13	14	11249	0	300	18	–
Bellie	456	20	38	36315	10610	10610	37	10
Speymouth	263	14	24	13705	2500	2500	17	–
Birnie	250	18	18	17202	1690	1690	14	–
Pluscarden	139	14	19	14711	1750	1750	14	–
Buckie North	664	38	85	51246	10190	11342	84	9
Buckie South and West	383	29	39	34946	5210	5210	41	42
Enzie	133	14	14	8011	699	816	17	–
Cullen and Deskford	501	39	73	33759	6730	6950	51	16
Dallas	64	5	14	10049	1580	1580	–	–
Forres St Leonard's	368	28	52	37857	5150	7074	–	–
Rafford	91	7	17	9630	1035	1035	–	–
Duffus, Spynie and Hopeman	465	41	45	42117	6440	6440	39	–
Dyke	214	16	19	19988	3390	3390	41	7
Edinkillie	99	12	–	18114	1730	1730	8	2
Elgin High	858	50	51	66768	12730	12730	67	25
Elgin St. Giles' and St. Columba's South	1782	97	97	101929	22020	22020	-	-
Findochty	69	8	20	16005	200	200	25	19
Portknockie	129	10	39	13298	300	300	22	–

Congregation	Com	Eld	G	In98	Ass	Gvn	3-11	-17
Rathven	153	17	29	11841	500	500	43	–
Forres St Laurence	713	38	55	59806	10730	11710	–	–
Grange	202	8	17	9031	213	2506	14	–
Rothiemay	231	12	13	7812	165	165	8	–
Keith North, Newmill and Boharm	578	49	28	71259	11080	11530	44	15
Keith St Rufus and Botriphnie	960	44	40	49547	8610	8610	49	15
Knockando, Elchies and Archiestown	281	14	14	11284	1100	1100	–	–
Rothes	354	18	22	20466	3770	3770	37	–
Lossiemouth St Gerardine's High	428	25	46	48645	7500	7500	32	4
Lossiemouth St James'	383	21	40	42482	5560	5560	33	5
Mortlach and Cabrach	530	32	46	23984	0	0	–	–
St Andrew's Lhanbryde and Urquhart	494	40	27	35039	6090	6090	49	16

36. ABERNETHY

Congregation	Com	Eld	G	In98	Ass	Gvn	3-11	-17
Abernethy	169	18	–	22215	2910	2910	39	13
Cromdale and Advie	114	5	–	9929	640	1252	–	–
Alvie and Insh	80	10	–	20197	6080	5241	20	11
Boat of Garten and Kincardine	115	10	14	20441	0	0	14	12
Duthil	76	9	14	8711	0	0	12	9
Dulnain Bridge	43	6	–	9149	412	412	4	–
Grantown-on-Spey	348	24	37	33167	6340	7340	33	10
Inveraven and Glenlivet	146	7	10	12035	0	0	6	3
Kingussie	129	16	–	20544	0	0	12	15
Kirkmichael and Tomintoul	89	5	–	10174	0	0	9	–
Laggan	42	5	–	8423	0	0	4	–
Newtonmore	105	9	–	13057	0	20	9	–
Rothiemurchus and Aviemore	110	7	-	17191	0	0	11	2

37. INVERNESS

Congregation	Com	Eld	G	In98	Ass	Gvn	3-11	-17
Ardclach	45	3	–	3828	0	0	2	–
Auldearn and Dalmore	102	8	19	12850	0	0	11	–
Ardersier	87	8	16	14220	0	100	32	–
Petty	69	9	-	11150	0	80	–	–
Cawdor	166	15	21	22665	0	1000	21	–
Croy and Dalcross	69	14	21	9176	0	308	15	–
Culloden The Barn	403	37	40	55729	8580	8580	67	23
Daviot and Dunlichity	66	6	–	13212	0	0	–	–
Moy, Dalarossie and Tomatin	37	4	8	7436	0	0	16	–
Dores and Boleskine	107	9	11	16060	0	0	18	–
Inverness Crown	835	91	90	95337	20620	31064	61	37
Inverness Dalneigh and Bona	273	16	28	53930	9730	9730	43	27
Inverness East	337	35	29	98322	21780	21780	71	20
Inverness Hilton	247	15	35	58735	0	0	75	12
Inverness Kinmylies	212	17	–	27474	0	0	41	10
Inverness Ness Bank	583	54	24	68239	11990	11990	48	27
Inverness St Columba (High)	280	37	23	46632	11570	11720	23	7
Inverness St Stephen's	440	38	21	45974	10420	10420	77	25
Inverness The Old High	199	30	–	32907	8430	8430	21	13
Inverness Trinity	420	42	33	60825	12750	12750	66	9
Inverness West	289	24	–	61558	13570	15750	24	10
Kilmorack and Erchless	139	13	17	26568	0	405	16	2

Congregation	Com	Eld	G	In98	Ass	Gvn	3-11	-17
Kiltarlity	54	6	7	12629	0	0	36	2
Kirkhill	90	8	16	15340	0	160	23	4
Nairn Old	998	61	34	76466	17120	17120	52	30
Nairn St Ninian's	352	19	35	30752	3980	3980	23	2
Urquhart and Glenmoriston	150	8	10	35866	4620	4620	53	8

38. LOCHABER

Congregation	Com	Eld	G	In98	Ass	Gvn	3-11	-17
Acharacle	40	4	–	11762	0	50	–	–
Ardnamurchan	18	4	–	4243	0	0	11	–
Ardgour	53	7	16	12229	0	200	16	–
Strontian	24	3	7	5370	0	54	8	–
Arisaig and The Small Isles	59	5	18	9384	0	0	10	–
Duror	49	8	16	11827	0	1750	–	–
Glencoe	76	10	19	15000	0	0	10	–
Fort Augustus	75	9	18	20930	0	146	22	–
Glengarry	37	7	11	9206	0	145	12	–
Fort William Duncansburgh	330	23	21	42137	8030	8641	27	12
Kilmonivaig	73	7	9	16089	3937	6777	5	14
Fort William MacIntosh Memorial	238	31	19	43666	6030	6030	21	12
Kilmallie	203	22	30	36357	8520	1704	41	9
Kinlochleven	88	9	24	19408	0	240	8	8
Nether Lochaber	72	5	–	12149	0	225	18	–
Mallaig St Columba and Knoydart	100	6	–	24217	0	0	25	5
Morvern	55	5	10	9191	0	0	–	–

39. ROSS

Congregation	Com	Eld	G	In98	Ass	Gvn	3-11	-17
Alness	141	15	27	35102	0	0	42	9
Avoch	32	5	12	12570	1730	1730	2	–
Fortrose and Rosemarkie	147	13	–	29761	4475	4475	30	15
Contin	67	12	–	15475	0	2000	–	–
Cromarty	77	6	16	10776	0	0	24	9
Dingwall Castle Street	164	18	21	42629	5000	5193	11	13
Dingwall St Clement's	265	26	20	39218	6990	6990	57	8
Fearn Abbey and Nigg Chapelhill	109	17	26	26668	0	0	16	–
Ferintosh	210	22	39	35018	1000	1000	52	9
Fodderty and Strathpeffer	176	18	26	23898	0	1557	30	21
Invergordon	250	19	25	42021	6150	7650	51	18
Killearnan	145	16	–	27498	0	400	36	4
Knockbain	74	6	8	13730	0	0	19	8
Kilmuir and Logie Easter	84	13	17	22241	0	3044	13	3
Kiltearn	92	5	5	27256	0	0	28	7
Lochbroom and Ullapool	65	3	12	19161	0	0	19	8
Resolis and Urquhart	106	11	–	24742	0	0	27	13
Rosskeen	169	12	36	32781	0	424	38	11
Tain	196	16	33	48714	7180	7180	57	16
Tarbat	70	11	20	18289	0	603	11	–
Urray and Kilchrist	145	22	29	33667	0	718	34	–

40. SUTHERLAND

Congregation	Com	Eld	G	In98	Ass	Gvn	3-11	-17
Altnaharra and Farr	32	2	–	9324	0	0	4	–
Assynt and Stoer	33	2	–	13464	0	0	20	14

Congregation	Com	Eld	G	In98	Ass	Gvn	3-11	-17
Clyne	98	9	–	18602	0	0	18	–
Creich	51	5	–	10295	0	325	17	–
Rosehall	24	1	–	6470	0	0	–	–
Dornoch Cathedral	412	31	61	57528	10780	12470	51	17
Durness and Kinlochbervie	45	4	12	15513	0	0	11	–
Eddrachillis	18	2	–	12835	0	200	16	–
Golspie	108	19	17	21182	2010	3000	13	28
Kildonan and Loth Helmsdale	42	4	19	13845	0	0	3	–
Kincardine Croick and Edderton	75	10	13	17363	0	0	–	28
Lairg	52	4	22	15558	0	0	22	4
Rogart	27	4	14	8730	0	0	3	–
Melness and Tongue	56	6	10	9190	0	0	24	1

41. CAITHNESS

Congregation	Com	Eld	G	In98	Ass	Gvn	3-11	-17
Berriedale and Dunbeath	19	3	–	7403	0	0	15	–
Latheron	24	1	–	7059	0	0	10	–
Bower	35	5	10	11195	0	45	19	3
Watten	46	4	8	9616	0	45	18	–
Canisbay	48	4	10	13419	0	20	15	–
Keiss	29	2	12	9445	0	100	11	–
Dunnet	22	2	9	3942	0	0	6	–
Olrig	58	5	11	9065	0	0	29	4
Halkirk and Westerdale	87	6	21	15414	0	0	49	10
Lybster and Bruan	43	8	31	18283	0	0	27	3
Reay	36	5	9	12832	0	250	12	–
Strathy and Halladale	34	5	16	10263	0	0	13	–
Thurso St Peter's and St Andrew's	253	22	47	52095	7620	7620	59	12
Thurso West	291	30	43	41322	3920	3920	61	4
Wick Bridge Street	190	14	15	25999	1960	2160	29	15
Wick Old	287	36	41	42084	4375	4575	74	17
Wick Pultneytown and Thrumster	268	18	36	50564	7950	8200	97	21

42. LOCHCARRON – SKYE

Congregation	Com	Eld	G	In98	Ass	Gvn	3-11	-17
Applecross, Lochcarron and Torridon	83	8	28	25280	200	200	36	3
Bracadale and Durinish	94	8	10	18427	0	0	54	23
Gairloch and Dundonnell	78	5	–	36911	4940	4940	31	–
Glenelg and Kintail	63	7	–	18726	0	0	33	15
Kilmuir and Stenscholl	70	11	–	26008	0	0	33	8
Lochalsh	121	8	23	32091	0	210	41	8
Portree	152	11	–	45453	5080	5080	63	7
Snizort	100	6	–	39311	600	600	39	12
Strath and Sleat	192	19	25	54115	8560	8560	72	32

43. UIST

Congregation	Com	Eld	G	In98	Ass	Gvn	3-11	-17
Barra	36	6	–	10421	0	200	11	–
Benbecula	80	11	25	27768	0	0	30	20
Bernera	22	3	–	9569	0	500	9	1
Carinish	75	9	25	32506	0	0	31	5
Kilmuir and Paible	32	8	-	23560	0	0	26	3
Lochmaddy and Trumisgarry	48	4	12	16499	0	0	15	–

Congregation	Com	Eld	G	In98	Ass	Gvn	3-11	-17
Manish – Scarista	50	4	–	23395	0	0	33	–
South Uist	61	12	12	16590	0	0	9	–
Tarbert	160	14	–	57260	9890	9890	55	17
44. LEWIS								
Barvas	95	11	–	32519	2125	2125	43	15
Carloway	44	1	–	21849	0	700	19	2
Cross Ness	55	7	–	24283	0	0	17	2
Kinloch	50	10	–	23509	0	0	26	4
Knock	82	6	–	33853	0	0	36	–
Lochs-in-Bernera	37	6	–	17216	0	0	13	1
Lochs – Crossbost	18	2	–	13716	0	0	21	3
Stornoway High	280	20	–	78174	16620	16620	89	19
Stornoway Martin's Memorial	123	6	19	40014	4030	4030	36	14
Stornoway St Columba	146	12	30	59719	10670	10670	50	26
Uig	57	8	–	16343	0	0	15	11
45. ORKNEY								
Birsay	115	12	18	9961	160	160	40	–
Harray and Sandwick	295	23	47	22919	970	970	35	15
Deerness	103	9	–	7892	1010	1010	13	–
Holm	149	11	17	11051	970	970	21	–
St Andrew's	89	10	11	7136	490	43	8	–
Eday	10	2	7	2512	0	0	–	1
Stronsay: Moncur Memorial	73	10	28	11080	0	0	12	–
Evie	57	5	–	4384	600	721	3	3
Firth	144	7	24	22358	2858	3056	19	67
Rendall	66	3	14	6994	800	800	12	4
Flotta	29	4	–	3122	0	0	8	–
Hoy and Walls	83	13	12	5230	0	0	13	–
Kirkwall East	577	47	71	47334	12330	12639	45	11
Kirkwall St Magnus Cathedral	846	78	36	68845	18610	18782	72	5
North Ronaldsay	18	3	–	1636	0	0	–	–
Sanday	112	9	18	9654	0	0	30	4
Orphir	146	11	20	18304	920	988	10	6
Stenness	98	9	15	13606	990	1060	12	–
Papa Westray	12	3	–	2549	0	0	6	–
Westray	74	14	24	19881	0	0	26	11
Rousay	33	4	12	2427	0	0	–	–
Shapinsay	76	10	–	8111	0	0	4	–
South Ronaldsay and Burray	218	12	15	16858	0	0	36	10
Stromness	433	23	35	36166	6860	5831	–	3
46. SHETLAND								
Burra Isle	55	7	25	6968	0	0	22	5
Tingwall	186	19	27	18029	0	0	56	6
Delting	123	9	-	15652	0	0	34	8
Nesting and Lunnasting	46	5	20	8083	0	0	–	–
Dunrossness	77	13	-	14861	0	0	27	19
Sandwick Cunningsburgh and Quarff	160	11	39	22663	0	300	27	1
Fetlar	23	3	–	1952	0	0	12	–

Congregation	Com	Eld	G	In98	Ass	Gvn	3-11	-17
Yell	152	12	39	11138	0	0	18	–
Lerwick and Bressay	595	46	–	49930	10250	10250	–	–
Northmavine	96	10	–	10169	0	0	–	–
Sandsting and Aithsting	59	13		9175	0	50	19	4
Walls and Sandness	54	11	27	7772	0	50	12	–
Unst	136	10	27	14685	0	0	25	3
Whalsay and Skerries	259	17	20	19582	0	0	–	–

47. ENGLAND

Congregation	Com	Eld	G	In98	Ass	Gvn	3-11	-17
Corby St Andrew's	374	27	33	30726	2510	2510	22	6
Corby St Ninian's	402	26	15	41527	6050	5445	23	5
Guernsey: St Andrew's in the Grange	236	19	–	35793	6130	6130	67	4
Jersey: St Columba's	145	22	–	37491	2800	2800	45	6
Liverpool: St Andrew's	54	6	9	10733	2280	2280	–	–
London Crown Court	326	44	10	72413	17670	17670	25	–
London St Columba's	1506	61	–	218684	41970	41970	99	4
Newcastle	132	20	9	13516	3370	3370	13	–

INDEX OF MINISTERS

NOTE: Ministers who are members of a Presbytery are designated "A" if holding a parochial appointment in that Presbytery, or "B" if otherwise qualifying for membership.

"A-1, A-2" *etc* indicate the numerical order of congregations in the Presbyteries of Edinburgh, Glasgow and Hamilton.

Also included are:

(1) Ministers who have resigned their seat in Presbytery (List 6-H)

(2) Ministers who hold a Ministerial Certificate (List 6-I),

(3) Ministers serving overseas (List 6-K).

(4) Auxiliary Ministers (List 6-A)

(5) Ministers who have died since the publication of the last Year Book (List 6-R)

NB *For a List of the Diaconate see List 6-G*

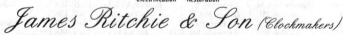

Patterson, J.M.	Edinburgh 1B	Rae, R.	Dundee 29B	Robb, R.P.T.	Stirling 23A
Patterson, J.W.	St Andrews 26B	Rae, S.M.	England 47B	Robertson, A.	Glasgow 16B
Pattison, K.J.	Ross 39A	Raeburn, A.C.	Glasgow 16A-51	Robertson, A.	Stirling 23B
Paul, Miss A.	Dumbarton 18A	Raemonn, P.	Europe 48A	Robertson, A.O.	List 6-R
Paul, I	Falkirk 22B	Ramage, A.E.	Dumbarton 18A	Robertson, B.	Glasgow 16B
Peat, S.W.	List 6-I	Ramsay, A.	Lochaber 38A	Robertson, B.	Europe 48B
Penman, I.D.	Edinburgh 1A-39	Ramsay, B.	Angus 30A	Robertson, C.	Edinburgh 1A-8
Penny, R.F.	Hamilton 17A-8	Ramsay, M.	Dunkeld/Meigle 27A	Robertson, C.	List 6-H
Perry, J.B.	Angus 30B	Ramsay, R.J.	Dundee 29A	Robertson, Miss C.	Angus 30A
Peterkin, W.N.	Glasgow 16B	Ramsay, W.G.	Glasgow 16B	Robertson, D.M.	Ayr 10B
Petrie, I.D.	Dundee 29A	Ramsden I.	Ross 39A	Robertson, D.R.	Lorn/Mull 21A
Petrie, K.L.	Aberdeen 31A	Randall, D.J.	Buchan 34A	Robertson, E.	West Lothian 2B
Petty, P.W.P.	List 6-H	Redmayne, G.	Irv/K'marnock 11A	Robertson, Miss E.M.D.	Stirling 23A
Philip, A.J.	Glasgow 16A-125	Redpath, J.G.	Dunfermline 24A	Robertson, F.A.	Inverness 37A
Philip, D.S	Europe 48B	Reid, Miss A.A.	Ardrossan 12B	Robertson, G.R.	Gordon 33A
Philip, G.M.	Glasgow 16B	Reid, A.A.S.	Stirling 23B	Robertson, I.M.	Falkirk 22B
Philip, J.	Edinburgh 1B	Reid, A.B.	Dunkeld/Meigle 27A	Robertson, I.W.	Dum'/K'cud 8B
Philip, M.R.	Dunkeld/Meigle 27A	Reid, A.D.	Jedburgh 6A	Robertson, J.	Lothian 3B
Phillips, J.S.	Ayr 10B	Reid, A.G.	Dunfermline 24A	Robertson, J.H.	Inverness 37A
Philp, Miss C.	Edinburgh 1B	Reid, D.	Dunfermline 24B	Robertson, J.T.	Moray 35B
Philp, R.A.	Glasgow 16B	Reid, D.T.	Stirling 23B	Robertson, M.	Inverness 37A
Pickering, J.M.	Perth 28A	Reid, I.M.A.	Lochcarron/Skye 42A	Robertson, Miss N.	Kin'/Dee' 32A
Pirie, D.	Lothian 3A	Reid, J.	Kirkcaldy 25A	Robertson, T.G.M.	St Andrews 26A
Pitkeathly, D.G.	Buchan 34A	Reid, Miss J.G.	Glasgow 16A-122	Robertson, T.P.	Dundee 29A
Pitkeathly, T.C.	Europe 48A	Reid, J.K.S.	Edinburgh 1B	Robertson, T.R.	D'um/K'cud 8B
Plate, Miss M.A.G.	Orkney 45A	Reid, M.R.B.C.	Kirkcaldy 25B	Robinson, K.S.P.	List 6-R
Pogue, V.C.	Dunfermline 24B	Reid, R.G.	Falkirk 22A	Robson, G.K.	Dundee 29A
Pollock, T.L.	Hamilton 17A-2	Reid, S.	Lanark 13A	Robson, J.	List 6-R
Pollock, W.	Lorn/Mull 21A	Reid, W.M.	Europe 48A	Rodger, M.A.	Gordon 33B
Poole, Mrs A.M.	Moray 35A	Reid, W.S.	Edinburgh 1B	Rodwell, Mrs A.S.	Greenock 15A
Pope, D.H.N.	Hamilton 17A-61	Rennie, A.J.T.	Edinburgh 1A-25	Rogers, J.M.	Dundee 29B
Portchmouth, R.J.	St Andrews 26B	Rennie, A.M.	Stirling 23B	Rogerson, A.E.	List 6-R
Porteous, A.	Greenock 15B	Rennie, C.A.J.	Falkirk 22A	Rogerson, S.D.	Hamilton 17A-76
Porteous, J.K.	St Andrews 26B	Rennie, D.B.	Kincard'/Deeside 32B	Rollo, G.B.	Moray 35A
Porteous, N.W.	Edinburgh 1B	Rennie, J.B.	Gordon 33B	Rooney, M.I.G.	Angus 30A
Porter, J.C.	Moray 35B	Rennie, J.D.	Annan'/Eskdale 7B	Rose, D.S.	Dum'/K'cud 8A
Porter, R.	Glasgow 16B	Rennie, Mrs M.A.	Dunfermline 24A	Ross, Mrs A.J.	South Argyll 19A
Pot, J.	Europe 48A	Rennie, S.	Angus 30	Ross, A.C.	Edinburgh 1B
Poustie, G.T.	List 6-R	Renton, I.P.	Edinburgh 1B	Ross, A.C.	Annan'/Eskdale 7B
Povey, J.M.	West Lothian 2A	Renton, J.P.	Gordon 33A	Ross, D.M.	Glasgow 16B
Powrie, J.E.	Dundee 29B	Renwick, C.C.	Glasgow 16A-90	Ross, D.S.	Buchan 34A
Prentice, D.K.	Duns 5B	Rettie, J.A.	Sutherland 40B	Ross, Ms E.B.	Aberdeen 31A
Prentice, G.	Paisley 14B	Riach, W.A.D.	List 6-R	Ross, E.J.	Dunfermline 24B
Preston, T.	Edinburgh 1A-59	Ribbons, F.	Lothian 3A	Ross, Ms F.C.	Ardrossan 12A
Price, Mrs A.	List 6-I	Richard, Mrs F.	Dunfermline 24A	Ross, H.G.	List 6-R
Price, P.O.	Hamilton 17B	Richardson, T.C.	Aberdeen 31A	Ross, J.	Glasgow 16B
Provan, I.W.	List 6-I	Richmond, J.	England 47B	Ross, Miss J.	Falkirk 22A
Pryce, S.F.A.	Stirling 23B	Riddell, J.A.	Jedburgh 6A	Ross, J.H.G.	List 6-H
Pryde, W.K.	St Andrews 26A	Riddell, T.S.	West Lothian 2A	Ross, K.R.	Edinburgh 1B
Purves, J.P.S.	Stirling 23A	Ridland, A.K.	Lothian 3A	Ross, K.W.	Glasgow 16A-145
Purves, J.S.	Glasgow 16A-73	Risby, Mrs L.	Aberdeen 31A	Ross, M.Z.	St Andrews 26A
Pyper, J.S.	Greenock 15B	Ritchie, A.	Edinburgh 1A-18	Ross, R.A.	List 6-I
		Ritchie, B.	Perth 28A	Ross, W.B.	Dundee 29A
Quigley, Mrs B.D.	List 6-I	Ritchie, G.W.M.	Jedburgh 6B	Roy, A.A.	Caithness 41A
		Ritchie, J.	Aberdeen 31A	Roy, A.J.	St Andrews 26B
Raby, S.	Hamilton 17A-84	Ritchie, J.McL.	Lothian 3B	Roy, I.M.	Ardrossan 12B
Rae, A.W.	Melrose/Peebles 4B	Ritchie, M.A.	South Argyll 19B	Roy, J.	Irv'/K'marnock 11B
Rae, D.L.	Glasgow 16B	Ritchie, W.M.	Lochcarron/Skye 42B	Roy, J.A.	Dundee 29A
Rae, P.C.	Dunfermline 24B	Robb, N.J.	St Andrews 26B	Rule, J.A.	Paisley 14B

INDEX OF PLACES

NOTE: Numbers on the right of the column refer to the Presbytery in which the district lies. Names in brackets are given for ease of identification. They either refer to the name of the Parish, which may be different from that of the district, or they distinguish places with the same name.

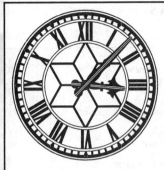

INDEX OF SUBJECTS

INDEX OF ADVERTISERS